CMBE

1st International Conference on Computational & Mathematical Biomedical Engineering
29th June – 1st July, 2009, Swansea University, UK

Edited by:

Perumal Nithiarasu
Civil and Computational Engineering Centre
School of Engineering, Swansea University
Swansea, UK

Rainald Löhner
Center for Computational Fluid Dynamics
College of Sciences, George Mason University
Fairfax, Virginia, US

Raoul van Loon
Civil and Computational Engineering Centre
School of Engineering, Swansea University
Swansea, UK

With support from:

Xianghua Xie, Igor Sazonov, Antonio Orlando, Antonio Gil
Swansea University, Swansea, UK

1st International Conference on Computational & Mathematical Biomedical Engineering, 2009, Swansea, UK

First edition, June 2009
© 2009 by the authors of the abstracts

Published by CMBE

ISBN: 978-0-9562914-0-0

PREFACE

It is our pleasure to welcome all participants of the *1st International Conference on Computational and Mathematical Biomedical Engineering* (**CMBE09**) to Swansea University. Computational and mathematical methods have had a profound impact on the understanding and advancement of engineering science and technology over the last few decades. It is becoming increasingly obvious that computational and mathematical methods will have a similar impact in the area of biomedical engineering and medicine. CMBE09 is a response to the expectation that computational methods are ready to make a change in the way in which diseases and disorders are treated, medical equipment is designed and health care is carried out. The conference aims to convene a diverse scientific audience of mathematicians, physicists, clinicians and computational scientists that have a communal interest in modelling within biomedical engineering. It is encouraging to learn that this conference represents an interdisciplinary forum of scientists with expertise ranging from imaging to CFD, from algorithmic developments to clinical applications and from respiratory flows to protein mechanics. We hope that the interaction between scientists during the conference leads to new topics of research and new collaborations.

CMBE09 consists of eight conference keynotes, one mini-symposium keynote, ten organized mini-symposia and eight standard sessions. We are grateful to all keynote speakers for accepting our invitation. We anticipate that some of the keynote lectures will be published in the '*International Journal for Numerical Methods in Biomedical Engineering*'.

We thank CMBE09 sponsors, supporters, mini-symposium organizers, executive, scientific and local committee members for their support.

Perumal Nithiarasu   Rainald Löhner
Swansea University   George Mason University
United Kingdom   United States of America

SPONSORS

SUPPORTING ORGANISATIONS

WIMCS

COMMITTEES

Co-chairs
P. Nithiarasu, UK
R. Löhner, USA

Executive Committee
F. Baaijens, The Netherlands
C. Constantinou, UK
R. Feijoo, Brazil
T.J.R. Hughes, USA
G.A. Holzapfel, Austria
R. Hose, UK
J. Humphrey, USA
K.E. Jordan, USA.
W.K. Liu, USA
P. Maini, UK
J. Middleton, UK
E. Oñate, Spain
K. Parker, UK

International Advisory Committee
A. Al-Jumaily, New Zealand
J. Cebral, USA
D. Drikakis, UK
L. Formaggia, Italy
K. Garikipati, USA
J-F. Gerbeau, France
A. Hazel, UK
M. Heil, UK
N. John, UK
R. Krishna Kumar, India
A. Lee, Singapore
X. Luo, UK
A.G. Malan, South Africa
K. Miller, Australia
L. Nokes, UK
J. Peiro, UK
T. Phillips, UK
R. Said, UK
S.J. Sherwin, UK
C.A. Taylor, USA
T. Tezduyar, USA
Y. Ventikos, UK
F. Van de Vosse, The Netherlands
W. Wall, Germany
G.W. Wei, USA
X.Y. Xu, UK

Local Organizing Committee
S. Ashraf, Morriston Hospital
J. Bonet, School of Engineering
M. Cross, School of Engineering
W. Dettmer, School of Engineering
E. De Souza Neto, School of Engineering
P. Ebden, Singleton Hospital
M.G. Edwards, School of Engineering
Y. Feng, School of Engineering
C. Fielder, School of Engineering
A.J.Gil, School of Engineering
H. Griffiths, School of Medicine
O. Hassan, School of Engineering
J.W. Jones, School of Engineering
P. Ledger, School of Engineering
K. Morgan, WIMCS & School of Engineering
A. Orlando, School of Engineering
D. Peric, School of Engineering
P.H. Saksono, School of Engineering
V. Sawlani, Morriston and Singleton Hospitals
I. Sazonov, School of Engineering
J. Sienz, School of Engineering
R. Van Loon, School of Engineering
M.F. Webster, School of Engineering
P.R. Williams, School of Engineering
X. Xie, Department of Computer Science

CONTENTS

MS-2: Multiphysics multiscale computational modelling of the cardiovascular system
Organised by P.J. Blanco and R.A. Feijoo

MS-3: Computational modelling of respiratory system
Organised by W.A. Wall and K.R. Lutchen

MS-4: Wales Institute of Mathematical and Computational Sciences (WIMCS)

Organised by K. Morgan

MS-5: Cerebral Aneurysm Haemodynamics

Organised by J.R. Cebral and R. Löhner

MS-6: Heart-valve modelling

Organised by R. van Loon and X. Luo

MS-7: Recent advances in computational and mathematical methods for imaging and image analysis

Organised by G. Wei

MS-8: Methodologies for analysing protein conformational changes

Organised by S. Guest and A. MacDonald

MS-9: Shape and deformable modelling in biomedical image analysis

Organised by X. Xie and M. Mirmehdi

MS-10: Patient-specific modelling of haemodynamics in aortic aneurysms

Organised by I. Sazonov, P. Nithiarasu and S. Ashraf

SS-1: Computational electrophysiology

SS-2: Image processing

SS-3: Modelling fluid-structure interaction in biomedical engineering

SS-4: Computational haemodynamics

SS-5: Computational tissue mechanics

SS-6: Modelling diagnosis and treatment procedures

SS-7: Modelling at cellular and molecular level

SS-8: Computational biomechanics

Keynote Lectures

CONSTRAINED MIXTURE MODELS OF ARTERIAL ADAPATATION: PAST SUCCESSES AND FUTURE PROMISES

J.D. Humphrey
Department of Biomedical Engineering and M.E. DeBakey Institute Texas A&M University, College Station, TX 77843-3120 USA jhumphrey@tamu.edu

ABSTRACT

The past four decades have brought forth tremendous advances in the continuum biomechanics of arteries [1]. Nevertheless, two conspicuous shortcomings remain. First, most constitutive relations and stress analyses have focused on conditions at a single instant, not how the material properties and stress fields evolve due to normal development or in response to perturbed loads, disease, injury, or clinical treatment; second, biomechanical analyses have been based on the assumption that arteries are materially uniform rather than consisting of many different constituents that turnover at different rates and to different extents while collectively defining the whole. The primary goal herein is to encourage a new direction in arterial mechanics whereby one models time-dependent changes in composition, structure, geometry, and properties that occur in response to changes in the biochemomechanical environment. Although it is not yet possible to identify many of the underlying mechanisms that are responsible for such growth and remodeling [2], expanding data bases provide sufficient guidance on salient aspects of development, adaptation, and disease progression, thus it is appropriate that we begin to interpret these data within mathematical frameworks. Toward this end, our approach will focus on the development, extension, and application of constrained mixture models of the biochemical processes that manifest at the tissue level as changes in structure, function, and biomechanical properties. As illustrative examples, we will consider adaptations to altered blood pressure, flow, and axial stretch and cerebral vasospasm [3,4].

REFERENCES

[1] J.D. Humphrey. *Cardiovascular Solid Mechanics: Cells, Tissues, and Organs*, Springer-Verlag, New York , 2002

[2] J.D. Humphrey, Vascular adaptation and mechanical homeostasis at tissue, cellular, and sub-cellular levels, *Cell Biochem Biophys* 50, 53-78, (2008)

[3] S. Baek, A. Valentin, J.D. Humphrey, Biochemomechanics of cerebral vasospasm and its resolution: II. Constitutive relations and model simulations, *Annl Biomed Engr* 35, 1498-1509, (2007)

[4] A. Valentin, L. Cardamone, S. Baek, J.D. Humphrey, Complementary vasoactivity and matrix remodeling in arterial adaptations to altered pressure and flow, *J R Soc Interface* 6, 293-306, (2009)

TOWARDS A COMPREHENSIVE COMPUTATIONAL MODEL FOR THE RESPIRATORY SYSTEM

W. A. Wall

Institute for Computational Mechanics, Technische Universität München, Boltzmannstr. 15, 85748 Garching b. Müunchen, Germany
wall@lnm.mw.tum.de

L. Wiechert

Institute for Computational Mechanics, Technische Universität München, Boltzmannstr. 15, 85748 Garching b. Müunchen, Germany
wiechert@lnm.mw.tum.de

A. Comerford

Institute for Computational Mechanics, Technische Universität München, Boltzmannstr. 15, 85748 Garching b. Müunchen, Germany
comerford@lnm.mw.tum.de

S. Rausch

Institute for Computational Mechanics, Technische Universität München, Boltzmannstr. 15, 85748 Garching b. Müunchen, Germany
rausch@lnm.mw.tum.de

ABSTRACT

Mechanical ventilation is a vital supportive therapy for critical care patients suffering from Acute Respiratory Distress syndrome (ARDS) in view of oxygen supply. However, heterogeneity of the ARDS lung predisposes patients towards ventilator induced lung injuries (VILI). These complications occur in terms of primary mechanical and secondary inflammatory injuries of lung tissue and are deemed the most important factors in the pathogenesis of ARDS.

Computational models of the respiratory system can provide essential insights into involved phenomena and support the development of improved patient-specific ventilation protocols in the long term. Notionally, we divided the respiratory system into two major subsystems, namely the conducting airways and the respiratory zone represented by lung parenchyma. Due to their respective complexity, both parts are themselves out of range for a direct numerical simulation resolving all relevant length scales. Therefore, we first developed detailed individual models for parts of the subsystems in turn. For the tracheo-bronchial region, CT-based geometries usually up to approximately seven generations were employed. We developed new robust schemes for fluid-structure interaction (FSI) simulations enabling the efficient coupling of incompressible flows and soft tissue. Thereby, we do not only consider the influence of the deformability of the airway walls but also embed the airway tree into homogenized lung parenchyma for the first time. Recently, we also used our elaborate models to study nanoparticle deposition in the human lung.

Since pulmonary alveoli are the main site of VILI, we also established a detailed model of alveolar ensembles considering the influence of the covering surfactant film as well as soft tissue behavior. Corresponding material parameters are determined in experimental studies on living lung tissue combined with an inverse analysis technique. Alveolar behavior is simulated using both artificial as well as CT-based alveolar geometries for the first time.

In order to model the unresolved parts of the respective subsystems appropriately, complex multi-scale approaches were developed. The dynamic behavior of lung parenchyma and local alveolar ensembles is investigated simultaneously by using novel nested multi-scale procedures, thereby obviating a direct numerical simulation of the completely resolved alveolar micro-structure. In the tracheo-bronchial region, physiological outflow boundary conditions are derived by considering the impedance of the unresolved parts of the lung in a fully coupled 3D-1D approach. First steps towards a coupling of the resulting parenchymal and airway models will be presented, opening up new vistas towards an all-encompassing 'virtual' lung model.

MULTI-LAYERED SOFT COLLAGENOUS TISSUES: CONSTITUTIVE MODELING AND INVERSE ANALYSIS

G. A. Holzapfel

Graz University of Technology, Institute of Biomechanics Center of Biomedical Engineering,
Kronesgasse 5-I, 8010 Graz, Austria, holzapfel@TUGraz.at
&
Royal Institute of Technology, Department of Solid Mechanics School of Engineering Sciences,
Osquars Backe 1, 100 44 Stockholm, Sweden

ABSTRACT

Several connective tissues consist of multiple layers and are composed primarily of collagen, a protein which gives the tissue strength, varying with, for example, age and pathology [1]. Cerebral aneurysmal walls, for example, are multi-layered structures with mean fiber alignments distinguishing one layer from another [2]. Walls of conducting arteries such as the aorta, subclavian, carotid, and iliac are other examples of soft collagenous tissues. They consist of multiple fenestrated elastic laminae separating the organized media into well-defined concentrically fiber-reinforced layers. The number of elastic laminae decreases toward the periphery. Quadricep tendons are also composed of multiple layers of collagenous tissue, and airway walls are multi-layered structures as well. A new versatile constitutive model for the mechanical response of multiple layers in collagenous tissues is presented [3]. It considers several layers with a mean collagen fiber alignment distinguishing one layer from another. The collagen fibers are embedded in a non-collagenous matrix material. By using that model a new method is presented for estimating the elastic properties of the inhomogeneous and anisotropic structure of, for example, saccular cerebral aneurysms by inverse analysis [4]. The distributions of anisotropic, elastic properties and wall stresses may be estimated. It is concluded that the wall stresses are accurate enough to facilitate the assessment of the risk of cerebral aneurysm rupture. There is an urgent need to consider the modeling of soft collagenous tissues at the molecular, cellular and tissue levels. A recent book [5] attempts to focus on this aspect covering a continuum biochemomechanical theory of soft tissue and cellular growth and remodeling (by JD Humphrey), the modeling of the heart (by H Schmid and PJ Hunter), anisotropy and nonlinear elasticity in arterial wall mechanics (by RW Ogden) and arterial tissue in health and disease (by GA Holzapfel) [5].

REFERENCES

[1]   G.A. Holzapfel, Collagen in arterial walls: Biomechanical aspects. In: P. Fratzl (ed). *Collagen Structure and Mechanics*, Springer-Verlag, Heidelberg, Chapter 11, 285-324, 2008.

[2]   P.B. Canham, H.M. Finlay, J.A. Kiernan and G.G. Ferguson, Layered structure of saccular aneurysms assessed by collagen birefringence, *Neurol Res* 21(7), 618626, (1999)

[3]   M. Kroon and G.A. Holzapfel, A new constitutive model for multi-layered collagenous tissues, *J. Biomech.*, 41, 2766-71, (2008)

[4]   M. Kroon and G.A. Holzapfel, Estimation of the distributions of anisotropic, elastic properties and wall stresses of saccular cerebral aneurysms by inverse analysis, *Proc. R. Soc. Lond. A*, 464, 807-25, (2008)

[5]   G.A. Holzapfel and R.W. Ogden (eds), *Biomechanical Modelling at the Molecular, Cellular and Tissue Levels*, Springer-Verlag, Wien, New-York, 2009.

PATIENT-SPECIFIC MODELING OF BLOOD FLOW AND VESSEL WALL DYNAMICS

C. A. Taylor
Department of Bioengineering Stanford University Stanford, CA 94305, USA
taylorca@stanford.edu

ABSTRACT

Hemodynamic factors including shear stress and pressure provide the stimuli for many acute and chronic changes in the vascular system and contribute to the initiation and progression of congenital heart diseases and acquired vascular diseases such as atherosclerosis and aneurysms. Furthermore, knowledge of hemodynamic variables is essential for properly assessing the severity of many vascular diseases and devising an appropriate therapeutic strategy.

While advances in cardiovascular imaging have provided unprecedented insight into vascular anatomy, noninvasive methods for quantifying physiologic variables are not as broadly applied, with the notable exceptions of phase contrast MRI and Doppler ultrasound. Yet, these imaging methods, no matter how advanced, can only provide data about the present state and do not provide a means to predict the outcome of an intervention or evaluate alternate prospective therapies. We have developed a computational framework for computing blood flow in anatomically relevant vascular anatomies with unprecedented realism. This framework includes methods for (i) creating subject-specific models of the vascular system from medical imaging data, (ii) specifying boundary conditions to account for the vasculature beyond the limits of imaging resolution, (iii) generating finite element meshes including anisotropy, adaptivity and boundary layers, (iv) assigning blood rheological and tissue mechanical properties, (v) simulating blood flow and vessel wall dynamics, and (vi) visualizing simulation results and extracting hemodynamic data. These methods have been applied to model blood flow and vessel wall dynamics in the aorta, the lower extremities, the cerebrovasculature, coronary and pulmonary arteries in children and adults. Such computational solutions of blood flow offer an opportunity to predict potential hemodynamic benefits of treatment strategies. An entirely new era in medicine could be created whereby doctors utilize simulation-based methods, initialized with patient-specific anatomic and physiologic data, to design improved treatments for individuals based on optimizing predicted outcomes. Furthermore, such methods have been applied to quantify hemodynamic conditions in animal models of human disease. Most recently, computational methods of blood flow and vessel wall dynamics have been coupled to growth and remodeling codes to simulate vascular adaptation in health and disease.

While significant progress in modeling blood flow and vessel wall dynamics has been made over the last decade, challenges remain. First, while three-dimensional anatomic data is readily available, physiologic (e.g. flow distribution, pressure, impedance spectra) and mechanical (e.g. vessel properties) input data are more difficult to obtain. Second, in vivo validation data is scarce and, as a result, theoretical methods development is greatly outpacing its experimental foundation. Third, state-of-the-art image-based modeling tools are only being used at a few elite research universities and institutions around the world due to the significant expertise required to produce meaningful results. Developing software systems for reliable patient-specific modeling of blood flow and vessel wall dynamics for biomedical researchers, clinicians and engineers who are not experts in biomedical computational science is a challenge for the future.

COMPUTATIONAL MODELLING OF OPTIC NERVE HEAD BIOMECHANICS

C.R. Ethier

Department of Bioengineering Imperial College London, London SW7 2AZ, UK

r.ethier@imperial.ac.uk

ABSTRACT

Glaucoma is the second most common cause of blindness in western countries, afflicting 65 to 70 million people worldwide [1]. All forms of glaucoma have a common clinical end point of visual field loss and characteristic changes to the optic nerve head (ONH), the region at the back of the eye where the axons forming the optic nerve leave the eye posteriorly. In the most common forms of the disease, the pressure within the eye (intraocular pressure, or IOP) is elevated, and IOP lowering is currently the only way to treat the disease. We do not yet understand the pathophysiology of blindness in glaucoma, but studies have strongly suggested that biomechanical factors acting within the optic nerve head are important. The working model is that high IOP leads to elevated mechanical stresses acting within the connective tissues of the ONH, which in turn lead to nerve fibre damage, probably through activation of Type 1-β astrocytes and/or other glial cells [2]. It is therefore important to understand the biomechanical environment within the ONH, e.g. to drive better cell culture models of the biology of the disease process. Unfortunately, the ONH is difficult to access experimentally, since it is located at the very posterior aspect of the eye and is composed of soft connective and neural tissue components surrounded by the extremely stiff sclera. We have therefore used numerical modelling based on anatomic reconstructions and ex vivo mechanical testing to better understand ONH biomechanics. In this presentation I will discuss the role of sensitivity analyses in deducing the most important factors that influence ONH biomechanics; how histologic and high-field MRI imaging have been used to drive finite elements simulations of ONH biomechanics; and the incorporation of biaxial mechanical testing results for sclera into current generation models of ocular biomechanics.

Support: Canadian Institutes of Health Research and Royal Society Wolfson Research Excellence Award.

REFERENCES

[1] H. A. Quigley and A. T. Broman, The number of people with glaucoma worldwide in 2010 and 2020, *Br J Ophthalmol* 90(3), 262-267, 2006

[2] M. R. Hernandez, The optic nerve head in glaucoma: role of astrocytes in tissue remodeling, *Progress in Retinal and Eye Research* 19(3), 297-321, 2000

MODELING COLLAGEN (RE)MODELING

F.P.T. Baaijens

Department of Biomedical Engineering, Eindhoven University of Technology, P.O. Box 513, 5600MB
Eindhoven, Netherlands

F.P.T.Baaijens@tue.nl

ABSTRACT

The collagen architecture of native heart valves and small diameter arteries is well organized and critical for their biomechanical function. Mimicking this architecture in tissue engineered heart valves and arteries may be necessary for their short- and long-term in vivo functionality. We assume that mechanical loads play a decisive role during the development of the collagen architecture. To understand the mechanobiology of collagen modeling a series of tissue engineering experiments were performed and computational models were developed with increasing complexity and predictive capability. In modeling collagen modeling we first assumed that newly formed collagen is aligned in the principal strain directions. This gave a fairly good prediction of the collagen architecture in heart valves, but could not predict the typical helix shaped collagen structure in arteries. We next assumed that collagen is aligned in between the principal strain (or stress) directions. With this assumption the helix shaped collagen architecture in arteries is predicted accurately, while a clear improvement of the predicted collagen structure in heart valves is obtained. Our understanding of the mechanism of load induced (mechanoregulation) collagen alignment is incomplete. The lecture focuses on what we do and dont understand about this mechanism, and which future experiments may enhance our understanding.

CLINICAL APPLICATION OF IMAGE-BASED CFD FOR CEREBRAL ANEURYSMS

J. R. Cebral
Center for Computational Fluid Dynamics George Mason University, USA
jcebral@gmu.edu

ABSTRACT

In this talk I will summarize our clinical investigations in cerebral aneurysms using image-based computational fluid dynamics. We have used these techniques to create a database of patient-specific hemodynamics models of cerebral aneurysm. A variety of studies have been conducted in order to validate the computational models. These include comparison to analytical solutions in simple geometries, comparison to in vitro models with both idealized and patient-specific geometries as well as comparison to blood flow patterns observed in vivo using dynamic X-ray angiography. Sensitivity studies have also been carried out in order to assess the effects of different modeling parameters, varying physiologic conditions, and motion of the arterial walls including both pulsation and translational motions observed in vivo with dynamic imaging techniques. Subsequently, these models have been used to relate hemodynamic characteristics to clinical observations with the objective of better understanding the mechanisms responsible for the pathogenesis, growth and rupture of intracranial aneurysms. In particular, it was found that in a sample of 60+ aneurysms, unruptured aneurysms tended to have diffuse inflow jets impacting on a large area of the aneurysm sac and associated simple/stable flow patterns. In contrast, ruptured aneurysms tended to have concentrated inflow jets impacting on a small area of the sac and complex/unstable flow patterns. In another sample of 30+ aneurysms of the anterior communicating artery it was found that ruptured aneurysms had higher values of maximum wall shear stress than unruptured aneurysms. In addition, it was observed that secondary lobulations or blebs tend to develop at or adjacent to regions of elevated aneurysm wall shear stress associated with the impingement of the inflow jet against the aneurysm wall. Once a bleb is formed a new flow recirculation zone is created opposing the main flow direction and the bleb always progresses towards a state of lower wall shear stress. In parallel to these studies, we have developed adaptive unstructured embedded grid techniques to model patient-specific blood flows in cerebral aneurysms after treatment with endovascular procedures. These techniques are being currently used to study the flow modification effects of different flow diverting stents in order to improve their design, and to relate the changes in the aneurysm hemodynamics to the outcome of endovascular interventions. The major safety concern with the use of stents to treat intracranial aneurysms if the possibility of occluding perforators or small arterial branches which can result in strokes. For this reason, we developed a methodology to assess the reduction in the flow rate in jailed arterial branches that uses the resistance of the distal vascular beds to apply appropriate outflow boundary conditions. Preliminary results suggest that, because the resistances of the vascular beds of small arteries are quite large, the flow rate in these arteries is preserved to a large degree even if a large percentage of the area of their origin is occluded by the stent. Although these models do not consider thrombosis or endothelization mechanisms, they are in agreement with clinical observation.

WALL STRESS ANALYSIS OF ABDOMINAL AORTIC ANEURYSMS AND ITS POSSIBLE USE FOR PERSONALIZED DIAGNOSTICS PLANNING

F.N. van de Vosse
Eindhoven University of Technology, Biomedical Engineering
&
Maastricht University Hospital, Vascular Surgery

L. Speelman
Eindhoven University of Technology, Biomedical Engineering
&
Maastricht University Hospital, Vascular Surgery

M. vant Veer
Catharina Hospital Eindhoven, Cardiology and Vascular Surgery

S. de Putter
Eindhoven University of Technology, Biomedical Engineering

E.A. van Dam
Eindhoven University of Technology, Biomedical Engineering

E.M.H. Bosboom
Maastricht University Hospital, Vascular Surgery

M.C.M. Rutten
Eindhoven University of Technology, Biomedical Engineering

M. Breeuwer
Philips Medical Systems, Healthcare Information Technology

G.W.H. Schurink
Maastricht University Hospital, Vascular Surgery

J. Buth
Catharina Hospital Eindhoven, Cardiology and Vascular Surgery

ABSTRACT

Introduction: An abdominal aortic aneurysm (AAA) is a dilatation of the aortic wall leading to an increase in diameter of at least 50%. If left untreated, most AAAs will increase in size until rupture causing a life threatening hemorrhage. Currently, the criterion for elective repair by endovascular or open surgery stent-graft placement is a maximum diameter of at least 5.5 cm. Multiple studies show that not only diameter but also peak or 99-percentile peak wall stress may be indicative for rupture risk. In these studies it is hypothesized that wall stress analysis may give indications why a number of small AAAs do rupture in an early stage and some large AAAs seem not to rupture at all.

Methods: Computations of the wall stress in abdominal aortic aneurysms are based on geometrical data obtained by CT or MRI imaging [1] and approximate (Finite Element) solutions of the momentum equation endowed with an appropriate constitutive relation between the state of stress and the state of strain [2]. In this presentation the role of non-linear stress-strain relations will be discussed in relation with the importance of the initial strain that will be present in the aortic wall at the moment is imaged [3]. Both in-vitro [4] and in-vivo assessment of the vessel wall and thrombus mechanical properties based on MRI imaging are carried out to obtain the material parameters to be used in the constitutive relations between stress and strain. In the presentation these methods will be discussed in view of their possible clinical application.

Results: First results of a pilot clinical study (20 patients), where aneurysm diameter and shape are related to 99-percentile peak stress based on the computational methods presented will be presented. The importance of non-linear modelling, initial stress inclusion and the role of thrombus will be discussed.

REFERENCES

[1] S. de Putter, M. Breeuwer, U. Kose, F.N. van de Vosse, F.A. Gerritsen, Automatic determination of the dynamic geometry of abdominal aortic aneurysm from MR with application to wall stress simulations, *ICS*, 1281, 339-344, (2005)

[2] B.J.B.M. Wolters, M.C.M. Rutten, G.W. Schurink, U. Kose, J. de Hart, F.N. van de Vosse, A patient-specific computational model of fluid-structure interaction in abdominal aortic aneurysms, *Med. Eng. Phys.*, 27(10), 871-883, (2005)

[3] S. de Putter, B.J.B.M. Wolters, M.C.M. Rutten, M. Breeuwer, F.A. Gerritsen, F.N. van de Vosse, Patient-specifc initial wall stress in abdominal aortic aneurysms with a backward incremental method, *J. Biomech.*, 40(5), 1081-1090, (2007)

[4] E.A. van Dam, S.D. Dams, G.W.M. Peters, M.C.M. Rutten, G.W.H. Schurink, J. Buth, F.N. van de Vosse, Determination of Linear Viscoelastic Behavior of Abdominal Aortic Aneurysm Thrombus, *Biorheology*, 43(6), 695-707, (2006)

Mini-Symposia

Prestressing patient–specific biomechanical problems under finite deformation

Michael W. Gee

Institute for Computational Mechanics, Technische Universität München,
Boltzmannstr 15, D -85747 Garching, Germany, gee@lnm.mw.tum.de

Wolfgang A. Wall

Institute for Computational Mechanics, Technische Universität München,
Boltzmannstr 15, D -85747 Garching, Germany, wall@lnm.mw.tum.de

ABSTRACT

In simulation of biomechanical structures the patient specific geometry of the object of interest is very often reconstructed from in–vivo medical imaging such as CT scans. Such geometries therefore represent a deformed configuration stressed by typical in–vivo conditions. Commonly, such structures are considered stress–free in simulation. In this contribution we present and compare two methods to introduce a physically meaningful stress/strain state to the obtained geometry for simulations in the finite strain regime and demonstrate the necessity of such prestressing techniques. One method is based on an inverse design analysis (ID) to calculate a stress–free reference configuration. The other method developed by the authors is based on a modified updated Lagrangian formulation (MULF). Formulation of both methods is provided and implementation issues are discussed. Applicability and accurateness of both approaches are compared and evaluated utilizing fully three dimensional patient specific abdominal aortic aneurysm structures within the context of wall stress and fluid–structure interaction analysis.

Key Words: *inverse design analysis, prestressing, prestraining, patient specific modeling, abdominal aortic aneurysm, fluid–structure interaction.*

1 Introduction

Through great progress in models and simulation approaches in biomechanics it is nowadays possible and desirable to use patient–specific geometries obtained from medical imaging to construct computational models of biomechanical structures. When in–vivo medical imaging is applied the resulting images and therefore reconstructed three dimensional geometries represent a configuration under in–vivo load such as e.g. blood pressure. A common approach in simulation of such patient specific geometries is to neglect the pre–deformation of the object of interest under in–vivo loads and to assume the obtained configuration as stress–free. As we will demonstrate, this simplified approach will lead to unphysically large deformations, strains and stresses at least in cases where finite deformations and maybe even large strains do occur. One interesting case where above comments apply is the simulation of abdominal aortic aneurysms (AAA) [1, 2]. Here, the in–vivo geometry represents a pre–deformed spatial configuration that is mainly loaded by blood pressure. It is also known from experiments [3] that aneurysm wall material undergoes large strains. Three dimensional AAA structures reconstructed from imaging are pre–loaded by time averaged blood pressure which accounts for a significant portion of the occurring peak loads. Taking the in–vivo geometry as stress–free is especially not suitable for fluid–structure interaction simulations as this assumption will lead to non–physical large deformations under realistic loading. Here, we consider two types of methods to introduce prestressing in computational patient specific biomechanics in the finite strain regime and apply them to AAA examples: The first is based on an inverse design analysis where we assume the load to be e.g. constant diastolic blood pressure at the time of medical imaging. We show how the resulting prestressed configuration is incorporated in a standard forward analysis within fluid–structure interaction or structural dynamics simulations. The second method is based on a modified Updated Lagrangian formulation (MULF), where a multiplicative split of the deformation gradient is used to produce a displacement–free prestrained/prestressed state. We compare results of the two approaches and discuss benefits and drawbacks of both methods applied to fully three dimensional patient specific abdominal aortic aneurysm structures.

2 Prestressing with inverse design analysis (ID)

Classically, an inverse design problem deals with the question how a body has to be shaped in the material configuration such that under a defined set of loads it takes on a prescribed shape. We consider the boundary value problem of finite deformation elasticity on an undistorted structure $\Omega_0 \subset \mathbb{R}^3$ in the stress–free material configuration which can be cast to a (deformed) spatial configuration $\Omega_t \subset \mathbb{R}^3$

$$\text{div}\boldsymbol{\sigma} + \mathbf{b}_t = \mathbf{0} \text{ in } \Omega_t \ , \quad \mathbf{u} = \mathbf{u}_D^t \text{ on } \gamma_D \ , \quad \boldsymbol{\sigma}\,\mathbf{n}_\gamma = \mathbf{t}_t \text{ on } \gamma_N \ . \tag{1}$$

We assume a hyperelastic material behavior as published in [3] for the AAA wall. We further introduce the inverse deformation gradient $\mathbf{f} = \partial \mathbf{X}/\partial \mathbf{x} = \mathbf{F}^{-1}$ that relates the (unknown) material configuration to the (known) spatial configuration. The method of weighted residuals is applied to the spatial balance equation in (1) resulting in the weak form

$$\delta\Pi_t = \delta\Pi_t^{int} - \delta\Pi_t^{ext} = \int_{\Omega_t} \delta\mathbf{e} : \boldsymbol{\sigma} \, \mathrm{d}\Omega - \int_{\Omega_t} \mathbf{b}_t \cdot \delta\mathbf{u} \, \mathrm{d}\Omega - \int_{\gamma_N} \mathbf{t}_t \cdot \delta\mathbf{u} \, \mathrm{d}\gamma = 0 \ . \tag{2}$$

Equation (2) is solved for the unknown material frame $\mathbf{X}$ using a finite element discretization method and appropriate nonlinear numerical solution techniques such as Newton–type methods. Implementation and linearization details can be found in more detail in [6].

3 Prestressing with Modified Updated Lagrangian Formulation (MULF)

Starting point of the method is a known spatial configuration obtained from imaging. We denote such a configuration as $\Omega_t \subset \mathbb{R}^3$ with $\mathbf{x}_t$ as corresponding coordinate vector field. The configuration Ω_t is subject to an external load $\mathbf{t}_t \neq \mathbf{0}$ that is known and in equilibrium with the stress state of the structure at the time when medical imaging was performed. The weak form of the balance equation in a material configuration with respect to Ω_t reads

$$\delta\Pi_t = \delta\Pi_t^{int} - \delta\Pi_t^{ext} = \int_{\Omega_t} \delta\mathbf{E} : \mathbf{S} \, \mathrm{d}\Omega - \int_{\gamma_N} \mathbf{t}_t \cdot \delta\mathbf{u} \, \mathrm{d}\gamma = 0 \ . \tag{3}$$

(3) can only be true in the non–trivial case $\mathbf{S} \neq \mathbf{0}$ if either a deformation gradient $\mathbf{F} \neq \mathbf{I}$ exists or displacements $\mathbf{u} \neq \mathbf{0}$ occur that result in a non–trivial deformation gradient. Therefore, a usual incremental load controlled calculation is performed with the only difference that the incremental summation of displacement increments is replaced by an incremental multiplicative update of an independent inprinted deformation gradient. The structure does not deform but builds up the inprinted deformation gradient in an incremental way [6, 8].

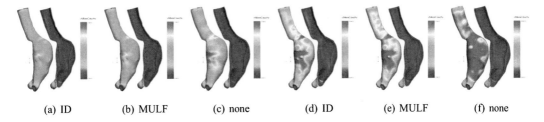

| (a) ID | (b) MULF | (c) none | (d) ID | (e) MULF | (f) none |

Figure 1: Figures (a) – (c): $Male71y$ prestressed state at $85mmHg$. Figures (d) – (f): Analysis at $120mmHg$ based on prestressed state in Figures (a) – (c). View and cut showing ILT geometry. Colors indicate von Mises Cauchy stresses.

4   Results and discussion

The presented approaches represent robust and applicable methods for determining the prestressing state of general patient-specific AAAs. We applied MULF and ID prestressing in a study of 39 aneurysms, of which two structures named $Male71y$ and $Female48y$ are utilized here to discuss the characteristics of the methods. The geometries obtained from medical imaging shown in Figs. 1 and 2

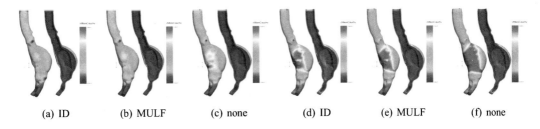

| (a) ID | (b) MULF | (c) none | (d) ID | (e) MULF | (f) none |

Figure 2: Figures (a) – (c): $Female48y$ prestressed state at $85mmHg$. Figures (d) – (f): Analysis at $120mmHg$ based on prestressed state in Figures (a) – (c). View and cut showing ILT geometry. Colors indicate von Mises Cauchy stresses.

account for the three dimensional geometry of the intraluminal thrombus (ILT) and assume a constant aortic wall thickness of $1mm$ as the aortic wall can not be seen in standard CT images clearly. For the aortic wall, an isotropic aortic aneurysm material model according to [3] is used, for the ILT a Neo–Hookean model is applied. It is assumed that diastolic blood pressure $p = 85mmHg$ was present at the time of imaging and therefore the aneurysm structures are prestressed with this load applying the ID and MULF prestressing techniques. Results for the prestressed stress state as well as a standard forward calculation assuming the initial imaged configuration to be stress–free are given in Figs. 1 and 2, respectively. In the ID and MULF case, the deformation is zero and the configuration corresponds to the one from medical imaging. In the forward analysis case (Figures 1(c) , 2(c)) the deformation of course is nonzero. The stress states from MULF and ID prestressing are comparable with stresses from MULF prestressing being slightly higher. Stresses in the no–prestressing analysis are significantly too large mainly due to the fact that the pressure load is applied with respect to the deformed configuration. After having obtained this prestressed state the load is further increased to the systolic pressure level $p = 120mmHg$. The aneurysms deform and the corresponding stress states are compared to the no–prestressing analysis in Figs. 1 and 2 in sub–Figures (d) through (f), respectively. Again, the deformations obtained from ID and MULF prestressing are comparable while the no–prestressing analysis overestimates displacements significantly. The no–prestressing simulation yields unrealistically large deformations in Figures 3(c) and 3(f) as expected. The inverse design analysis (ID) does not yield a unique stress–free material configuration in the finite deformation context. Due to non–uniqueness, the

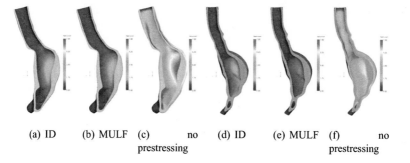

(a) ID   (b) MULF   (c)   no   (d) ID   (e) MULF   (f)   no
                      prestressing   prestressing

Figure 3: AAAs $Male71y$ ((a)–(c)) , $Female48y$ ((d)–(f)) under $120mmHg$. Comparison of deformation for ID, MULF and no–prestressing case. Grey slice indicates spatial configuration from medical imaging. Color indicates displacements.

material configurations have to be evaluated with great care. The MULF prestressing technique does not yield a stress–free reference configuration but approximates the prestressed state directly. The resulting prestressed state is unique. This represents a major advantage over the ID prestressing method.

References

[1] J. Humphrey, C. Taylor, Intracranial and abdominal aortic aneurysms: Similarities, differences, and need for a new class of computational models, Ann. Rev. Biomed. Eng. 10 (2008) 221–246.

[2] D. Vorp, Biomechanics of abdominal aortic aneurysms, Journal of Biomechanics 40 (2007) 1887–902.

[3] M. Raghavan, D. Vorp, Toward a biomechanical tool to evaluate rupture potential of abdominal aortic aneurysm: identification of a finite strain constitutive model and evaluation of its applicability, Journal of Biomechanics 33 (2000) 475–482.

[4] J. Lu, X. Zhou, M. Raghavan, Inverse elastostatic stress analysis in pre–deformed biological structures: Demonstration using abdominal aortic aneurysms, Journal of Biomechanics 40 (2007) 693–696.

[5] J. Lu, X. Zhou, M. Raghavan, Inverse method of stress analysis for cerebral aneurysms, J. Biomech Model. Mechanobiol. 7 (2008) 477–486.

[6] M.W. Gee, C. Förster, W.A. Wall, A computational strategy for prestressing patient–specific biomechanical problems under finite deformation, Communications in Numerical Methods in Engineering with Biomedical Applications, in press.

[7] U. Küttler, M.W. Gee, C. Förster, A. Comerford, W.A. Wall, Coupling strategies for biomedical fluid-structure interaction problems, Communications in Numerical Methods in Engineering with Biomedical Applications, in press.

[8] M.W. Gee, C. Reeps, H.H. Eckstein, W.A. Wall, Prestressing in finite deformation abdominal aortic aneurysm simulation, submitted to J. Biomechanics.

[9] V. Fachinotti, A. Cardona, P. Jetteur, Finite element modelling of inverse design problems in large deformation anisotropic hyperelasticity, International Journal for Numerical Methods in Engineering 74 (2008) 894–910.

1ˢᵗ International Conference on Mathematical and Computational Biomedical Engineering – CMBE2009
June 29 – July 1, 2009, Swansea, UK
P. Nithiarasu and R. Löhner (eds)

COMPUTATIONAL FLUID DYNAMICS: CLINICAL APPLICATION IN HUMAN CORONARY ARTERIES

Frank Gijsen
Biomedical Engineering, Thoraxcenter, ErasmusMC, f.gijsen@erasmusmc.nl
Jolanda Wentzel
Biomedical Engineering, Thoraxcenter, ErasmusMC, j.wentzel@erasmusmc.nl
Hans Schuurbiers
Biomedical Engineering, Thoraxcenter, ErasmusMC, j.schuurbiers@erasmusmc.nl
Anton van der Steen
Biomedical Engineering, Thoraxcenter, ErasmusMC, a.vandersteen@erasmusmc.nl
Patrick Serruys
Interventional Cardiology, Thoraxcenter, ErasmusMC, p.w.c.serruys@erasmusmc.nl

Key Words: *shear stress, atherosclerosis, coronary arteries*

1. INTRODUCTION

It is well established that atherosclerotic plaques generally develop in low shear stress regions, including curved arterial segments and bifurcations[1]. Once these plaques intrude into the lumen, the shear stress they are exposed to alters with hitherto unknown consequences. We hypothesize that in the more advanced stages of the disease, shear stress has an important impact on plaque composition in such a way that high shear stress enhances plaque vulnerability through its biological impact on the endothelium[2].
If we want to investigate this and other hypotheses we need to study the relationship between shear stress and markers of atherosclerosis in human coronary arteries, several requirements have to be met. Shear stress distribution can be obtained through computational fluid dynamics (CFD). To apply this method, we need detailed information on the 3D geometry of coronary arteries (a real challenge in these small, moving arteries), boundary conditions and material properties. If we want to study the impact of shear stress on atherosclerosis, we also have to identify the relevant markers of the disease and preferably determine how these markers change over time. The most important input parameter for application of CFD is the 3D geometry of the coronary arteries. We developed an imaging technique[3] in which we combine biplane angiography with intravascular ultrasound (IVUS). The IVUS images were acquired during a pullback, contours of the lumen of the artery were drawn in the IVUS images and subsequently stacked on the 3D reconstruction of the path of the catheter (figure 1, left panel). The other input data for application of CFD are also patient derived. Flow measurements with a Doppler wire and viscosity measurements with a capillary viscometer.

Atherosclerosis is characterized by local thickening of the vessel wall. Several wall components can be responsible for the increased wall thickness, including lipid accumulation, fibrous tissue and calcifications. The thickness of the plaque is a measure for the 'age' of the disease, while plaque composition is important to determine the plaque phenotype. Vulnerable plaques for example are characterized by a large lipid pool, covered by a thin fibrous cap, which is often infiltrated by macrophages.

Several imaging techniques can be used to determine surrogate markers for atherosclerosis in vivo. The one that is used most frequently is wall thickness, which can easily be derived from IVUS. Other IVUS based imaging techniques (palpography and virtual histology) are capable of providing information on plaque composition.

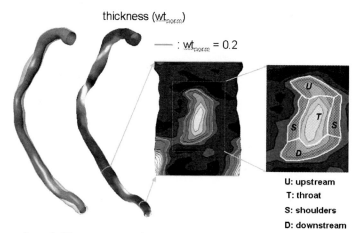

U: upstream
T: throat
S: shoulders
D: downstream

figure 1: 3D reconstration of a coronary artery (left) and plaque definition

In this current study we focus on two experimental methods to determine markers of atherosclerosis, palpography and virtual histology, and we study how they are related to shear stress in human coronary arteries.

2. SHEAR STRESS VS PALPOGRAPHY

Palpography[3] was applied to measure radial strain, which is a surrogate marker for plaque composition. After matching the ultrasound data sets, we were able to study the relationship between shear stress and strain. To do so, each plaque was divided into 4 regions: upstream, throat, shoulder and downstream (see figure 1). Average shear stress and strain were determined in each region. A subset of the arteries was also imaged at a follow-up procedure after six months. After matching the strain data from index and follow up, we can infer how strain changed over time in each region and as a function of the shear stress levels at index.

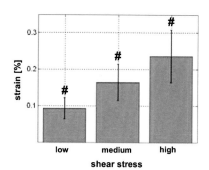

figure 2: pooled data for averaged normalized shear stress versus strain

The data for the plaque regions from the index procedure[4] showed that shear stress in the upstream, shoulder, throat and the downstream region were 2.55±0.89 Pa, 2.07±0.98 Pa, 2.32±1.11 Pa and 0.67±0.35 Pa respectively. Shear stress in the downstream region was significantly lower. Strain in the downstream region was also significantly lower than the values in the other regions (0.09±03% vs 0.19±0.06%, 0.19±0.05%, and 0.17±0.07% for the upstream, shoulder and throat region respectively). Pooling all regions, dividing shear stress per plaque into tertiles and computing average strain showed a positive correlation: for low, medium and high shear stress, strain was 0.09±0.04%, 0.16±0.06% and 0.24±0.07%, respectively (figure 2).

Preliminary data from the follow-up measurements (n=16) revealed that strain increased mostly in the upstream region (+0.03%), followed by the shoulder (+0.02%), and throat (+0.01%) region. In the downstream region, strain decreased by –0.01%.

Instead of looking at the separate regions, we analyzed the results like we did for the strain values from the index procedure. All data were pooled, and we investigated how the strain changed in the regions that were exposed to low, medium and high shear stress at the index. In figure 3, it can be seen that those regions exposed to low and medium shear stress showed a slight decrease in strain, while the regions exposed to high shear stress showed a clear increase in strain.

Low strain co-localizes with low shear stress downstream of a plaque, indicating that stiffer wall material is present there. Higher strain can be found in all other plaque regions, with highest strain found in regions exposed to the highest shear stresses. The follow-up data indicate that there is a prevalence of increase in strain in the upstream region of the plaque, while strain decreases in the downstream region. The regions exposed to the highest shear stress values show an increase in strain over time. This indicates that weaker underlying wall material at those locations, and these regions might be more prone to rupture.

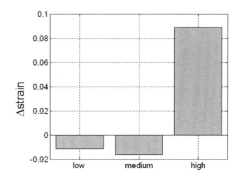

figure 3: change of strain as a function of normalized shear stress

3. SHEAR STRESS VS VIRTUAL HISTOLOGY

We investigated the relationship between shear stress and plaque composition from virtual histology (VH) in 10 coronary arteries from 10 patients. For the acquisition of the VH images a continuous pullback with an IVUS catheter (Volcano, USA) was performed in the same artery. The radiofrequency data was processed to obtain color-coded tissue maps of each cross-section[5]. The VH images were matched with the 3D lumen reconstruction from the ANGUS procedure (figure 4). Per cross section the average shear stress was calculated. For each cross section, we defined low shear stress as lower than 0.95 times the average value, and high shear stress as higher than 1.05 times the average value. In order to investigate the influence of the severity of the disease on the relationship between shear stress and location of necrotic core, cross sections were divided into 2 groups, based on the size of either plaque burden (<40%, >40%)

figure 4: fusion of the 3D imaging procedure ANGUS and virtual histology in a human coronary artery

or necrotic core area (<10%, >10%). Plaque burden <40% was considered as surrogate marker for early atherosclerosis with minimal lumen narrowing and plaque burden >40% represents the more advanced stage of atherosclerosis. Necrotic core >10% is one of the criteria for identification of IVUS derived vulnerable plaque.

In the 863 matched cross sections, 51 cross sections did not contain a necrotic core. The cross sections with a necrotic core had a smaller lumen area (9.0± 5.1 vs 11.7±6.5, p<0.05) and larger wall thickness (0.6±0.2 vs 0.3±0.1 mm, p<0.05) than the cross sections without a necrotic core. Table I present the characteristic of the cross sections containing a necrotic core with a plaque burden <40% and >40%, and a necrotic core size <10% and >10%. Cross sections with a plaque burden <40% had in average a larger lumen area, media bounded area and smaller wall thickness values than cross sections with plaque burden >40%. Comparing the cross sections with a large necrotic core (>10%) to the ones with a small necrotic core (<10%), it could be observed that plaques with a large necrotic core had, as expected, the largest plaque burden and wall thickness (p<0.05).

In the cross sections with necrotic core, the shear stress ranged from 0.35 to 19.36 Pa with an average of 4.12±3.83 Pa. Per cross section the average shear stress was calculated and the shear stress at the locations of necrotic core was compared to the average shear stress. For 30% of the cross sections the necrotic core was located at low shear stress, while 47% was located at high shear stress.
For cross sections with plaque burden <40%, the necrotic core was almost equally distributed over the high shear stress and low shear stress regions (fig 5A, 36% vs 42%). However, for cross sections with a plaque burden >40%, the necrotic core was more frequently found in the high shear stress region than in the low shear stress region (52% vs 25%).

Subsequently the cross sections were divided into two groups based on the size of the necrotic core (fig 5B). With increasing necrotic core size the percentage cross sections for which the necrotic core was located at low shear stress decreased from 32% to 21%, while, interestingly, the percentage cross sections for which the necrotic core was located at high shear stress remained the same (47% vs 49%). Subsequently the cross sections were divided into 4 groups based on both the plaque burden and the necrotic core size. We observed that plaques with a necrotic core >10%, but still having a plaque burden < 40% were in 58% of

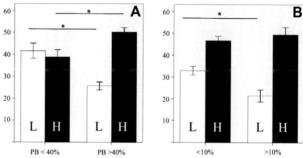

figure 5: shear stress at locations with necrotic core for different plaque burdens (A) and necrotic core area (B). L= lower shear stress, H= higher shear stress.

the cases located at low shear stress regions (fig 6A). That percentage decreased to 17% when plaque burden exceeded 40% (p<0.05). However, for plaques with a necrotic core <10%, the plaque burden did not make too much of a difference as to have the necrotic core located at low shear stress or at high shear stress (39% vs 30%, p<0.05). Both plaques with a necrotic core <10% and >10%, showed a slightly increased shear stress with increasing plaque burden (fig 6B).

The current results show that even in early atherosclerosis, a significant amount of the plaques are exposed to elevated shear stress levels, indicating that lumen narrowing probably already occurs at plaque burden below 40%. Furthermore, we showed that especially the lipid rich lesions are subjected to changes in shear stress during the progress of atherosclerosis. In the early phase of the disease, the lipid rich plaques are predominantly located in low shear stress regions,

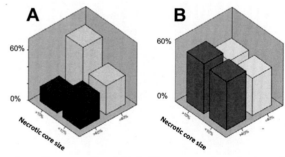

figure 6: cross section divided with respect to plaque burden and necrotic core size. Regions exposed to low WSS are given in (A) and regions exposed to high WSS in (B).

while in the more advanced phase of the disease, they are exposed to higher shear stress. This change in shear stress might trigger biological mechanisms that lead to plaque destabilization.

References:

1) Malek et al., JAMA, vol 282, pp 2035-2042, 1999
2) Slager et al., Nature Clinical Practice, 2, 456-464, 2005
3) Schaar et al., Circulation, vol 108, pp 2636-2641, (2003).
4) Gijsen et al., Am J Physiol Hear Circ Physiol, 295(4), 2008
5) Nair et al., Circulation, 106, 2002.

1st International Conference on Mathematical and Computational Biomedical Engineering - CMBE2009
June 29 - July 1, 2009, Swansea, UK
P.Nithiarasu and R.Löhner (Eds.)

UNSTEADY FLUID SOLID INTERACTION ANALYSIS OF A BIFURCATION IN A HUMAN HEALTHY LEFT CORONARY ARTERY.

M. Malvè, J. F. Rodríguez, A. García, M. A. Martínez, M. Doblaré
Group of Structural Mechanics and Materials Modelling. Aragón Institute of Engineering Research (I3A), University of Zaragoza. Networking Center in Bioengineering, Biomaterials and Nanomedicine (CIBER-BBN). C/ Maria de Luna s/n - 50018 - Zaragoza (Spain), mmalve@unizar.es

J. Ohayon
Laboratoire TIMC-IMAG, Equipe DynaCell, CNRS/URM5525, Pavillon Taillefer, Faculté de Médicine de Grenoble, 38700 La Tronche, France, jacques.ohayon@univ-savoie.fr

ABSTRACT

In this study, a fluid solid interaction analysis (FSI) of a MRI reconstructed left coronary artery was analyzed. The arterial wall was modeled as fiber reinforced hyperelastic material following the recent model of Holzapfel et al. (2005). The shear stress of the arterial wall was computed in order to investigate a correlation between flow-induced wall shear stress and geometry of the artery. In particular, since the most usual atheromatous plaque locations in the human coronaries are the arterial bifurcations, the relationship between blood flow and plaque formation near the bifurcations taking into account the arterial wall deformation was studied. An unsteady state FSI analysis with a commercial software (AD-INA) was performed in order to evaluate the maximum and the minimum wall shear stress as a function of the flow regime and the arterial wall deformation in the left coronary. The material modes were included in the code by using a user subroutine. The wall shear stress (WSS) values were quantified and correlated with the usual location of atheromatous plaque formation.

Key Words: *fluid solid interaction, fiber reinforced arterial wall, blood flow, wall shear stress.*

1 INTRODUCTION

Nowdays, cardiovascular diseases represent the most frequent cause of death in the modern civilization. In particular they are the 49% of the death diseases in Europe and the 38% in United Stated [1]. The common index for those pathologies, known as CVD (*Cardio-Vascular Disease*) includes different kinds of cardiovascular diseases and it is considered as one the most important reference of the world human health [1].

Cardiovascular diseases are divided in different classes: infarction (ischemic or hemorragic), thrombosis and aneurism. One of the most important class is surely the coronary disease, included in the category of cardiovascular diseases with the index CAD (*Coronary Artery Disease*). In this class, the most important role is played by atherosclerotic diseases caused by formation, developing and rupture of atheromatous plaques.

Studies on coronary arteries are normally focused on hemodynamics aspect, neglecting the interaction between blood flow and arterial walls, evaluating the WSS at the rigid walls and connecting it with atheromatous pathologies (Fukumoto et al., 2008, Asakura et al., 1990). Gijsen et al. (2007) analyzed a left arterial bifurcation showing the hemodynamics of a left main arterial bifurcation of just one patient.

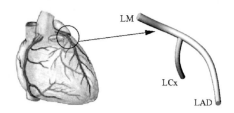

Figure 1: Geometry of the studied left coronary artery.

Soulis et al. (2006) studied a left main arterial bifurcation of the main, the ascending and the circumflex arterial branches but using a mean geometry. Goubergrits et al. (2009) performed a CFD simulation of a rigid wall based left arterial bifurcation comparing the results with a silico experimental model. Moreover, recently some FSI studies of vulnearable atheromatous plaques have been performed.

The aim of this work is the understanding of how the blood flow patterns can affect the arterial wall and how the plaque formation can be influenced by the WSS. This understanding will help the develop of more efficient strategies to treat pathological patients.

2   MATERIALS AND METHODS

The 3D coronary artery model of a 60 years old healthy patient was made with help of computer imaging technics. A patient specific geometry and the heart movement were reconstructed using computed tomography (CT) scans and magnetic resonance imaging (MRI) in one point of time of the cardiac cycle. As shown in the Figure 1, the arterial tree considered in this study included the left main coronary artery (LM) and its principle branches: the left descending artery (LAD) and the left circumflex artery (LCx). The real data were imported in the commercial sofware $FEMAP^{©}$ in the way to smooth the rough geometry and generate the computational mesh.

A full hexaedral mesh of the arterial wall was generate using the commercial code $I - DEAS^{©}$ (Figure 2). The fluid tetrahedrical mesh, made with the commercial code $FEMAP^{©}$ (Figure 2) was performed starting from the internal shell that represents the fluid solid interface domain. The final mesh was imported in the software package $ADINA^{©}$ where the fluid-solid interaction was performed.

The arterial wall was characterized with the Holzapfel model [7] as 3-layers (*intima, media* and *adventitia*) fiber reinforced hyperelastic material. As the reconstructed artery came from an healthy patient, the blood was supposed as Newtonian and incompressible ($\rho = 1008 \ Kg/m^3$, $\mu = 3.5 \ cPoise$) under unsteady conditions [8] [11]. Moreover, the blood flow was assumed laminar (the Reynolds number was in the range $0 < Re < 200$).

As boundary conditions, time dependent inlet and outlet velocity conditions were used. Starting from a spatially uniform, time variable velocity inlet profile (Sankaranarayanan et al. 2005), outlet velocities were calculated on each instant of the cardiac cycle with the well known Murray Law (Murray et al., 1926). At the fluid-solid interface the *no-slip* boundary condition was imposed.

3   RESULTS

The WSS has been evaluated by postprocessing the velocity field. Its distribution on the arterial wall is shown in figure 3.

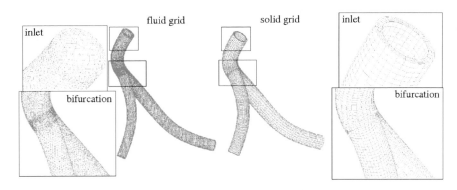

Figure 2: Computational grid (fluid on left, solid on right).

Near the bifurcation, due to geometrical reasons (the angle between the LCx branch and the LM is nearly $90°$), the blood flow separated from the arterial wall and generated a recirculation area on the inferior side of the LCx branch. As a results a high WSS value on the LM branch was visible while a low WSS was present inside the LCx branch (see figure 3). A cause of the change of flow direction, a recirculation area even with smaller intensity was generated on the superior side of the LAD branch. As a results the wall shear stress showed a low value also in the LAD superior side (see figure 3).

The computed WSS values ($0.8 - 3\ Pa$) were compared with those found in literature and well matched other studies in this field [4] [5] [8]. The computed blood flow velocity field causing the WSS distribution on the arterial tree was according with the most frequently atheromatous plaque location [11] [12]. The deformed shape of the arterial bifurcation is shown in figure 4. The computed displacement were in the range of $0.1 - 1\ mm$.

4 CONCLUSIONS

This study demonstrates that region with low WSS, connected with detached blood flow, are possibly predisposed to the atherosclerosis development since the velocity gradient is low. In particular for geometrical reasons, these regions are located near the arterial bifurcations, where the flow divided and different flow regimes develop. The importance of this study was the understanding of how the low/high velocity gradients affect the WSS distribution, a relevant aspect in the treatment of pathological patients.

REFERENCES

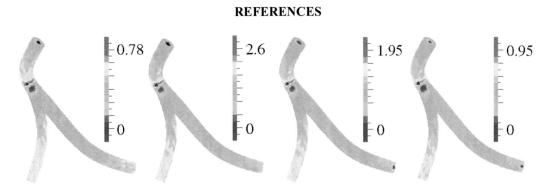

Figure 3: Shear stress distribution on the arterial wall [N/m^2].

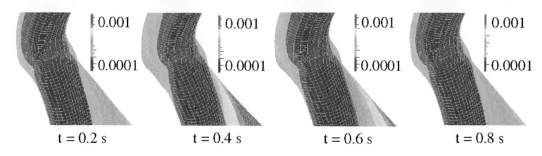

| t = 0.2 s | t = 0.4 s | t = 0.6 s | t = 0.8 s |

Figure 4: Deformed shapes of the left coronary artery in the bifurcation region (displacement in [mm]).

[1] World Health Organization Regional Office for Europe. *European Health Report for 2002*, Number 97 in European Series, World Health Organization 2002.

[2] Fry D., Acute vascular endothelial changes associated with increased blood velocity gradients, Vol 22, 1968, pp 165-197. *Circulation Research*.

[3] Asakura T., Karino T., Flow patterns and spatial distribution of atherosclerotic lesions in human coronary arteries, Vol 66 (4), 1990, pp 1045-1066. *Circulation Research*.

[4] Fukumoto Y., Hiro T., Fujii T. Hashimoto G., Fujimura T., Yamada J., Okamura T., Matsuzaki M., Localized Elevation of Shear Stress Is Related to Coronary Plaque Ropture - A 3-Dimensional Intravascular Ultrasound Study With In-Vivo Color Mapping of Shear Stress Distribution. *Journal of the American College of Cardiology*, Vol 51, 2008, pp 645-650, Elsevier, (ISSN: 0735-1097).

[5] Gijsen F.J.H., Wentzel J.J., Thury A., Lamers B., Schuurbiers J.C.H., Serruys P.W., van der Steen A.F., A new imaging technique to study 3-D plaque and shear stress distribution in human coronary artery bifurcations in vivo. *Journal of Biomechanics*, Vol 40, 2007, pp 2349-2357, Elsevier.

[6] Goubergrits L., Wellnhofer E., Kertzscher U., Affeld K., Petz C., Hege C.H., Coronary Artery WSS Profiling Using a Geometry Reconstruction Based on Biplane Angiography. *Annals of biomedical Engineering*.

[7] Holzapfel G.A., Sommer G., Gasser C.T., Regitnig P.. Determination of layer-specific mechanical properties of human coronary arteries with nonatherosclerotic intimal thickening and related constitutive modeling, *American Journal of Physiology - Heart and Circulatory Physiology*, 289, 2048-2058, 2005.

[8] Soulis J.V., Fermakis M., Giannoglou G.D., Louridas G.E., Wall shear stress in normal left coronary artery tree. *Journal of Biomechanics*, Vol 39, 2006, pp 742-749, Elsevier.

[9] Sankaranarayanan M., Chua L.P., Ghista D.N. Tan Y.S. Computational model of blood flow in the aorto-coronary bypass graft. *Biomedical Engineering Online*, Vol 4, 2005, pp 1-14.

[10] Murray C.D., The physiological Principle of Minimum Work, The Vascular System and the Cost of Blood Volume. *Proc Natl Acad Sci USA*, Vol 12, 1926, pp 207-214.

[11] Joshi A. K., Leask R.L., Myers J.G., Ojha M., Butany J. Ethier C.R., Intimal Thickness Is Not Associated With Wall Shear Stress Pattern in the Human Right Coronary Artery. *Arteriosclerosis, Thrombosis and Vascular Biology - Journal of the American Heart Association*, Vol 24, 2004, pp 2408-2413 (ISSN: 1524-4636).

1st International Conference on Mathematical and Computational Biomedical Engineering - CMBE2009
June 29 - July 1, 2009, Swansea, UK
P. Nithiarasu and R. Löhner (Eds.)

SIMULATION OF BLOOD FLOW IN THORACIC AORTA FOR PREDICTION OF LONG-TERM ADVERSE EVENTS

H. Suito
Okayama University/JST, Okayama, Japan, suito@ems.okayama-u.ac.jp

T. Ueda
Stanford University, Stanford, USA, takueda@stanford.edu

G.D. Rubin
Stanford University, Stanford, USA, grubin@stanford.edu

ABSTRACT

Numerical simulation of blood flow in the thoracic aorta based on finite difference approximation is presented. Aorta shapes are taken from centerline data of CT scans. Based on the flow field during several cardiac cycles, the time-averaged stress field is computed and a 1D-reduced force field is obtained, which might be responsible for elongation and other morphological changes of the aorta.

Key Words: *blood flow, stent graft, aneurysm*

1 INTRODUCTION

Thoracic endovascular aortic repair (TEVAR), or stent-graft treatment, has become widely accepted as an important option for treatment of thoracic aortic diseases. Many studies have prove the safety and efficacy of TEVAR with satisfactory short-term to mid-term outcomes. Even if the initial TEVAR treatment technically succeeds, some patients demonstrate recurrence and progression of diseases many years after treatment. Based on long-term follow-up examinations, such long-term morphological change and effect of hemodynamic flow seem to interact synergically. Constant pulsatile hemodynamic effects from blood flow seem to induce degeneration of the underlying aorta to induce its morphological change and induced minor morphological change to alter the hemodynamic state. These changes finally end up to cause long-term adverse events. This study is intended to investigate the constant effect of vascular hemodynamics on long-term adverse events using computational fluid dynamics based on finite-difference approximation with an immersed boundary – fictitious domain approach.

2 NUMERICAL METHODS

Navier–Stokes equations for an incompressible viscous fluid with a continuity equation are used, where blood is assumed to be a non-Newtonian fluid. In this study, flow equations are discretized using finite difference approximations. Finite difference meshes are generated using centerline data detected by the median axis transform technique from CT scans. Then the shapes of aortic walls are reconstructed in the centerline-fitted generalized coordinate (ξ, η, ζ) using radius data at each point on the centerline.

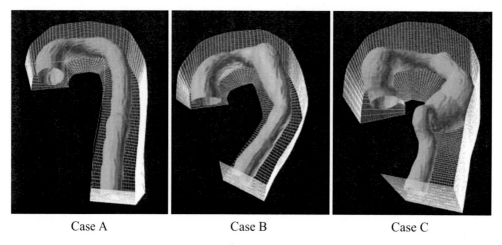

Case A	Case B	Case C

Figure 1: Finite difference grids

The shapes are represented by characteristic functions $\lambda(\xi, \eta, \zeta)$, which are used in the fictitious domain method. Figure 1 depicts finite difference meshes and contour surfaces of λ.

A collocate arrangement of flow variables on the generalized coordinate has been adopted. For approximation of the advection term, a third-order upwind scheme is used. A Poisson equation for the pressure is solved using GP-BiCG method with incomplete LU factorization as a preconditioner.

3 NUMERICAL RESULTS

First, time-dependent flow fields are computed for 10 cardiac cycles. Figure 2 portrays instantaneous flow velocities, as in the aneurysm of Case C, in which swirling flows are evident in the aneurysm.

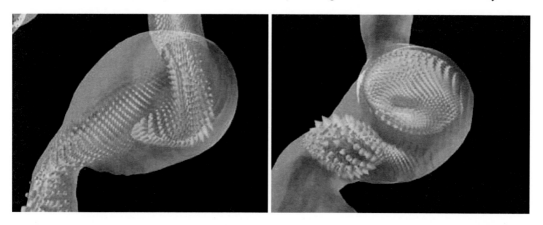

Figure 2: Swirling flow in an aneurysm

Next, using time-dependent flow data, time-averaged flow fields are computed for the last five cardiac cycles. Figure 3 presents averaged wall shear stresses.

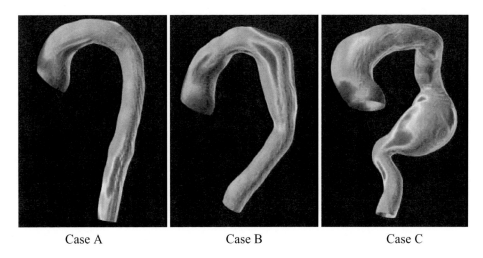

| Case A | Case B | Case C |

Figure 3: Averaged shear stresses

Then, using the time-averaged flow fields, we compute the reduced force distribution, which is defined as

$$F^e(s) = \int_{\Gamma(s)} \sigma_n d\Gamma, \tag{1}$$

$$F_i^b(s) = \int_{\Gamma(s)} \sigma_n n_i d\Gamma. \tag{2}$$

Here, σ_n is a time-averaged outward normal component of the stress exerted on the aortic wall;

$$\sigma_n = \sigma_{ij} n_j n_i. \tag{3}$$

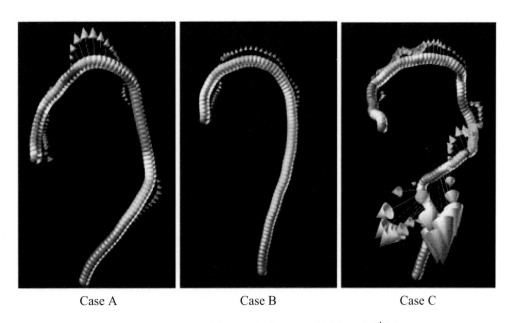

| Case A | Case B | Case C |

Figure 4: Reduced force distributions $F^e(s)$ and $F_i^b(s)$

Parameter s is the length along the centerline and $\Gamma(s)$ is the cross-section perpendicular to the centerline at s. The outward normal vector n_i can be computed as a gradient of the characteristic function:

$$n_i = \frac{\partial \lambda}{\partial x_i}. \tag{4}$$

In Fig. 4, the colors of the centerlines represent $F^e(s)$; the vectors on them indicate that $F_i^b(s)$. These forces are considered responsible for aortal elongation and other morphological changes.

4 CONCLUSIONS

As described in this paper, we propose a computational approach to predict constant effects of vascular hemodynamics on long-term adverse events in the thoracic aorta. The combination of finite difference approximation on centerline-fitted generalized coordinate system and fictitious domain method works well with reasonable computational cost. Although development remains in a preliminary stage, it is anticipated that such reduced force field representation is effective for prediction of long-term adverse events.

Acknowledgements

The authors would like to thank Prof. C.A. Taylor and Dr. C.A. Figueroa for their helpful comments and suggestions.

REFERENCES

[1]   C.A. Figueroa, C.A. Taylor et al., A coupled momentum method for modeling blood flow in three-dimensional deformable arteries, *Comput. Methods Appl. Mech. Engrg.*, 195, 5685–5706, 2006.

[2]   H. Fujita, H. Kawahara and H. Kawarada, Distribution theoretic approach to fictitious domain method for Neumann problems, *East–West Journal of Numerical Mathematics*, 3(2), 111–126, 1995.

[3]   D. Goldstein, R. Handler and L. Sirovich, Modeling a no-slip boundary with an external force field, *Journal of Computational Physics*, 105, 354–366, 1993.

[4]   J.D. Humphrey and C.A. Taylor, Intracranial and Abdominal Aortic Aneurysms: Similarities, Differences, and Need for a New Class of Computational Models, *Annu. Rev. Biomed. Eng.*, 10, 221–246, 2008.

[5]   G.D. Rubin, D.S. Paik, P.C. Johnson and S. Napel, Measurement of the aorta and its branches with helical CT, *Radiology*, 206, 823-829, 1998.

[6]   M. Tillich, R.E. Bell, D.S. Paik, D. Fleischmann, M.C. Sofilos, L.J. Logan and G.D. Rubin, Iliac arterial injuries after endovascular repair of abdominal aortic aneurysms: correlation with iliac curvature and diameter, *Radiology*, 219, 129–136, 2001.

[7]   T. Ueda, D. Fleischmann, G.D. Rubin, M.D. Dake and D.Y. Sze, Imaging of the Thoracic Aorta Before and After Stent-Graft Repair of Aneurysms and Dissections, *Semin. Thorac. Cardiovasc. Surg.* 20 (4), 348-357, 2008.

[8]   I.E. Vignon-Clementel, C.A. Figueroa, K.J. Jansen and C.A. Taylor, Outflow boundary conditions for finite element modeling of blood flow and pressure in arteries, *Comp. Methods Appl. Mech. Eng.*, 195, 3776–3796, 2006.

A multi-model approach to intravenous filter optimization

Yuri V. Vassilevski
RAS Institute of Numerical Mathematics, 119333, Gubkina St. 8, Moscow, Russia,
vasilevs@dodo.inm.ras.ru

Sergey S. Simakov
Moscow Institute of Physics and Technology, 141700, Institutski Lane 9, Dolgoprudny, Russia,
simakovss@ya.ru

Sergey A. Kapranov
Department of Interventional Radiology, City Hospital N 1, 117049, Leninskiy pr. 8, Moscow, Russia

ABSTRACT

We present a multi-model approach to the study of side-effects of endovascular implants. A 2D model of elastic walls and a local 3D model of blood flow are combined with a global blood circulation model. The three numerical models form an endovascular computational stand.

Key Words: *blood flow, endovascular implants, cava filter optimization.*

1 INTRODUCTION

Development of endovascular devices is one of the most challenging problems of contemporary medicine. Millions of endovascular implants are successfully installed annually. The design and installation of the devices-implants should minimize perturbations of the blood flow in the vessel as well as the impact to the vessel wall. This requires optimization of the device structure, choice of appropriate materials, study of the place and the method of the device fixation, estimation of the impact to the global circulation, evaluation of chemical species transport in the case of dissoluble devices. Our work addresses modeling side-effects due to intravenous filters (Fig. 1) which are implanted into veins to capture and dissolute migrating thrombi. In particular, we consider correct filter placement, computation of flow in the vicinity of the filter and captured thrombus, impact of the installed filter to the elastic properties of the venous wall, transport of polymeric material in case of dissoluble filter.

2 METHODS

Three numerical models of different dimensionality are proposed for the minimization of side-effects due to installation of intravenous implants. The detailed disturbance of the blood flow in the vicinity of the implant should be considered by means of 3D incompressible fluid flow model. Global response to the local perturbations should be analyzed in the scope of 1D closed circulation model. The elastic vessel wall response to the device fixation and flow pulsations should be taken into account through the 2D model of elastic structures and fluid-structure interaction problem.

Computational domains of these models differ considerably. In the 3D fluid flow model the domain is a complex 3D channel with complex obstacles in it (Fig. 2). The numerical scheme is based on the

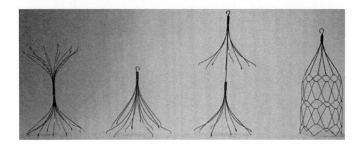

Figure 1. Samples of intravenous filters (Comed Co.).

finite volume discretization of Navier-Stokes equations on octree meshes. In the elastic wall model the domain is the two-dimensional manifold whose position in space can vary. The numerical scheme is based on representation of the vessel wall as a set of elastic fibers of different types. It computes the stress caused by vessel's motion.

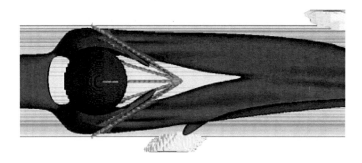

Figure 2. 3D model of the flow in the vicinity of a captured thrombus.

In the global circulation model the domain is a set of 1D flexible channels connected in a closed network (Figs. 3, 4). Blood flow is considered as pulsatile flow of incompressible fluid streaming through the network of vessels. For every vessel we have mass and momentum conservation equations

$$\partial S_k/\partial t + \partial (S_k u_k)/\partial x = \varphi_k(t, x, S_k, u_k, \chi_{ki}) \tag{1}$$

$$\partial u_k/\partial t + \partial (u_k^2/2 + p_k/\rho)/\partial x = \psi_k(t, x, S_k, u_k, \chi_{ki}), \tag{2}$$

where t denotes time, x is coordinate along the vessel, ρ is blood density, k is vessel's index, $S_k(t, x)$ is vessel's cross section area, $u_k(t, x)$ is flow velocity averaged over the vessel's cross section, p_k is pressure (relative to the atmospheric pressure), φ_k is mass inflow/outflow (e.g. due to the damage of the vessel's wall or blood transfusion), ψ_k denotes external forces (e.g. gravity, friction, etc.), χ_{ki} are parameters describing the impact i on the kth vessel. Elastic properties of the vessel's wall are described by the state equation

$$p_k(S_k) - p_{*k} = \rho c_{0k}^2 f_k(S_k), \tag{3}$$

where c_{0k} is the rate of small disturbance propagation, p_{*k} is pressure in the tissues surrounding the vessel (transmural pressure). The function $f_k(S_k)$ depends on the vessel's type. In this work we set

$$f_k(S_k) = \begin{cases} \exp(S_k/\bar{S}_k - 1) - 1, & S_k > \bar{S}_k \\ \ln(S_k/\bar{S}_k), & S_k \leqslant \bar{S}_k, \end{cases} \tag{4}$$

where $\bar{S}_k$ is vessel's cross section area under zero transmural pressure and zero velocity.

All the vessels must be connected each other and to the heart by the appropriate boundary conditions in nodes, that are Poiseuille's pressure drop conditions and mass conservation law combined with appropriate compatibility conditions for (1),(2).

$$p_k \left(S_k \left(t, \tilde{x}_k \right) \right) - p_l \left(t \right) = \varepsilon_k R_k^l S_k \left(t, \tilde{x}_k \right) u_k \left(t, \tilde{x}_k \right), k = k_1, k_2, \ldots, k_M \tag{5}$$

$$\sum_{k=k_1,k_2,\ldots,k_M} \varepsilon_k S_k \left(t, \tilde{x}_k \right) u_k \left(t, \tilde{x}_k \right) = 0, \tag{6}$$

where l is node index. For branches incoming into a node (terminal point) we set $\varepsilon_k = 1, \tilde{x}_k = L_k$, whereas for outgoing branches (entry node) we set $\varepsilon_k = -1, \tilde{x}_k = 0$. In the case of the heart junction, the product $S_k \left(t, x \right) u_k \left(t, x \right)$ in (5),(6) should be replaced with volumetric flow to the appropriate chamber of the heart Q_k.

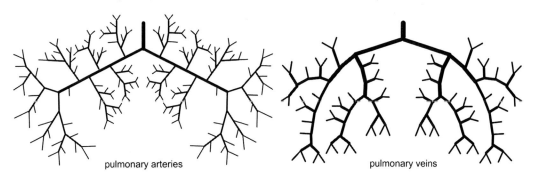

pulmonary arteries

pulmonary veins

Figure 3. 1D structure of the pulmonary vessels.

For each vessel equations (1),(2) are solved by a combination of the first and second order explicit schemes. This model also include a set of stiff ODE's describing the heart functioning that requires A- and L-stable methods.

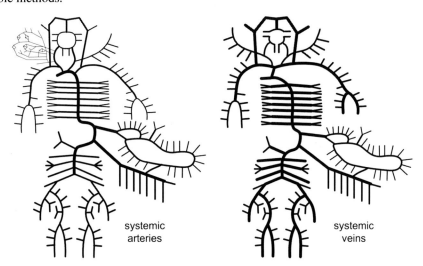

systemic
arteries

systemic
veins

Figure 4. 1D structure of the systemic vessels.

Interaction between the 1D, 2D, and 3D models is diverse. The elastic 2D wall is combined with 3D fluid flow in the framework of the fluid-structure interaction problem. The elastic 2D model is sensitive to implant installation and modifies the state equation (4) for the 1D global circulation model. The 1D global model affects boundary (inflow/outflow) conditions for the 3D model which enforces the vessel wall position.

3   RESULTS & CONCLUSIONS

We combined the above models in the framework of multi-model software, the endovascular computational stand. This stand is intended for the use by manufacturers and clinicians as well as the educational tool.

REFERENCES

[1]   S.S. Simakov and A.S. Kholodov, Computational study of oxygen concentration in human blood under low frequency disturbances, *Mathematical models and computer simulations*, 1(2), 283-295, 2009.

[2]   S.S. Simakov, A.S. Kholodov, Ya. A. Kholodov, et. al., Global dynamical model of the cardiovascular system, *Proceedings of the III European conference on computational mechanics*, 1467.1-1467.15, 2006.

[3]   Y.V. Vassilevski and S.A. Kapranov, Parallel modeling of blood flow peculiarities in the vicinity of cava filter with captured clot, *Mathematical modeling*, 17(11), 3-15, 2005.

1st International Conference on Mathematical and Computational Biomedical Engineering - CMBE2009
June 29 - July 1, 2009, Swansea, UK
P.Nithiarasu and R.Löhner (Eds.)

Towards in vivo Identification of Cerebral Aneurysm Wall Properties

Jia Lu
Department of Mechanical and Industrial Engineering, Center for Computer Aided Design,
The University of Iowa, Iowa City, IA 52242-1527
jia-lu@uiowa.edu

Xuefeng Zhao
Department of Mechanical and Industrial Engineering, Center for Computer Aided Design,
The University of Iowa, Iowa City, IA 52242-1527
xuefeng-zhao@uiowa.edu

ABSTRACT

We introduce a method for identifying cerebral aneurysm wall properties under the condition that the stress-free configuration of the sac is not known. The method is an indispensable intermediate step towards using dynamic image data to characterize the wall caliber of cerebral aneurysms. We have developed a pointwise identification method that enables an organ level characterization of the heterogeneous anisotropic properties in aneurysm sac under the assumption of known stress-free configuration; in this work, the assumption about the reference configuration is removed. We show that, in the context of parameter identification, the unknown reference configuration can be represented locally by a metric tensor, and the components of which can be identified together with the wall elastic properties from pointwise stress strain data extracted from the inflation motion.

Key Words: *Cerebral aneurysms, tissue property, in vivo identification, inverse elastostatics.*

1 INTRODUCTION

Cerebral aneurysms are focal dilatations of the intracranial arterial wall, whose rupture is believed to be caused by the pressure induced wall stress. Although the stress-strain property is fundamental to the understanding of the mechanical behavior and natural history of these lesions, currently there is no effective method for extracting patient-specific wall properties. Recently, the present authors proposed a method to identify the heterogeneous anisotropic nonlinear elastic properties of cerebral aneurysm sac in its intact state [1]. The method builds on the idea of pointwise identification [2] and utilizes organ-level inflation data as the input. The stress in an inflated state is computed using the finite element inverse elastostatics methods without invoking the material property in question. The material parameters are characterized directly from pointwise stress-strain data. The method opens a pathway for developing in vivo identification technologies based on recorded physiological surface motion. However, at present the method assumes a known stress-free reference configuration. This assumption is reasonable for in vitro experiments as one can use a slightly inflated state to approximate the stress-free configuration. To be the basis of in vivo identification, this assumption must be eliminated because the stress-free configuration is not known from in vivo images. Information about the stress-free configuration is not essential for stress analysis, but is indispensable for parameter identification because the strain data depend directly on the choice of reference configuration.

2   MATERIAL MODEL

2.1   Local stress-free configuration

Thin membranes typically collapse when unloaded. They can have multiple stress-free configurations which may not attain a smooth convex shape. To develop a theoretical framework suitable for parameter identification, it is imperative to have a constitutive description that permits a stressed configuration to be used as the reference. This can be achieved using the concept of local stress-free configuration, which associates each infinitesimal material element with a stress-free configuration that can be reached independently of the surrounding material. The stress-free state of the material body is a virtual configuration comprised of the union of the local configurations. The energy function at each material point is characterized with respect to the local stress-free state, whereas the deformation is measured relative to the chosen reference configuration. The notion of local configuration was initially proposed by Noll [3] and was later adapted in various forms to describe material inhomogeneity, plasticity, residual stress, initial strain, and so on.

If we let $\mathbf{K}^{-1}$ denote the local deformation that elastically releases the stress in an infinitesimal surface element and brings the material element to a local stress-free configuration. The local deformation is measured relative to a chosen reference configuration which is not necessarily stress-free. A line element $d\mathbf{X}$ in the reference configuration will have a released length

$$dS^2 = \mathbf{K}^{-1}d\mathbf{X} \cdot \mathbf{K}^{-1}d\mathbf{X} = d\mathbf{X} \cdot (\mathbf{K}^{-T}\mathbf{K}^{-1})d\mathbf{X}.$$

Therefore it makes sense to introduce the metric tensor

$$\mathfrak{G} = \mathbf{K}^{-T}\mathbf{K}^{-1}$$

to describe the local stress-free geometry of the material element. Note that $\mathfrak{G}$ is a tensor living on the reference configuration. During a normal deformation, the tangent tensor to be used in the constitutive equation is $\mathbf{FK}$ where $\mathbf{F}$ is the regular deformation gradient relative to the chosen reference configuration. Therefore, the (surface) Green-Lagrangian deformation tensor that enters a hyperelastic constitutive equation is

$$\mathbf{C} = \mathbf{K}^T\mathbf{F}^T\mathbf{FK}.$$

The principal invariants of $\mathbf{C}$ are $I_1 = \operatorname{tr}(\mathbf{K}^T\mathbf{F}^T\mathbf{FK})$, $I_2 = \det(\mathbf{K}^T\mathbf{F}^T\mathbf{FK})$. If we further introduce a convected coordinate system which bears the bases $(\mathbf{G}_1, \mathbf{G}_2)$ in the reference configuration, let the components of $\mathfrak{G}$ relative to these bases be $\mathfrak{G}_{\alpha\beta}$, and introduce the convected current bases $\mathbf{g}_\alpha = \mathbf{FG}_\alpha$, then,

$$I_1 = g_{\alpha\beta}\mathfrak{G}^{\alpha\beta}, \qquad I_2 = \frac{\det[g_{\alpha\beta}]}{\det[\mathfrak{G}_{\alpha\beta}]}. \tag{1}$$

2.2   Wall tissue energy function

We assume that the cerebral aneurysm wall is composed of a random elastin network, reinforced by two families of orthogonal collagen fibers. An anisotropic structural strain energy function proposed by Holzapfel et al. [4] is used to model the elastic behavior of the cerebral aneurysm sac. The strain energy function takes the form

$$w = k_1 (I_1 - 2\log J - 2) + \sum_{i=4,6} \frac{k_i}{a} \left\{ \exp\left[a (I_i - 1)^2 \right] - 1 \right\}, \tag{2}$$

36

where k_i $(i = 1, 4, 6)$ are 2D elastic stiffness parameters having the dimension of force per unit length and a is a dimensionless material constant. In the energy function, I_1 is the first principal invariant introduced above, $J = \sqrt{I_2}$, and I_4 and I_6 are square stretches of line elements in the two fiber directions. With the notations introduced above, the last two invariants are written as

$$I_4 = \frac{N_1^\alpha g_{\alpha\beta} N_1^\beta}{N_1^\alpha \mathfrak{G}_{\alpha\beta} N_1^\beta}, \qquad I_6 = \frac{N_2^\alpha g_{\alpha\beta} N_2^\beta}{N_2^\alpha \mathfrak{G}_{\alpha\beta} N_2^\beta}. \tag{3}$$

Here N_I^α is the component of fiber tangents in the convected system. It is clear that the stress depends on the material parameters (k_1, k_4, k_6, a), the deformation gradient $\mathbf{F}$, and the three components ($\mathfrak{G}_{11}$, $\mathfrak{G}_{22}$, $\mathfrak{G}_{12}$) of the local metric tensor. In the proposed method, the material parameters and the metric tensor will be treated as unknown model parameters. They will be identified pointwise from local stress-strain data acquired independently from stress analysis and surface measurement.

3   NUMERICAL EXPERIMENT

A virtual (numerical) test is conducted to verify the feasibility of the proposed method. A three-dimensional model of a patient-specific cerebral aneurysm is adopted from a separate study. The material property of the cerebral aneurysm is assumed to be heterogeneous; the elastic stiffness decreases linearly with respect to the height from the neck. The two fiber directions in one of the deformed state are assumed to be known. Within the proposed mathematical framework, this means that the components N_I^α, $I = 1, 2; \alpha = 1, 2$ are specified. The unknown model parameters are therefore the material constants and the components of the metric tensor. The numerical experiment consists of the following steps:

1. Perform (forward) finite element analyses on the aneurysm sac to generate 15 deformed configurations under different pressure levels;

2. In each of the deformed configurations, perform inverse stress analysis to determine the stress distribution;

3. Select the first deformed configuration (the one under the lowest pressure) to be the (stressed) reference, compute the deformation gradients relative to this configuration. Compute the geometric quantities $g_{\alpha\beta}$ and $\mathbf{N}_I^\alpha g_{\alpha\beta} \mathbf{N}_I^\beta$;

4. Use the acquired stress-strain data, identify the local model parameters using nonlinear regression. The objective function used in this step is

$$\Phi = \sum_{i=1}^{N} \| ^{(i)}\boldsymbol{\sigma} - {}^{(i)}\hat{\boldsymbol{\sigma}} \|^2$$

where, $^{(i)}\boldsymbol{\sigma}$ and $^{(i)}\hat{\boldsymbol{\sigma}}$ are the modeled and experimental stresses in the ith deformed configuration, and $N = 15$ is the total number of deformed states. The parameter a is not identified because the membrane stress is extremely insensitive to this parameter.

Figure 1 shows the distribution of the identified parameters k_i. Qualitatively judged from the figure, the prescribed linear variation of elastic parameters over the height was recovered, except for the region where the stress determination was not accurate enough, i.e., near the clamped boundary and at the fundus. Figure 2 shows the identification error between the identified parameters and the realistic ones computed at each nodal point according to $Error(k_i) = \left| \left(k_i - \tilde{k}_i \right) / \tilde{k}_i \right| \times 100\%, (i = 1, 4, 6)$, where

k_i and $\tilde{k}_i$ are identified and realistic elastic parameters, respectively. The identification error is less than 15%, 5% and 9% for k_1, k_4 and k_6, respectively, in the bulk region of the aneurysm sac which is in blue in Figure 2.

4 CONCLUSIONS

We proposed a novel non-destructive method for the identification of anisotropic heterogeneous properties in cerebral aneurysms without knowing the stress-free configuration. We discussed the theoretical underpins and demonstrated the method using a numerical experiment. A noteworthy attribute of the method is that, the unknown stress-free configuration is locally represented by three parameters, and these parameters are identified together with material parameters pointwise from local stress-strain data, without solving coupled large-scale optimization problem. The numerical experiment clearly highlighted the feasibility and effectiveness of the method.

REFERENCES

[1] X. Zhao, M. L. Raghavan, and J. Lu, Identifying the Distribution of Heterogeneous Anisotropic Elastic Properties in Cerebral Aneurysms. *Biomechanics and Modeling in Mechanobiology*, in review.

[2] J. Lu, X. Zhao, and X. Chen, Pointwise identification of elastic properties in nonlinear hyperelastic membranes. Part I: Theoretical and computational developments; Part II: Experimental validation, *Journal of Applied Mechanics*, 2009 (in press).

[3] W. Noll, A new mathematical theory of simple material. *Archive for Rational Mechanics and Analysis*, 48,1-50, 1972.

[4] G. A. Holzapfel, T. G. Gasser and R. W. Ogden, A new constitutive framework for arterial wall mechanics and a comparative study of material models, *Journal of Elasticity*, 61, 1-48, 2000.

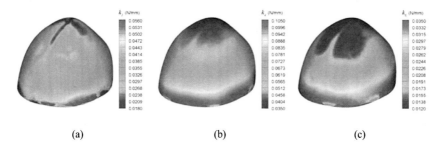

Figure 1: Distribution of the identified elastic parameters: (a) k_1, (b) k_4, (c) k_6.

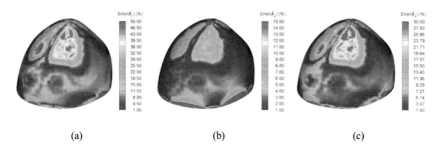

Figure 2: Distribution of the identified error: (a) Error(k_1), (b) Error(k_4), (c) Error(k_6).

1st International Conference on Mathematical and Computational Biomedical Engineering - CMBE2009

June 29 - July 1, 2009, Swansea, UK

P.Nithiarasu and R.Löhner (Eds.)

Filtering-based data assimilation in fluid-structure interaction: towards personalization of vascular models

Cristóbal Bertoglio

INRIA, REO team, 78153 Le Chesnay Cedex, France, cristobal.bertoglio@inria.fr

Miguel A. Fernández

INRIA, REO team, 78153 Le Chesnay Cedex, France, miguel.fernandez@inria.fr

Jean-Frédéric Gerbeau

INRIA, REO team, 78153 Le Chesnay Cedex, France, jean-frederic.gerbeau@inria.fr

Philippe Moireau

INRIA, MACS team, 78153 Le Chesnay Cedex, France, philippe.moireau@inria.fr

ABSTRACT

In this work we introduce a procedure for the estimation of model parameters in systems involving the mechanical interaction of a viscous incompressible fluid and an elastic structure. For the joint state-parameter estimation we consider a sequential approach, inspired by filtering strategies recently reported in the literature, assuming only measured wall displacements. The proposed approach is illustrated numerically through an example inspired from vascular biomechanics.

Key Words: *fluid-structure interaction, data assimilation, particle filtering, medical imaging.*

1 INTRODUCTION

During the last decade, the numerical modeling of three-dimensional blood flow in compliant arteries has become a very active field of research (see e.g. [5] and the references therein). Examples of applications include disease research, where fluid mechanical conditions are correlated to atherosclerosis regions (see e.g. [14]), and endo-vascular devices design, in which the impact of the device on blood hemodynamics is numerically modeled (see e.g. [7, 4]).

In this work, the numerical model is exploited within a data assimilation purpose. In other words, we address the estimation of uncertain physical parameters involved in the fluid-structure bio-mechanical model, from a set of available (non-invasive) measurements of the system. This methodology could be used, for instance, as a diagnosis tool where estimation of the wall compliance allows to asses the risk and location of atherosclerosis disease (see e.g. [13]).

Typically, data assimilation of distributed mechanical systems is performed within a variational approach (see e.g. [1]) that is, by minimizing a least square criterion which balances observation error and regularization. One of the main difficulties related to this approach lies in the iterative evaluation of the criterion and its gradient - typically adjoint-based - which requires a high computational effort. Somehow this explains the fact that, to the authors best knowledge, data assimilation of three-dimensional fluid-structure systems has not yet been addressed in the literature. The existing approaches are exclusively based on the usage of simplified models (see e.g. [8]).

In this work we consider another family of methods to perform data assimilation, the so-called *sequential approachs* (e.g., Kalman filtering). Here, the model prediction for a next time is improved by means of the statistical information from observations and model output [2]. Even though, classical Kalman filtering is not tractable for distributed systems, some effective sequential procedures for mechanical systems were introduced recently in [11, 12, 10]. They are based on the construction of physics-specific *Luenberger observers* [9] to perform the estimation of the model trajectory. This allows also to reduced the uncertainty space to the parameters - which are typically much less than the degrees of freedom of the state. Therefore, we can use the reduced version [10] of the so-called *Unscented Kalman Filter* (UKF) [6] for the joint-state parameter estimation, that avoids the computation of tangent operators. Moreover, the total computational effort of the estimation is practically the same of one direct simulation because of the parallel feature of the particles propagation.

Finally, we perform the estimation of the compliance distribution in a vessel from displacement measurements of the fluid-structure interface.

2 PROBLEM SETTING

2.1 The direct problem

Mathematical formulation   We consider the mechanical interaction between a fluid and a surrounding structure. The fluid is described by the incompressible Navier-Stokes equations (within an arbitray Lagrangian-Eulerain formulation), and the structure by the non-linear elastodynamic equations (see e.g. [5, Chapter 3]).

Discretization   For the space discretization of the coupled PDE's system, we consider for instance finite elements for both the fluid and the structure and assume (without loss of generality) that the fluid and solid discretizations match at the interface. The resulting semi-discretized formulation can be written as a (coupled) dynamical system of the type $B\dot{X} = A(X) + R$, where the state X contains the degrees of freedom of the solid displacement and velocity, and the fluid velocity and pressure. Next, after the discretization in time, the problem can be written in the form $X_{n+1} = F_{n+1,n}(X_n)$, where $F_{n+1,n}$ is usually called *evolution operator*.

2.2 The inverse problem

State estimation   Our goal is to find an estimation $\hat{X}$ of the real state X by means of some set of observations of the real system $Z = Z(X)$ (usually noised), in such a way that the error $\|X - \hat{X}\|$ tends to zero rapidly. For this purpose, we use a convenient sequential procedures recently reported in [11, 12, 10], based on the construction of physics-specific *Luenberger observers*. Hence, the dynamical system for the estimator can be written as $B\dot{\hat{X}} = A(\hat{X}) + R + K(Z, \hat{X})$, where the observer $K(Z, \hat{X})$ is proportional to the error between the estimate and the observations.

In the case of displacement measurements obtained from medical imaging, the observations that can be extracted are essentially contours. Then, the observation error is proportional to the distance of each node of the structure mesh to the discrete surface obtained after segmentation of the images. Therefore, the feedback $K(Z, \hat{X})$ is only introduced in the structure solver, modifying the equation of compatibility between velocities and the displacements derivative [12]. It can be shown, under some reasonable conditions, that this is actually enough to control the error of the entire fluid-structure system $\|X - \hat{X}\|$.

Joint state-parameter estimation   Generally, one would like to estimate additionally some parameters of the model that we call θ. In Kalman filtering approaches, the extension of the estimation process is formally simple and consists in augmenting the dynamical system with an equation for $\dot{\theta}$. Then, we can write the sequential state-parameter estimator, in an abstract way, as $\hat{X}_{n+1} = \hat{F}_{n+1,n}(\hat{\theta}_n, \hat{X}_n, Z, K)$ and $\hat{\theta}_{n+1} = \hat{G}_{n+1,n}(\hat{\theta}_n, \hat{X}_n, Z)$. In [11, 10], a convenient method to estimate both state and parameters together taking advantage of the Luenberger-type filtering mentioned above is reported. This procedure corresponds to a reduced-order version of the UKF, in the sense that the uncertainty space is reduced to the parameters because of the existence of the Luenberger observer in $\hat{F}_{n+1,n}$. Then, it allows to limit the computation of the covariance to the parametric space whose dimension is typically much more coarser. Moreover, the UKF method involves only the computation of a very reduced number of particles, that approaches the estimated mean and covariances up to the second order, without the computation of any tangent - or parametric sensitivity - operator.

2.3   Numerical example

As a preliminary example, we illustrate here some features of the proposed approach in the linear case (Stokes-linear elasticity coupling). We estimate the compliance distribution of straight vessel under the effect of a fluid pressure wave propagating along the tube. The vessel has a length of $L = 5\,cm$ and a radius of $R = 0.5\,cm$. The thickness of the wall is $\epsilon = 0.1\,cm$. The vessel is divided into five sections along the longitudinal axis, each one with a Young's modulus of $E = 3 \times 10^5\,Pa$, except the third in which $E = 4 \times 10^5\,Pa$. The fluid and the structure are initially at rest and an over pressure of $1333\,Pa$ is imposed, between the inlet and outlet boundaries, during 5×10^{-3} seconds. The fluid and solid equations have been discretized using the explicit staggered scheme reported in [3].

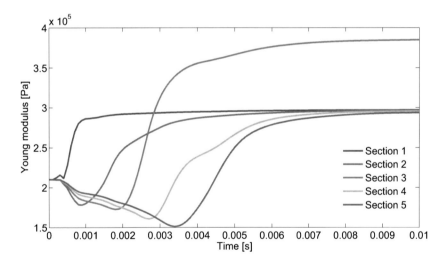

Figure 1: Sequential estimation of the Young modulus distribution in a linear compliant vessel.

In the identification process, the uncertainty comes only from the initial guess of the five Young's modulus, which are all set to $2.1 \times 10^5\,Pa$. The wall displacements are measured, on the wall fluid-structure interface, at each time step, the time step length being $10^{-4}\,s$. Figure 1 illustrates the evolution of the estimated parameters, using 6 particles in the reduced UKF algorithm. We can observe that the Young's modulus distribution is recovered with the propagation of the pressure wave trough each section.

3 CONCLUSIONS

A state-of-the-art scheme to perform sequential joint-state parameter estimation is applied to a fluid-structure interaction problem. Preliminary 3D numerical examples inspired from vascular biomechanics encourage to extend its application to more complex FSI problems and real clinical data.

References

[1] H. T. Banks and K. Kunisch. *Estimation techniques for distributed parameter systems*, volume 1 of *Systems & Control: Foundations & Applications*. Birkhäuser Boston Inc., Boston, MA, 1989.

[2] A. Bensoussan. *Filtrage optimal des systèmes linéaires*. Dunod, 1971.

[3] E. Burman and M.A. Fernández. Stabilization of explicit coupling in fluid-structure interaction involving fluid incompressibility. *Comput. Methods Appl. Mech. Engrg.*, 198(5–8):766–784, 2009.

[4] M.A. Fernández, J.-F. Gerbeau, and V. Martin. Numerical simulation of blood flows through a porous interface. *M2AN Math. Model. Numer. Anal.*, 42:961–990, 2008.

[5] L. Formaggia, A. Quarteroni, and A. Veneziani, editors. *Cardiovascular Mathematics. Modeling and simulation of the circulatory system*, volume 1 of *Modeling, Simulation and Applications*. Springer, 2009.

[6] S. Julier, J. Uhlmann, and H. Durrant-Whyte. A new approach for filtering nonlinear systems. In *American Control Conference*, pages 1628–1632, 1995.

[7] C. Kleinstreuer, Z. Li, and M.A. Farber. Fluid-structure interaction analyses of stented abdominal aortic aneurysms. *Annu Rev Biomed Eng.*, 9:169–204, 2007.

[8] P.-Y. Lagrée. An inverse technique to deduce the elasticity of a large artery. *Eur. Phys. J. AP*, 9:153–163, 1999.

[9] D. G Luenberger. An introduction to observers. *IEEE Transactions on Automatic Control*, 16:596–602, 1971.

[10] P. Moireau and D. Chapelle. Reduced-order unscented kalman filtering with application to parameter identification in large-dimensional systems. Submitted to COCV, 2009.

[11] P. Moireau, D. Chapelle, and P. Le Tallec. Joint state and parameter estimation for distributed mechanical systems. *Computer Methods in Applied Mechanics and Engineering*, 197:659–677, 2008.

[12] P. Moireau, D. Chapelle, and P. Le Tallec. Filtering for distributed mechanical systems using position measurements: Perspective in medical imaging. *Inverse Problems*, 25(3):035010–035035, March 2009.

[13] W.A. Riley, R.W. Barnes, G.W. Evans, and G.L. Burke. Ultrasonic measurement of the elastic modulus of the common carotid artery. The atherosclerosis risk in communities study. *Stroke*, 23:952–956, 1992.

[14] D. Tang, C. Yang, S. Mondal, F. Liu, G. Canton, T.S. Hatsukami, and C. Yuan. A negative correlation between human carotid atherosclerotic plaque progression and plaque wall stress: in vivo MRI-based 2D/3D FSI models. *J Biomech.*, 41(4):727–736, 2008.

1st International Conference on Mathematical and Computational Biomedical Engineering - CMBE2009
June 29 - July 1, 2009, Swansea, UK
P.Nithiarasu and R.Löhner (Eds.)

Mathematical and numerical models for healthy and diseased arterial wall

Mariarita de Luca
MOX-Dipartimento di Matematica, Politecnico di Milano,
Piazza Leonardo da Vinci 32, 20133 Milan, Italy
mariarita.deluca@polimi.it

ABSTRACT

In this work are discussed mathematical and computational strategies related to the use of a multi-mechanism model for cerebral arterial tissue, introduced by *Wulandana and Robertson* [1]. The multi-mechanism model has been proposed to model the onset and early growth of cerebral aneurysms. A *cerebral aneurysm* (also known as intracranial or intracerebral aneurysm) consists of an abnormal localized dilation of blood vessel in the brain, filled with blood. In particular in this work, we implement the multi-mechanism model in a C++ Finite Element library, called *LifeV*. The characteristic of the mathematical model is to involve a different treatment of each mechanism. The material is supposed to be hyperelastic and homogeneous, as identified by a specific strain energy function. The material models are the *St. Venant Kirchhoff*, the *Neo-Hookean*, and the exponential model, in the range of finite deformations. In the literature it is a common practice to consider biological tissues as incompressible materials. For our implementation, all materials are treated as weakly compressible by including a penalty term in the strain energy functions. The formulated mechanical problem consists in solving the *linear momentum equation* with suitable boundary conditions in a three dimensional framework. All the numerical simulations were carried out using a real three dimensional geometry of a carotid artery with a giant aneurysm obtained from clinical images.

Key Words: *cerebral aneurysm, arterial wall deformation.*

1 INTRODUCTION

The multi-mechanism model is based on the behavior of collagen and elastin, passive structural components of the arterial wall. They enter the model a separate mechanisms with different material response and unloaded reference configurations. In cerebral arteries, elastin is mostly located in a specific layer of arterial wall, called internal elastic lamina (IEL), and early stage cerebral aneurysms are characterized by the disruption of IEL. After elastin fragmentation, the mechanical behavior of the aneurysm wall is only due to collagen, that is usually found in the adventitia layer of artery. The multi-mechanism model is based on the assumption that under physiological stress, both elastin and collagen contribute to load bearing, but after a certain level of deformation the elastin undergoes rupture and for further stress only the collagen is able to contribute to load bearing. This theory is supported by the fact that once elastin is gone, the body is not able to replace it, while it can always build new collagen fibers. The behavior of elastin and collagen under stress determine the nonlinear and inelastic behavior of arterial wall deformations.

2 MAIN BODY

We assume to have two mechanisms and that each of them behaves as a single hyperelastic material. We consider $\Omega(t)$ the current configuration of the body and t is the current time. Ω_1 and Ω_2 are respectively the reference configurations of the first and second mechanism. The motion of the body with respect to each mechanism reference configuration is described by the corresponding deformation gradients

$$\mathbf{F}_1(\mathbf{X}_1, t) \quad \text{and} \quad \mathbf{F}_2(\mathbf{X}_2, t - t_2), \tag{1}$$

where t_2 is the time at which the second mechanism is activated. A simple measure of the deformation is a scalar invariant function of the first deformation gradient [1]:

$$s(t) = \hat{s}(\mathbf{F}_1(\mathbf{X}_1, t), \mathbf{x}). \tag{2}$$

The scalar function s identifies when the collagen fibers are recruited and when the elastin breaks.

The strain energy function W_1 per unit volume, in the reference configuration Ω_1, when only the first mechanism is active reads

$$W(t) = W_1(\mathbf{F}_1(\mathbf{X}_1, t)). \tag{3}$$

During the motion, we assume that the collagen recruitment is dictated by the value $s_a = s(t_2)$ of the scalar function (2). Note that it is assumed that all the collagen fibers are recruited simultaneously at some points $\mathbf{x}$. As the body continues to deform, corresponding to increased values of $s > s_a$, both mechanisms are active and contribute the load bearing. We can relate the deformation gradients of the two mechanisms by the relation

$$\mathbf{F}_2(\mathbf{X}_2, t - t_2) = \mathbf{F}_1(\mathbf{X}_1, t) \, \mathbf{F}_1^{-1}(\mathbf{X}_1, t_2). \tag{4}$$

The computation of their determinants gives

$$J_2(t - t_2) = \det(\mathbf{F}_2(\mathbf{X}_2, t - t_2)), \quad \text{and} \quad J_1(t) = \det(\mathbf{F}_1(\mathbf{X}_1, t), \tag{5}$$

so that

$$J_2(t - t_2) = J_1(t) \, J_1(t_2)^{-1} \tag{6}$$

where $J_1(t_2)^{-1}$ is related to the reference configuration Ω_2 and it is a known constant value.

After the collagen recruitment, when $s > s_a$ the strain energy function associated to the hyperelastic material has contribution from both mechanisms

$$W(t) = W_{12}(\mathbf{F}_1(\mathbf{X}_1, t), \mathbf{F}_2(\mathbf{X}_2, t - t_2)). \tag{7}$$

When a second critical value s_b of the scalar function s is reached, the elastin breaks (deactivation of the first mechanism). Also for the breakage of elastin, if the phenomenon happens at different time and positions, the scalar value s_b will be a function of time and position too. For further deformations, that correspond to the scalar values $s > s_b$ the elastin is no more contributing, and so only the collagen fibers are load bearing. Now the strain energy function per unit volume with respect to Ω_2 depends only on $\mathbf{F}_2(\mathbf{X}_2, t - t_2)$ as

$$W(t) = W_2(\mathbf{F}_2(\mathbf{X}_2, t - t_2)). \tag{8}$$

The last assumption that is needed to derive the full model is that the two mechanisms are independent and do not interact between them, so that the strain energy function when both elastin and collagen are active is

$$W_{12} = W_1 + W_2 \tag{9}$$

We observe that we can simply sum the contributions of the two mechanism in the current configuration.

To avoid the problem of having the configuration as another unknown we need to reformulate the model with respect to only one fixed reference configuration. There is not a specific reason to prefer the configuration Ω_1 or Ω_2. In this description we choose Ω_1. Now, we have to compute the total energy in the reference configuration Ω_1. The total energy as sum of the contributions of the two mechanisms reads

$$U_{tot} = \int_{\Omega_1} W_1 \mathrm{d}\Omega_1 + \int_{\Omega_1} J_2^{-1}(t-t_2)J_1(t)W_2 \mathrm{d}\Omega_1 = \int_{\Omega_1} W_1 \mathrm{d}\Omega_1 + \int_{\Omega_1} J_1(t_2)W_2 \mathrm{d}\Omega_1 \qquad (10)$$

where we substituted equation (6) in the previous expression.

Now, we can get rid of the integrals since all of them are referred to the volume occupied by the body in the reference configuration Ω_1. If we define now W_{tot} the total strain energy function per unite volume in Ω_1, such that when both mechanism are active, we have

$$W_{tot} = W_1 + J_1(t_2)W_2, \qquad (11)$$

finally we can express the contribution of the two mechanisms in the reference configuration Ω_1 as

$$W_{tot} = \begin{cases} \theta W_1 & \text{for } 0 \le s \le s_a \\ \theta W_1 + J_1(t_2)W_2 & \text{for } s_a \le s \le s_b \\ J_1(t_2)W_2 & \text{for } s \ge s_b \end{cases} \qquad (12)$$

where θ is a scalar parameter that takes into account the deactivation of the first mechanism. In particular when the first mechanism is still active, $\theta = 1$, after the elastin breakage $\theta = 0$.

In order to treat the materials as weakly compressible, we employ the multiplicative decomposition of both deformation gradients [2]

$$\mathbf{F}_1 = \hat{\mathbf{F}}_1 \overline{\mathbf{F}}_1 \quad \text{and} \quad \mathbf{F}_2 = \hat{\mathbf{F}}_2 \overline{\mathbf{F}}_2 \qquad (13)$$

where $\hat{\mathbf{F}}_1$ and $\hat{\mathbf{F}}_2$ take into account the change in volume of the body during the motion and $\overline{\mathbf{F}}_1$ and $\overline{\mathbf{F}}_2$ are referred to an isochoric motion. For both mechanisms, the following definition holds:

$$\overline{\mathbf{F}}_i = J^{-\frac{1}{3}} \mathbf{F}_i \quad \text{and} \quad \hat{\mathbf{F}}_i = J^{\frac{1}{3}} \mathbf{I}, \quad \text{for } i = 1, 2. \qquad (14)$$

With such decomposition, the correspondent strain energy function of each mechanism, decomposes in an additive way. W_{1vol} and W_{2vol} take into account the changes in volume of the body during the motion, while W_{1iso} and W_{2iso} represent the incompressible contributions [3]. In this framework, the energy of the double-mechanism model (12) becomes

$$W_{tot} = \begin{cases} \theta(W_{1vol} + W_{1iso}) & \text{for } 0 \le s \le s_a \\ \theta(W_{1vol} + W_{1iso}) + J_1(t_2)(W_{2vol} + W_{2iso}) & \text{for } s_a \le s \le s_b \\ J_1(t_2)(W_{2vol} + W_{2iso}) & \text{for } s \ge s_b \end{cases} \qquad (15)$$

The first Piola-Kirchhoff stress tensor, for the multi-mechanism model, that we use in the balance of linear momentum written in the reference configuration Ω_1 reads

$$\mathbf{P} = \begin{cases} \theta(\mathbf{P}_{1vol} + \mathbf{P}_{1iso}) & \text{for } 0 \le s \le s_a \\ \theta(\mathbf{P}_{1vol} + \mathbf{P}_{1iso}) + J_1(t_2)(\mathbf{P}_{2vol} + \mathbf{P}_{2iso}) & \text{for } s_a \le s \le s_b \\ J_1(t_2)(\mathbf{P}_{2vol} + \mathbf{P}_{2iso}) & \text{for } s \ge s_b \end{cases} \qquad (16)$$

In order to compute the first Piola-Kirchhoff stress tensor in equation (16), we can use different material models for each mechanism, namely

Neo-Hookean: $W_{iso}(\mathbf{C}) = \frac{\mu}{2}(I_C - 3)$;

Exponential: $W_{iso}(\mathbf{C}) = \frac{\alpha}{2\gamma}(e^{\gamma(I_C-3)} - 1)$;

Volumetric part: $W_{vol}(J) = \frac{K}{4}((J-1)^2 + (\ln J)^2)$.

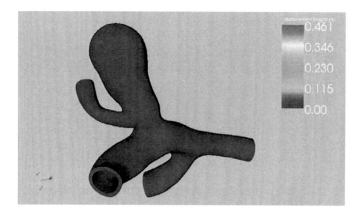

Figure 1: Segment of internal carotid artery with a giant aneurysm obtained by clinical data.

3   CONCLUSIONS

Numerical simulations are first carried out with a cylindrical geometry, with circular cross section. In those simple cases, we are able to match the numerical solutions with the analytic solution of the inflating problem, computed with the assumption of incompressibility of the structure. The next numerical simulations correspond to the inflation of the geometry in Figure 1, obtained from clinical data (courtesy of the ANEURISK project). The mesh is composed by 266873 tetrahedra. We are able to compare the mechanical behavior of the nonlinear constitutive models implemented.

These models are stable in the case of one mechanism model, while they show a parameter dependence and a mesh dependence within the two mechanism model. The current work in progress is the testing of the code with the nonlinear constitutive models implemented in the two mechanism model framework.

Acknowledgements: This work has been carried out in collaboration with Anne M. Robertson, Department of Mechanical Engineering and Material Science (MEMS), University of Pittsburgh; Alessandro Veneziani, Department of Mathematics and Computer Science, Emory University and Modeling and Scientific Computing (MOX), Dipartimento di Matematica, Politecnico di Milano; Davide Ambrosi, Modeling and Scientific Computing (MOX), Dipartimento di Matematica, Politecnico di Milano; and Paolo Biscari, Dipartimento di Matematica, Politecnico di Milano.

REFERENCES

[1]   R. Wulandana, A. M. Robertson, An Inelastic multi-mechanism constitutive equation for cerebral arterial tissue. *Biomech Model Mechanobiol*, **4**, 235-248, 2005.

[2]   G. A. Holzapfel, *Nonlinear Solid Mechanics: A Continuum Approach for Engineering*. Wiley, Chichester, 2000.

[3]   S. Hartman, P. Neff, Polyconvexity of generalized polynomial-type hyperelastic strain energy functions for near-incompressibility. *International Journal of Solids and Structures*, **40**, 27672791, 2003.

[4]   A. Quarteroni, A. Valli, *Numerical Approximation of Partial Differential Equations*. Second Ed., Springer-Verlag, 1997.

[5]   P. G. Ciarlet, *Mathematical Elasticity*, Volume I. North Holland, 1993.

1st International Conference on Mathematical and Computational Biomedical Engineering – CMBE2009
June 29 – July 1, 2009, Swansea, UK
P. Nithiarasu and R. Löhner (eds)

HOW DO RESIDUAL STRESSES ARISE IN ARTERIES?

Luca Cardamone
Department of Civil Engineering, University of Salerno, Italy, lcardamo@unisa.it
Jay D. Humphrey
Biomedical Engineering Department, Texas A&M University, USA,
jhumphrey@tamu.edu

ABSTRACT

The arterial wall is built by several constituents that contribute in different ways to the structural properties and functions of the vessel. The structural protein elastin, in particular, endows large arteries with unique biological functionality and mechanical integrity; hence its disorganization, fragmentation, or degradation can have important consequences on the progression and treatment of vascular diseases. There is, therefore, a need in arterial mechanics to move from materially uniform, phenomenological, constitutive relations for the wall to those that account for separate contributions of the primary structural constituents. In this study, we employ a constrained mixture model of the arterial wall and show that prestretched elastin contributes significantly to both the retraction of arteries that is observed upon transaction and the opening angle that follows the introduction of a radial cut. We also show that the transmural distributions of elastin and collagen, compressive stiffness of collagen, and smooth muscle tone play complementary roles. Axial prestretch and residual stresses in arteries contribute to the homeostatic state of stress *in vivo* as well as adaptations to perturbed loads, disease, or injury. Understanding better the development of and changes in wall stress due to individual extracellular matrix constituents thus promises to provide considerable clinically important insight into arterial health and disease.

Key Words: *Vascular development, Elastin, Aging, Marfan syndrome, Opening angle, Residual stress.*

1. INTRODUCTION

Several experimental evidences, starting from the 1960s, reveal that arteries retract when transected, thus suggesting the existence of an axial prestretch that defines the favorable length *in vivo*. Dobrin and colleagues [1] in 1975 showed that that this axial prestretch increases nearly linearly with age during postnatal development and suggested that it can be "attributed to stretching of the vessels by growth and to changes in connective tissue composition." Subsequent studies demonstrated that nearly all axial prestretch in healthy arteries is due to the presence of intramural elastin, not collagen.

Findings in the 1960s revealed further that stress exists in an artery even when there is no intramural pressure. Later studies confirmed the existence of residual stresses in arteries, which appear to arise from non-uniform growth and remodeling processes during development [2], they can change in response to disease or injury in maturity, and furthermore depend primarily on intramural elastin, not collagen or smooth muscle. Zeller and Skalak in 1998 [3] suggested that the net residual stresses in an excised artery likely depend on different residual stresses within individual constituents, with elastin having a residual tension and collagen a residual compression. Indeed, this suggestion is consistent with current thinking that elastin is deposited during the perinatal period and its half-life is normally on the order of the lifespan of the organism, thus causing it to undergo extensive elastic deformations during normal biological growth. On the other hand, collagen turns over continuously and is likely deposited at a preferred deposition stretch independent of the current state of the artery in maturity [4], thus yielding a more modest collagen prestretch.

The existence of residual stress in an excised arterial segment, revealed for example by the opening angle that follows the introduction of a radial cut, suggests a net compressive stress in the inner wall and a net tensile stress in the outer wall, which is captured easily by both standard stress analyses [5] and computational models of arterial growth [6]. Such models are based on materially uniform, phenomenological, constitutive relations, however, and thus have not been capable of assessing the potential roles of individual constituents or how they are formed or reorganized during development or maturity. The goal of this study, therefore, is to employ a recently proposed materially non-uniform, structurally motivated, constrained mixture model of the arterial wall to study the means by which elastin plays such an important role in the development of axial prestress and residual stress in the normal arterial wall. We submit further that the constrained mixture model employed herein can be used to build residual stresses into patient-specific computational models without the need to define clinically unattainable spatially and temporally changing opened configurations, a feature that could be particularly advantageous in modeling complex arterial geometries and diseased states.

2. METHOD

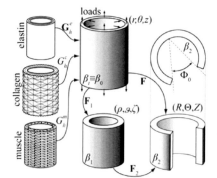

Figure 1: Schema of the constrained mixture model of an arterial segment consisting of elastin, multiple families of collagen fibers, and circumferentially oriented smooth muscle.

Following the semi-inverse approach of finite elasticity, we prescribe the kinematics for an idealized axisymmetric artery via two successive motions: mappings of material points from a physiologically-relevant *in vivo* configuration $\beta_t \equiv \beta_0$ (with coordinates r, θ, z) to an intact but traction-free excised configuration β_1 (with coordinates ρ, ϑ, ζ) and finally to a nearly stress-free, radially-cut configuration β_2 (R, Θ, Z) (see Figure 1). The deformation gradients for these motions are

$$\mathbf{F}_1 = \text{diag}\left[\frac{\partial \rho}{\partial r}, \frac{\rho}{r}, \frac{1}{\lambda}\right], \quad \mathbf{F}_2 = \text{diag}\left[\frac{\partial R}{\partial \rho}, \frac{(\pi - \Phi_O)R}{\pi \rho}, \frac{1}{\Lambda}\right], \tag{1}$$

with Φ_O and Λ the residual stress related opening angle and axial stretch, respectively, and λ the additional axial stretch related primarily to the *in vivo* "prestretch". The total deformation gradient is thus computed via $\mathbf{F} = \mathbf{F}_2 \mathbf{F}_1$ and incompressibility is assumed to hold during transient motions, but not overall growth and remodeling, hence $\det \mathbf{F} = 1$ herein. The Cauchy stress $\mathbf{t}$ (associated with $\mathbf{F} = \mathbf{F}_1$, or $\mathbf{F} = \mathbf{F}_2 \mathbf{F}_1$) can be computed via

$$\text{div} \mathbf{t} = \mathbf{0}, \quad \mathbf{t} = -p\mathbf{I} + \frac{\partial W}{\partial \mathbf{F}} \mathbf{F}^{\text{T}} + \mathbf{t}^{\text{act}}, \tag{2}$$

where p is a Lagrange multiplier that enforces incompressibility, W is the net strain energy function for the passive behavior of the wall, and $\mathbf{t}^{\text{act}}$ accounts for smooth muscle activity. Consistent with [7] we employ a rule-of-mixtures constitutive relation for the passive response, namely

$$W = \phi^e W^e(\mathbf{F}^e) + \sum_{k=1,4} \phi^k W^k(\lambda^k) + \phi^m W^m(\lambda^m), \tag{3}$$

where ϕ^i are mass fractions for each structurally significant constituent and W^i are individual strain energy functions ($i=e$ for amorphous elastin, $i=1,2,3,4$ for four oriented families of collagen fibers, and $i=m$ for circumferentially oriented passive smooth muscle). Moreover, $\mathbf{F}^e$, λ^k, and λ^m represent the elastin deformation gradient, collagen fiber stretch, and smooth muscle stretch, respectively. These quantities are defined with respect to individual stress-free configurations (see Figure 1) and this aspect represents one of the most important features of the present model.

Equilibrium of the *in vivo* configuration β_0 requires

$$\int_{r_i}^{r_a} (t_{\theta\theta} - t_{rr}) \frac{dr}{r} = P, \qquad 2\pi \int_{r_i}^{r_a} t_{zz} r dr = f, \tag{4}$$

where r_i and r_a denote intimal and adventitial radii in β_0 (associated with the deformation $\mathbf{F} = \mathbf{I}$) and P and f are the *in vivo* luminal pressure and axial force, respectively. To ensure radial equilibrium at the prescribed *in vivo* luminal pressure, equation $(4)_1$ was solved for the adventitial radius r_a; equation $(4)_2$ gives for the *in vivo* axial force. In this way, the material parameters, intimal radius, and luminal pressure were kept the same in all the simulations regardless of the assumed distributions of constituent prestretches and mass fractions (with slight variations in outer radius maintaining radial equilibrium). Equilibrium of the unloaded configuration β_1 similarly requires

$$\int_{\rho_i}^{\rho_a} (t_{\vartheta\vartheta} - t_{\rho\rho}) \frac{d\rho}{\rho} = 0, \qquad \int_{\rho_i}^{\rho_a} t_{\zeta\zeta} \rho d\rho = 0 \tag{5}$$

where ρ_i and ρ_a denote intimal and adventitial radii in β_1 (associated with the deformation $\mathbf{F} = \mathbf{F}_1$). Equations (5) can be solved to determine the inner radius ρ_i and the net *in vivo* axial prestretch λ for prescribed material properties and distributions of constituent prestretches and mass fractions, with zero transmural pressure and axial force. Finally equilibrium of the excised, radially-cut configuration β_2 can be satisfied via (cf. Taber and Humphrey in [6])

$$\int_{R_i}^{R_a} (t_{\Theta\Theta} - t_{RR}) \frac{dR}{R} = 0, \qquad \int_{R_i}^{R_a} t_{ZZ} R dR = 0, \qquad \int_{R_i}^{R_a} t_{\Theta\Theta} R dR = 0, \tag{6}$$

where R_i and R_a denote intimal and adventitial radii in β_2 (associated with the deformation $\mathbf{F} = \mathbf{F}_2 \mathbf{F}_1$). Note that the additional global equilibrium equation $(6)_3$ enforces zero applied moments on the radially-cut section. The three global equations can be solved for the inner radius R_i, the net *in vivo* axial prestretch $\ddot{\text{E}}\lambda$, given λ from above, and the residual stress related opening angle $\ddot{\text{O}}_0$, all for the prescribed material properties and distributions of constituent prestretches and mass fractions, again with zero transmural pressure and axial force.

Concerning the constitutive relations, coherently with [7], we assumed the amorphous elastin matrix to be described by the neo-Hookean strain energy, collagen fibers and passive smooth muscle by a Fung-type exponential behavior. In particular collagen was assumed to behave differently in compression and tension in order to account for the potential buckling of the fibers and the bearing capability of proteoglycans in compression. Also the active muscular stress $\mathbf{t}^{\text{act}}$ was modeled according to [7].

3. RESULTS

Several simulations were performed using constituents mass fractions typical of human basilar arteries, one of the primary arteries that supplies blood to the brain, assuming different hypothesis on the transmural distribution of the constituents and their prestretch. Numerical results herein support the hypothesis that elastin is cross-linked soon after deposition in development hence outer layers of elastin likely experience less circumferential prestretch in maturity than do the inner layers. Results showing up to a 30% reduction in the opening angle $\ddot{\text{O}}_0$ with loss of elastin in the basilar artery, are consistent qualitatively with experimental and theoretical results (see [7] and references therein). For small radial gradients in elastin prestretch, computed residual stresses in the intact unloaded configuration were qualitatively comparable to those reported in [6] where phenomenological constitutive relations were employed. The predicted axial retraction from the intact, unloaded configuration to the radially-cut, unloaded configuration was about 1%, consistent with a reinterpretation of the Chuong and Fung data. The present results also confirm those in [6] that the radially-cut, unloaded configuration is completely stress-free only if the material is homogeneous; for non-uniform distributions, the radially-cut configuration was still residually stressed and the rings obtained by the introduction of a circumferential cut manifested different opening angles, with the inner ring opening more than the outer one, according to experimental evidences. Moreover, we showed that a distribution of elastin prestretches that decreases from the intima to the adventitia helps render the *in vivo* distribution of stress more uniform through the thickness for all values of physiological pressure during the cardiac cycle, perhaps enhancing the performance of the artery as a load-bearing thick-walled structure as well as its mechanobiological responses. Consistent with experimental findings, our results suggest that the compressive mechanical behavior of proteoglycan-supported collagen plays a particularly important role in determining the unloaded length of the artery: the *in vivo* axial prestretch λ decreased and became dramatically less sensitive to the transmural distribution of elastin prestretch when the collagen was stiffer in compression. Moreover, the sensitivity of the opening angle to the distribution of elastin prestretches decreased with increases in the compressive stiffness of collagen. When muscle activity was included in the unloaded, radially-cut configuration, the model predicted changes with increases of constrictor concentration in qualitative agreement with experimental results reported in the literature. Finally, the simulations showed that a gradual, age-related reversal of radial gradients in elastin and collagen (cf., for example, [8]) could explain, in part, the observed increases in opening angle with age.

Based on the present results, we submit that axial prestresses and residual stresses arise in arteries largely due to the deposition of remarkably stable, highly elastic, elastin during development and the continual turnover of collagen and smooth muscle at consistent, preferred stretches within an important ground substance matrix. That is, residual stresses arise due to the different natural configurations of individual constituents, and they can be influenced greatly by transmural gradients therein as well as changes in the relative mass fractions and degrees of cross-linking. Our results, based on a simple constrained mixture model, qualitatively recover most of the accepted observations in the literature and thereby provide further motivation to formulate mixture models of arterial growth and remodeling in diverse cases important to studies of clinical and basic science. Moreover, because residual stresses arise naturally using this constrained mixture model, such constitutive relations promise to simplify the inclusion of residual stresses, and their changes with disease, within finite element models of complex arterial geometries without needing to define evolving opened-up configurations at each axial position, the residual stress field itself, or the existence of a homeostatic *in vivo* stress.

REFERENCES

[1]   P. B. Dobrin, T. Canfield, and S. Sinha, Development of longitudinal retraction of carotid arteries in neonatal dogs, *Experientia*, 31, 1295-1296, 1975.

[2]   Y. C. Fung, *What principle governs the stress distribution in living organism?*, Science Press, Beijing, 1983.

[3]   P. J. Zeller and T. C. Skalak, Contribution of individual structural components in determining the zero-stress state in small arteries, *J. Vasc. Res.*, 35, 8-17, 1998.

[4]   J.D. Humphrey and K. R. Rajagopal, A constrained mixture model for growth and remodeling of soft tissues, *Math. Model. Meth. Appl. Sci.*, 12, 407-430, 2002.

[5]   C. J. Chuong, Y. C. Fung, On residual stress in artery, *J. Biomech. Eng.*, 108, 189-192, 1986.

[6]   L. A. Taber, J. D. Humphrey, Stress-modulated growth, residual stress, and vascular heterogeneity, *J. Biomech. Eng.*, 123, 528-535, 2001.

[7]   L. Cardamone, A. Valentín, J. F. Eberth, J. D. Humphrey, Origin of axial prestretch and residual stress in arteries, *Biomech. Model. Mechanobiol.*, (in press) DOI 10.1007/s10237-008-0146-x.

[8]   S. A. Feldman and S. Glagov, Transmural collagen and elastin in human aortas: reversal with age, *Atherosclerosis*, 13, 385-394, 1971.

Modelling Controlled Drug Release and Transport Phenomena in the Arterial Wall

Sara Minisini, Luca Formaggia
MOX, Mathematics Department - Politecnico di Milano,
Via Bonardi 9, 20133 Milano,
sara.minisini@polimi.it, luca.formaggia@polimi.it

ABSTRACT

Polymeric matrices are widely used in medical devices to store a drug and release it at a prescribed rate. We investigate the drug release from polymeric matrix systems into the arterial tissue using a two dimensional numerical model. The main phenomena taken into account are the dissolution and diffusion of the drug inside the material and the erosion of the matrix. A mathematical model of the drug dissolution and release processes in the erodible matrix has been formulated in terms of two coupled nonlinear partial differential equations in a moving domain. In the tissue another system of equations describes diffusion, convection due to plasma filtration and reversible biochemical binding. Suitable interface condition have been devised to couple the two models and thus describe the whole release process. Numerical investigations applied to drug eluting stents show the impact on the release profile of the different phenomena involved as well as the influence of the characteristics of the drug and of the polymeric material.

Key Words: *controlled drug delivery, drug dissolution, polymer erosion, drug eluting stent.*

1   INTRODUCTION

When modeling the complete process of drug elution, from a drug eluting stent (DES) into arterial wall we need to describe phenomena that take place on different scales in space and time. DES for cardiovascular applications are miniaturized metal structures which are coated with a polymeric micro-layer whose thickness generally lays within the range of microns. As regards the time scales, the release of drug into the tissue persists until a few weeks after the stent implantation. While, the local phenomena that influence drug release take place inside the coating within much shorter time scales, typically minutes or even seconds. Usually, deterministic models are used to describe the phenomena both at the macroscale, identified with the tissue level [8], and at the mesoscale identified with the coating [3].

In this work we focus on mathematical and numerical models which allow to study some of the parameters responsible[2] of the efficacy of the therapeutic treatment. These elements are the characterization of the drug and tissue properties and that of the drug delivery system. To better understand the mechanisms involved in the drug release mechanism, one has to focus on the structure of the device. In one possible configuration, the drug is uniformly distributed throughout the polymer matrix giving a mono-lithic devices, [5], such as microspheres, slabs or beads. Initially, the release is controlled by desorption of the drug from the device surface, followed by drug diffusion through porous channels. Afterwards, it is governed by dissolution, diffusion and in the case of a biodegradable material by the mass loss of the matrix that can contain residual drug. Depending on which of the phenomena prevails the drug

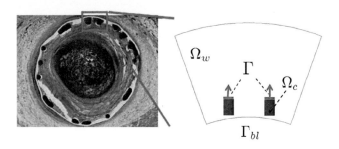

Figure 1: *Detail of a stented artery and of the associated two dimensional discrete model.*

release could be diffusion/dissolution controlled, or erosion controlled. When erosion is faster than drug diffusion, drug release is erosion controlled. In this case a part from the classical physical mass transport processes chemical reaction due to degradation of the polymeric chains (due to hydrolysis) occurs. There are two main patterns of erosion. Erosion can take place throughout the whole matrix, this case is referred as homogeneous or bulk erosion, or can be restricted to the device surface [4]. The latter process is named heterogeneous or surface erosion and is the one we consider.

In fact, the surface erosion is considered as the preferable erosion mechanism in medical devices, because it is highly reproducible, and the degradation rate of the material can be manipulated by just changing the surface contact area with the surrounding solvent.

2 Mathematical modeling of drug release

The dissolution is the physical process for with a solid element dissolves in the surrounding solution. In our work we refers to the dissolution as the process that transform the solid drug contained in the matrix into its dissolved state inside the porous network of the polymer that can flow out by diffusion. The basic step of the dissolution is the reaction that takes place at the liquid-solid interface. The mathematical model that we use to describe the dissolution/diffusion in a two dimensional rectangular slab, Ω_c, is a based on a reformulation of the Noyes-Whitney equation that found as the governing force of the dissolution is the difference between the solubility c_s and the dissolved concentration of the drug inside the matrix. The system of equation, as proposed in [3] reads:

$$\frac{\partial c}{\partial t} = \nabla(D_c \nabla c) + k_d s^{2/3}(c_s - c), \quad \text{in } \Omega_c,$$

$$\frac{\partial s}{\partial t} = -k_d s^{2/3}(c_s - c), \qquad \text{in } \Omega_c,$$

(1)

where c, and s are the dissolved and solid drug inside the domain, k_d is the dissolution rate constant (1/sec) and D_c is the diffusion coefficient. The system of equations will be solved with suitable boundary condition to describe the release in the tissue. The model (1) is then extended to consider the erosion process. We assume that matrix boundaries in contact with the solution erode following a linear law, as experimental trials show for a large class of polymer. The model is equivalent to (1) but reformulated on a moving domain $\Omega_c(t) = (0, L(t)) \times (0, H)$, where the length of the slab changes according to experimental laws. The mass transport in the tissue, modelled as an homogeneous porous media, is described by means of an advection diffusion reaction system of equations . In agreement with experimental evidences [1] diffusion and convection are in competition in the distribution of the drug inside the wall. The velocity of the plasma filtration $\mathbf{u_w}$ due to the pressure gradient between the lumen and the adventitia, is computed by means of Darcy's law [7]. Moreover the ability of the drug to bind reversibly with specific sites [6] is considered. Under these assumptions we have:

$$\frac{\partial a}{\partial t} + \mathbf{u}_w \nabla a - D_w \Delta a = -k_1 ab + k_2(b0 - b), \quad \text{in } \Omega_w,$$

$$\frac{\partial b}{\partial t} = -k_1 ab + k_2(b0 - b), \qquad\qquad \text{in } \Omega_w,$$

(2)

where $\Omega_w(t)$ is a section of the arterial wall as shown in figure 2. The drug inside the tissue assumes two different states: the state where the drug is dissolved into the plasma permeating the interstices between cells, whose volume averaged concentration is $a(t, \mathbf{x})$. The drug moves by convection and diffusion. The state where the drug attaches reversibly to specific sites of the extra-cellular matrix of the tissue. If we denote with $b(t, \mathbf{x})$ the density of the free binding sites in the tissue, with $b0(\mathbf{x})$ their initial concentration in the arterial, the volume averaged concentration of the bound drug is $b0(\mathbf{x}) - b(t, \mathbf{x})$. The system of equation (2) needs a suitable set of boundary and coupling conditions. We assume that the mass drug transfer between the two domains takes place only through Γ (as shown in Fig.2), where we assume assume continuity of the flux and discontinuity of the concentrations if the topcoat (a layer used to slow down the release process) is considered. Let summarize the boundary conditions:

$$\mathbb{B} := \begin{cases} a = 0, & \text{on } \Gamma_{bl}, \\[2ex] D_w \dfrac{\partial a}{\partial \mathbf{n}_w} = 0, & \text{on } \partial\Omega_w \backslash \{\Gamma_{bl} \cup \Gamma\}, \\[2ex] D_c \dfrac{\partial c}{\partial \mathbf{n}_w} = 0, & \text{on } \partial\Omega_c \backslash \{\Gamma\}. \end{cases}$$

(3)

and the coupling condition on Γ,

$$-D_c \frac{\partial c}{\partial \mathbf{n}_c} = P_c \left(\frac{c}{k_c \epsilon_c} - \frac{a}{k_w \epsilon_w} \right), \quad \text{and} \quad D_w \frac{\partial a}{\partial \mathbf{n}_w} = -D_c \frac{\partial c}{\partial \mathbf{n}_c},$$

(4)

The first equation of (4), takes into account for the topcoat presence, otherwise, the continuity of the dissolved concentration, $c = a$ is prescribed. As initial conditions we set, $a(0, \mathbf{x}) = 0$, $b(0, \mathbf{x}) = b0$, in Ω_w and $c(0, \mathbf{x}) = 0$, $s(0, \mathbf{x}) = 1$ in Ω_c. The complete problem (1), (2) and (3) is then extended to the case of a biodegradable matrix and reformulated on moving domains $\Omega_c(t)$ and $\Omega_w(t)$. In particular to preserve the mass balance of the system and consider that both the phases can be released from the matrix new coupling boundary condition are devised. Our numerical results let us describe the distribution of both the drug phases, and to quantify the release dynamic in terms of mass stored in the stent $M_c = \int_{\Omega_c} c + s \, d\Omega$ and that released in the tissue $M_w = \int_{\Omega_w} (a + b0 - b) \, d\Omega$. The distribution of the dose and the release pattern, two important parameters in the definition of the efficacy of the treatment are analyzed in dependence of the nature of the drug (hydrophobic or hydrophilic) and the characteristic of the polymeric matrix. Moreover, the effect of the matrix erosion is deeply investigated and the effect of a dose dumping to an abrupt release of drug is analyzed.

3 CONCLUSIONS

From the analysis of important quantities such as the dose and the residence time it is found as the distribution of the drug inside the wall is not uniform and it is strongly influenced by the coating features and the characterization of the tissue [7], [9]. Thus, improved models to describe the characteristics of the tissue and the polymeric matrix have been studied. The ability of the drug to bind with specific binding sites with a reversible kinetic was considered. Inside the delivery material we consider a dissolution-diffusion and erosion model. This model improved the simple one used in [7], [9], where

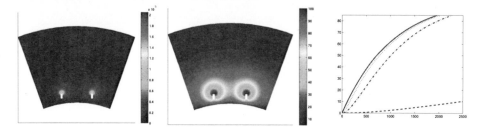

Figure 2: *Distribution of the dissolved concentration (left) and percentage of free binding sites (middle). Percentage of release drug in the tissue against time in minutes (right). The release profiles have an increasing value of the dissolution coefficient from right to left*

it was assumed that the drug was completely dissolved in the matrix and the release was governed by diffusion only. A sensitivity analysis highlighted those parameters that played an important role in the definition of the release rate, the dissolution coefficient and the drug solubility. By using these parameters, we had more control on the release process and its kinetics. The extension introduced to take into account for the erosion was based on experimental evidences. We introduced some simplification, as the linear degradation of the matrix and the hypothesis that the eroding front remains planar during the erosion process. Even though the approach we used to define the boundary condition when describing the release in the tissue from eroding matrices could be applied, and improved laws to describe the eroding matrix could allow us to describe a wide class of situations.

References

[1] Creel, C. J., Lovich, M. A., Edelman, E.R., Arterial paclitaxel distribution and deposition, *Circ. Res.*, 2000, 86, pp.879-884.

[2] Bourgeois, E., Delfour, M.C., General patterns and asymptotic dose in the design of coated stents, *Compu. Methods Biomech. Biomed. Eng.*, 2008, 11(4), pp.323-34

[3] Frenning, G., Theoretical investigation of drug release from planar matrix systems: effects of a finite dissolution rate, *J. Control. Rel.*, 2003, 92, pp.331-339.

[4] Göpferich, A., Mechanisms of polymer degradation and erosion, *Biomaterials*, 1996, 17, pp.103-114.

[5] Heller, J., Biodegradable polymers in controlled drug delivery, *Crit. Rev. Ther. Drug Carrier Sys.*, 1984, pp.39-90.

[6] Levin, A. D., Vukmirovic, N., Hwang, C., Edelman, E.R., Specific bindings to intracellualr proteins determines arterial transport for rapamycin and pclitaxel, *Proc. Natl. Acad. Sci. USA*, 2004, 101(22), pp.9463-9467.

[7] Migliavacca, F., Gervasio, F., Prosi, M., Zunino, P., Minisini, S., Dubini, G., Formaggia, L., Expansion and elution model of a coronary stent, *Comput. Method Biomech. Biomed. Eng. J.*, 2007, 10(1), pp.66-73.

[8] Quarteroni, A., Formaggia, L., Mathematical modelling and numerical simulation of the cardio-vascular system, *Handbook of numerical analysis*, 2004, Vol. XII, pp. 3-127, North-Holland, Amsterdam.

[9] Vergara, C., Zunino, P., Multiscale boundary conditions for drug release from cariovascular stent, *SIAM, Multiscale Model. Simul.*, 2008, pp.565-588.

A 3D FLUID STRUCTURE INTERACTION NON-NEWTONIAN MODEL FOR BLOOD FLOW USING 1D ABSORBING BOUNDARY CONDITIONS

A. Moura, J. Janela and A. Sequeira
CEMAT, Center for Mathematics and its Applications, IST, Instituto Superior Técnico, Technical University of Lisbon, Av. Rovisco Pais, n. 1, 1049-001, Lisbon, alexandra.moura@math.ist.utl.pt

ABSTRACT

We consider three main difficulties in modelling blood flow in arteries: the pulse propagation phenomena is captured by using a 3D fluid-structure interaction model; the shear-thinning behaviour of blood is accounted throught a generalized Newtonian model; and the systemic circulation is considered by means of reduced 1D models, coupled to the 3D FSI non-Newtonian one, acting as proper absorbing boundary condition to the 3D model. The models and couplings are presented and analyzed, and comparative numerical results, between the Newtonian and non-Newtonian models, are presented in several geometries.

Key Words: *non-Newtonian fluids, fluid-structure interaction, 1D model, blood flow, pulse propagation, absorbing boundary condition.*

1 INTRODUCTION

The human circulatory system is extremely complex and its modelling and simulation constitute a very difficult and challenging task. Blood exhibits complex rheological characteristics such as shear-thinning viscosity, viscoelasticity or yield stress [3], and non-Newtonian models should be considered. Moreover, blood flow in arteries is characterized by travelling pressure waves due to the interaction of blood with the vessel wall, and 3D fluid-structure interaction (FSI) models are required [1]. On the other hand, the cardiovascular system is highly integrated and a whole hierarchy of models for the simulation of blood flow in the vascular system has been developed, giving rise to the so-called *geometrical multiscale modelling* of the cardiovascular system [4], which consists in coupling different models operating at different space scales, 3D, 1D and 0D, involving local and systemic dynamics.

Very little can be found in literature regarding 3D FSI models for blood using non-Newtonian fluids, as well as the coupling of reduced blood flow models with 3D non-Newtonian ones. Here, we extend the 3D FSI model to generalized Newtonian fluids, and perform the coupling between 3D generalized Newtonian models with reduced 1D models, that can act as proper physiological absorbing boundary condition. The energy estimate for the 3D FSI coupling, using a non-linear elastic structure model for the vessel wall, as well as the energy estimate or the 3D FSI - 1D coupling in [1] are extended to the generalized Newtonian case [2]. Several numerical results are presented, comparing the Newtonian and non-Newtonian cases for different geometries.

2   THE MATHEMATICAL MODELS

The 3D non-Newtonian fluid model.   Let $\Omega^t \subset \mathbb{R}^3$ be a bounded domain representing a portion of a blood vessel at time t. The part of the boundary representing the wall is Γ_w^t, while the remaining parts of the boundary are the so-called *artificial boundaries* [1]. We consider the fluid equations [3]:

$$\begin{cases} \rho \left(\dfrac{\partial \mathbf{u}}{\partial t} + \mathbf{u} \cdot \nabla \mathbf{u} \right) - \operatorname{div} \boldsymbol{\sigma}(\mathbf{u}, P) &= \mathbf{0}, \quad \text{in } \Omega^t, \forall t \in I, \\ \operatorname{div} \mathbf{u} &= 0, \quad \text{in } \Omega^t, \forall t \in I, \end{cases} \tag{1}$$

where $I =]0, T]$ is the time interval and $\rho = 1 g cm^{-3}$ the density of blood. The unknowns are the velocity $\mathbf{u}$ and the pressure P, while $\boldsymbol{\sigma}(\mathbf{u}, P)$ is the Cauchy stress tensor. For a generalized Newtonian fluid we have $\boldsymbol{\sigma}(\mathbf{u}, P) = -P\mathbf{I} + 2\mu(\dot{\gamma})\mathbf{D}(\mathbf{u})$, where $\mathbf{D}(\mathbf{u})$ is the strain rate tensor and $\mu(\dot{\gamma})$ is the dynamical viscosity, dependent on the shear rate $\dot{\gamma} := \sqrt{\frac{1}{2}\mathbf{D}(\mathbf{u}) : \mathbf{D}(\mathbf{u})}$. For both mathematical and physical reasons we will focus on bounded viscosity laws of the general type:

$$\mu(\dot{\gamma}) = \mu_\infty + (\mu_0 + \mu_\infty)F(\dot{\gamma}), \tag{2}$$

Where $F(\cdot)$ is a continuous monotonic function such that $\lim_{\dot{\gamma} \to 0} F(\dot{\gamma}) = 1$ and $\lim_{\dot{\gamma} \to +\infty} F(\dot{\gamma}) = 0$. In the case of blood flow we are interested in desribing a shear-thinning behaviour, and therefore the asymptotic viscosities verify $\mu_0 > \mu_\infty > 0$. For the Carreau-Yasuda generalized Newtonian model, that describes a shear-thinning fluid [3], we have $\mu(\dot{\gamma}) = \mu_\infty + (\mu_0 - \mu_\infty) \times (1 + (\lambda\dot{\gamma})^a)^{\frac{n-1}{a}}$, with $\lambda > 0$, and $n, a \in \mathbb{R}$ model constants to be estimated from experimental data. In the particular case of $a = 2$ we obtain the Carreau model. System (1) is endowed with the initial condition $\mathbf{u} = \mathbf{u}_0$.

The 3D structural model.   We consider the 3D non-linear model of hyperelasticity [1,2]. The structure domain is bounded: $\Sigma^t \subset \mathbb{R}^3$. The structure equations are written in *Lagrangian* coordinates, *i.e.* with respect to a reference configuration, chosen to be the domain at the initial time Σ^0:

$$\rho_w \frac{\partial^2 \boldsymbol{\eta}}{\partial t^2} - \operatorname{div}_0 (\mathbf{P}) = \mathbf{0}, \quad \text{in } \Sigma^0, \forall t \in I, \tag{3}$$

where $\boldsymbol{\eta}$ is the displacement vector with respect to the reference configuration Σ^0, ρ_w the wall density, div_0 the divergence operator with respect to the Lagrangian coordinates and $\mathbf{P} = \mathbf{P}(\boldsymbol{\eta})$ the first Piola-Kirchhoff tensor (see [1]). We consider a St. Venant-Kirchhoff material [1,2], and endow equations (3) with proper initial conditions.

The 3D fluid-structure interaction coupling.   The FSI coupling occurs at the wall interface Γ_w^t, through the matching conditions between the fluid and the solid [1,2]. These are the no-slip condition $\mathbf{u} = \dot{\boldsymbol{\eta}}, \forall t \in I$, on Γ_w^t, and the continuity of the stresses $-(\det \nabla_0 \boldsymbol{\eta}) (\boldsymbol{\sigma}(\mathbf{u}, p) + p_{ext}\mathbf{I}) (\nabla_0^{-T}\boldsymbol{\eta}) \cdot \mathbf{n}_0 = \widehat{\boldsymbol{\Phi}}$ for $t \in I$, on Γ_w^0, where p_{ext} is a given external pressure, $\widehat{\boldsymbol{\Phi}}$ is the structure force per unit reference surface area on Γ_w^0, ∇_0 indicates the gradient with respect to the Lagrangian coordinates, and $\mathbf{n}_0$ is the outward unit vector to Γ_w^0. We adopt the Arbitrary Lagrangian Eulerian (ALE) framework to account for the deformation of the fluid domain, due to the interaction with the structure wall.

An energy decay property for this FSI non-Newtonian coupling has been demonstrated in [2], taking into consideration that we are interested in a bounded viscosity of the type (2).

The 1D hyperbolic model. One-dimensional (1D) models can be derived from the incompressible Navier-Stokes equations coupled with a structure model for the vessel wall, by making some simplifying assumptions and integrating over the cross section of the artery (see [1] and references therein). Under these assumptions, and assuming a specific axial velocity profile, the 1D model for blood flow in a cylindrical vessel is given by the following system:

$$
\begin{cases}
\dfrac{\partial A}{\partial t} + \dfrac{\partial Q}{\partial z} = 0, \\[2mm]
\dfrac{\partial Q}{\partial t} + \dfrac{\partial}{\partial z}\left(\dfrac{\alpha Q^2}{A}\right) + \dfrac{A}{\rho}\dfrac{\partial \overline{p}}{\partial z} = -2\pi\nu(\alpha+2)\dfrac{Q}{A},
\end{cases}
\qquad z \in (a,b), t \in I,
\tag{4}
$$

Here $(b-a)$ is the vessel length, z denotes the axial direction, α is the momentum flux correction coefficient, ν is the fluid dynamic viscosity and ρ is the fluid density; α, ν and ρ are assumed constant and we take $\alpha = 1$, corresponding to a flat velocity profile. The unknowns are the cross-section area A, the flow rate Q and the averaged pressure $\overline{p}$. System (4) is closed by providing an algebraic relation linking pressure and area: $\psi(A; A_0, \beta) = \beta\dfrac{\sqrt{A} - \sqrt{A_0}}{A_0}$, with $\beta = \dfrac{\sqrt{\pi}h_0 E}{1-\nu^2}$.

The 3D FSI - 1D coupling. The prescription of boundary conditions on the 3D fluid artificial sections is done by coupling them with a 1D model, that can represent a network of the main arteries. The coupling is performed imposing the continuity of the mean total pressure and of the fluxes at the interfaces.

Using an iterative procedure to get the solution of the coupled problem, the 3D FSI model provides pointwise information on the velocity, which is integrated to obtain the flow rate to be given to the 1D model as a boundary condition on the interfacing point. In turn, the 1D model provides the mean total pressure to be prescribed as boundary conditions at the artificial sections of the 3D model (see [4]).

With this choice for the coupling, following [1], and taking into account the energy estimate for the 3D FSI non-Newtonian problem [2], an energy estimate for the 3D FSI - 1D coupling with a 3D generalized Newtonian fluid can be straightforwardly derived.

3 NUMERICAL RESULTS

As a first numerical test we consider a shear-thinning Carreau fluid model with parameters chosen as in [4], in a cylindrical geometry. At the inflow we take a pressure impulse of $10mmHg$, and at the outflow the 3D model is coupled with a 1D model. In Fig. 1 it can be seen that the 3D FSI - 1D coupling works as expected, with the 1D model absorbing the pulse pressure wave, also for generalized Newtonian fluids.

Secondly, we consider a curved tube (see Fig. 2), with the same pressure impulse at the inflow boundary as before and compare the Carreau and Newtonian models. At outflow the 3D FSI model is again coupled with a 1D tube. In Fig. 2 we compare the wall shear stress (WSS) for both cases, showing qualitative and quantitative differences between them.

4 CONCLUSIONS

We have extended the 3D FSI - 1D coupling to generalized Newtonian fluids, demonstrating the couplings work very well. An energy estimate for the 3D FSI coupling and its coupling with 1D model

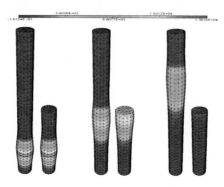

Figure 1: Comparison of the pressure distribution between the 3D FSI generalized Newtonian - 1D coupling (right) and the equivalent 3D FSI generalized Newtonian model (left), at three different time steps.

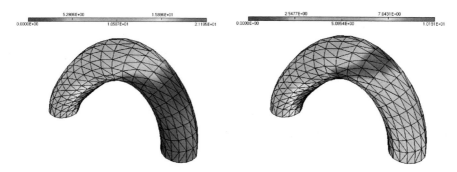

Figure 2: Comparison of WSS distribution between the 3D FSI Newtonian - 1D coupling (left) and the 3D FSI generalized Newtonian - 1D coupling (right) at $t = 0.01s$.

was obtained. From the results, significative differences are found between the Newtonian and non-Newtonian models, which should be carefully studied and taken into account when performing blood flow simulations. Work is on going to apply these models to real patient specific geometries and medical data.

Acknowledgments. This work has been partially supported by the research center CEMAT/IST through FCT's funding program and by the project PTDC/MAT/68166/2006. A. Moura is funded by FCT through grant SFRH/BPD/34273/2006.

REFERENCES

[1] L. Formaggia, A. Moura and F. Nobile. On the stability of the coupling of 3D and 1D fluid-structure interaction models for blood flow simulations. *Mathematical Modelling and Numerical Analysis*, 41(4), 743-769, 2007.

[2] J. Janela, A. Moura and A. Sequeira. A 3D fluid-structure interaction non-Newtonian model for blood flow. 2009. Submitted.

[3] A. Robertson and A. Sequeira. Hemorheology. In: G. P. Galdi, R. Ranacher, A. Robertson and S. Turek editors, *Haemodynamical Flows: Modelling Analysis and Simulation*, vol 37, 63-120. Birkhauser, 2008.

[4] A. Sequeira, A. Moura and J. Janela. Towards a geometrical multiscale approach to non-Newtonian blood flow simulations. In: *Advances in Mathematical Fluid Dynamics*. Springer, Berlin and Heidelberg, 2009. In press.

1st International Conference on Mathematical and Computational Biomedical Engineering - CMBE2009
June 29 - July 1, 2009, Swansea, UK
P.Nithiarasu and R.Löhner (Eds.)

Massively Parallel Cardiac Computational Electrophysiology in Anisotropic Media

R. Arís, G. Houzeaux and M. Vázquez
Barcelona Supercomputing Center, Campus Nord UPC, Barcelona, Spain, mariano.vazquez@bsc.es

Debora Gil, Jaume Garcia-Barnes
Computer Vision Center, Campus Bellaterra, Universitat Autonoma de Barcelona, Spain

ABSTRACT

This paper presents a multi-disciplinary joint work, focusing in the High Performance Computational Mechanics aspect of a massively parallel cardiac computational electrophysiology model. It represents an effort to put advanced computational tools in the hands of the research community, capable of simulating efficiently and accurately this extremely complex problem.

Key Words: *Cardiac Computational Electrophysiology, Parallelization, Fenton-Karma models, Finite element methods*

1 INTRODUCTION

The present work proposes a computational method for reaction-diffusion electro-physiological models, subjected to the following two premises. Firstly, the model must be capable of running as fast as possible in large-scale supercomputers allowing to solve either simple models very rapidly or Grand Challenge ones in a reasonable amount of time. Secondly, the model must be flexible enough to be used by Physiologists including all kind of models.

2 A Cardiac Computational Electrophysiology Model

During the past two decades, different modeling approaches have been developed for bridging the physical scales corresponding to the different levels of the heart structural description [5,6]. This process is part of a concept called integrative biological modeling, which is currently an active research topic that includes structural, functional and data integrations [7]. Currently, the most conspicuous ideas for bridging scales correspond either to cellular automata or reaction-diffusion systems. The former are based on two components: discrete network of cells representing the spatial structure, and *a priori* definition of simple communication rules between cells in order to reproduce the propagation wave. The latter are based on conservation laws and use systems of partial and ordinary differential equations to describe the excitation and propagation process in cardiac tissue (excitable media). The present paper is based on this second line of action, mainly relying in the models studied or proposed in works like [8,9]. In this paper, we are not focused in the validity of the physiology of the models themselves, but in their Computational Mechanics side.

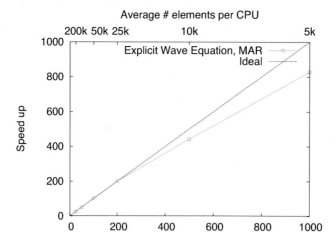

Figure 1: Hard scalability of Alya for the diffusion operator: speed-up vs. number of CPU cores.

2.1 Physiological models

In this paper, we follow the line of modeling the electrophysiology potential $\phi(x_i, t)$ problem using a propagation equation through a macroscopic continuous media combined with a microscopic model, which should be properly projected to the large scales. The basic form of the electrical activation potentials ϕ_α propagation equation is[1]:

$$\frac{\partial \phi_\alpha}{\partial t} = \frac{\partial}{\partial x_i}\left(D_{ij}\frac{\partial \phi_\alpha}{\partial x_j}\right) + L(\phi_\alpha). \tag{1}$$

Greek subindices label the number of activation potentials involved. In this case we focus on mon-odomain models, being $\alpha = 1$. The diffusion term is governed by the diffusion tensor D_{ij}. $L(\phi_\alpha)$ is the non-linear operator corresponding to the cell model for the ionic current I_{ion}. The equation is set in a fixed reference frame and D_{ij} must describe the cable (i.e. cardiac tissue fibers) orientation in the fixed reference frame. Then, $D_{ij} = C_{ik}^{-1} D_{lk}^{\text{loc}} C_{lj}$ where C_{lk} is the base change matrix from the local fiber-aligned reference frame (a_i, c_i^1, c_i^2) (i.e. one axial vector and two crosswise ones) to the global reference frame. D_{lk}^{loc} is the local diagonal diffusion matrix, whose diagonal components are the axial and crosswise fiber diffusions. In this work, the activation potential model used is the of the Fenton-Karma (FK) type [3,11] (see these references for a complete description of the models).

The differential equations are solved using a variational formulation together with a FEM-based spacial discretization and a FD-based Euler time integration. A similar scheme was introduced in [12]. The weak form is: find $\phi \in \mathcal{V}$ such that $\forall \psi \in \mathcal{W}$ which verifies

$$\frac{\partial}{\partial t}\int_\Omega \psi\phi\, dV = \int_{\partial\Omega} \frac{D_{ij}}{C_m S_v}\frac{\partial\phi}{\partial x_j}\, n_j dS - \int_\Omega \frac{D_{ij}}{C_m S_v}\frac{\partial\psi}{\partial x_i}\frac{\partial\phi}{\partial x_j}\, dV + \int_\Omega I_{\text{ion}}\, dV \tag{2}$$

Spaces $\mathcal{W}$ and $\mathcal{V}$ are the usual FEM trial and interpolation function spaces (see [13]). The simulation domain is Ω and its boundary is $\partial\Omega$. The first term on the right hand side is used to impose Neumann boundary conditions, for instance when considering the effect of the media surrounding the simulation domain. As a first approximation, we will set the fluxes on the boundaries to zero. No Dirichlet conditions are directly imposed. The weak form Eq. (2) is discretized in space using the Finite Element Method and in time with a trapezoidal rule allowing backwards or forward Euler and Crank-Nicholson formulations. In this paper we explore the explicit scheme.

---

[1] Einstein convention on repeated indexes is used.

2.2 Fibers

For many years, the ventricular myocardium was described as a continuum in which myocite fibers orientation varied smoothly from the external side of ventricular wall (epicardium) to the internal side (endocardium). The defenders of this idea have been interpreting positively experimental evidence although one key issue remained obscure: "how". How does a heart with this morphology contract to achieve the pumping rate observed?

A second idea was left aside. It states that the cardiac ventricular tissue is configured as a helicoidal band with two spiral turns. Since recent years, this model is being reconsidered, as new evidence is gathered which solidly confirm it. The father of this theory, named Ventricular Myocardial Band (VMB) concept is F. Torrent-Guasp [14]. One of the strong points of the VMB concept is that, as cited in [15]: "The confirmation of oblique-oriented myocardial fibers may help explain the observations of Sallin and co-workers in 1969, in which 50-60% ejection fraction could only be achieved with 15% shortening fibers if they were in a helical arrangement, compared to circumferential (EF 30%) or simply longitudinally oriented (EF 15%)." A very interesting point is that a great deal of previous experiments can be re-interpreted under this new light, like that of [16,17].

Muscle biomechanics strongly depends on the spatial disposition of its fibers. In order to understand their behavior, both function and anatomy should be taken into account. In the case of myocardium and according to the concept of Torrent Guasp's band [1], fibers follow a complex distribution, they have an helical disposition. Nowadays, anatomic fiber information is taken from the diffusion tensor, using techniques such as those of [17]. In this paper we propose a novel strategy for performing simulations taking into account these facts. In it, the diffusion tensor D_{ij} is recomputed locally depending on the **fibers gradient**. When it is small, there is only one privileged direcion: along the fiber. On the other hand, when large, it appears a second privileged direction, which is colinear with the gradient. Another issue studied in this paper is the how sensible is the activation potential propagation to the experimental error in the fiber's directions. We show that, for the models here presented, the sensitivity is low up to 30 degrees of random error in the fiber orientations.

2.3 Computational aspects: parallelization

The simulation models to be presented at the conference are implemented in the Alya System, conceived for simulating complex computational mechanics problems in parallel. High Performance Computational Mechanics techniques are used to allow the computer code that is derived from this work to run in the most efficient way in parallel environments like clusters of multi-core computers. This is achieved by using MPI-based, OpenMP-based or a hybrid MPI / OpenMP based strategy. All three possibilities are programmed in Alya, however, in this paper we will show results for the external MPI-based strategy. An **MPI-based strategy** is an *external* parallelization, based in a divide-and-conquer strategy. In a pre-process stage, the original problem is divided in several sub-problems that in the analysis stage are solved in parallel, interchanging information only when required to match boundaries between neighboring sub-problems. Sub-problem partition is achieved by using an automatic mesh partitioner (METIS). This strategy demands a large development effort but gives the best scalability figures.

3 CONCLUSIONS

In this project, the goal is to make a model that integrates anatomy and functionality of the left ventricle (LV). For each patient we obtain the three-dimensional functionality and the LV geometry, together with the information coming from studies that give the average model of the fibers. Both geometry and average model are the input on the simulation. The activation potential so obtained is compared with experimental data to validate the model and adapt it to the individual patients. The scheme is fully parallelized and scales well for thousands of processors. We have introduced a novel way of computing the diffusion tensor and we have assessed the experimental error in fiber orientation. The final outcome of this project is to provide the MD a "computational heart" to better understand, predict and diagnose cardiac diseases and to plan healing treatments.

REFERENCES

[1]   F. Torrent-Guasp, El ciclo cardíaco, *Madrid, Espasa Calpe*, 1954.

[2]   F. Fenton, A.Karma *Vortex dynamics in three-dimensional continuous myocardium with fiber rotation: Filament instability and fibrillation*, Chaos, Vol 8, Num. 1, 1998.

[3]   F. Fenton, E.M. Cherry, A.Karma, W-J.Rappel *Modeling wave propagation in realistic heart geometries using the phase-field method* , Chaos, Vol 15 013502, 2005.

[4]   A. Nasiraei-Moghaddam, M. Gharib *Evidence for the existence of a functional helical myocardial band* , Am J Physiol Heart Circ Physiol 296: H127-H131, 2009.

[5]   M.E. Belik and T.P. Usyk and A.D. McCulloch. *Computational Methods for Cardiac Electrophysiology* , Computational Models for the Human Body, Handbook of Numerical Analysis Vol XII, P.G. Ciarlet Editor, N. Ayache Guest Editor, Elsevier, 129–187, 2004.

[6]   R.L. Winslow and D.F. Scollan and A. Holmes and C.K. Yung and J. Zhang and M.S. Jafri. *Electrophysiological Modeling of Cardiac Ventricular Function: From Cell to Organ* , Ann Rev Biomed Eng, **2**: 119–155, 2000.

[7]   A.D. McCulloch and G. Huber. *Integrative biological modeling 'in silico'* , 'In Silico Simulation of Biological Processes, Novartis Foundation Symposium 247, John Wiley & Sons, G. Bock and J.A. Goode Eds., 4–19, 2002.

[8]   M. Murillo and X.C. Cai. *A fully implicit parallel algorithm for simulating the non-linear electrical activity of the heart* , Numerical Linear Algebra with Applications, **11**: 261–277, 2004.

[9]   F.H. Fenton and E.M. Cherry and A. Karma and W. Rappel *Modeling wave propagation in realistic heart geometries using the phase-field method* , Chaos, **15**,013502, 2005.

[10] F.B. Sachse. *Computational Cardiology: Modeling of Anatomy, Electrophysiology, and Mechanics* , Springer, Lecture Notes in Computer Science, Vol 2966, 2004.

[11] F.H Fenton and A. Karma *Vortex dynamics in three-dimensional continuous myocardium with fiber rotation: Filament instability and fibrillation* , Chaos, **8**,No.1, 1998.

[12] A. Rosolen, S. Ordás and M. Vázquez. *Numerical schemes for the simulation of three-dimensional cardiac electrical propagation inpatient-specific ventricular geometries.* , Proceedings of the European Conference on Computational Fluid Dynamics ECCOMAS CFD 2006, Egmond aan Zee, The Netherlands. 2006.

[13] K. Eriksson and D. Estep and P. Hansbo and C. Johnson *Computational Differential Equations* , Cambridge University Press, 1996.

[14] F. Torrent-Guasp, M.J. Kocica, A.F. Corno, M. Komeda, F. Carreras-Costa, A. Flotats, J. Cosin-Aguillar and Han Wen *Towards new understanding of the heart structure and function* , European Journal of Cardio-Thoracic Surgery **27**:191-201, 2005

[15] M. Castella, G.D. Buckberg, S. Saleh and M. Gharib *Structure function interface with sequential shortening of basal and apical components of the myocardial band* , European Journal of Cardiothoracic Surgery **27**, 980-987, 2005

[16] D. Durrer, R.Th. Van Dam, G.E. Freud, M.J. Janse, F.L. Meijler, R.C. Arzbaecher *Total Excitation of the Isolated Human Heart* , Circulation. **41**:899-912, 1970

[17] P.A. Helm *A Novel Technique for Quantifying Variability of Cardiac Anatomy: Application to the Dyssynchronous Failing Heart* , PhD Thesis. Johns Hopkins University. 2005

EFFICIENT PARTITIONED PROCEDURES FOR FLUID-STRUCTURE INTERACTION ALGORITHMS

Fabio Nobile

MOX, Dipartimento di Matematica, Politecnico di Milano, Piazza L. Da Vinci 32, 20133 Milano, Italy. `fabio.nobile@polimi.it`

Christian Vergara

Dept. of Information Technology and Mathematical Methods, Università degli Studi di Bergamo, Viale Marconi 5, 24044 Dalmine (BG), Italy. `christian.vergara@unibg.it`

ABSTRACT

Key Words: *Fluid-structure interaction, Robin boundary conditions, haemodynamics*

Partitioned procedures for the solution of the monolithic Fluid-Structure Interaction (FSI) problem, arising when a fluid interacts with a structure, allows to use available fluid and structure codes. In this sense, these strategies are modular. Of course, a partitioned procedure solves the two subproblem in an iterative framework. In this way, at convergence, when the FSI interface conditions (namely the continuity of the velocity and of the normal stress) are satisfied, the solution of the monolithic problem is reached. The most classical partitioned procedure is the *Dirichlet-Neumann* (DN) scheme, consisting in solving a Dirichlet problem for the fluid (with interface velocity given by the structure) and a Neumann problem for the structure (with normal stress given by the fluid).

It is well known in the literature that when the ratio between the densities of the fluid and of the structure are quite similar (or, even, if the structure density is higher than the fluid one) the convergence properties of the DN scheme are very poor, since it needs a small relaxation to converge (see [2]).

In order to improve the performances of the DN scheme, in [1] it has been proposed to consider a linear combination of the interface conditions, namely

$$\alpha_f \mathbf{u}^{n+1} + \mathbf{T}_f^{n+1}\mathbf{n} = \alpha_f \frac{\eta^{n+1} - \eta^n}{\Delta t} + \mathbf{T}_s^{n+1}\mathbf{n}, \qquad \text{on } \Sigma^*,$$
$$\frac{\alpha_s}{\Delta t}\eta^{n+1} - \mathbf{T}_s^{n+1}\mathbf{n} = \frac{\alpha_s}{\Delta t}\eta^n + \alpha_s \mathbf{u}^{n+1} - \mathbf{T}_f^{n+1}\mathbf{n}, \qquad \text{on } \Sigma^*, \tag{1}$$

where $\mathbf{u}$ and p are the fluid velocity and pressure, η is the structure displacement, $\mathbf{T}_f$ and $\mathbf{T}_s$ the Cauchy stress tensors, Σ^* is the FSI interface (extrapolated by previous time steps or subiterations) and α_f and α_s are suitable coefficients. We point out that the interface conditions are discretized in time with a backward Euler method and Δt is the time step.

The convergence properties of the schemes based on FSI interface conditions (1) (*Robin-Robin (RR) schemes*) depends clearly on the choice of the parameteres α_f and α_s. In [1] it has been proposed to use the following expression

$$\alpha_f = \frac{\rho_s H_s}{\Delta t} + \beta H_s \Delta t$$

where ρ_s is the structure density, H_s the structure thickness and β a parameter that takes in to account for transversal membrane effects and comes from the reduction of the 3D equations of linear elasticity to a reduced model (see [3]). The numerical results have shown better convergence properties of the

Robin-Neumann (RN) scheme ($\alpha_s = 0$) with respect to the DN scheme, in particular when the added mass effect is high.

Here we study new strategies for the determination of optimal values of α_f and α_s, which guarantee good convergence properties. Moreover, we apply these partitioned procedures to realistic cases, in particular in the haemodynamics contest.

References

[1] S. Badia, F. Nobile, and Ch. Vergara. Fluid-structure partitioned procedures based on Robin transmission conditions. *Journal of Computational Physics*, 227:7027–7051, 2008.

[2] P. Causin, J.F. Gerbeau, and F. Nobile. Added-mass effect in the design of partitioned algorithms for fluid-structure problems. *Computer Methods in Applied Mechanics and Engineering*, 194(42-44):4506–4527, 2005.

[3] F. Nobile and C. Vergara. An effective fluid-structure interaction formulation for vascular dynamics by generalized Robin conditions. *SIAM Journal on Scientific Computing*, 30(2):731–763, 2008.

Finite Element Methods for a Mesoscopic Constitutive Model of Blood

Alexandre Iolov and Yves Bourgault

Department of Mathematics and Statistics, University of Ottawa, Ottawa, Canada K1N 6N5,
aiolo040@uottawa.ca, ybourg@uottawa.ca

André Fortin and A. Kane

Département de mathématiques et de statistique, Université Laval, Québec, G1V 0A6

Robert Owens

Département de mathématiques et de statistique, Université de Montréal, Montréal, Québec, H3C 3J7

ABSTRACT

A finite element method is proposed to solve a new constitutive model for blood flows. This model accounts for red blood cell clustering and related shear-thinning effects. Numerical results reproducing experiments in a rheometer are presented.

Key Words: *haemorheology, Stabilized Finite Elements.*

1 INTRODUCTION

Several constitutive models have been used to represent the non-Newtonian behaviour of blood that occurs, for instance, in smaller arteries (see [1] for a review). Most of the rheological models attempted so far for blood flows are phenomenological in the sense that they do not account for the fact that blood is a complex suspension of platelets, white and red blood cells. Owens [2] recently proposed a microstructure-based model where the main non-Newtonian effects in blood arise from the aggregation and disaggregation of the red blood cells (RBCs) into and out of coinstack-like rouleaux. As shown in [2] using 0-D simulations, this new microstructure-based model can predict the viscous stress and rheological hysteresis seen in experiments using triangular-variations in shear rate in a rheometer [3].

We propose a finite element method to implement this rheological model and extend its use to 2-D and 3-D flows in geometries relevant to haemodynamics. Our finite element method is an extension of the discrete Elastic-Viscous-Split-Stress (DEVSS) method presented in [4]. A difficulty associated with this rheological model is that it necessitates the solution of a pure advection-reaction equation for the average RBC rouleaux size coupled with the equations for all the other variables (pressure, velocity, extra-stress tensor) appearing in common viscoelastic models (such as the Oldroyd-B model).

This paper will briefly describe the microstructure-based model, the extension of the DEVSS finite element method and the first numerical results obtained for this new rheological model.

2 THE PHYSICAL MODEL

The model of Owens [2] for the microstructure rheology of blood postulates that the contribution of the RBC's to the extra-stress τ can be represented by a function of the average size of the rouleaux, N.

More precisely, N denotes the average size of the rouleaux in a given infinitesimal volume. N affects the elastic contribution in the fluid's stress tensor and is in turn affected by the shear rates arising from the flow of the fluid. Simulations for such a flow then require solving an advection-reaction equation for N, an Oldroyd-B type equation for the extra-stress tensor τ and the regular Navier-Stokes (NS) equations for the fluid.

The resulting system reads as:

$$D_t N + \frac{1}{2}b(\dot{\gamma})(N^2 - 1/2) = \frac{1}{2}b(\dot{\gamma})(N_{st}^2 - 1/2) \tag{1}$$

$$\tau + \mu \overset{\triangledown}{\tau} = 2\eta_p \dot{\gamma} \tag{2}$$

$$Re D_t u - \eta_s \nabla \cdot (\dot{\gamma}(u)) - \nabla \cdot \tau + \nabla p = f \tag{3}$$

$$\nabla \cdot u = 0$$

where N_{st} is the average size of the rouleaux at steady shear, b is an aggregation-disaggregation (a reaction) rate, and $\dot{\gamma}$ is the shear rate (which is proportional to the deformation rate tensor $\dot{\gamma}$). Most importantly, the first and second equation are coupled via μ, the relaxation time in the Oldroyd-B model for τ, which is a function of N. Usual boundary conditions are applied for the velocity and pressure, while the advection equations for N and τ require inlet BC's only.

3 FINITE ELEMENT METHOD

Our finite element method consists in using the Discrete-EVSS method [4], (DEVSS), for which an extra tensor d is added to the NS equations. The addition of this tensor leads to a stable FEM where only pressure and velocity are required to satisfy a compatibility condition, as is usual for the NS equations for Newtonian fluids. The discrete variational form for the NS equations becomes:

$$Re < D_t u, \phi_u > -2\alpha < d, \phi_u > +2(\alpha + \eta_s) < \dot{\gamma}(u), \nabla \phi_u >$$
$$- < \nabla \cdot \tau, \phi_u > - < p, \nabla \cdot phi_u >=< f, \phi_u >; \quad \forall \phi_u$$

$$< d - \dot{\gamma}(u), \phi_d >= 0; \quad \forall \phi_d$$

where α is a parameter of the algorithm.

Due to the hyperbolic nature of the advection equations for N and τ, we used the Streamline-Upwind-Petrov-Galerkin (SUPG) method (see e.g. [5]) to discretise these equations. The stable Taylor-Hood element is used for velocity and pressure. All the other variables are discretised with continuous linear elements.

The resulting system is marched forward in time using the implicit Euler scheme. Due to the non-linearity of the system, the three equations are solved one at a time using a Picard-type iterative method - first solving for N, then τ and finally (u, p, d) until convergence. The computations are performed using the MEF++ library developed by the Groupe Inter-disciplinaire de Recherche en Éléments Finis (GIREF, Université Laval).

4 NUMERICAL RESULTS

We present two test cases, all based on the 2-D geometry of a rheometer shown on Fig. 1. The two cylinders are separated by a thin region (the fluid region) which has inner radius = 1 and width = .05 (non-dimensional units). The outer cylinder moves while the inner cylinder remains fixed. This geometry was meshed using 117696 triangular cells, giving a layer of about 40 elements between the cylinders.

A first test case is a classical experiment on the viscoelasticity of blood which involves applying a ramp-type shear in a microviscometer and measuring the resulting stresses. This experiment was reproduced in [2] using 0-D computations. We reproduce the results with our 2-D geometry. All the variables are initially taken and remain uniform in space. During the experiment, the flow is accelerated in the form of a ramp function. Our results for this test case are presented on Fig. 2. These closely reproduce the results from Owens' paper [2], which in turn closely match the experimental work in [3].

In the second test case, a non-uniform (in space) rouleaux size is used, keeping all the other variables as in our first test case. In particular, the shearing flow is kept steady. Figure 3 shows the time evolution of the average rouleaux size. An initially non-uniform N relaxes to N_{st} as time increases.

More results will be presented at the conference, including haemodynamically relevant geometries.

References

[1] P. Neofytou, D. Drikakis, Effects of blood models on flows through a stenosis, *International Journal for Numerical Methods in Fluids* 43, 597-635, 2003.

[2] R. Owens, A new microstructure-based constitutive model for human blood, *Journal of Non-Newtonian Fluid Mechanics*, 140, 57-70, 2006.

[3] M. Bureau, J.C. Healy, D. Bourgoin, M. Joly, Rheological hysteresis of blood at low shear rate, *Biorheology* 17, 191-203, 1980

[4] A. Fortin, R. Guenette, R. Pierre, On the discrete EVSS method *Computer Methods in applied mechanics and engineering* 189, 121-139, 2000.

[5] T. De Mulder, Stabilized finite Element Methods (SUPG, GLS, ...) for incompressible flows *28th CFD Lectures Series at the von Karman Institute for Fluid Dynamics*, March, 1997.

Figure 1: Geometry of rheometer; inner radius = 1 , width = .05

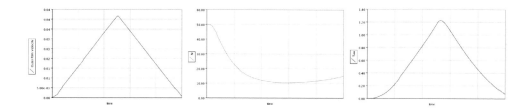

Figure 2: Ramp-shear test case in a viscometer. Left: applied shear. Middle: N. Right: τ

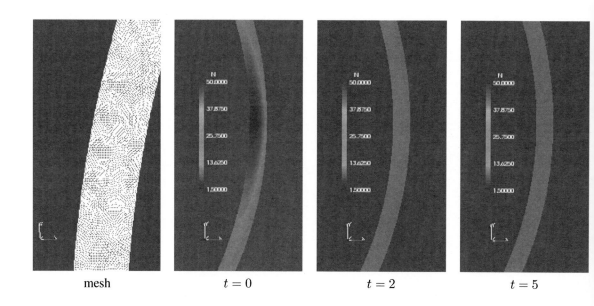

mesh $t = 0$ $t = 2$ $t = 5$

Figure 3: Time evolution of the average rouleaux size N

1st International Conference on Mathematical and Computational Biomedical Engineering - CMBE2009
June 29 - July 1, 2009, Swansea, UK
P.Nithiarasu and R.Löhner (Eds.)

LES OF NON-NEWTONIAN PHYSIOLOGICAL BLOOD FLOW

Md Mamun Molla & Manosh C Paul
Department of Mechanical Engineering, University of Glasgow, Glasgow, G12 8QQ, UK. E-mail:
m.paul@mech.gla.ac.uk

ABSTRACT

Large Eddy Simulation (LES) is performed to study the physiological pulsatile transition to turbulent non-Newtonian blood flow through a 3D model of arterial stenosis using the different non-Newtonian blood viscosity models. The computational domain has been chosen is a simple channel with a biological type stenosis formed eccentrically on the top wall. The physiological pulsation is generated at the inlet of the model using the fourth harmonic of the Fourier series of the physiological pressure pulse (Womersley [1]). The computational results are presented in terms of the post-stenotic re-circulation zone, shear stress, mean and turbulent kinetic energy.

Key Words: *non-Newtonian blood flow, re-circulation zone, wall shear stress, stenosis, LES.*

1 INTRODUCTION

The term arterial stenosis refers the narrowing of an artery where the cross-sectional area of blood vessel reduces. Blood is a non-Newtonian incompressible viscoelastic fluid (Fung [2], pp.53). At shear rates above about 100 s^{-1}, the blood viscosity tends towards an asymptotic value. If the shear rates fall below that asymptotic level, the viscosity of blood increases and the non-Newtonian properties of blood being exhibited (Berger and Jou [3]), especially when the shear rates drop below 10 s^{-1} (Huang *et al.* [4]).

Very few studies which are related to the non-Newtonian blood flow in arterial stenosis, such as Tu *et al.* [5], Buchanan *et al.* [6], Neofytou and Drikakis [7], Hron *et al.* [8] and Valencia and Villanueva [9] used different blood viscosity models, however, all these studies are conducted only for laminar flow. Most recently Paul *et al.* [10] have investigated the pulsatile turbulent blood flow through a model of arterial stenosis applying the LES technique. Using the first harmonic of the Fourier series of the pressure pulse, a Large-eddy simulation of the physiological pulsatile flow in the same model is performed by Molla *et al.* [11]. In these papers, the investigation has been done assuming that the blood is a Newtonian fluid. However, the recent investigation shows that the global maximum shear rate during some periods of pulsation receives a result which is less than the range of the non-Newtonian shear rate (100 s^{-1}). Therefore, it would be quite reasonable to account in the computation the blood as a non-Newtonian fluid to get more accurate insight of the transition of the blood flow through the stenosis. In this regard, various blood viscosity models are applied and their effects are examined in the paper.

The geometry chosen in the simulation (Fig. 1(a)) consists of a 3D channel with one sided cosine shape stenosis on the upper wall centred at $y/L = 0.0$ with a 50 cross-sectional area reduction at the centre. In Fig. 1(b)-(c), the inlet velocity profile is presented for one pulsation for the Reynolds number of 2000 and the Womersley number of 10.5. Note that the velocity in frame (b) is recorded at very close to the bottom wall. In the simulation, no slip boundary conditions are used for both the lower and upper walls

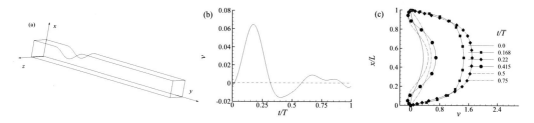

Figure 1: (a) A schematic of the model with coordinate system and (b-c) Streamwise inlet velocity.

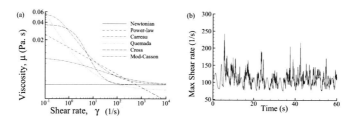

Figure 2: (a) Relation between the apparent shear rate and viscosity for the different models (b) Global maximum shear rate $|\dot{\gamma}|$ against time for the Power-law model

of the model, and a convective boundary condition at the outlet For the spanwise boundaries, periodic boundary conditions are applied for modelling the spanwise homogeneous flow.

The LES code is written based on the finite volume method with collocated grid arrangement which is second order accurate in space and time. For the present computation the grid arrangement is taken as $50 \times 200 \times 50$ along the cross-stream, streamwise and spanwise direction, respectively, with a constant timestep of 10^{-3}. The sensitivity tests on grid and timestep are performed and the above grid arrangment is sufficient to resolve the large scale flows. In addition, the code is validated with suitable experimental data, the details are available in Molla [12].

2 RESULTS AND DISCUSSION

The relation between the apparent shear rates and the viscosity for the five non-Newtonian blood viscosity models along with the Newtonian one is presented in Fig. 2(a). From this figure, it is seen that for low shear rates (e.g. $< 100 \text{ s}^{-1}$) the non-Newtonian blood viscosity is higher than that of the Newtonian model. Moreover, the necessity of using the non-Newtonian model is very much clear by observing the range of the global maximum shear rate in Fig. 2(b) for the Power-law model. Similar distributions of the shear-rate are found for the other models.

Fig. 3(a-f) depict the post-stenotic re-circulation zones in terms of the mean streamlines for the different models. The length of the re-circulation region is enlarged in the non-Newtonian models, which is an alarming condition at the pathological point of view since the blood in the re-circulation region is re-circulated for a long time and is stagnant in this region that could cause the blood clot or thrombosis.

The mean shear stress, $\tau_{xy}/\rho\bar{V}^2$, distributions are plotted in Fig. 4(a-b) respectively at the upper wall and lower wall. At the upper wall the stress drop is higher in the cases of non-Newtonian model than that of the Newtonian model and the maximum stress drop is found for the Power-law model. The magnitude of this stress drops to -0.07730 which is about 32 higher than the Newtonian model for which it is $-0.058\ 9$. Interestingly, the stress drop for all the models is occurring at a same streamwise

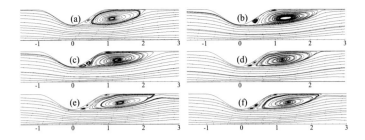

Figure 3: Post-stenotic recirculation zone at (a) Newtonian (b) Power-law (c) Carreau (d) Quemada (e) Cross and (f) Modified-Casson models.

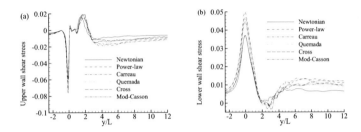

Figure 4: Shear stress at the (a) upper wall and (b) lower wall for the different blood viscosity models.

location, $y/L = -0.12505$. The difference between the non-Newtonian and Newtonian models of the shear distribution is distinguishable in the post-stenosis region, however, in the laminar region a small difference is found. Moreover, in the further downstream region, the upper wall shear stresses for all the non-Newtonian models are always smaller than the case of Newtonian model. On the other hand, the maximum shear stress at the lower wall occurs at $y/L = -0.059$ for all the models, but the most largest value is found again for the Power-law model which is 0.04989. In contrast to the upper wall, the non-Newtonian models give higher shear stress at the lower wall in the further downstream region of the stenosis.

The effects of various non-Newtonian models on the mean and turbulent kinetic energy are illustrated in Fig. 5. The mean kinetic energy in the turbulent region ($1.0 < y/L < .0$) varies in the non-Newtonian models with the magnitude that is slightly higher in the Carreau and Quemada models compared to the Newtonian model. However, the curves are identical at the upstream of the stenosis. The significant effects are reported on the results of the turbulent kinetic energy in frame (b). The peak in the post-lip region ($1.0 < y/L < 3.0$) occurs in the Newtonian model, while all the non-Newtonian models produce higher turbulent kinetic energy in the further downstream because of the fact that the physiological oscillation is reduced by the higher viscosity in the non-Newtonian models which causes delay in the transition process.

3 CONCLUSIONS

Non-Newtonian physiological flow in the model of arterial stenosis has been investigated by using the LES technique. The global maximum shear rate for the different viscosity models falls below the non-Newtonian range of $100\ \text{s}^{-1}$ which clearly indicated the necessity of applying the various non-Newtonian blood viscosity models in the investigation. The post-stenotic re-circulation region is extended slightly in the non-Newtonian models, in the pathological point of view, this usually increases the possibility of thrombosis or blood clot. The shear stress results are influenced by the non-Newtonian

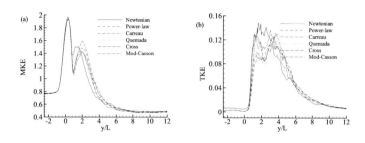

Figure 5: (a) Mean and (b) turbulent kinetic energy for the different blood viscosity models.

models producing the maximum rise at the lower wall while dropping significantly at the upper wall. The intensity of the turbulent kinetic energy is also affected by the choice of the blood viscosity models. Despite the simplicity in the vessel model, the LES results of the non-Newtonian blood flow presented in the paper would provide a better insight in the understanding of the flow transition and turbulent downstream of a real stenosed artery and the formation of atherosclerosis. The natural extension of this work is to consider a more biological realistic model, e.g. circular and flexible artery and apply the LES to study the transition of the non-Newtonian blood flow.

References

[1] J. R. Womersley, Method for the calculation of velocity, rate of flow and viscous drag in arteries when the pressure gradient is known, *J. Physiology*, 155 (1955) 553–563.

[2] Y. C. Fung, Biomechanics: Circulation, 2nd edition, Springer,1997.

[3] S. A. Berger, L.-D. Jou, Flows in stenotic vessels, *Annu. Rev. Fluid Mech.*, 32 (2000) 347–382.

[4] C. R. Huang, W. D. Pan, H. W. Chen, A. L. Copley, Thixotropic properties of whole blood from healty human subjects, *Biorheology* , 24 (1987) 795–801.

[5] C. Tu, M. Delville, Pulsatile flow of non-Newtonian fluids through arterial stenosis, *J. Biomechanics*, 29 (7) (1996) 899–908.

[6] J. R. B. Jr, C. Kleinstreuer, J. K. Comer, Rheological effects on pulsatile hemodynamics in a stenose tube., *Computers and Fluids*, 29 (2000) 695–724.

[7] P. Neofytou, D. Drikakis, Effects of blood models on flows through a stenosis, *Int. J. Numer. Meth. Fluids*, 43 (2003) 597–635.

[8] J. Hron, J. Malek, S. Turek, A numerical investigation of flows shear-thinning fluids with applications to blood rheology, *Int. J. Numerical Methods in Fluids* , 32 (2000) 863–879.

[9] A. Valencia, M. Villanueva, Unsteady flow and mass transfer in models of stenotic arteries considering fluid-structure interaction, *Int. Communication Heat and Mass Transfer*, 33 (2006) 966–975.

[10] M. C. Paul, M. M. Molla, G. Roditi, Large-eddy simulation of pulsatile blood flow, *Medical Engineering and Physics*, 31 (2009) 153–159.

[11] M. M. Molla, M. C. Paul, G. Roditi, Physiological flow in a model of arterial stenosis, *J. Biomechanics*, 41(S1) (2008) S243.

[12] M. M. Molla, Large eddy simulation of pulsatile flow in the models of arterial stenosis and aneurysm, PhD thesis (in preparation) 2009, University of Glasgow, UK.

1st International Conference on Mathematical and Computational Biomedical Engineering – CMBE2009
June 29 – July 1, 2009, Swansea, UK
P. Nithiarasu and R. Löhner (eds)

A THREE DIMENSIONAL PROTOTYPE ELECTRO-FLUID-STRUCTURE MODEL OF THE LEFT VENTRICLE

T. N. Croft
School of Engineering, Swansea University, Singleton Park, Swansea SA2 8PP, UK,
t.n.croft@swan.ac.uk
D. Carswell
School of Engineering, Swansea University, Singleton Park, Swansea SA2 8PP, UK,
d.carswell@swan.ac.uk
M. Cross
School of Engineering, Swansea University, Singleton Park, Swansea SA2 8PP, UK,
m.cross@swan.ac.uk
M. Devereux-Cole
School of Engineering, Swansea University, Singleton Park, Swansea SA2 8PP, UK,
365146@swan.ac.uk
A. K. Slone
School of Engineering, Swansea University, Singleton Park, Swansea SA2 8PP, UK,
a.k.slone@swan.ac.uk
A. J. Williams
School of Engineering, Swansea University, Singleton Park, Swansea SA2 8PP, UK,
Alison.j.williams@swan.ac.uk

ABSTRACT

This short paper outlines the progress being made on the design and implementation of a fully functional computational model of the left ventricle and associated valve of the human heart in three dimensions. The basis for the work reported here is a two dimensional model previously developed by the authors, using a simplified geometry, that predicts the interaction of the electro-chemical induced contraction of the heart wall, the flow in the ventricle due to the wall motion and the fluid loads on the wall. This contribution reports the initial stages of the extension of the model to three dimensions using a realistic geometrical representation of the heart with appropriate adaptations to the boundary conditions. The presentation will show some early results of this work, which is targeted at supporting the assessment of micro-pumps within the cardio environment.

Key Words: *Left ventricle, Electro- fluid-structure interaction, Blood flow, wall shear, mesh movement; multi-physics, mixed finite volume and finite element methods.*

1. INTRODUCTION

In the design of heart pumps, it is not only important to use simulation based technologies to evaluate and optimize designs, it also useful to simulate the evaluation of their performance in the cardiological context. This provides a motivation to develop reasonably functional computational models of important domains within the human heart, such as, the left ventricle. Hence, one might argue that any such model, to act as a useful virtual environment for testing the performance of micro-pumps should provide a reasonably realistic reflection of the heart's behaviour. Of course, the heart is a complex system which involves sophisticated interactions amongst what engineers would characterize as fluid, structural, chemical and electrical phenomena. Developing from the pioneering work of Noble [1][2], using a simple model to investigate cardiac action, an enduring worldwide iterative modelling and experimental activity to develop a very sophisticated understanding of the electrochemical behaviour of the heart has developed. This understanding has been embedded within a wide range of mathematical models, normally based upon what are called bi-domain equations, of which those by the teams of Tranayova *et al.*, Plank and Vigmond, are typical, although probably the most comprehensive is due to the work of Noble, Panilov and their co-workers [3]. This work has provided the basis for genuine significantly functional virtual heart models that may be used in clinical research and treatment assessment.

Considerable work on the mechanics of the heart has been led over the years by Hunter and co-workers [4]. Based upon the work of McCulloch *et al.* [5] the structure of the heart wall has been characterised and recorded digitally. Hunter amongst others has developed a range of models to capture the behaviour of the heart wall, both with respect to its detailed geometric structure and its non-linear material properties. There have been a number of attempts to capture the interaction between an electro-chemical bi-domain model and a structural response, see for example the work of Nash and Panilov [6]

In parallel with this work on electrochemical models, work on fluid-structure interaction (FSI) has also been pursued. Computational FSI brings its own challenges, and there are a number of workers who have attempted such activity in a cardiological context, including Peskin and McQueen together with their co-workers [7] who have used what is termed the immersed boundary method. More recently, there have been other attempts at modelling an aorta or a ventricle by Baajens *et al*, Howard and Patterson *et al.* Wood *et al.*, and van Loon *et al.* amongst others. These models capture the interaction between the 'blood' and the heart wall, but still require the wall dynamic deformation to be specified (in reality, of course, this is a consequence of the electrochemical action).

In recent times there are two groups who have attempted a computational model which couples the electro-chemical and fluid-structure interaction phenomena. Watanabe *et al.* [8] developed a two dimensional model based upon an electrochemical model of Luo and Rudy [9] although the structural movement was somewhat restricted. The other effort by Croft *et al* [10], describes a two dimensional model which captures the impact of a cyclic electric field (arising from Clayton and Holden's electro-chemical model [11]]) on a right ventricle geometric structure containing a 'blood'-like fluid, simulating both its filling and emptying. This paper describes the strategy for extending Croft's model from two to three dimensions, and setting it within a rather more realistic geometrical context.

2.   COMPUTATIONAL MODELLING OVERVIEW

2.1 Overview of the mathematical model

As indicated above the computational model is concerned with a realistic geometry of the left ventricle of a human heart [12]. The model itself has three components:

a)   a cyclic electro-chemical model.
b)   a fluid model to describe the flow of 'blood'.
c)   a structural model to describe the contraction and relaxation of the 'heart' wall in response to the cyclic electric field.
and their interactions.

2.1.1   Clayton and Holden's electrochemical model. The Clayton Holden model [11] is essentially an attempt to capture the action potential propagation throughout the ventricle as a continuous mono-domain. It is based on the concept of a membrane voltage, V_m, given by a cable equation and including a membrane patch current, I_{ion}, which include equations to capture the fast and slow inward (depolarizing) currents corresponding broadly to Na^+ and Ca^{2+} currents and a slow outward (polarizing) current corresponding to K^+ currents. The membrane voltage, V_m, is scaled with both the resting potential, V_0, and the Nernst potential of the fast inward current, V_{fi}, as a combination of a primary, u, and two secondary, v and w, action potentials:

$$\frac{\partial u}{\partial t} = \nabla.\mathbf{D}\nabla u - (J_{fi} + J_{si} + J_{so})$$

$$\frac{\partial v}{\partial t} = \Theta(u_c - u)\left[\frac{1-v}{t_v^-(u)}\right] - \Theta(u - u_c)\left[\frac{v}{t_v^+}\right]$$

$$\frac{\partial w}{\partial t} = \Theta(u_c - u)\left[\frac{1-w}{t_w^-}\right] - \Theta(u - u_c)\left[\frac{w}{t_w^+}\right]$$

(1)

where $\Theta(x)$ denotes a Heaviside step function. The currents in the equation above are described in [11], where J_{fi}, is the fast input current, J_{si} is the slow input current and J_{so} is the slow output current. The above model was solved numerically subject to zero flux conditions, for each of the three potentials, on the boundaries of the heart wall.

2.1.2   The 'blood' fluid model. The 'blood' is modelled as a slightly compressible Newtonian fluid. Hence, the flow should be well characterised by the Navier Stokes equations. Moreover the Reynolds numbers are such that the flow regime is reasonably well characterised as laminar. Of course, the fluid is flowing within a domain that is itself moving, see below, subject to a range of boundary conditions [10].

2.1.3   *The structural mechanics model.* This is initially as simplistic as possible, using a linear strain–displacement formulation using the small strain assumption, which is valid for strains of the order of a few percent. It is assumed within each time (i.e. load) step that the structure reaches its steady solution which simplifies the structural mechanics analysis.

2.1.4   *Coupling amongst the component phenomena.* The couplings amongst the component models are conceived as follows:
   a)   The electric field, as represented by its potential, provides a load for the structure. The total strain now contains both an elastic and electric component

$$\varepsilon = \varepsilon_{el} + \varepsilon_{elec}$$

(2)

which results in an extra term in the stress-strain equations. The electric strain is calculated from:

$$\varepsilon_{elec} = -\alpha\,V(1,1,1,0,0,0)^{\mathrm{T}}$$

(3)

where V is the input voltage and α is the electric strain equivalent of the thermal expansion coefficient in the thermal strain.
   b)   The consequent interaction between the fluid and the structural domains is represented through a conventional fluid-structure interaction procedure:
   •   The traction load by the fluid on the structure is as follows [13]

$$\mathbf{t}_p = \left(-p\mathbf{I} + \mu\left\{\nabla\mathbf{u} + (\nabla\mathbf{u})^T\right\} - \frac{2}{3}\mu(\nabla\cdot\mathbf{u})\mathbf{I}\right)\mathbf{n}\quad \text{on } \Gamma_s$$

(4)

where p and μ are the fluid pressure and dynamic viscosity respectively, $\mathbf{u}$ is the fluid velocity, $\mathbf{I}$ is the identity matrix and $\mathbf{n}$ is the normal to the fluid-structure interface.

- The deformation of the structure affects the fluid domain through a consistent movement of the fluid domain - structure boundary. In response to this boundary motion the mesh in the fluid domain is adapted to maintain element quality in such a way as to obey the geometric conservation law. Thus the fluid velocity, **u**, in the convection term of the Navier Stokes equation and the continuity equation must be replaced by the relative velocity. Details of the mesh adaption algorithm and the calculation of the mesh velocity can be found in [13].

The overall solution strategy is summarised in Croft *et al* [10]; this is implemented within the PHYSICA multi-physics modelling software technology [14]. In going from two to a three dimensional model, some of the boundary conditions obviously have to be adapted and although the concept of a single mesh is maintained, the mesh now becomes a mix of tetrahedral, wedge and hexahedral elements with about 100,000 nodes. The compute times also increase by an order of magnitude and so the simulations are typically run scalably in parallel on a 16 processor cluster with high speed processor interconnect.

3. CONCLUSIONS

The paper will show progress in implementing and testing the extension of the Croft *et al* [10] model applied to the left ventricle and associated valve of the human heart. Once completed, the objective is to utilise the computational model as a host within which to evaluate the performance of novel micro-pumps in the virtual heart environment.

REFERENCES

[1]   Noble D, Cardiac action and pacemaker potentials based on the Hodgkin-Huxley equations, *Nature* **188**:495-497, 1960.

[2]   Noble D, Modeling the heart – from genes to cells to the whole organ, *Science*, **295**:1678-1682, 2001.

[3]   ten Tusscher KHWJ, Noble D, Noble PJ and Panilov AV, A model for human ventricular tissue, *American Journal of Physiology - Heart and Circulatory Physiology* , **286**:1573-1589, 2004

[4]   Nickerson DP, Smith NP and Hunter PJ, A model of cardiac cellular electromechanics. *Phil Trans R Soc Lond A*, **359**:1159-1172, 2001.

[5]   Usyk TP, LeGrice IJ and McCulloch AD, Computational model of three dimensional cardiac electromechanics, *Computing and Visualisation in Science*, 4:249-257, 2002.

[6]   Nash MP and Panifilov AV, Electromechanical model of excitable tissue to study re-entrant cardiac arrhythmias, *Progress Biophysics & Molecular Biology*, **85**:501-522, 2004.

[7]   Kovacs SJ, McQueen DM and Peskin CS, Modelling cardiac fluid dynamics and diastolic function, *Phil Trans R Soc Lond A*, 359:1299-1314, 2001.

[8]   Watanabe W, Segiura S, Kafuku H and Hisada T, Multiphysics simulation of the left ventricular filling dynamics using fluid-structure interaction finite element method, *Biophysical Journal*, **87**:2074-2085, 2004.

[9]   Luo C and Rudy Y, A model of the ventricular cardiac action potential depolarisation, repolarisation and their interaction, *Circ Res*, **68**:1501-1526, 1991.

[10]   T N Croft, A J Williams, A K Slone and M Cross, A two dimensional prototype multi-physics model of the right ventricle of the heart, *Int J. Numer. Meth. Fluids*, **57**:583-600, 2008

[11]   Clayton RH and Holden AV, A method to quantify the dynamics and complexity of re-entry in computational models of ventricular fibrillation, *Physics in Medicine and Biology*, **47**:225-238, 2002.

[12]   Zygote Inc; http://www.zygote.com

[13]   Slone AK, K Pericleous K, Bailey C and Cross M, Dynamic fluid-structure interaction using finite volume unstructured mesh procedures, *Computers & Structures*, **80**:371-390, 2002.

[14]   PHYSICA, see http://www.physica.co.uk

Application of Viscoelastic Constitutive Models to Blood Flow

C.-B. Liu
School of Engineering, Swansea University, C.B.Liu@Swansea.ac.uk

P. Nithiarasu
School of Engineering, Swansea University, P.Nithiarasu@Swansea.ac.uk

ABSTRACT

In the present work, non-Newtonian viscoelastic models are considered as constitutive models for blood. The characteristic based split scheme is used for the solution of the governing equations. The results obtained for blood flow through a tube are compared against available experimental data.

Key Words: *steady blood flow, Oldroyd-B model, Generalized Oldroyd-B (GOB) Model, CDS scheme, unstructured grids, finite element.*

1 INTRODUCTION

Blood flow in large, normal human arteries are normally assumed to be Newtonian. However, the non-Newtonian effects may be important even in large vessels when the blood related diseases such as sickles are present[1]. It is also evident from the literature that the non-Newtonian nature dominates when blood is experimented outside the body [2]. It appears that the velocity profile obtained from the generalised Oldroyd-B model is in good agreement with experimental measurements obtained for porcine blood flow through a three-dimensional straight plexiglass tube at steady state[2]. It is thus reasonable to assume that the blood is viscoelastic in nature when it is pumped through extracorporeal systems such as ventricular pumps. However, appropriate non-Newtonian flow models in general is not very conclusive and this area deserves some experimental and constitutive modelling research. In the present work, we test viscoelastic flow models against available experimental data.

It is known that plasma in blood is normally Newtonian in nature. The second major constituent of blood, red blood cells (RBCs), are essentially suspended in plasma. They belongs to a class of material which allows instantaneous elastic responses as they are subjected to deformation. It is also recognised that RBCs aggregate (rouleaux) and become solid-like material to store elastic energy with decreasing shear rates and fails to retain the elastic behaviour at higher shear rates as it changes into fluid. One of the two reasons for increase in viscosity and the elasticity is the rouleaux formation. Another potential reason for the blood to become viscoelastic when in contact with foreign bodies is the tendency to form blood clots. Thus, the assumption of blood being a viscoelastic material outside a living body is justified.

According to a thermodynamic framework presented in the literature [3], blood can be represented by a stored energy function of elastic response from a neo-Hookean solid and a rate of dissipation due to response of viscous Newtonian fluid. A generalised Oldroyd-B (GOB) thus developed[3] has been demonstrated to be in good agreement with the experimental data [4]. In the present study, three different models- Newtonian, standard Oldroyd-B and generalised Oldroyd-B (GOB) fluid models - have been considered. These constitutive equations are solved along with incompressible Navier-Stokes equations using the finite element method. An artificial-dissipation-based CBS-AC scheme has been used to solve the equations[5]. The test problem studied is the blood flow through a circular tube. The velocity profiles obtained are compared with the experimental measurements available in the literature [4].

2 GOVERNING EQUATIONS

2.1 Non-dimensional Form of Standard Viscoelastic Flow Models

The scales used to describe non-dimensional form of the governing equations in the present work are:

$$u_i^* = \frac{u_i}{u_\infty}; \quad \rho^* = \frac{\rho}{\rho_\infty}; \quad x_i^* = \frac{x_i}{l};$$

$$t^* = \frac{t u_\infty}{l}; \quad p^* = \frac{p}{\rho_\infty u_\infty^2}; \quad \tau_{ij}^* = \frac{\tau_{ij} l}{\eta_o u_\infty} \tag{1}$$

where subscript ∞ indicates a free stream value and l is a characteristic length. The non-dimensional governing equations can be written as:

Continuity equation:

$$\frac{\partial U_i^*}{\partial x_i^*} = 0 \tag{2}$$

Momentum equation:

$$\frac{\partial U_i^*}{\partial t^*} + \frac{\partial}{\partial x_j^*}(u_j^* U_i^*) =$$
$$-\frac{\partial p^*}{\partial x_i^*} + \frac{1}{Re}\left[(1-\alpha)\left(\frac{\partial u_i^*}{\partial x_j^*} + \frac{\partial u_j^*}{\partial x_i^*} - \frac{\partial u_k^*}{\partial x_k^*}\delta_{ij}\right) + \frac{\partial \tau_{ij}^*}{\partial x_j^*}\right] \tag{3}$$

Constitutive equation:

$$\frac{\partial \tau_{ij}^*}{\partial t^*} + \frac{\partial}{\partial x_k^*}\left(u_k^* \tau_{ij}^*\right) = -\frac{1}{De}\left(1 + \frac{\epsilon De}{\alpha}\tau_{kk}^*\right)\left[\frac{1 + \frac{De}{\alpha L^2}\tau_{kk}^*}{1 - \frac{3}{L^2}}\right]\tau_{ij}^*$$
$$+ \frac{\alpha}{De}\left[\frac{1 + \frac{De}{\alpha L^2}\tau_{kk}^*}{1 - \frac{3}{L^2}}\right]\left(\frac{\partial u_i^*}{\partial x_j^*} + \frac{\partial u_j^*}{\partial x_i^*} - \frac{\partial u_k^*}{\partial x_k^*}\delta_{ij}\right)$$
$$+ \tau_{ik}^*\frac{\partial u_j^*}{\partial x_k^*} + \tau_{jk}^*\frac{\partial u_i^*}{\partial x_k^*} \tag{4}$$

where viscosity rate is $\alpha = \eta_p/\eta_o$ in which η_p is the dynamic viscosity of viscoelastic fluid, $\eta_o = \eta_s + \eta_p$ represents the total viscosity in which η_s is the dynamic viscosity of solvent Newtonian fluid. The Reynolds number Re and Deborah number De are defined as:

$$Re = \frac{\rho_\infty u_\infty l}{\eta_o}; \quad De = \frac{\lambda u_\infty}{l} \tag{5}$$

where λ is the relaxation time and characteristic length l here is assumed to be the diameter of the tube.

In the above Equation (4) when extensible parameter $L^2 \to \infty$, the constitutive equation describes the standard Oldroyd-B model (constant viscosity) with $0 < \alpha < 1$ and $\epsilon = 0$. The upper-convected Maxwell (UCM) model is obtained by substituting $\alpha = 1$ and $\epsilon = 0$. When $0 < L^2 \ll \infty$, the viscoelastic fluid indicates FENE-MCR model with $0 < \alpha < 1$ and $\epsilon = 0$. For simplified Phan-Thien/Tanner (PTT) model, $L^2 \to \infty$, $\alpha = 1$ and $\epsilon \neq 0$.

2.2 Generalised Oldroyd-B(GOB) Model of Rajagopal-Srinivasa

To make the application of boundary conditions easier, non-dimensional viscoelastic stress is redefined as:

be

$$\tau_{ij}^* = \frac{\tau_{ij}}{\rho_\infty u_\infty^2} \tag{6}$$

The non-dimensional form of momentum and GOB constitutive equations should be rewritten as:

Momentum equation:

$$\frac{\partial U_i^*}{\partial t^*} + \frac{\partial}{\partial x_j^*}(u_j^* U_i^*) = -\frac{\partial p^*}{\partial x_i^*} + \frac{\beta}{Re}\left[\frac{1}{2}\left(\frac{\partial u_i^*}{\partial x_j^*} + \frac{\partial u_j^*}{\partial x_i^*}\right)\right] + \frac{\partial \tau_{ij}^*}{\partial x_j^*} \tag{7}$$

Constitutive equation:

$$\tau_{ij}^* + \frac{De}{2}\left[\frac{\partial \tau_{ij}^*}{\partial t^*} + \frac{\partial}{\partial x_k^*}\left(u_k^* \tau_{ij}^*\right) - \tau_{ik}^* \frac{\partial u_j^*}{\partial x_k^*} - \tau_{jk}^* \frac{\partial u_i^*}{\partial x_k^*}\right] = \frac{\phi}{De\, Re}\Lambda^* \delta_{ij} \tag{8}$$

where Newtonian viscosity ratio is $\beta = \eta_s/\eta_\infty$, viscoelastic viscosity ratio is $\phi = \eta/\eta_\infty$ in which η is the viscosity and Λ^* is the non-dimensional material modulus that depends on velocity gradient and elastic shear modulus $\mu = \eta/\lambda$. The definition of Deborah number De is the same as non-dimensional standard viscoelastic models. The Reynolds number Re is defined as:

$$Re = \frac{\rho_\infty u_\infty l}{\eta_\infty} \tag{9}$$

where η_∞ is the viscosity obtained at high shear rates.

3 STEADY POISEUILLE FLOW IN A TUBE

A circular tube of diameter l is assumed. The inlet Reynolds number used is 16.33024615. This is defined based on the density of human blood, $\rho = 1.05\ g/ml$, the mean inlet flow velocity, $u_\infty = 1.592$ cm/sec, the viscosity at high shear rate, $\eta_\infty = 6.5\ cP$ and the diameter of a tube $l = 0.635\ cm$ obtained from Yeleswarapu et al's experiment [2]. The parameters used by Anand and Rajagopal [4] are also used here. They include elastic shear modulus, $\mu = 0.0388\ N/m^2$ and the viscosity of blood, $\eta = 0.387$ $Pa.s$. The Deborah number obtained is 25.00625051.

The viscosity rate $\alpha = 0.41$ is assumed for the standard Oldroyd-B model. Due to the asymptotic viscosity of blood, $\eta_1 = 2\eta_\infty$ with $\eta_1 = 0.013$ Pa.s and $\eta = 2(\eta_{zo} - \eta_\infty)$ with $\eta_{zo} = 200\ cP$ (indicating the viscosity at low shear rate) are used. A Newtonian viscosity rate of $\beta = 2$ and viscoelastic viscosity rate of $\phi = 59.53846154$ are used in the GOB model.

The velocity profile of three-dimensional poiseuille flow at inlet is obtained by solving the problem of uniform flow in a tube to obtain a fully developed profile. No slip boundary conditions are assumed at solid walls. No negative eigenvalues of the conformation stress tensor are allowed to occur in the computational domain.

The governing equations are solved using the above parameters and boundary conditions using the CBS scheme [5]. The material modulus is based on the incompressibility condition. For poiseuille velocity profile at inlet section, the non-dimensional form of material modulus is $\Lambda^* = 1/[1 + 0.25(u_{1,2}^* De)^2 + 0.25(u_{1,3}^* De)^2]^{1/3}$ and $\Lambda^* = 1$ is used for uniform flow inlet.

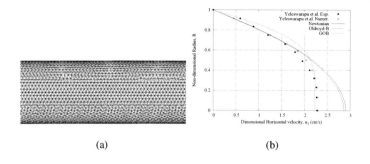

| (a) | (b) |

Figure 1: Blood flow in a straight tube. (a) Surface mesh (Volume mesh: Nodes: 59474; Elements: 326415); (b) Horizontal velocity profile.

The L_2 norm of the residuals of the momentum and constitutive equations are reduced down to at least 10^{-6} to assume a steady state. The mass conservation is also checked to make sure that the conservation is obtained.

Figure 1(a) shows the mesh used in the study. The typical element size used near the wall is about 0.06.Figure 1(b) shows the comparison of horizontal velocity profiles between Yeleswarapu et al's experimental data and present results. As seen, the standard Oldroyd-B model provides a velocity profile quite similar to the results obtained from Newtonian fluid assumption. With the GOB model, the horizontal velocity profile of blood is closer to the experimental data.

4 CONCLUSIONS

This study was aimed at using an artificial-dissipation-based CBS-AC scheme to numerically solve three different blood flow models. The best fit against Yeleswarapu et al's experimental data was obtained from generalized Oldroyd-B (GOB) model introduced by Rajagopal and Srinivasa.

5 ACKNOWLEDGEMENTS

This work was partially funded by EPSRC grants EP/C515498/1 and EP/D070554/1.

REFERENCES

[1] R.A. Freitas Jr., *Nanomedicine, Volume I: Basic Capabilities.*, Landes Bioscience, Georgetown, TX, 1999.

[2] K.K. Yeleswarapu, M.V. Kameneva, K.R. Rajagopal and J.F. Antaki, The flow of blood in tubes: Theory and experiment , *Mechanics Research Communications*, 25, 257–262, 1998.

[3] K.R. Rajagopal and A.R. Srinivasa, A thermodynamic frame work for rate type fluid models, *Journal of Non-Newtonian Fluid Mechanics*, 88, 207–227, 2000.

[4] M. Anand and K.R. Rajagopal, A shear-thinning viscoelastic fluid model for describing the flow of blood, *International Journal of Cardiovascular Medicine and Science*, 4, 59–68, 2004.

[5] C.B. Liu and P. Nithiarasu, An artificial-dissipation-based fractional step scheme for upper-convected Maxwell (UCM) fluid flow past a circular cylinder, *International Journal for Numerical methods in Fluids*, 57, 1171–1187, 2008.

1st International Conference on Mathematical and Computational Biomedical Engineering – CMBE2009
June 29 – July 1, 2009, Swansea, UK
P. Nithiarasu and R. Löhner (eds)

Synthesizing Imaging and Structural Models to Probe Airways and Airway Structures Responsible for Asthma

Kenneth R. Lutchen
Boston University, 44 Cummington Street, Boston, MA klutch@bu.edu
Adam Laprod
Boston University, 44 Cummington Street, Boston, MA klutch@bu.edu
Lisa Campana
Boston University, 44 Cummington Street, Boston, MA klutch@bu.edu
Mitchell Albert
University Massachusetts Medical, Worchester, MA Mitchell.Albert@umassmed.edu

ABSRACT

Key Words: *Oscillatory Mechanics, Hyperpolarized Imaging, Airways, Ventilation.*

1. INTRODUCTION

Asthma treatments range from targeting molecular events (inflammation) to structural intervention (bronchial thermoplasty to ablate smooth muscle). Regardless, efficacy remains inconsistent and asthma prevalence remains on the rise. There is a glaring need to understand if or how biological and physiological events that alter specific structures in the lung can or will impact function. Modeling approaches in the past have been helpful, but unless explicitly driven by and coupled to data and specific questions, models alone are insufficient (3). Recently, anatomically consistent models (2,4,5) have advanced the capacity to link structure to function. We will review our current approach designed to understand the multi-scale nature of the defects associated with degraded function in <u>human</u> asthma.

2. MAIN BODY

At the whole-lung level we synthesize quantitative measures from Hyperpolarized Helium Magnetic Resonance Imaging (Hyp ^{3}He MRI) and oscillatory mechanics data with personalized 3D airway models (2,4). Because of their anatomic fidelity these computational models present a powerful approach to identify which airway sizes and constriction patterns most contribute to asthma. We have acquired data from healthy and asthmatic subjects pre and post broncho-provocation and pre and post deep inspirations at both baseline and post provocation (2,6). We compare a variety of approaches for synthesizing the model with the data, ranging from airway tree model creation with constraints on parent airways leading to defects (4) to the level of quantitative matching that these models match both the imaging ventilation data and the mechanics (2). Our applications show that while constriction in some larger airways likely occurs in asthma, heterogeneous severe constriction in very small airways are necessary for establishing the simultaneous functional degradation in both ventilation and mechanics during human asthma (2,7). These results motivate the question of how mechanisms at the individual airway or airway smooth muscle level integrate to cause whole lung behavior. Here we will also show some recent mechanics and imaging data from isolated airways along

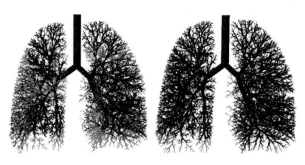

Figure 1: Model airway tree for asthmatic subject post broncho-constriction with methacholine(left) and post albuterol (right). In black are airways that are ventilated, in red are airways that are not being ventilated due to methacholine. Visually a large number of airways which are unventilated, after albuterol some airways are recovered but not all.

with modeling analysis (3). The data and models point largely to the smooth muscle as the primary locus of defect for asthmatic lungs.

3. CONCLUSIONS

Ultimately, these studies will provide a mechanism for determining whether treatments designed to address a crucial biophysical mechanism are capable of targeting essential small airways responsible for clinical symptoms in asthma.

REFERENCES

[1]   Affonce, D.A and K.R. Lutchen. New perspectives on the mechanical basis for airway hyperreactivity and hypersensitivity in asthma. *J. Appl. Physiol.* 101: 1710-1719, 2006

[2]   Campana, L., J. Kenyon, S. Zhalehdoust-Sani, Y-S. Tzeng, Y. Sun, M Albert, K.R. Lutchen. Probing Airway Conditions Governing Ventilation Defects in Asthma via Hyperpolarized MRI Image Functional Modeling *J. Appl. Physiol* (in press)

[3]   Laprod, A. and K.R. Lutchen. Respiratory impedance measurements for assessment of lung mechanics: focus on asthma. Review Article. *Respiratory Physiology and Neurobiology.* 163: 64-73, 2008.

[4]   Mullally, W. M. Betke, M. Albert, and K.R. Lutchen. Explaining Clustered Ventilation Defects via a Minimal Number of Airway Closure Locations. *Annls of Biomedical Engineering*. 37: 286-300, 2009.

[5]   Tgavalekos N., M. Tawhai, R. S. Harris, G. Mush, M. Vidal-Melo, J Venegas , K. R. Lutchen. Identifying airways responsible for heterogeneous ventilation and mechanical dysfunction in asthma: An image-functional modeling approach. *J. Appl. Physiol*. 99:2388-2397, 2005.

[6]   Tzeng, Y-S, J, Gereige, J. Mansour, N. Shah, X. Zhou, G. Washko, E. Stepp, M. Cho, J. B. Szender, S. Z. Sani, E. Israel, K. Lutchen, M. Albert. The difference in ventilation distribution and ventilation heterogeneity between asthmatic and healthy subjects quantified from hyperpolarized ^{3}He MRI. *J. Appl. Physiol* 106: 813-822, 2009

[7]   Venegas JG, Winkler T, Musch G, Vidal Melo MF, Layfield D, Tgavalekos N, Fischman AJ, Callahan RJ, Bellani G, and Harris RS. Self-organized patchiness in asthma as a prelude to catastrophic shifts. *Nature* 434: 777-782, 2005.

Computational modelling of paranasal sinus gas exchange

Christina M. Hood
Department of Bioengineering, Imperial College London,
South Kensington Campus, London SW7 2AZ, c.hood06@imperial.ac.uk

Robert C. Schroter
Department of Bioengineering, Imperial College London,
South Kensington Campus, London SW7 2AZ, r.schroter@imperial.ac.uk

Denis J. Doorly
Department of Aeronautics, Imperial College London,
South Kensington Campus, London SW7 2AZ, d.doorly@imperial.ac.uk

ABSTRACT

Impaired sinus gas exchange is often proposed as a factor in sinus disease, a common and debilitating condition. In this study computational fluid mechanics (CFD) techniques were used to study gas exchange in simplified geometries representing the maxillary sinus. Convection, diffusion and mucociliary transport effects were examined. Flow patterns in the ostium match those given by independent driven cavity analytical solutions. Convective transport is very slow for typical ostium sizes, but increases for larger ostia. Sinuses with two ostia have greatly increased transport compared to single ostia as they form a flow path in parallel to the nose rather than a reservoir attached to it. Diffusive effects are dominant for small ostia and increased concentration differences, as used in previous experimental studies. Mucociliary transport is important for sinus health but was not found to have any interaction with gas exchange.

Key Words: *nose, maxillary sinus.*

1 INTRODUCTION

Clinical interventions to treat sinusitis often try to improve ventilation of the sinuses, but the relationship between sinus anatomy and gas exchange is not well understood. Sinus ventilation is difficult to study *in vivo* as the sinuses are small and inaccessible, hence this study has used computational modelling techniques to examine several possible physical mechanisms.

The maxillary sinuses are the largest of the human sinuses and particularly susceptible to disease. The geometries used for modelling are based on the typical shapes and dimensions of the maxillary sinus, the middle meatus (part of the nasal cavity) and the ostium which connects them, as shown in Figure 1. Simplified geometries were used to represent various anatomical variants, with the effects of the presence of an additional ostium being of particular interest.

Aust and Drettner (1) conducted experiments where the air in model and real sinuses was replaced by pure nitrogen and the recovery of the oxygen concentration to atmospheric values monitored. The diffusion modelling in this study aimed to match and extend the understanding of their results, as the transport mechanisms involved are not clear.

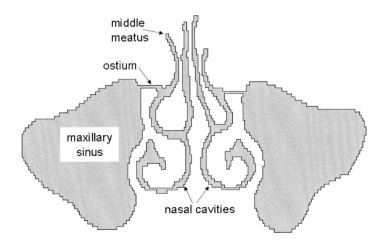

Figure 1: Diagram of nasal and maxillary sinus anatomy, adapted from CT scan slice

2 Modelling Methods

Commercial software (Fluent 6.3.26) was used to model steady airflow, convective and diffusive transport between the sinus and middle meatus. Geometries were modelled in 2D and 3D with quadrilateral and hexahedral meshes respectively. Pressure boundary conditions for each end of the middle meatus were obtained from an existing computational model of the whole nasal airway (3). Order of magnitude calculations, for example using Fick's Law for first-order diffusion, were also performed for comparison with the more detailed CFD simulations.

3 Results

3.1 Convection

Single ostium models have no net flow through the ostium and very slow gas exchange, with a typical geometry requiring more than 80 hours for 90% exchange. However, the air in the ostium and sinus does show vortical motions driven by the shear flow in the nasal cavity, matching the classic driven cavity solution. Increasing the cross-sectional area of the ostium and/or reducing its length increases the velocities in the ostium and reduces the exchange time. In contrast, a sinus with two ostia has net flow through it and a much faster 90% exchange time of 96 seconds. Contours of x-velocity and streamlines in a typical single ostium are shown in figure 2.

3.2 Mucociliary Transport

The walls of the sinus, ostium and nasal cavity were generally considered to be stationary, whereas in reality they are covered with ciliated epithelium transporting a layer of mucous. Some 2D and 3D simulations with moving walls were carried out to investigate this effect. The mucociliary velocities altered the flow patterns in the sinus but did not affect the convection or diffusion exchange times.

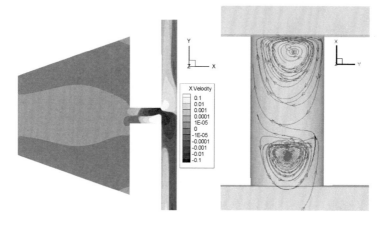

Figure 2: Plots of x-velocity contours and streamlines for 3mm diameter, 6mm long ostium

3.3 Diffusion

Diffusive transport is thought to be an important factor in Aust and Drettner's sinus wash-out experiments, due to the increased concentration difference between the sinus and the nasal cavity. Fick's law was used to make a first-order estimate of the time required to exchange 90% of sinus air by diffusion through a 4mm diameter ostium, this calculation gave an exchange time of 7.6 minutes.

Diffusive transport of an inert gas was also added to the Fluent simulations to give a more precise estimate. A diffusion-only simulation had an exchange time of 7.1 minutes and a simulation with both convection and diffusion gave an exchange time of 6.4 minutes. These times are similar but somewhat longer than Aust and Drettner's result of 4.2 minutes in a physical model. A summary of the calculation and simulation results for three ostium diameters is given in table 1 and a graph of the changes in sinus oxygen concentration relative to atmosphere over time as figure 3.

Ostium Diameter (mm)	Time to Replace 90% sinus air (min)				
	Aust	Fick	CFD		
			Convection	Diffusion	Conv+Diff
3	-	13.6	5040	12	12
4	4.2	7.6	840	7.1	6.4
6	2.5	3.4	5.2	3.4	2.3

Table 1: Summary of convective and diffusive calculated exchange times, experimental results from (1)

3.4 Acoustics

Several experimental studies have found that humming increases NO transport from the sinuses to the nose (4,5 among others). This process is however difficult to model computationally, as direct simulation of acoustics requires very fine spatial and temporal discretisations (2). A 1D simulation of the sinus as a non-linear Helmholtz resonator, with a program adapted from Zhao and Morgans (6), showed a resonance in the vocal frequency range, but did not seem to explain the increased transport due to humming. It would be interesting to model the interaction between acoustic and diffusive effects but this is not currently possible.

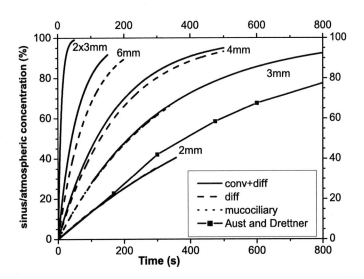

Figure 3: Graph tracking sinus oxygen concentration with time for different ostium diameters

4 Discussion and Conclusions

The modelling in this study has shown that normal sinuses only have very limited gas exchange, with a convective exchange time of 80 hours for a 3mm diameter ostium. However, larger or shorter ostia can have shorter convective exchange times. Adding an extra ostium to allow flow through the sinus or increasing the concentration difference between the sinus and the nose can reduce the exchange times significantly, to 96 sec and 12 min respectively. Excessive ventilation could be harmful due to depletion of the protective NO in the sinus. Diffusive transport is likely to be most important to narrow ostia and convective transport to wide ostia. Mucociliary transport is very important to sinus health but does not interact with ventilation. Humming has dramatic effects on sinus transport but currently can not be adequately modelled.

REFERENCES

[1] Aust, R. and Drettner, B., Experimental Studies of the Gas Exchange through the Ostium of the Maxillary Sinus, *Uppsala J. Med. Sci.*, 79, 177-186, 1974.

[2] Colonius, T. and Lele, S.K., Computational aeroacoustics: progress on non-linear problems of sound generation, *Progress in Aerospace Sci.*, 40, 345-416, 2004.

[3] Doorly, D.J. et al., Mechanics of airflow in the human nasal airways, *Respir Physiol Neurobiol*, doi:10.1016/j.resp.2008.07.027, 2008

[4] Maniscalco et al., Nasal nitric oxide measurements before and after repeated humming maneuvers, *Eur J. Clin Inv*, 33, 1090-1094, 2003.

[5] Menzel, et al., Temporal nitric oxide dynamics in the paranasal sinuses during humming, *J. Appl Physiol*, 98, 2064-2071, 2005.

[6] Zhao, D. and Morgans, A., Tuned Passive Control of Combustion Instabilities Using Multiple Helmholtz Resonators, *AIAA* 2007-3243, 2007.

1st International Conference on Mathematical and Computational Biomedical Engineering – CMBE2009
June 29 – July 1, 2009, Swansea, UK
P. Nithiarasu and R. Löhner (eds)

Modeling Respiratory Flow in a CT-Scanned Upper and Lung Airway

H.Y. Luo, Y.X. Liu and Y. Liu*
Department of Mechanical Engineering, The Hong Kong Polytechnic University
Hung Hom, Kowloon, Hong Kong
mmyliu@polyu.edu.hk

ABSRACT

The inspiratory flow characteristics in a CT-scanned human upper airway and lung model were numerically investigated using low Reynolds number (LRN) κ-ω turbulent model and large eddy simulation (LES). The airway is extracted from the mouth to segmental bronchi of a 60-year-old Chinese male patient. Computations were carried out in the Reynolds number range of 900 ~ 2100, corresponding to mouth-air breathing rates of 190 ~ 440 ml/s. Flow patterns on the Re = 2100 and flow rate distribution were presented. In this model, the flow pattern is very complex, and the effect of laryngeal jet on trachea inlet is well simulated. The result of different turbulent approaches is compared.

Key Words: *upper airway, lung airway, CT-scanned.*

1. INTRODUCTION

The air flow in the bifurcating airway is one of the most basic and revealing problems in the general case of breathing physiology, which can provide useful information for drug particle delivery patterns, pollution dispersion, etc. Numerous studies on bifurcating flow have been carried out to investigate the effect of bifurcation on air flow pattern and particle deposition, and they considered the human lung as either symmetric bifurcation airways or asymmetric airways, and most of these models were based on the Weibel human lung model [1]. The Weibel model takes the human lung as 23 generation regularly bifurcated airways, however, the actual human lung airways show distinct irregular features, and the regular airway models may not reflect the realistic flow characteristics in the human lung.

The development of computational capability and computerized tomography (CT) makes it possible to generate a real lung model for CFD simulation. In this paper, we extended our previous study [2] to a real CT-scanned human upper airway and lung model, and the flow pattern and flow rate distribution are studied in detail.

2. THE MODEL AND RESULT

Thoracic CT scans were taken from a 60-year-old Chinese male patient using a single-slice helical CT scanner (SS-CT). The images were obtained in the axial plane with a resolution of 0.7×0.7 mm^2, and slice thickness is 0.625 mm. The 3D surface geometry of the upper and lung airway was reconstructed using the image processing software Mimics and the generated real lung model is shown in Figure 1. The tracheal wall contains some C-shaped rings of hyaline cartilage. The open posterior parts of the cartilage rings are smooth muscle fibers. Therefore, the shape of the cross-section of the trachea is approximately D-shaped. To avoid any influence of the outlet boundary conditions on the computed solution, each branch exit was artificially lengthened with a straight tube. Medical statistical regularity exists from the trachea to the fifth-order segmental bronchi for the same race and gender (Beachey 1998), therefore we focus on the upper airway and the fifth-order airways which would be representative for Asian male.

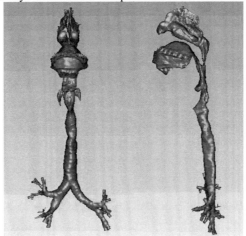

Figure 1 Schematic view of the airway

Acknowledgement

Support given by the Research Grants Council of the Government of the HKSAR under Grant No. PolyU 5238/08E and by the Hong Kong Polytechnic University under Central Research Grant Nos. G-U377 is gratefully acknowledged.

REFERENCES

[1]   E.R. Weibel, Morphometry of the Human Lung, New York Academic Press, Springer-Verlag. 1963.

[2]   H.Y. Luo and Y. Liu, Modeling the Bifurcating Flow in an CT-Scanned Human Lung Airway, *J. Biomechanics*, 41: 2681-2688, 2008.

Fluid Structure Interaction of a human trachea under different ventilation conditions

A. Perez del Palomar, M. Malve and M. Doblare
Group of Structural Mechanics. Aragon Institute of Engineering Research, Maria de Luna s/n 50018 Zaragoza, mmalve@unizar.es

ABSTRACT

Although the understanding of the ventilation patterns in the trachea is a challenging aspect due to their implications in the success of tracheal prostheses implantation, few studies have analyzed the behaviour of the trachea under different ventilation conditions. The interest of this is specially relevant in patients that have to be mechanically ventilated. In this study, a finite element model of a human trachea based on CT images from a 70 years old man is developed. A fluid structure interaction analysis using a commercial software code (ADINA) was modeled in order to study the deformations of the the trachea under different ventilation conditions. The trachea was assumed as a fiber reinforced hyperelastic material in which the different orientation of the collagen fibers was introduced. The fluid in this case was air since different ventilation patterns were analyzed, normal breathing and mechanical ventilation. The deformations of the cartilage rings and the muscle membrane of the trachea were analyzed and the differences in the tracheal behaviour between normal and forced breathing were investigated.

Key Words: *human trachea, breathing patterns, mechanical ventilation.*

1 INTRODUCTION

The trachea is able to adapt itself to regulate the pressure during the different ventilation situations. The main components that constitute the trachea are the cartilaginuos rings, and the muscular membrane. Tracheal cartilaginous structures role is to maintain the windpipe open despite interthoracic pressure during respiratory movements. Smooth muscle contraction and transmural pressure generate bending in the cartilage and collapse it to regulate the air flow. Although the understanding of how this process is performed is a challenging aspect, few studies have analysed the behaviour of the trachea under different ventilation conditions.

Most of the developed numerical studies in the respiratory system analyze the airflow patterns using rigid and approximated airways geometry (Liu et al., 2002). Only few studies are based on "real", i.e. based on 3D imaging, airway geometries (Cebral et al., 2004). Almost all studies, both with artificial and real geometries, do not take airway deformations and fluid-structure interaction (FSI) effects into account (Ma et al., 2006). FSI studies in lower airway geometries were done only in the lower cartilage-free generations of the lung (Hazel and Heil 2003). On the other hand, regarding the constitutive modeling of the tracheal walls, there is a large dispersion of the mechanical properties of the different tissues that are included in the trachea, and only few studies have analyzed their mechanical behaviour for humans (Clive et al, 1998).

The final aim of this work is to understand the breathing/ventilation process in the respiratory system in order to develop strategies to better ventilate patients using FSI techniques.

2 MATERIAL AND METHODS

The finite element model of the human trachea was made based on a CT performed to a 70 years old healthy male patient. The segmentation of the DICOM files was made using MIMICS. A full hexaedrical mesh of the trachea was made using PATRAN (Figure 1). Regarding the fluid domain, a tethraedral-based fluid grid was generated filling the tracheal channel using the commercial software FEMAP. The final mesh was then imported in the software package ADINA where the fluid-solid interaction (FSI) was performed.

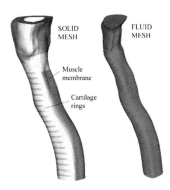

Figure 1: Finite element meshes of the solid and the fluid

To determine the properties of the different tissues of the trachea different experimental tests were conducted. The histology revealed that in the cartilage rings, the collagen fibers run randomly, therefore an isotropic material can be use to define its behaviour. However, the muscular membrane presented two perpendicular family of collagen fibers, one of the family runs longitudinally and the other transversely. Therefore, for this tissue a constitutive model that takes into account the anisotropy was used. For the cartilage, a Neo-Hookean model $\Psi = C_1(\bar{}_1 - 3)$ was used to fit the experimental results. Concerning the smooth muscle, the well known Holzapfel strain energy function (Holzapfel 2000) for one family of fibers was used,

$$\Psi = C_1(\bar{}_1 - 3) + \frac{K_1}{2K_2}\{exp[K_2(\bar{}_4 - 1)^2] - 1\} + \frac{K_3}{2K_4}\{exp[K_4(\bar{}_6 - 1)^2] - 1\} + \frac{1}{D}(\ - 1)^2$$

where C_1 is the material constant related to the ground substance, $K_i > 0$ are the parameters which identify the exponential behavior due to the presence of collagen fibres and D weights tissue incompressibility modulus (see Figure 2 for the constants fitting).

The fluid (air) was supposed newtonian ($\rho = 1.205\ Kg/m^3$, $\mu = 1.83 \cdot 10^{-5}\ Kg/m \cdot s$) and incompressible under unsteady flow conditions. Flow was assumed turbulent, thus, the $\ - \epsilon$ model was used. The boundary conditions under normal breathing and mechanical ventilation conditions are shown in Figure 3 (Wall et al., 2008). In the FSI model the fluid domain is deformable so that the numerical approach uses the well known ALE formulation. For the solid domain, a typical Lagrangian formulation (Bathe, 2004) is used.

3 RESULTS

In Figure 4 the amplified deformed shape of the trachea is shown for normal breathing. It can be seen the different stages of the breathing process. In the first phase the trachea dilatates to increase the air

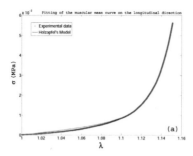 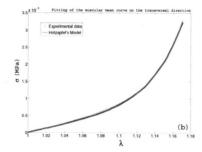

Figure 2: Uniaxial tests performed to tracheal muscle samples (a) Fitting of the Holzapfel's model to the experimental results obtained in the longitudinal direction of the trachea (C_1=0.87KPa, K_1=0.154 KPa, K_2=34.15) ; (b) Fitting of the Holzapfel's model to the experimental results obtained in the transversal direction of the trachea (C_1=0.87KPa, K_3=0.34 KPa, K_4=13.9)

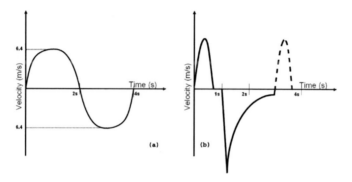

Figure 3: (a) Sinusoidal boundary conditions for normal breathing;(b) Flow time history of the respirator for the mechanically ventilated lung

volume in the lungs (from 0 to 1s), then in the second stage (during the expiration) the trachea collapses. During this normal breathing, it can be seen how the fluid goes inside the lungs (the first two seconds) and in the second stage (expiration) the air goes out the lungs (Figure 5). Comparing the results of

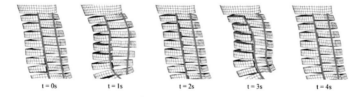

Figure 4: Deformed shape of the cartilage rings during natural breathing (scale magnification 10)

stresses and deformations of breathing and mechanical ventilation patterns, not too many differences can be addressed, since the mechanical ventilation tries to simulate a normal breathing of a patient. The most important fact is that in the mechanical ventilated trachea the applied pressure is always positive, therefore the trachea is always subjected to non zero pressue.

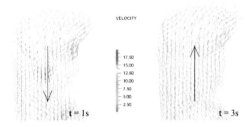

Figure 5: Air flux during normal breathing. On the left direction of the air flux during inspiration; on the right, the air direction during expiration.

4   CONCLUSIONS

We have presented an approach and detailed simulation results of FSI under different ventilation conditions. We found that under inspiratory flow, the mechanical response of the tracheal walls and the flow patterns were similar in normal breathing or mechanical ventilation. However, during expiration more differences could be found between both situations. It has been demostrated that using FSI techniques the deformations and stresses that the trachea undergoes can be seen. This would be the relevant importance to design better mechanical ventilation techniques or to analyze how the implantation of a endotracheal prostheses can affect the flow patterns or the mechanical response of the human trachea.

5   AKNOWLEDGEMENTS

This project was funded by Carlos III Health Institute, Spanish Ministry of Science and Innovation.

REFERENCES

[1]   Liu Y, So RMC, Zhang CH. Modeling the bifurcation flow in a human lung airway. *Journal of Biomechanics* 2002; 35:465-473.

[2]   Cebral JR, Summers RM. Tracheal and central bronchial aerodynamics using virtual bronchoscopy and computational fluid dynamics. *IEEE Transactions on Medical Imaging* 2004; 23(8):1021-1033.

[3]   Ma B, Lutchen KR. An anatomically based hybrid computational model of the human lung and its application to low frequency oscillatory mechanics. *Annals of Biomedical Engineering* 2006; 34(11):1691-704.

[4]   Hazel AL, Heil M. Three-dimensional airway reopening: the steady propagation of a semi-infinite bubble into a buckled elastic tube. *Journal of Fluid Mechanics* 2003; 478:47-70.

[5]   Clive R. Roberts, Jeffrey K. Rains, Peter D. Par, David C. Walker, Barry Wiggs, Joel L. Bert. Ultrastructure and tensile properties of Human traqueal cartilage. *J Biomech*, 81-86, 1998.

[6]   Holzapfel GA. Nonlinear Solid Mechanics. Wiley, New Yor, 2000

[8]   Wall W.A., Rabczuk T., Fluid-tructure Interaction in lower airways of CT-based lung geometries. *International Journal for Numerical Methods in Fluids*, vol. 57, pp 653-675, 2008, Wiley InterScience.

[8]   Bathe K.J., Zhang H., Finite element developments for general fluid flows with structural interactions, *International Journal for Numerical Methods in Engineering*, vol. 60, pp. 213-232, 2004.

Nanoparticle Mass Transfer in a Patient Specific Human Lung

A. Comerford
Institute for Computational Mechanics, Technische Universität München, D-85747 Garching,
Germany

W. A. Wall
Institute for Computational Mechanics, Technische Universität München, D-85747 Garching,
Germany

ABSTRACT

The time dependent mass transport of nanoparticles was studied in a patient specific model of the human lungs. The transport of the nanoparticles was simulated via the convection diffusion equation under varying mass diffusivities, or more specifically Schmidt numbers (Sc). These were Sc=10, 100 and 500 representing small to larger particles respectively. From the results it was found that the realistic geometry plays an important role in the delivery of these particles throughout the geometry and also to the lung wall. For example as the flow becomes more convection dominated (Sc increasing) the geometric variations have a greater impact on the resulting transport/deposition to the surface. In particular, secondary flow characteristics induced by the bifurcating tree were a major controller of the particle transport. Interestingly, higher generations were very susceptible to large variations in transport processes. The effects of Sc on particle concentration within the domain showed marked variation; a low Sc resulted in higher convection into the bulk fluid and higher Sc meant the mass transfer boundary layer was constricted to a thin region on the lung wall. Time dependent effects were observed to play a secondary role to geometric variations.

Key Words: *Air flow, Lung , Mass transfer.*

1 INTRODUCTION

Nanoparticle deposition in the Human lung is of considerably interest. Due to the very small diameter of these particles they are efficiently transported through the lungs[1]. In particular, the lungs are seem as a potentially attractive route for targeted drug delivery of pulmonary and non pulmonary diseases[2]. Such diseases include diabetes (for insulin delivery) and also diseases of the pulmonary airway itself. Currently the experimental measurement of small particles in the lung remains an elusive area due to a number of measuring related difficulties. Further to drug delivery, exposure to various nanoparticulates resulting from nanomaterial production, such as carbon nanotubes, are potentially hazardous, hence there is significant interest in how these distribute and effect the lung.

Previously, there has been attention given to steady state mass transport using idealised lung geometries, such as Weibel based geometries[3]. However it is well known that the lung exhibits significant homogeneity, and Weibel based geometries fail to produce the relevant dynamics of the human lung. Furthermore realistic geometry, particularly irregular walled geometries can lead to mass transfer characteristics which can not be predicted from idealised geometries, as has been highlighted previously for arterial geometries[4]. For this reason the present study focuses on the transport of nanoparticles in a patient specific lung geometry. This is in order to provide understanding of how nanoparticles are transported to the higher generations (higher implies towards peripheral vessels) of the lung.

2 METHODOLOGY

The geometry used in the simulations was segmented using the commercially available segmentation software Mimics (Materialise). The standard CT scans had a resolution of 0.6mm. This allowed up to seven generations of the bronchial tree to be obtained. Following segmentation the outlets of the geometry where cut normal to the flow direction and the geometry was exported in stl format. Figure 1 shows the lung model with outlets cut normal to the flow direction.

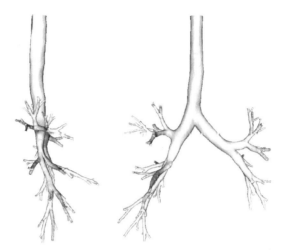

Figure 1: Segmented seven generation lung model used in the numerical simulations.

The lung geometry was meshed using the commercially available meshing software Harpoon (Sharc). Due to the specific nature of the study, very fine boundary layers were fitted in the near wall region in order to capture relevant mass transfer characteristics. In particular, on all interior walls wedge shape mesh elements were inserted with an initial off wall spacing of 2e-5mm growing over six layers to a total thickness of 0.2mm. This is considered sufficient based on the the hydrodynamic parameters. Overall the mesh consisted of 4 million tetrahedral elements and 900000 wedge elements.

The governing equations for airflow in the trachea-bronchial region are the time dependent incompressible Navier-Stokes Equations,

$$\frac{\partial \mathbf{u}}{\partial t} + \rho(\mathbf{u} \cdot \nabla)\mathbf{u} = -\nabla p + \mu \nabla^2 \mathbf{u}, \tag{1}$$

$$\nabla \cdot \mathbf{u} = 0. \tag{2}$$

where $\mathbf{u}$ represents the velocity vector ($\mathbf{u} = [u, v, w]$), p the air pressure, ρ the density and μ the dynamic viscosity. The inflow boundary conditions used in the present simulations was a sinusoidal inspiratory profile, $q(t) = A sin(\omega t)$, where A represents the flow amplitude and ω the circular frequency. The mean flow in the present study was 15 L/min. At the outlets of the computational domain traction free conditions were utilised. We have previously investigated impedance of the peripheral vessels using a Dirichlet to Neumann approach. From this study it was found that the flow is only marginally affected by the peripheral vessels, hence when investigating flow related phenomena, such as mass transfer, more simplified conditions suffice.

The mass transfer field was solved via the convection-diffusion equation, given by,

$$\frac{\partial \phi}{\partial t} + \mathbf{u} \cdot \nabla \phi = D \nabla^2 \phi \qquad (3)$$

with ϕ the mass concentration and D the diffusion coefficient. For mass transfer, Schmidt numbers ($Sc = \nu/D$) of 10, 100 and 500 were investigated, this represents an increase in the convective dominance of the flow and also represents a diameter increase of the particles. The boundary conditions for the mass transfer assumed a uniform concentration of $\phi=1$ at the inlet of the domain and the concentration of $\phi=0$ at all the lung walls, this condition is assuming that when a particle interacts with the wall it is completely absorbed, which for small nano sized particles is considered a reasonable condition.

The numerical simulations were performed in our *in house* multi-physics research code BACI.

3   CONCLUSIONS

From the results it is clearly evident that the realistic geometry plays an important role in the transport of nanoparticles to the lung wall. Specifically, considering Figure 2, it is clear that the distribution of Sherwood number (ie. non dimensional mass transfer coefficient) is driven by the variational wall geometry. The dominant area of high deposition is consistently at the apex of the bifurcation. However, there are regions where the wall non-uniformity leads to higher deposition in other areas, this is most noticeable in the higher Schmidt number model. These additional high concentration regions are brought about by near wall airflow separation and attachment resulting in mass transport boundary layer growth and reduction.

Figure 2: Sherwood distribution at max inspiration, Sc=10 and 100 left and right respectively, Sherwood number range is from 0 (blue) to 60 (red). Non-uniform mass transfer results directly from the non-uniform geometry, where the surface deposition is effected by growing and shrinking of the mass transfer boundary layer. This is most notable in the higher Schmidt number model, where regions of highest surface gradients do not always occur at the bifurcation points.

When comparing the difference between particle distribution in the second generation downstream of the major bifurcation of the trachea (see Figure 3), for Sc=10, 100 and 500 (from left to right), it is shown that for the lower Sc number there is a greater growth of the mass transfer boundary layer. In addition, the location of maximum depletion, irrespective of the Sc, is located at the inner wall of the bifurcation (left hand side of each individual cross-section). This location is the meeting of two counter rotating vortices (evidenced by secondary flow streamlines) resulting from the bifurcating airway. However as oppose to symmetric uniform geometries, the realistic geometry exhibits *3D curvature*, meaning the counter rotating vortices are a superposition of effects (ie centripetal acceleration is dominant in the bifurcation plane, however there is also an influence from other curvature directions). This means the vortices are no longer corresponding to the the centre of the inner wall. This is important to the distribution of these particles. The greater depletion that is observed into the domain, under lower Schmidt number conditions, is primarily due to the greater influence of convection ie. the particles are *diffused* more effectively.

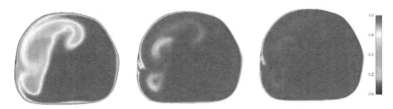

Figure 3: Spatial concentration in a cross section of the second generation of the lung. From left to right Sc=10, 100 and 500 respectively. Clearly with lower Schmidt number the particles are convected more into the bulk domain.

Actual temporal effects seem to be relatively insignificant in the the first few generations. However in the higher generations some areas are exposed to relatively high temporal variations and are in line with the haemodynamic phenomena in these areas, such as profile skewing towards a specific wall during the acceleration phase. This leads to around a five fold increase in transport to the surface. Overall, the distribution is driven by geometric features and the temporal mean distribution is similar to the distribution observed at the equivalent point in the time cycle. Work is currently being undertaken in order to see if this is Reynolds number dependent and whether steady state simulations at the equivalent Reynolds number suffice in order to obtain essential transport characteristics.

Future work will couple the present method with our vast FSI implementations in our *in house* research code. This has been been done previously for pure fluid simulations by our group[5]

REFERENCES

[1] C. Kleinstreuer, Z. Zhang and Z. Lia, Modeling airflow and particle transport/deposition in pulmonary airways, *Respiratory Physiology & Neurobiology* , 163, 128-138, 2008.

[2] S. Azarmia, W. H. Roac and R. Löbenberg, Targeted delivery of nanoparticles for the treatment of lung diseases, *Advanced Drug Delivery Reviews* , 60, 863-875, 2008.

[3] Z. Zhang, C. Kleinstreuer and C. S. Kim, Airflow and Nanoparticle Deposition in a 16-Generation Tracheobronchial Airway Model, *Annals of Biomedical Engineering* , 36, 2095-2110, 2008.

[4] A. Comerford and T. David, Computer Model of Nucleotide Transport in a Realistic Porcine Aortic Trifurcation, *Annals of Biomedical Engineering*, 36, 1175-1187, 2008.

[5] U. Küttler, M. Gee, C. Förster, A. Comerford and W. A Wall, Coupling strategies for biomedical fluid-structure interaction problems, *Communications in Numerical Methods in Engineering with Biomedical Applications*, *in press*, 2009.

1st International Conference on Mathematical and Computational Biomedical Engineering - CMBE2009
June 29 - July 1, 2009, Swansea, UK
P.Nithiarasu and R.Löhner (Eds.)

SIMULATING PHARMACEUTICAL AEROSOL BOLUS DISPERSION AND DEPOSITION IN HUMAN UPPER AIRWAYS: RANS, LES or DES?

Santhosh T. Jayaraju
Dept. Mechanical Engineering, Vrije Universiteit Brussel, Pleinlaan 2, 1050 Brussel, Belgium,
Santhosh.Jayaraju@vub.ac.be

Chris Lacor
Dept. Mechanical Engineering, Vrije Universiteit Brussel, Pleinlaan 2, 1050 Brussel, Belgium

Sylvia Verbanck
Respiratory Division, Academic hospital Brussel, Laarbeeklaan 101, 1090 Brussel, Belgium

ABSTRACT

Air flow and pharmaceutical aerosol bolus dispersion/deposition is studied in a realistic representation of human upper airway geometry. The most commanly used modeling methods such as Reynolds Averaged Navier Stokes (RANS), Detached Eddy Simulation (DES) and Large Eddy Simulation (LES) are tested in the present work. In case of RANS, the most widely used SST $k - \omega$ turbulence model is employed. DES is based on Spalart-Allmaras model for the near-wall region. In case of LES, two subgrid scale models, namely the Smagorinsky-Lilly and the WALE model are tested. The frozen LES method proposed by Matida et al. [5] is also tested. All the results are compared with the experimental data to analyze their reliability.

Key Words: *RANS, LES, DES, Aerosol Dispersion, Aerosol Deposition*

1 INTRODUCTION

Inhaled medication is generally the preferred method of drug administration to the lung for the first-line therapy of asthma and chronic obstructive pulmonary diseases. The complexity of extrathoracic pathway which involves bends, sudden cross-sectional changes, and non-symmetry of the geometry generally results in major deposition of inhaled medication in the pathway before reaching the lungs [3, 5]. With the upper airway flow being transitional, the use of two-equation RANS models, which are basically developed for turbulent flows may result in poor prediction. Reviewing the previous works, Matida et al. [5] conclude that the RANS as well as Reynolds Stress Model (RSM) does not capture relevant features of the flow and highlighted the need to switch towards LES. The present work evaluates the performance of RANS, LES as well as DES in predicting the aerosol deposition.

Besides the deposition of an aerosol bolus, its degree of volumetric dispersion also offers a sensitive tool to characterize aerosol transport [4]. Indeed, aerosol boluses delivered to different lung depths are being used to quantify all aerosol mixing processes, except for Brownian diffusion, that are collectively referred to as *convective mixing* [1]. The degree of aerosol bolus dispersion induced on a bolus transiting the upper airway model is studied using RANS methodology. The ability of RANS in accurately predicting the dispersion induced by the upper airway is discussed.

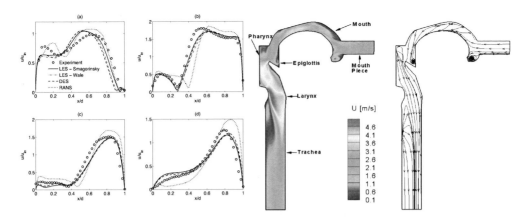

Figure 1: Left: Comparison of normalized 2 component velocity magnitude at (a) Five millimeters above epiglottis (b,c,d) One, two and three tracheal diameters downstream of larynx. Right: Velocity magnitude and vector lines in the central-sagittal plane of the model.

2 MAIN BODY

Fluid Flow Results

As can be seen in Fig. 1, the LES Smagorinsky model does slightly better than the WALE model. It is also interesting to see that DES performs as good as the Smagorinsky model. The time-averaged velocity magnitude along with vector lines are shown for Smagornisky model at 30 L/min. The velocity profiles are highly skewed with many recirculation zones due to the complex nature of the domain. The flow entering through mouth-piece impinges on the tongue and accelerates as it moves through the middle region of the mouth. At the end of the mouth, the flow takes a 90 degree bend and enters the pharynx region. This acceleration and bending of flow may have considerable effect on particle deposition. The vectorline representation shows recirculation regions in the epiglottis and upper part of pharynx region as a result of the oropharyngeal jet. A sharp step at the end of pharynx on the posterior side results in a laryngeal jet beginning from the glottal region and developing towards the anterior side of trachea. This jet may also dominate the particle deposition on the anterior side of trachea. As a result of laryngeal jet, there is a big flow separation on the posterior side.

Aerosol Deposition Results

Fig. 2 summarizes the simulated total deposition percentages for different particle diameters along with the experimental curve fit of Grgic et al. [2], obtained from deposition measurements in 7 different model casts representative of over 80 image-based mouth-throat structures. For the 2 and 4 μm particles, LES and DES show particle depositions that are much closer to the experimental curve than those obtained with RANS $k - \omega$, while for the 8 and 10 μm particles, RANS, LES and DES perform equally well. Alternatively, RANS $k - \omega$ with mean flow tracking, i.e. without EIM, consistently underestimates deposition for all particle diameters greater than 2 μm. The same is true for the frozen LES method. Considering that 5 μm is generally referred to as the upper limit of the respirable range for inhalation drugs (represented by the dash-dotted line in Fig. 2), our findings suggest that in the mouth-throat geometry, the prediction of medication aerosol deposition inhaled at normal flow rates were more accurate for LES and DES than for the RANS $k - \omega$ model. At a first glance, DES can then

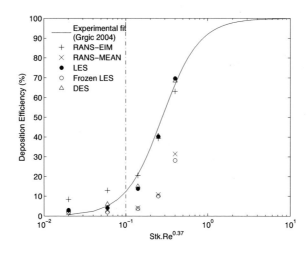

Figure 2: Simulated total deposition (expressed as % of particles at model inlet) as a function of Stokes and Reynolds number as defined by Grgic et al. [2]. The solid line represents the experimental best fit curve. The dash-dotted line corresponds to a 5 μm particle at 30 l/min. In case of RANS, '+' represents turbulent tracking i.e. considering EIM; '×' represents mean flow tracking i.e. without EIM.

be seen as the preferred method over LES due to reduced computational requirements. To be certain regarding DES being better than LES, an additional LES simulation was performed on the DES mesh. It is observed that LES did as good as DES for both fluid and particle phase. This clearly means that LES would remain the preferred method among the models tested, as it obviates solving an additional equation for ν_t required for DES. For the description of particle transport with diameters above 5 μm (e.g., in the upper range of air pollutant particle distributions) or for small diameters but inhaled at greater inhalatory flows (e.g., dry powder inhalers), RANS with its vastly lower computational requirements suffices to adequately predict aerosol deposition.

Aerosol Dispersion Results

Fig. 3 shows the CFD simulated particle concentration traces at the model outlet, which were normalized to their respective bolus peaks, for 250 ml/s (thick solid lines) and 500 ml/s (normal solid lines). The bolus halfwidths corresponding to the CFD simulated particle concentration curves were much smaller for exhalation than for inhalation at both 250 ml/s ($HW_{in} = 69$ ml; $HW_{ex} = 20$ ml) and 500 ml/s ($HW_{in} = 49$ ml; $HW_{ex} = 20$ ml). Also superimposed on the inhalatory traces of Fig. 3A are the corresponding analytical solutions with $D = 200$ cm^2/s, for 250 ml/s (dotted lines) and 500 ml/s (dashed lines). In Fig. 3B, the analytical solution with $D = 25$ cm^2/s is also displayed, merely to illustrate the degree of underestimation of axial bolus dispersion for the exhalatory UAM configuration. The marked difference in halfwidth between the CFD generated boluses in panels A and B of Fig. 3 is in contrast to the very similar halfwidths obtained in bolus experiments with the upper airway model in inhalatory and exhalatory configuration. Given that CFD tools are currently finding such a widespread use in the prediction of the fate of aerosols in the lungs, and that the transitional laminar-turbulent flow regime in the upper airway poses a particular challenge, it is recommended that the bolus dispersion be used as a sensitive tool to validate emerging CFD approaches such as LES.

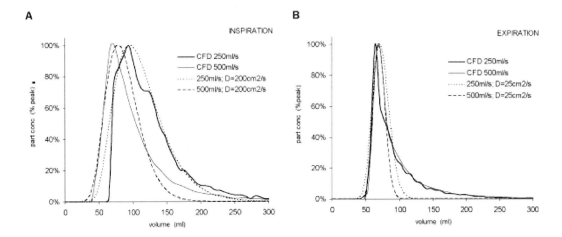

Figure 3: Panel A: CFD simulated outlet profiles with the UAM geometry in inhalatory configuration for flows of 250 ml/s (thick solid lines) and 500 ml/s (normal solid lines) and corresponding theoretical solutions using D = 200 cm^2/s for both flows. Panel B: CFD simulated outlet profiles with the UAM geometry in exhalatory configuration for flows of 250 ml/s (thick solid lines) and 500 ml/s (normal solid lines) and corresponding theoretical solutions using D = 25 cm^2/s for both flows.

3 CONCLUSIONS

1. 5 μm is generally referred to as the upper limit of respirable range for inhalation drugs. For the micro-particles below 5 μm considered in the present study, LES and DES more closely match experimental aerosol deposition than RANS.

2. RANS simulations for aerosol dispersion matched the experimental results for inhalation, but not for exhalation, indicating that the turbulence models should be further scrutinized to adequately simulate all aspects of aerosol transport in the upper airway.

References

[1] C Darquenne and M Paiva. Gas and particle transport in the lung. in: Complexity in structure and function of the lung, m.p. hlastala and h.t. robertson, eds. *Lung Biology in Health and Disease Series*, 121, 1998.

[2] B Grgic, W H Finlay, P K P Burnell, and A F Heenan. In vitro intersubject and intrasubject deposition measurements in realistic mouth-throat geometries. *Journal of Aerosol Science*, 35:1025–1040, 2004.

[3] S T Jayaraju, M Brouns, S Verbanck, and C Lacor. Fluid flow and particle deposition analysis in a realistic extrathoracic airway model using unstructured grids. *Journal of Aerosol Science*, 38:494–508, 2007.

[4] S T Jayaraju, M Paiva, M Brouns, C Lacor, and S Verbanck. Contribution of upper airway geometry to convective mixing. *Journal of Applied Physiology*, 105:1733–1740, 2008.

[5] E A Matida, W H Finlay, M Breuer, and C F Lange. Improving prediction of aerosol deposition in an idealized mouth using large eddy simulation. *Journal of Aerosol Medicine*, 19:290–300, 2006.

1st International Conference on Mathematical and Computational Biomedical Engineering - CMBE2009
June 29 - July 1, 2009, Swansea, UK
P.Nithiarasu and R.Löhner (Eds.)

Numerical investigation of the flow field in the upper human airways

A. Henze

Institute of Aerodynamics, RWTH Aachen University, Wüllnerstrasse 5a, 52062 Aachen, Germany,
a.henze@aia.rwth-aachen.de

R. K. Freitas
r.freitas@aia.rwth-aachen.de

G. Eitel
g.eitel@aia.rwth-aachen.de

W. Schröder
office@aia.rwth-aachen.de

ABSTRACT

The flow in a realistic model of the human lung is numerically simulated at steady and unsteady inspiration and expiration. A model of a human lung ranging from the trachea down to the sixth generation of the bronchial tree is used for the simulation. The numerical analysis is based on a Lattice Boltzmann method which is particularly suited for flows in extremely intricate geometries such as the upper human airways. The results for steady air flow at inspiration and expiration for a diameter based Reynolds number of $Re_D = 1250$ evidence secondary vortex structures and air exchange mechanisms. It is shown that the asymmetric geometry of the human lung plays a significant role for the development of the flow field in the respiratory system. Secondary vortex structures observed in former studies are reproduced and described in detail. Additionally, results for the unsteady flow field for a whole respiration cycle are presented. The solutions allow a detailed analysis of the temporal formation of secondary flow structures whereas the time dependence is much more pronounced at inspiration than at expiration.

Key Words: *computational fluid dynamics, Lattice-Boltzmann method, respiratory system, human lung, unsteady flow.*

1 INTRODUCTION

The understanding of the flow processes in the upper human airways is of great importance to develop aerosol drug delivery systems and to improve the efficiency and usability of artificial respiration. Numerous experimental and numerical investigations of lung flow have been conducted so far [1, 2, 3, 4, 5]. Most of the investigations are based on simplified models of the lung structure where the so-called Weibel model [6] is the most common. In many studies only the first three to five generations are considered and a planar representation is favored for simplicity.

The present work focuses on the detailed investigation of the three-dimensional flow in a realistic model of the human lung based on an actual lung cast. The geometry covers the trachea and the bronchial tree down to the sixth generation. A silicon model of the same geometry has been experimentally investigated in [3]. The flow field is simulated via a Lattice-Boltzmann method (LBM) [7] where the geometry is represented by an automatically generated Cartesian mesh. Unlike former numerical and experimental investigations, in which a simplified geometry was used, the present method can be efficiently applied to variable, realistic airway geometries. For instance the flow field downstream of the laryngeal region has recently been investigated in [8] by an LBM. The numerical results allow an extended analysis of the three-dimensional flow structures observed in [3].

The steady flow field at inspiration and expiration has been simulated for a constant mass flux. Furthermore, the flow field at time dependent inhalation and exhalation has been computed. The results mainly serve to fundamentally understand the three-dimensional flow structures within the upper bifurcations of the human lung under normal breathing conditions and the time-dependent development of the flow field. In this extended abstract, the main results for the steady and unsteady flow field at inspiration and expiration are outlined and some conclusions are drawn.

2 RESULTS

2.1 Steady flow field

To understand the global structure of the flow field, simulations have been performed for steady inspiration and expiration at a constant Reynolds number of $Re_D = 1250$. The value for Re_D is based on the hydraulic diameter of the throat and corresponds to a volume flux of 240 ml/s. To validate the solutions, the results have been compared with experimental data (Fig. [1]) obtained by Particle Imaging Velocimetry (PIV) measurements [3]. The velocity distributions and contours in the left primary bronchus at four cross sections described in Fig. [2] (left) are shown in Fig. [2] (center and right).At inspiration Fig. [2] (center) shows that the main mass flux is located near the lower wall indicated by a high stream-wise velocity. Downstream of the first bifurcation a pair of counter-rotating vortices develops in which air is transported away from the high speed region along the outer walls. The vortex pair has also been observed in the experiment [3]. Additionally, the analysis of the numerical data emphasizes the strong asymmetry of the vortical structures. When the next bifurcation is reached, the vortices do separate and each one enters a branch of the next bronchial generation as shown in Fig. [2] (d) at inspiration.

At expiration the stream-wise velocity is fully distributed and the indicated vortical structures clearly possess a much smaller ratio of azimuthal momentum to stream-wise momentum than at expiration. In conclusion, the findings of the steady flow field confirm that much more secondary flow structures are generated at inspiration than at expiration.

2.2 Unsteady flow field

In order to investigate the temporal development of the secondary flow structures, extensive simulations concerning the unsteady behavior of the flow field during oscillating respiratory ventilation have been performed. Simulations of oscillating flows have been conducted for a peak Reynolds number $Re_D = 1050$ and a Womersley number $\alpha = 3.27$ corresponding to a breathing period of $T = 3.7$ s which describes a normal respiration at rest. The temporal change of the mass flux has been prescribed by a sinusoidal curve. The results evidence that the temporal rate of change of the velocity at initiating inspiration has a strong impact on the development of the flow field in the bifurcations. When the mass flux peaks, the flow field is almost identical with the steady case distribution. The elementary vortical structures and the high speed region which have been observed at maximum inspiration are already encountered at a Reynolds number of $Re_D = 590$. This is in agreement with the experiment where the size of the counter-rotating vortices has been found to be Reynolds number independent as long as it is above a critical level. At expiration the overall flow structure does not appear to change noticeably in time. The comparison with the time dependent PIV findings from [3] shows the temporal behavior of the numerically determined flow field to be in good agreement with the experimental results.

3   CONCLUSIONS

The flow field in a realistic model of the human lung at steady inspiration and expiration and at unsteady respiration has been simulated via the LBM. The LBM has proved to be an efficient tool to simulate flows through highly intricate geometries.

The steady flow field at inspiration and expiration has been analyzed for a constant flow rate of 240 ml/s. The visualization has evidenced the intricate three-dimensional character of the flow field. A pair of counter-rotating vortices and a region of high speed flow have been observed downstream of the first bifurcation in the left bronchus. The results have been compared with PIV measurements and showed to be in very good agreement with the experimental findings.

In order to evidence the impact of an oscillating mass flux, the unsteady flow field has been analyzed at a Womersley number of $\alpha = 3.27$ and a maximum Reynolds number of $Re_D = 1050$. At inspiration the growth of the vortical structures in the left branch of the first bifurcation has been investigated in detail and evidenced a strong dependence of the shape and size of the secondary flow structures on the instantaneous mass flux. At Reynolds numbers greater than $Re_D = 600$ the overall shape of the flow field does not change. At expiration the steady and unsteady flow solutions are found to be very similar since hardly any secondary flow structures have been observed.The obtained results reveal insight into the overall structure of the flow field in a realistic lung geometry and emphasize the unsteady character of the flow field when the flow conditions reverse. This knowledge is essential for the improvement of artificial respiration devices and for the development of aerosol drug delivery systems.

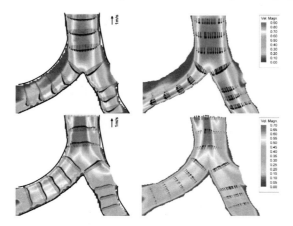

Figure 1: Velocity contours and vectors for inspiration (upper) and expiration (lower). Experiment (left) and numerical solution (right).

REFERENCES

[1] J. K. Comer, C. Kleinstreuer, C. S. Kim, Flow structures and particle desposition patterns in double-bifurcation airway models. Part 1. Air flow fields 435 (2001) 25 – 54.

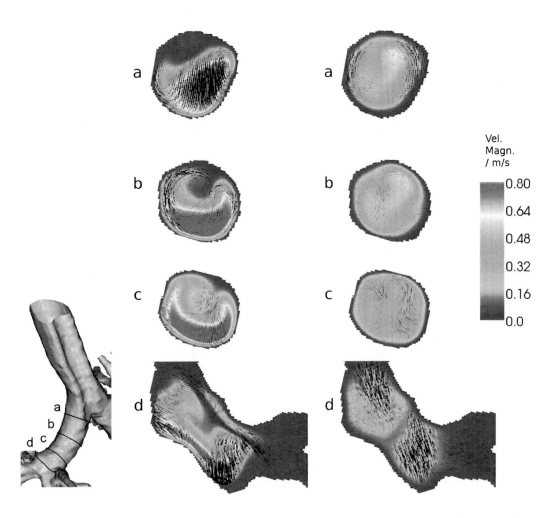

Figure 2: Left: Definition of the location of the cross sections. In-plane velocity distributions (arrows) and axial velocity contours (color) at steady inspiration (center) and steady expiration (right).

[2] N. Nowak, P. P. Kakade, A. V. Annapragada, Computational Fluid Dynamics Simulation of Airfoil and Aerosol Deposition in Human lungs, Annals of Biomedical Eng. 31 (2003) 374 – 390.

[3] S. Große, W. Schröder, M. Klaas, A. Klöckner, J. Roggenkamp, Time resolved analysis of steady and oscillating flow in the upper human airways, Experiments in Fluids 42 (2007) 955–970. doi:10.1007/s00348-007-0318-y.

[4] S. Große, W. Schröder, M. Klaas, Time-Resolved PIV Measurements of Vortical Structures in the Upper Human Airways, in: Particle Image Velocimetry, Vol. 112/2008 of Topics in Applied Physics, Springer Berlin/Heidelberg, 2008, pp. 35–53.

[5] C. van Ertbruggen, C. Hirsch, M. Paiva, Anatomically based three-dimensional model of airways to simulate flow and particle transport using computational fluid dynamics, J. Appl. Physiol. 98 (2005) 970–980.

[6] E. Weibel, Morphometry of the human Lung, Springer Berlin, 1963.

[7] R. Benzi, S. Succi, M. Vergassola, The Lattice Boltzmann Equation: Theory and Applications, Physics Reports 222 (No. 3) (1992) 145–197.

[8] C. G. Ball, M. Uddin, A. Pollard, Mean flow structures inside the human upper airway, Flow, Turbulence and Combustion 81 (2008) 155 188.

Forcing of low Reynolds Number Alveolar Flows in the Lung

David Borer
ETH Zürich, Institute of Fluiddynamics, Sonneggstr. 3, 8092 Zürich, Switzerland,
dborer@ifd.mavt.ethz.ch

Thomas Rösgen
ETH Zürich, Institute of Fluiddynamics, Sonneggstr. 3, 8092 Zürich, Switzerland,
roesgen@ifd.mavt.ethz.ch

ABSTRACT

The air flows deep inside the lung are not only important in gas exchange processes but they also determine the efficiency of particle deposition and retention. The study aims at quantifying the possibility and efficiency of external forcing, relying on the mechanism of internal acoustic streaming. A viscous oscillating boundary layer flow is converted into a steady, viscosity-independent bulk motion which is very efficient at low Reynolds numbers. The streaming can be controlled by external parameters (excitation amplitude, frequency, beam shape) and may thus be of diagnostic and therapeutic relevance. Numerical simulations are performed to analyze the flow patterns in 3D model geometries and to measure deposition rates.

Key Words: *lung flows, particle deposition, acoustic streaming.*

1 Introduction

In order to exchange oxygen and carbon dioxide within the body, blood and air must be brought into close contact over a large surface area, nearly the size of a tennis court (approximately $130\,m^2$) in the human lung. For this to happen in an orderly fashion, a system of branched airways that have their origin in the trachea has evolved to connect all of the 300 million alveoli, which constitute the gas exchanger, to the outside air.

In the human and mammalian lung, the airways are built as dichotomous (dividing into two parts) trees. In the human lung, this repeats for approximately 23 generations, and since the number of branches doubles with each generation, there will be approximately 2^{23} (or 8 million) end branches, generally called alveolar sacs. This, of course, remains an average value as the number of branching generations needed to reach the alveolar sacs is quite variable (from about 18 to 30).

The airway tree is thus divided into two major functional zones: the first (approximately) 14-16 generations consist of conducting airways. This is followed by about 9 generations of acinar airways where axial channels (called alveolar ducts) are enclosed by a sleeve of alveoli with gas exchange tissue on their surface. A useful definition is the acinar generation number z', which will be defined by $z' = 0$ at airway generation 15 and going to $z' = 8$ for the alveolar sacs.

This work is concerned with investigating aerosol deposition rates and possible enhancement measures, such as induced acoustic streaming.

2 Flow regime

With appropriate non-dimensional variables the Navier–Stokes equation can be written as:

$$Wo^2 \frac{\partial u}{\partial t} + Re(u \cdot \nabla u) = -\nabla(p/\rho) + \nabla^2 u$$

The Reynolds number Re gives the relation between inertial and viscous forces. For pipe flows the critical Reynolds number at which laminar–turbulent transition occurs, is around ~ 2300.

The Womersley number $Wo = \frac{D}{2}\left(\frac{\omega}{\nu}\right)^{1/2}$ provides a measure of the importance of the unsteady term compared to the viscous term. It appears originally in the solution for a laminar flow in a circular pipe driven by a sinusoidally oscillating pressure gradient [6]. For $Wo \gg 1$ the velocity profile differs from the well–known parabolic Poiseuille profile for laminar flows, with a plug flow in the bulk of the pipe and an out–of–phase flow near the walls.

Figure 1 shows the governing parameters for sedentary tidal volume breathing at $\dot{Q} = 18\ l/min$. Airway diameters are taken from Finlay [1]. In the acinar region the governing equation can therefore be written as $\mu \nabla^2 u = \nabla p$. This is called Stokes flow (or creeping flow), which is a laminar viscous flow without explicit time–dependance. By neglecting the convective term, the equations are linear. This allows for superposition of basic solutions.

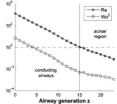

Figure 1: Re, Wo at Gen. z.

3 Acoustic streaming

Acoustic streaming is a steady current forced by the viscous damping and rectification of high frequency (acoustic) oscillations. By decomposing the velocity into a first order oscillating (i.e. acoustic) particle velocity and a second order steady (i.e. streaming) velocity, a set of equations can be derived (Nyborg [4]):

$$\mu \nabla^2 u_2 - \nabla p_2 + F = 0, \quad \text{where} \quad F = -\rho_0 \langle u_1 \cdot \nabla u_1 + u_1 \nabla \cdot u_1 \rangle.$$

Here, $\langle \cdot \rangle$ denotes a temporal averaging operator. Steady streaming flows can occur around solid boundaries, with an amplitude $u_2 \sim \frac{u_1^2}{\omega L}$ that is independent of viscosity. An oscillatory flow over a solid surface must vanish on the surface due to the no–slip condition. The vorticity generated at the wall spreads diffusively with diffusivity ν, so that wall effects are effectively confined to a distance over which vorticity can diffuse in one cycle before it is annihilated. This confined, oscillatory boundary layer (also known as a Stokes layer) is of size $\delta = \sqrt{\frac{2\nu}{\omega}}$, where ω is the angular frequency of the acoustic excitation. The flow field can therefore be split into two regions: a rotational flow in the near wall region and an irrotational flow outside the boundary layer.

Such a flow field may be characterized using a dimensionless frequency parameter, $M = \frac{D}{2}\sqrt{\frac{\omega}{\nu}}$, which was introduced in [7]. D is the characteristic diameter of the hemispherical cavity, $\omega = 2\pi f$ the angular frequency of oscillation, and ν the kinematic viscosity of air. The parameter M takes the same form as the Womersley number, but in this case may be interpreted as the ratio of a body length scale D to a viscous length scale δ.

Experiments were carried out with an elastic spherical cavity in an acoustic field by J. Sznitman, [5]. For the frequencies investigated, the resulting frequency parameter ranges between $M = [120 - 306]$, and the generated flows are steady and reproducible. The streaming flow in the sphere (excluding the Stokes layer) is essentially a creeping flow and can be solved for by expanding the pressure field in a series of solid spherical harmonics, for more detail see [2,3]. This results in a set of solutions for the velocity field, which can be identified in the experimental results. For an alveolus of diameter $D \simeq 200\,\mu m$ the frequency scales to the order of $1\,MHz$.

Figure 2 shows as an example the experimental and corresponding analytical result, as well the flow field obtained in the CFD calculation for $M = 306$. On the right are the analytically derived velocity equations for a sphere of unit radius.

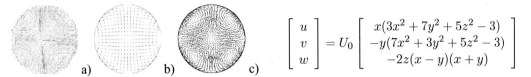

$$\begin{bmatrix} u \\ v \\ w \end{bmatrix} = U_0 \begin{bmatrix} x(3x^2 + 7y^2 + 5z^2 - 3) \\ -y(7x^2 + 3y^2 + 5z^2 - 3) \\ -2z(x-y)(x+y) \end{bmatrix}$$

Figure 2: M=306: a) Experimental (Sznitman [5]), b) analytical, c) CFD.

4 Results and Conclusions

For a simple duct model of an alveolus of the acinar generation $z' = 4$ the streaming is simulated under self similar breathing motion, which is modelled with by the sinusoidal scale function $L(t) - L_0 \left[1 + \frac{\beta}{2}\left(1 - \cos\left(\omega t\right)\right)\right]$. The velocity boundary condition of the alveolar walls is set to the analytically derived expression. The main unknown in this approach is the amplitude of the acoustic streaming velocity. Therefore the simulations are intended to demonstrate and quantify the effect of the streaming on the particle deposition for varying streaming intensities. We calculate the streaming for different velocity ratios $\hat{u}_a = \frac{u_{streaming}}{u_{duct}}$, which are set set to $\{0.01, 0.03, 0.1\}$. This is in the range of streaming velocities encountered in the experiments. Two breathing cycles were calculated with the commercial CFD package Ansys CFX.

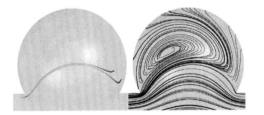

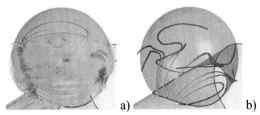

Figure 3: Cavity flow without streaming, single particle path on left.

Figure 4: Particle paths at $M = 306$: a) $\hat{u}_a = 0.1$, b) $\hat{u}_a = 0.01$.

Figure 3 shows the flow field for the case without steady streaming. The near reversible character of the particle transport is demonstrated on the left by the single particle path over two breathing cycles. If streaming is included, the particles exhibit a much more complex behavior due to constant streaming velocities perpendicular to the undisturbed flow (Figure 4). This leads to more particles entering the alveolus, leading to a higher deposition rate. The residence time in the alveolus is also greatly increased.

In Figure 5 the deposition efficiency is calculated as n/N, where n is the number of particles deposited in the alveolus and N is the total number of particles simulated. The effect

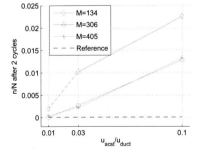

Figure 5: Deposition efficiency for varying values of M and $\hat{u}_a$.

varies depending on the flow field induced, e.g. on M. For levels of streaming two orders lower than the duct velocity an effect is still observable. Even if the streaming that can achieved in the lung is lower, this might still have a significant effect on the particle mixing and deposition.

REFERENCES

[1]   W. H. Finlay. The Mechanics of Inhaled Pharmaceutical Aerosols. An Introduction. Academic Press, 2001.

[2]   J. Happel, H. Brenner, Low Reynolds Number Hydrodynamics Kluwer, 1983.

[3]   H. Lamb, Hydrodynamics, Sixth Edition. Dover Publications, 1993.

[4]   W. L. Nyborg, Acoustic streaming due to attenuated plane waves, J. Acoust. Soc. Am. 25 (1953), pp. 6875.

[5]   J. Sznitman, Th. Rösgen, Acoustic Streaming Visualization in Elastic Spherical Cavities, J. Vis. vol. 11 4, 2008.

[6]   J. M. Womersley, Method for the calculation of velocity rate of flow and viscous drag in arteries when the pressure gradient is known. J. Physiol., 127:553563, 1955.

[7]   H. Zhao, S. S. Sadhal, and E. H. Trinh, Internal circulation in a drop in an acoustic field. J. Acoust. Soc. Am., 106:32893295, 1999.

Integrative modelling of tissue deformation and blood flow distribution in the lung

Kelly S. Burrowes
Oxford University Computing Laboratory, Wolfson Building, Parks Road Oxford, OX1 3QD, U.K.
kelly.burrowes@comlab.ox.ac.uk

M H. Tawhai
Auckland Bioengineering Institute, University of Auckland, Private Bag 92019, Auckland Mail Centre, Auckland 1142. m.tawhai@auckland.ac.nz

ABSTRACT

Inversion of posture from supine to prone is known to influence the distribution of ventilation and perfusion within the lung. Relatively recent measures have shown that the change in flow gradients measured in these respective postures are largely due to tissue deformation with only a minor effect of postural change on the distribution of ventilation and perfusion gradients within the isolated conducting networks [1]. In order to more fully understand the interaction between parenchymal tissue mechanics and pulmonary blood flow we have developed a subject-specific model of regional pulmonary blood flow coupled to a model of soft-tissue deformation. This has enabled us to investigate the effect of posture and lung volume on tissue behaviour and pulmonary blood flow.

Key Words: *subject-specific models, blood flow, tissue mechanics.*

1 INTRODUCTION

A large amount of interdependence exists between various components within the lung. Function of both the blood and air transport systems are dependent on material properties and resultant mechanical behaviour of the parenchymal tissue to which each transport tree is tethered. Using a validated theoretical model to understand the interdependence between structure, fluid transport, and mechanical function in the lung provides the advantage of exact control over functional parameters and the geometry of the solution domain. A computational model of the pulmonary blood flow network coupled to a model of parenchymal soft-tissue mechanics has been developed to examine the dependence of pulmonary blood flow distributions on elastic recoil pressures exerted by the parenchymal tissue and tissue deformation when the lung is in different postures and at different volumes.

2 MAIN BODY

2.1 Subject-specific models

We use a combination of MDCT (multi detector computed tomography) data and computational algorithms to construct subject-specific models of the lung and pulmonary arterial blood vessels. The human imaging data applied in the current study was acquired at the University of Iowa Comprehensive

Lung Imaging Center (I-Clic). The imaging data forms part of an imaging-based Human Lung Atlas that is currently under development [2]. The geometry of the left lung of a single subject was modelled and used for simulation in this study.

A curvilinear finite element volume mesh was fitted to the geometric data points that were calculated to lie on the rendered MDCT lung surface at TLC (total lung capacity). A second pleural surface was fitted to surface data for the lung at FRC (functional residual capacity). The lung was considered as a continuous solid, and the lobes were not modelled separately. The computational and visualisation software package CMISS (www.cmiss.org) was used for geometry fitting, and for later computation of tissue stress and strain and blood flow calculations.

The largest blood vessels were also extracted from MDCT data. A volume-filling branching algorithm was applied [3] within the lung volume to represent the geometry of additional blood vessels unidentifiable via imaging.

2.2 Soft-tissue mechanics (finite deformation elasticity)

Volume changes of the lung are predicted using equations describing finite deformation (large strain) theory. The parenchymal material is described using a strain-energy density function with coefficients such that uniform inflation pressures are approximated to be 5 cmH_2O at FRC and 25 cmH_2O at TLC. The reference geometry is taken as a uniform scaling from TLC to 25% of TLC.

Volume change and distribution of stress and strain were compared at FRC and TLC in the prone and supine postures under a normal gravitational load (9.81 $m.s^{-2}$). The deformed lung model is contained by a contact 'pleural' body that changes geometry from TLC to FRC. Contact is enforced between the lung and the pleural surfaces, but the lung is free to slide within the cavity. An important point to note is that the shape of the cavity did not change between postures: in each case the cavity shape was that of the surface geometry for the supine (imaged) lung. Neither the heart, chest wall, nor diaphragm was displaced during inversion of posture.

Elastic recoil pressure was calculated as the average of the principal Cauchy stresses. The mean elastic recoil pressure can be considered as an estimate of the pleural pressure magnitude. Elastic recoil pressure varies within iso-gravitational slices, with more variation evident when the model is supine. Figure 1(a) and (b) illustrate the surface (pleural) pressures developed in the lung model in response to gravity in the prone and supine model, respectively. The same colour scale is used for each simulation ranging from approximately 3 (dark blue) to 7 (red) cmH_2O. The tissue is pulled in the direction of gravity, but the displacements are smallest in the prone lung.

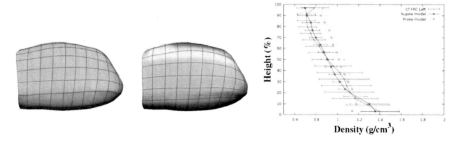

Figure 1: *Tissue mechanics predictions at FRC: Pleural pressures on the lung surface in (a) prone and (b) supine postures. Spectrum: 3-7 cmH_2O. (c) Normalised tissue density versus vertical height (dorsoventral axis) for the model (prone and supine) and MDCT measurements (supine). Results are presented as averages within 10 mm thick iso-gravitational sections (± standard deviation). 0% height corresponds to the dorsal surface for the supine results, and the ventral surface for the prone results.*

Comparisons are made between tissue density measurement and the model prediction for the left lung of a single subject at FRC. Figure 1(c) plots the normalised (relative to mean) density distribution with respect to gravitationally-dependent height (dorsoventral axis) for model predictions in the prone and supine posture and values calculated from the MDCT imaging (supine posture) for this subject. These results display the close correlation of model predictions with imaging measurements. Model predictions show a more uniform tissue density in the prone posture which agrees with experimental measurements [1,4].

2.3 Blood flow coupled to tissue deformation

By applying conservation of mass, the 1D Poiseuille flow equation, and an empirically-based pressure-radius relationship we predict pressure, radius, and flow distributions within the arterial model. By assuming steady-state, fully-developed laminar flow within vessels of constant radius, the Poiseuille equation gives an exact solution to the Navier-Stokes equations. Pressure boundary conditions are applied at inlet and outlet locations in the model.

The vascular model is embedded within the lung volume finite element mesh and the coordinates of the arterial model are updated based on the lung tissue deformation vector at different lung volumes and in different postures (Figure 2). The deformation of the blood vessels within the parenchymal tissue is reflected by a change in the length and radius of each vessel, which influences the vascular resistance. The elastic recoil pressure acting on each vessel is predicted from the soft-tissue mechanics model. This pressure is included into the elastic vessel pressure-radius relationship.

Figure 2: *Pressure in the upright arterial model of the left lung: (a) FRC (50% lung volume), (b) TLC (100% lung volume). Spectrum: 0.6 (blue) to 3.4 (red) kPa.*

With the coupled mechanics-flow model we can calculate perfusion gradients using different methods of normalisation. Figure 3 displays (a) blood flow, (b) density, and (c) density-normalised blood flow per voxel in the supine model at FRC plotted with respect to vertical height (dorsoventral axis). A voxel volume of $250\ mm^3$ is used for this analysis. After normalisation of blood flow to tissue density the gradient is reduced from -6.1%/cm to -2.1%/cm illustrating the large influence of tissue density on perfusion gradient, previously highlighted via imaging measurements [1,5].

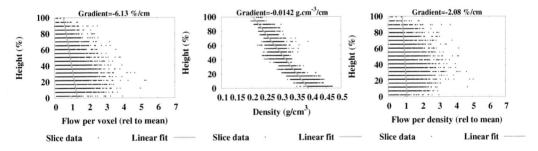

Figure 3: *Blood flow predictions in the supine arterial model at FRC. (a) Blood flow (relative to mean), (b) tissue density (g/cm^3) and (c) density-normalised flow (relative to mean) per voxel plotted against vertical height (dorsoventral axis). Voxel volume=250 mm^3.*

A large amount of blood flow heterogeneity was observed within iso-gravitational planes in all postures and lung volumes. Maximal flow rates were present in the central regions of the lung with persistent regions of decreased flow in the more peripheral regions indicating that vascular geometry plays a key role in governing the distribution of flow [6].

3 CONCLUSIONS

We have developed a model of soft-tissue mechanics to predict tissue density and elastic recoil pressures within the lung at different volumes and in different postures. A model of blood flow within the arterial network has been coupled to this model to enable realistic predictions of regional blood flow within the lung under various conditions.

We have used a combined approach of imaging and computational modelling to study the uniformity of tissue density and elastic recoil pressure. Results suggest that an underlying feature of the prone posture is a more uniform density distribution and less heterogeneity in density or elastic recoil pressure than when in the supine posture. These differences are present even in the absence of heart, chest wall, or diaphragm displacement, although they are expected to be exaggerated by any displacements or shape changes that are associated with the change in posture.

Blood flow results show increased flow towards the dependent lung region, however after normalisation by tissue density the flow gradient is greatly reduced. This confirms the hypothesis that flow gradients are largely influenced by lung tissue distribution.

REFERENCES

[1]   J Petersson, M Rohdin, A Sanchez-Crespo, S Nyren, H Jacobsson, S Larsson, S G E Lindahl, D Linnarsson, B Neradilek, N L Polissar, R W Glenny. Posture primarily affects lung tissue distribution with minor effect on blood flow and ventilation, *Respir Physiol Neurobiol*, 156(3), 293-303, 2007.

[2]   B Li, G E Christensen, E A Hoffman, G McLennan, J M Reinhardt. Establishing a normative atlas of the human lung: Intersubject warping and registration of volumetric CT images, *Acad Radiol*, 10, 255-265, 2003.

[3]   MH Tawhai, P Hunter, J Tschirren, J Reinhardt, G McLennan, EA Hoffman. CT-based geometry analysis and finite element models of the human and ovine bronchial tree, *J Appl Physiol*, 97(6), 2310-21, 2004.

[4]   G K Prisk, K Yamadam A C Henderson, T J Arai, D L Levin, R B Buxton, S R Hopkins. Pulmonary perfusion in the prone and supine postures in the normal human lung, *J Appl Physiol*, 103, 883-894, 2007.

[5]   SR Hopkins, AC Henderson, DL Levin, K Yamada, T Arai, RB Buxton, GK Prisk. Vertical gradients in regional lung density and perfusion in the supine human lung: the Slinky effect. *J Appl Physiol*, 103(1), 240-8, 2007.

[6]   KS Burrowes and MH Tawhai. Computational predictions of pulmonary blood flow gradients: Gravity versus structure. *Respir Physiol Neurobiol*, 154(3), 515-523, 2006.

1st International Conference on Mathematical and Computational Biomedical Engineering - CMBE2009
June 29 - July 1, 2009, Swansea, UK
P.Nithiarasu and R.Löhner (Eds.)

Surfactant dynamics with SPH

S. Adami, X.Y. Hu and N.A. Adams
Institute of Aerodynamics, Technische Universität München, 85748 Garching, Germany,
stefan.adami@aer.mw.tum.de

ABSTRACT

We propose a Lagrangian particle method for the simulation of multiphase flows with surfactant. The transportation model of the surfactant accounts for advection and diffusion of surfactants on an arbitrary interface and in the bulk phase. Within our method, we can simulate insoluble surfactants as well as interfacial transportation such as adsorption or desorption. The method is validated with analytic solutions for the isolated physical phenomena of surface diffusion and surfactant dynamics. More complex simulations of the oscillating bubble experiment, the bubble deformation in shear flow and the Marangoni-force driven bubble show the capabilities of this method to simulate interfacial flows with surfactants.

Key Words: *surfactant dynamics, dynamic surface tension, surface diffusion.*

1 INTRODUCTION

The presence of surfactant in the liquid-lining layer of pulmonary alveolar structures has a major impact on the surface tension at the air-liquid interface. With increasing surfactant concentration at the interface, surface tension decreases and consequently the breathing process is influenced, i.e., the work required for respiration is reduced [1]. Furthermore, many engineering and scientific applications use the effect of surfactants on interfaces, e.g., to manipulate the deformation of drops and bubbles in shear flows [2].

Experimental investigations on the behavior of lung surfactant in vitro frequently use a bubble surfactometer [5, 7]. With this instrument, a nearly spherical bubble of air is formed at the end of a narrow tube and exposed to a liquid suspension containing surfactant. Oscillating the bubble volume with time, the dynamic behavior of the surface tension due to the surfactant at the air-liquid interface can be measured. The surface tension is not measured directly but rather the pressure drop across the bubble surface (pulsating bubble surfactometer [3]) or the changing shape of the bubble (captive bubble surfactometer [8]) is estimated.

To the knowledge of the authors, this is the first time a multi-phase SPH method is proposed to simulate multiphase flows with surfactants. The model is based on the multi-phase smoothed particle hydrodynamics (SPH) framework in Hu and Adams [4]. The main advantage of the Lagrangian formulation is the adaptive interface representation. Therefore no complicated interface tracking or capturing technique is needed and the simulation of more complex cases including more than two phases is straightforward. The surfactant dynamics are written in conservative form. Thus, mass conservation of surfactant is ensured. On the interface, we solve a diffusion equation for the surfactant and due to our Lagrangian method advection is naturally included. The exchange of surfactant between the interface and the bulk phase follows an adsorption-limited model taking into account adsorption and desorption

[7]. As constitutive equation to determine the surface tension in dependence of the interfacial surfactant concentration two linearly isothermal regions are used.

2 RESULTS AND DISCUSSION

The present numerical method is validated with analytic solutions for the isolated physical phenomena of diffusion and surfactant dynamics. As an example, Fig. 2(a) shows the results for the surface diffusion on a drop interface. To show the capabilities of this method to simulate interfacial flows with surfactants we perform more complex simulations like the Marangoni-force driven bubble, see Fig. 2(b). Here, the force caused by a surface tension gradient along the interface produces a counterclockwise rotation and moves the bubble down.

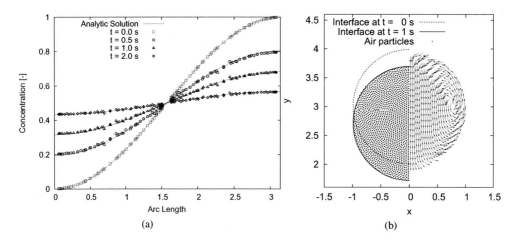

Figure 1: (a) Validation of the surface diffusion model. (b) Vectorplot of the particle velocities for the Marangoni-force driven bubble.

After validating our model, we simulate the oscillating bubble experiment and study the effect of surfactant diffusion in the bulk phase. Fig. 2(a) shows the temporal evolution of the bulk surfactant concentration directly underlying an interface with and without considering the diffusion effect. In agreement with Morris et al. [6] we find that diffusion effects in the bulk phase can be dominant and strongly affect the surface tension loop, see Fig. 2(b). In these cases the bulk phase is assumed to be infinitely large. For the more realistic situation, where the liquid layer has only a certain width, diffusion effects are expected to be even more pronounced than seen in this example.

3 CONCLUSIONS

We implemented a new model based on a smoothed particle hydrodynamics formulation to simulate the dynamic behavior of surfactants on interfaces. So far, we have applied our model to simulate the adsorption to a constant-area bubble of air suspended to a liquid solution containing surfactant and the dynamic behavior of surface tension while oscillating the bubble size. In both cases we were able to predict the transient behavior of the transportation from the bulk solution to the interface with reasonable accuracy. Our simulations confirm the findings of Morris et al., who simulated as first the influence of the diffusion process in the bulk phase on the dynamic cycling based on a one-dimensional model.

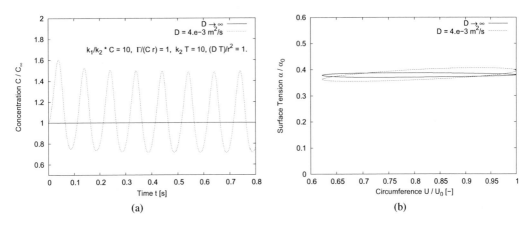

Figure 2: Comparison between the adsorption-limited ($D \to \infty$) and the diffusion-limited model ($D = 4 \cdot 10^{-3} m^2/s$). (a) Evolution of the surfactant concentration in the bulk phase directly underlying the interface. (b) Corresponding surface tension loops.

REFERENCES

References

[1] Hans Bachofen and Samuel Schurch. Alveolar surface forces and lung architecture. *Comparative Biochemistry and Physiology - Part A: Molecular & Integrative Physiology*, 129(1):183–193, May 2001.

[2] Ivan B. Bazhlekov, Patrick D. Anderson, and Han E.H. Meijer. Numerical investigation of the effect of insoluble surfactants on drop deformation and breakup in simple shear flow. *Journal of Colloid and Interface Science*, 298(1):369–394, June 2006.

[3] G. Enhorning. Pulsating bubble technique for evaluating pulmonary surfactant. *Journal of Applied Physiology*, 43(2):198–203, 1977.

[4] X. Y. Hu and N. A. Adams. A multi-phase SPH method for macroscopic and mesoscopic flows. *Journal of Computational Physics*, 213(2):844–861, April 2006.

[5] E. P. Ingenito, L. Mark, J. Morris, F. F. Espinosa, R. D. Kamm, and M. Johnson. Biophysical characterization and modeling of lung surfactant components. *Journal of Applied Physiology*, 86(5):1702–1714, May 1999.

[6] J. Morris, E.P. Ingenito, L. Mark, R.D. Kamm, and M. Johnson. Dynamic behavior of lung surfactant. *Journal of Biomechanical Engineering*, 123:106–113, 2001.

[7] D. R. Otis, E. P. Ingenito, R. D. Kamm, and M. Johnson. Dynamic surface tension of surfactant TA: experiments and theory. *Journal of Applied Physiology*, 77(6):2681–2688, December 1994.

[8] Samuel Schurch, Francis H. Y. Green, and Hans Bachofen. Formation and structure of surface films: captive bubble surfactometry. *Biochimica et Biophysica Acta (BBA) - Molecular Basis of Disease*, 1408(2-3):180–202, November 1998.

1st International Conference on Mathematical and Computational Biomedical Engineering – CMBE2009
June 29 – July 1, 2009, Swansea, UK
P. Nithiarasu and R. Löhner (eds)

A Time Varying Heterogeneous Lung Model for Airway Impedance

Del Leary
Dalhousie University, 5981 University Avenue
Halifax, Nova Scotia
CANADA B3H 1W2, dleary@dal.ca
Geoff N. Maksym
Dalhousie University, 5981 University Avenue
Halifax, Nova Scotia
CANADA B3H 1W2, geoff.maksym@dal.ca

ABSTRACT

Key Words: *airway impedance modeling, asthma, heterogeneity*

1. INTRODUCTION

Several lung models have been recently developed to explore variability and heterogeneity as mechanisms for changes in lung function in obstructive lung diseases such as asthma[1,2]. These models incorporate recent advances in understanding of airway function and provide mechanisms for the development of spatial heterogeneity and patchiness of airway ventilation observed using lung imaging techniques. Such spatial heterogeneity must evolve temporally, and may lead to changes in lung impedance that can be measured using the forced oscillation technique. However, the contribution of temporal variation to changes in airway impedance is not understood. Airway resistance (Rrs) recorded by the forced oscillation technique exhibits temporal variability, attributed to both tidal fluctuation in airway diameter and variations in airway smooth muscle activity. However, while variation of Rrs has been recently quantified, it is unknown how much of the variation of Rrs can be attributed to airway smooth muscle activity[4,5,and6]. Here we present a branching airway lung model to simulate airway diameter variation and compute variation in Rrs.

Using an anatomically correct 64895 airway tree provided by M. Tawhai (U. Aukland) that uses a Monte Carlo volume filling method[3], we have constructed a multi-branching model that allows for temporal variations. A graphic of the airway tree up to twelve generations is shown in Figure 1 where each colour indicates a different generation. The impedance was calculated at the mouth, thereby incorporating the entire airway tree, using a lumped element approach. This static model was altered so that it could be driven by input volumetric flow at the airways, breathe with fixed tidal volume, and airway diameters could be controlled to simulate airway narrowing. We simulated airway narrowing that would result from activation of airway smooth muscle ASM including randomized distributed airway calibre constriction for every airway throughout the tree. The resulting distribution of lung resistance from the multi-branching system was compared to a simplified single airway model. Both Gaussian distributed airway constriction and uniform distribution were used in both models. The effect of breathing was also simulated, via sinusoidal tidal volume changes and heterogeneous patchy ventilation, by selectively closing chosen regions of the lung.

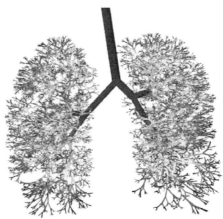

Figure 1. The airway tree displaying to twelve generations, of the 26 generation airway tree comprising 64895 airways, each modelled as a resistance with time varying diameter and terminated by an elastance element.

2. MAIN BODY

Methods: Similar to Tgavalekos et al[2], each airway was modelled as a tube with Newtonian resistance. The total airway resistance for the lung, Rrs, was computed during each time step, and each airway diameter was updated 200 times per breath. The airways were linked by boundary conditions at each airway having equal pressure at a junction and a pressure drop due to Poiseuille resistance across an airway. Flow was considered incompressible and was fractioned into downstream branching airways based on the impedance ratio of the higher generation (smaller diameter) airways found at the junction. Airway diameters were then varied by increasing amounts of airway constriction according to different distribution functions at each time step described below. For each parameter set, the model was simulated for 10 breaths, totalling 40 seconds, providing 2000 points of airway pressure and flow for the calculation of the distribution of Rrs.

Distribution functions: Two different distribution functions were used to vary the airway diameters, but the mean diameters were adjusted in separate simulations with narrowing by 2.5, 7.5, 12.5, 17.5, 22.5, and 27.5%. *Gaussian distributed* airway diameters was simulated with a standard deviation of 10% of the constricted airway diameter, thus keeping the coefficient of variation constant in each simulation. For comparison the resistance of the single airway model was assigned a baseline diameter as the average diameter of the multi-branch model up to the twelve generations that were studied then adjusting the length of the single airway to 57 cm to achieve an equal resistance to the multi-branch model. *Uniformly random distributed* airway diameters were also simulated, with the range of the diameter distribution equal to the constriction percentage given above. Constriction either occurred coherently with all airways varying together or incoherently with all airways free to vary differently but within the distributions. *Variation in airway constriction with breathing* was simulated by employing the uniformly random distributed constriction model with tidal variation in airway diameter. Finally, a model with *variation in airway constriction with breathing with enforced patchiness of ventilation* was simulated by narrowing a branch at either the 8th generation (Fig. 3c) or the 4th generation (Fig. 3d) to 10% of its initial diameter.

Results: When we varied airway constriction with fixed standard deviation Gaussian distributed airway diameters, we found that with a single airway (Fig. 2, left panel) Rrs was distributed approximately log-normally and that with increasing airway constriction the mean Rrs increased and the variation in Rrs increased. Indeed, the standard deviation increased proportionally to the mean Rrs yielding a coefficient of variability of ~0.46 for the single airway and coherent multi-branch model, and 0.05 for the incoherent multi-branch model. Comparing the results from the applied constriction in Figure 2 shows that the coherently varying multi-branch model (Fig 2c) had similar histograms of Rrs to the single airway model, as would be expected since each airway is behaving identically, while the multi-branch model with incoherent variation (Fig 2b) exhibits similar rightward shifts in mean Rrs but less variation. This smaller variation in Fig. 2b is emergent phenomena, since it cannot be predicted using a simplified single airway lumped element model and requires the multi-branch model before this behaviour is exhibited. This behaviour occurred because some airways narrowed while others compensated for this at the same point in time by dilating. This could mean that in the constricting lung in vivo variation should decrease relative to changes in mean airway resistance. However, it may be that in a diseased lung, some regions would exhibit some coherent changes in airway diameters, due to similarities in local airway remodelling and possibly to the serial structure of the airway, leading to cascading of airway narrowing[1]. Thus a more realistic scenario would be behaviour somewhere in between Figures 2b and 2c.

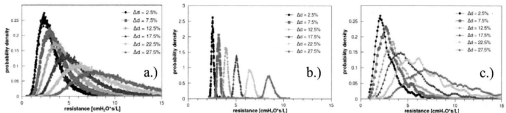

Figure 2. Histograms of lung Rrs resulting from diameter narrowing by 2.5, 7.5, 12.5, 17.5, 22.5, and 27.5% for a.) the single airway model, b.) the multi-branch model where all the airways have incoherent random Gaussian variation through the airway tree, and c.) all the airways in the airway tree and have coherent Gaussian variation .

When the airway diameters were permitted to vary within a uniform distribution incoherently (Figure 3a), results were similar to Gaussian distributed airway diameters (Figure 2b), but the variation of the effect of compensation was stronger, narrowing the distribution in Rrs relative to the Gaussian distributions, which may be due to small differences in standard deviations or the shape of the distributions. However, when breathing was then added to the model using a controlled tidal volume in Figure 3b, the distributions widened approaching behaviour in between Figure 2b and 2c.

When patchiness of ventilation was incorporated with dramatically narrowing an 8th generation airway to 10%, we found further increases in mean Rrs and further broadening of the distribution of airway resistance (Figure 3c). When patchiness was increased by constriction of a fourth generation airway, we found a further rightward shift of the airway resistance, as expected, coupled with greater increase in airway diameter variation (Figure 3d). It is important to note that the imposed large scale heterogeneity in a single airway constriction can significantly increase variation in Rrs. Interestingly, the distribution functions appear to develop two peaks or modes near their edges particularly at lower levels of airway constriction. This is likely due to the choice of sinusoidal variation in airway diameter for tidal ventilation, giving greater residence time for variation at the limits of inspiration and expiration.

Distribution functions of Rrs from healthy subjects and asthmatics have been previously reported and appear largely lognormal. Thus the above distributions are similar to those previously reported[5,4]. Diba et al. and Lall et al. reported that the standard deviation of airway resistance was correlated with mean or median airway resistance. We have shown that this occurs with both signal airway models and also with multi-branch models, but when airway diameter variation occurs incoherently this breaks down and resistance and variation in resistance become decoupled (Figure 2b). However, the behaviour is to reduce variation relative to the mean, but all reports indicate increased variation with airway narrowing.

Figure 3d shows that with imposed patchiness of ventilation, the standard deviation is increased greatly compared to homogenous (albeit random) constriction shown in Figure 3b. This is important, since we have previously reported that changes in variation more frequently exceed changes in airway resistance, either in substantial constriction in healthy adults[5] or in dilation in children with asthma[6]. This may have been due to heterogeneous airway constriction in the adults or relief from heterogeneous constriction in the children with asthma.

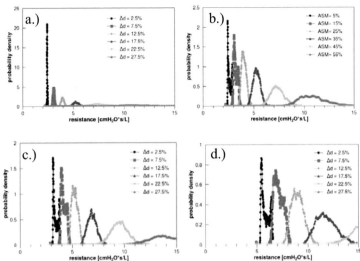

Figure 3. Comparing histograms using the same amount of ASM with combining of more physiological mechanisms. Starting a.) with random variability at various ASM, b.) adding breathing, c.) adding a small amount of heterogeneity, and d.) adding a large amount of heterogeneity.

3. CONCLUSIONS

These results indicate that variation in Rrs can be measured and can indicate effects of temporally and spatially heterogeneously varying airway calibre. Multi-branching models show more realistic trends when compared to FOT data by accounting for spatially incoherent variation and asymmetric distributions. Results predicted from single airway models can easily oversimplify the dynamics of a human lung. More importantly, with physiological realistic distributed constriction, variation appears to follow reported measured variation in airway resistance.

REFERENCES

[1]   T. Winkler and J G. Venegas, Complex Airway Behavior and Paradoxical responses to Bronchoprovication, *Journal of Applied Physiology*, 103, 655-663, 2007.

[2]   N. T. Tgvalekos, M. Tawhai, R. S. Harris, G. Mush, M. Vidal-Melo, J. G. Venegas, and K R. Lutchen, Identifying Airways Responsible for Hetergeneous Ventilation and Mechanical Dysfunction in Asthma: An Image Functional Modeling Approach, *Journal of Applied Physiology*, 99, 2388-2397, 2005.

[3]   M. H. Tawhai, A. J. Pullan, and P. J. Hunter, Generation of an anatomically based three-dimensional model of the conducting airways, *Annals of Biomedical Engineering*, 28, 793-802, 2000.

[4]   C. Diba, C. M. Salone, H. K. Reddel, C. W. Thorpe, B. Toelle, and G. G. King, Short Term Variability of Airway Calibre – A Marker of Asthma?, Journal of Applied Physiology, 103, 296-304, 2007.

[5]   C. Que, C. M. Kenyon, R. Olivenstein, P. T. Macklem, and G. N. Maksym, Homeokinesis and short-term variability of human airway caliber, *Journal of Applied Physiology*, 91 1131-1141, 2001.

[6]   C. A. Lall, N. Cheng, P. Hernandex, P. T. Pianosi, Z. Dali, A. Abouzied, and G. N. Maksym, Airway Resistance Variability and Response to Bronchodilator in Children with Asthma, *European Respiratory Journal*, 30, 260-268, 2007.

1st International Conference on Mathematical and Computational Biomedical Engineering – CMBE2009
June 29 – July 1, 2009, Swansea, UK
P. Nithiarasu and R. Löhner (eds)

Numerical Investigations of the Flow in Models of the Upper Central Airways

Lars Krenkel
Lars.Krenkel@dlr.de, Dept. Fluid Systems
Roland Kessler
Roland.Kessler@dlr.de, Dept. C²A²S²E
Claus Wagner
Claus.Wagner@dlr.de, Dept. Fluid Systems

German Aerospace Center (DLR), Bunsenstr.10, 37073 Göttingen, Germany

ABSTRACT

Key Words: *Artificial Ventilation, Endotracheal Tube, CFD, Modeling of the Pulmonary System, Gas Exchange.*

1. INTRODUCTION

Since a large number of patients admitted to the intensive care unit require artificial ventilation support, the development of lung protective ventilation strategies is an important subject in biomedical research. The central airways of the lung are a complex system of bifurcations and pipes with characteristic diameters ranging from approx. 15 mm to 20 mm at the trachea to approx. 50 μm to 250 μm at alveolar level. The primary objective of the lung to ensure the gas exchange is therefore intimately depending on the fluid mechanical transport mechanisms governing the complex branching system. For patients suffering from adult respiratory distress syndrome (ARDS), acute lung injury or at the worst from acute lung failure, mechanical ventilation is the fundamental life saving therapy but even after years of practical experience and research the mortality rate is still high. This is related to inspiratory lung epithelia overstretching and repeated collapse and re-expansion of alveoli which results in adverse shear forces which tend to aggravate the aetiopathology finally leading to ventilator associated lung injury (VALI).

In case of artificial ventilation support with the necessity of using airway management devices (i.e. endotracheal tubes) the complexity of the system even increases and a complete understanding of the ventilation and oxygenation mechanisms is of major interest in order to ensure protective oxygenation and ventilation of the patient.

In this particular study the effect of endotracheal tubes in combination with different gas mixtures on the resulting flow regime in models of the upper central airways is investigated. In a second step, special interest is laid on the distribution of gas in a 4th generation model of a lung and parametrically varied tube positions and orientations. Finally, first results of a newly implemented open boundary condition for oscillatory flow will be presented. The total pressure boundary condition allows for simulating the oscillatory flow in a model of the upper central airways during a complete ventilation cycle (inspiration and expiration) and should allow for in- and outflow at the same time depending on the local flow field in the vicinity of the boundary condition. In future, this boundary condition will be linked to a transfer function for taking into account the behavior of the numerically not resolved parts of the lung (e.g. compliance and resistance, shunt, pendeluft, and gas exchange).

2. Impact of Endotracheal Tubes and Gas Mixtures on the Flow Field

According to Haberthür et al.[1] and Guttmann et al.[2], in tracheally intubated and mechanically ventilated patients, expiratory resistance of an endotracheal tube or a tracheostomy can cause dynamic lung hyperinflation by impending lung emptying. Furthermore, analysing experimental data from animal HFO ventilation experiments and results from experiments in the magnetic resonance tomograph at the University of Mainz focusing on the governing flow field in a generic trachea with endotracheal tube as well as from other research groups (e.g. [3]) it became apparent that the flow in the endotracheal tube strongly affects the flow field in the lung. Another important fact is that due to different length scales in the airways including the airway management devices (tube, connector, etc.), the Reynolds number varies from below 1000 in the upper central airways to 4000 or even higher in the endotracheal tube. Even if the flow may be assumed to be laminar almost everywhere in the central airways, it is expected to be turbulent within and in the vicinity of the endotracheal tube.

To ensure optimum conditions for the numerical investigations, firstly, numerical investigations on the impact of the geometry's level of detail and of different numerical models as well as the impact of different volume mesh resolutions were carried out. The set-up consisted of a generic trachea with abstracted endotracheal tube. The level of detail was changed stepwise beginning with a very simple model of a straight tube's ending up to a highly resolved tube with bending, connector, and Murphy's eye. Figure 1 illustrates two typical geometries and the flow results obtained for a highly resolved tube in terms of turbulent kinetic energy distribution.

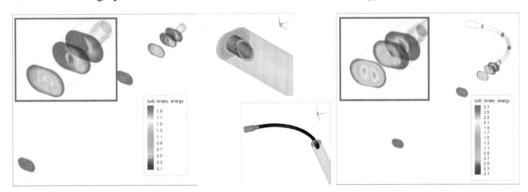

Figure 1   Distribution of turbulent kinetic energy for two geometrical set-ups

The bulk inlet velocity was adjusted for a mean tracheal Reynolds number based on the mean velocity of 1500 in the generic trachea, resulting in a maximal Reynolds number of 3330 in the endotracheal tube. The tracheal profile consists of two semi-circles (Ø20 mm) which are pulled apart 10 mm in one direction (characteristic lengths: height 20 mm, width 30 mm). For the more detailed model which includes the tube's bending together with the connector, secondary flow structures are obtained which are more pronounced than those obtained for the simplified set-up. The right side of Figure 1 illustrates the formation of two regions with high turbulent kinetic energy values for the complex geometric set-up, as a result of the secondary velocity rolls which are generated due to the tube's bending. In contrast and as expected, no secondary flow structures are generated for the simplified straight tube.

All numerical results were obtained with the unstructured DLR in-house Reynolds-averaged Navier-Stokes (RANS) code THETA. Analysis of experimental artificial ventilation data with respect to typical velocity fields and characteristic Reynolds numbers revealed that in most cases turbulent regions with Reynolds numbers exceeding 2300 are only expected in or in the vicinity of the endotracheal tube and the first few bifurcations at very high inspiratory or expiratory flow rates. For higher branch generations and at lower flow rates the flow regime is supposed to be laminar. From a theoretical point of view it seems to be straight forward that an accurate prediction of the turbulent flow is only possible with either Direct Numerical Simulations (DNS) or Large Eddy Simulations (LES) or suitable to the well known limited extend with RANS and a properly chosen turbulence model as well as an optimized mesh geometry. Thus, the question arises, whether the applied RANS solver also provides accurate predictions for the mostly laminar flow regime regions apart from the endotracheal tube and its vicinity.

Results based on preliminary numerical investigations indicate that it is appropriate to use the solver with turbulence model even if the turbulent flow regimes are limited to the tube and the vicinity of the outlet. The production rate of turbulent kinetic energy in regions with expected laminar character is negligible [4]. The parametric study included numerical simulations on differently resolved meshes and simulations with different turbulence models (k-ε and k-ω) as well as reference cases without turbulence model (laminar case).

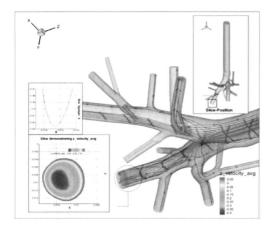 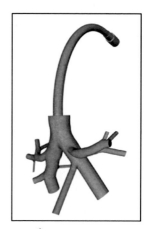

Figure 2   **Left**: numerical result of the steady flow through a 4th generation lung
Right: geometry for the investigation of endotracheal tube impact on the flow regime in a 4th generation lung model

Secondly, the influence of tube placing and orientation parameters as well as Reynolds number effects on gas distribution due to usage of gas mixtures (e.g. Heliox®, Solkane®) are studied numerically on a 4th generation model of a lung. Figure 2 shows on the left hand side a first example of the predicted flow in a 4th generation model of a lung for steady inflow conditions.

The picture illustrates the flow field in terms of stream traces and color coded velocity magnitudes in the outlet plane of a single branch. The laminar flow characteristic at the outlet of the chosen branch can be clearly identified with the 2D velocity profile, which tends to be slightly asymmetric. The observed asymmetric profile is supposed to be a result of the 3 dimensional bending and branching of the geometry which is also illustrated in Fig. 2. The picture on the right hand side depicts the geometrical set-up used to investigate the impact of an endotracheal tube and its orientation on the resulting flow regime in the model of the lung. The endotracheal tubes size, the placement, and the orientation have been found to affect the general flow regime and therefore the gas distribution. In further investigations, the influence of gas mixtures with different fluid properties (Reynolds number effects) on the gas distribution will be carried out.

Finally, first results of a newly implemented total pressure *"open boundary condition"* will be presented. The new boundary condition is essential for simulating oscillatory flows (e.g. full artificial ventilation cycle) by allowing in- and/or outflow at the same time depending on the flow field in the vicinity of the boundary condition governed by the properties of a closed system (i.e. elasticity, compliance, resistance of a lung). The newly implemented boundary condition will be tested stepwise, beginning with simple geometries (e.g. generic trachea and single bifurcation) and finally with a complex model of the lung. As a first step, simple pressure-volume relations will be used as governing properties of the open boundary condition. In a second step, a simplified transfer model in terms of a *forward process* in biomathematical modeling sense will be integrated for taking into account gas exchange and patho-physiological processes. Figure 3 illustrates the concept of a forward process model [5].

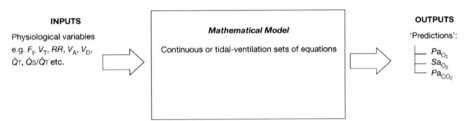

Figure 3   **Concept of the *forward process* in biomathematical modeling as it will be implemented as simplified transfer function [5]**

3. CONCLUSIONS

Numerical and experimental investigations of the impact of endotracheal tubes on the flow in a lung model revealed that endotracheal tubes strongly affect the flow in the trachea and accordingly in the central airways of the lung. A numerical parameter study of tubes with different levels of detail revealed that it is necessary to model not only the tube ending but also the bending and additional connectors since they are responsible for the development of secondary flow structures. Additional important parameters are the tube's size, the placement, and the orientation of the endotracheal tube. First results of ongoing investigations on the Reynolds number effect on the gas distribution using different gas mixtures also indicate a strong effect on the gas distribution in a 4th generation model of the lung with endotracheal tube. Finally, a concept for numerical simulations of a full artificial ventilation cycle with newly implemented total pressure open boundary conditions has been described.

REFERENCES

[1]   C.Haberthür, A.Mehlig, J.F.Stover et al., Expiratory automatic endotracheal tube compensation reduces dynamic hyperinflation in a physical lung model, *Critical Care*, Vol.13, No.1, 2009.

[2]   J.Guttmann, L.Eberhard, L.Fabry et al., Time constant/volume relationship of passive expiration in mechanically ventilated ARDS patients, *Eur Respir J*, Vol.8, 114-120, 1995.

[3]   P.R.M.Rocco, W.A.Zin., Modelling the mechanical effects of tracheal tubes in normal subjects, *Eur Respir J*, Vol.8, 121-126, 1995.

[4]   L.Krenkel, C.Wagner et al., Protective artificial lung ventilation: investigation of the air flow in a generic model of the lung, accepted for *Notes on Numerical Fluid Mechanics and Multidisciplinary Design, Springer Verlag.*

[5]   C.E.Hahn and A.D.Farmery, Gas exchange modelling: no more gills, please, *British Journal of Anaesthesia*, Vol.91, No.1, 2-15, 2003.

Numerical Modelling of the Air Flow in the Respiratory Tract

A. Devys

INRIA Lille Nord Europe, SIMPAF Project team, B.P. 70478, F-59658 Villeneuve d'Ascq Cedex, France.   anne.devys@math.univ-lille1.fr

C. Grandmont

INRIA Paris-Rocquencourt, REO Project team, BP 105, F-78153 Le Chesnay Cedex, France. celine.grandmont@inria.fr

B. Grec

Université Claude Bernard Lyon 1, Institut C. Jordan, F-69622 Villeurbanne Cedex, France. grec@math.univ-lyon1.fr

B. Maury

Université Paris-Sud, Laboratoire de mathématiques, Bâtiment 425, bureau 130, F-91405 Orsay Cedex, France. Bertrand.Maury@math.u-psud.fr

D. Yakoubi

INRIA Paris-Rocquencourt, REO Project team, BP 105, F-78153 Le Chesnay Cedex, France. driss.yakoubi@inria.fr

ABSTRACT

This work was partially funded by the ANR-08-JCJC-013-01 project headed by C. Grandmont.

Key Words: *air flow in the lung, Navier–Stokes equation, numerical simulation.*

In this contribution we focus our attention on the modelling of the air flow in the proximal part of bronchial tree. The model of the respiratory tract we consider has already been described by C. Grandmont, Y. Maday and B. Maury in [2]. The idea is to decompose the respiratory tract in three parts:

- **the upper part** (up to the 7th–9th generation), where the incompressible Navier–Stokes equations hold to describe the fluid;

- **the distal part** (from the 8th–10th to the 17th generation), where one can assume that the Poiseuille law is satisfied in each bronchiole;

- **the acini**, where the oxygen diffusion takes place and which are embedded in an elastic medium, the parenchyma. We will suppose that the parenchyma is modeled by a simple box that have one part (representing the diaphragm muscl) that moves in one direction. The motion of diaphragm is thus described by a simple spring model.

We obtain a coupled problem corresponding to the Navier-Stokes equations with nonstandard boundary conditions at the outlets Γ_i and at the inlet Γ_0. After time discretization it reduce to resistive boundary conditions where the flux of the fluid velocity u appear

$$\sigma_f(u,p) \cdot n + R\left(\int_\Gamma u \cdot n\right) n = g, \text{ on } \Gamma$$

where σ_f is the fluid stress tensor. Thus, if we consider a finite element discretization and an implicit scheme to treat the boundary flux (to avoid numerical instabilities), then all the degree of freedom at each outlet would be coupled and the underlying finite element matrix would have a non standart pattern. Consequently, these boundary conditions cannot be easily and directly implemented in a any FEM solver, for instance in `FreeFEM++` [3], without going deeply into the code. To get rid of this difficulty, the idea is to pre–compute a set of solutions with Neumann boundary conditions on each Γ_i, and then to define the solution as a linear combination of these solutions and of a correction term. This correction term solves also a Navier–Stokes problem with standard boundary conditions, the coefficients of the linear combination being calculated so that the solution satisfies the dissipative boundary conditions, see [1]. Note here that the convection part of the Navier-Stokes system is treated either explicilty or using the characteristic method.

After the description of the method, we shall present bi–dimensional and three–dimensional simulations based on different time discretizations (mixed method, Chorin–Temam projection scheme). We will also present a sensibilty study with respect to the parameters of the coupled model in order to illustrate its capacity to reproduce normal or pathological behavior of the respiration.

REFERENCES

[1] A. Devys, C. Grandmont, B. Grec, B. Maury and D. Yakoubi, Numerical method for the 2D simulation of the respiration *submitted*

[2] C. Grandmont , Y. Maday and B. Maury, A multiscale / multimodel approach of the respiration tree, *Proceedings of the International Conference, New Trends in Continuum Mechanics, 8-12 September 2003, Constantza, Romania Theta Foundation Publications, Bucharest,* 2003.

[3] F. Hecht, A. Le Hyaric, K. Ohtsuka and O. Pironneau, *Freefem++, Finite Elements Software* `http://www.freefem.org/ff++`.

HIGH-PERFORMANCE COMPUTATIONAL MODELLING OF NASAL AIRFLOW

Donal J. Taylor[1,2], Denis J. Doorly[1], Robert C. Schroter[2], Joaquim Peiró[1],
Esther Blenke[3], Robert Almeyda[3], Neil Tolley[3]
[1]Aeronautics, [2]Bioengineering, [3]ENT Surgery at Saint Mary's Hospital,
Imperial College London, South Kensington Campus, London SW7 2AZ - UK,
d.doorly@imperial.ac.uk

Guillaume Houzeaux, Mariano Vázquez
Barcelona Supercomputing Center, Dep. of Computer Applications in Science and Engineering CASE
Nexus II - Campus Nord UPC, C. Jordi Girona 29, 08034 Barcelona - Spain,
mariano.vazquez@bsc.es

ABSTRACT

The complexity and inaccessibility of the nasal passageways precludes detailed measurements in vivo, but Computational Fluid Dynamics can generate patient-specific high resolution flow simulations in such complicated geometries.

Computed tomography images (CT scans) of a healthy nasal anatomy were segmented to yield a surface representation of the walls of the nasal air space. This surface was then used to generate the volume mesh and computational simulations were conducted using two numerical codes: the commercial finite-volume flow solver Fluent and the research finite-element parallel flow solver Alya, developed at BSC-CNS. The results of computational simulations performed under conditions of quiet restful breathing show how the complex internal anatomy of the nasal airways directs and controls the airflow, identify the regions of high shear stress (and thus the high heat and mass transfer zones) on the turbinates and reveal complex recirculation regions in the flow.

Key Words: *nasal flow simulations, high-performance computing.*

1 INTRODUCTION

The nose performs many functions, including: heating, humidifying and filtering inspired air as well as providing one's sense of smell. The healthy function of the nose is highly dependent on the fluid dynamic characteristics of airflow in the nasal cavities. The interest in studying the nasal cavity is not only to increase the understanding in respiratory physiology, but also in the significant advances that this might bring to areas of application such as surgery, drug delivery and toxicology.

The morphology of the nasal airway is shown in Figure 1. It is complex and furthermore it has been seen to vary greatly between patients [1]. The complexity and inaccessibility of the nasal passageways precludes detailed measurements *in vivo*. While relatively few studies have been concerned with morphological variation (e.g. [1]), no means to quantitatively describe and represent the 3D geometry of the whole nasal cavity geometry have been developed. However, Computational Fluid Dynamics can generate high resolution results in such complicated geometries.

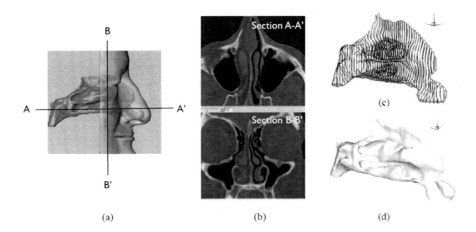

Figure 1: Anatomy of the nasal cavity showing its geometrical complexity: (a) general view; (b) CT images of axial (top) and sagittal (bottom) sections; (c) view of a set of axial sections; and (d) reconstructed surface.

2 MODELLING OF NASAL FLOW

The proposed approach to study the nasal cavity requires first an anatomically realistic 3D virtual model. The nasal airway geometry data is given in the form of a stack of medical images in grey scale obtained from *in vivo* Computed Tomography (CT) and comprising of the order of 80 axially acquired images of: 512×512 pixels, 1.3 mm slice thickness, 0.7 mm slice spacing, 0.39×0.39 mm pixel size. Two views of sections in the axial and sagittal planes are shown in Figure 1b. The airway anatomy was determined to be normal by a consultant radiologist.

The procedure to obtain a surface from each medical image stack involves firstly the delineation of the airway boundary using Amira [2]. Medical image segmentation to identify the boundary of the airway and the surrounding tissue is based on an initial constant value of grey-scale. A refinement to the segmentation is required to exclude secondary conduits such as sinuses as well as to identify image noise and interpreting the data accordingly. The reconstructed surface definition is smoothed to remove the stair-stepping artefacts of the imaging process, thus yielding the anatomically realistic surface definition depicted as a set of sections and a shaded triangulation in Figures 1c and 1d, respectively.

This surface was then used to generate the volume mesh using TGrid [3]. This mesh is hybrid and composed of 6 352 819 elements with three layers of prisms within a boundary layer adjacent to the wall (1 183 488 prisms) and a tetrahedron core (5 169 331 tetrahedra). The height of the prismatic elements nearest to the wall is 3.5×10^{-5} m corresponding to corresponding to 1% of the local channel width. The simulations can be considered nominally mesh independent as the pressure drop and average wall shear stress magnitude across the nasal boundary were found to be within 2.9% and 3.2%, respectively, of those computed using a mesh of 29 million hybrid elements in [4].

The inflow boundary condition is taken to be a blunt velocity profile with a volume flux of 100 ml/s (1.01 m/s inflow velocity at the naris); $Re \approx 900$ based on the hydraulic diameter of the nasal valve and is low enough for the flow to be laminar. This volume flux is equivalent to quiet restful breathing and thus the flow is assumed to be incompressible, laminar, Newtonian and steady.

The first computational simulation is performed using Fluent 6.2.16 [3]. This is a finite volume approach where the pressure is solved using a second-order accurate scheme, it is coupled to the velocity using the SIMPLE method and the momentum is approximated using a third-order upwind scheme. The segregated approach to solving the algebraic equations of continuity and momentum is used because it is less demanding on the memory despite taking additional iterations to converge.

The second simulation was performed using the research flow solver Alya [5], developed at BSC-CNS. It is a fractional-step finite element method based on a predictor-corrector scheme that solves the momentum and a modified continuity equations consecutively in order to converge to the monolithic solution avoiding fractional errors. One of the advantages of this approach is that simpler preconditioners can be used to solve the non-symmetric momentum equations (GMRES) and the symmetric continuity equation (CG). The parallelization strategy is based on a mesh partitioning technique using a master-slave MPI-based strategy. A further degree of parallelization is achieved by opening threads in internal loops using OpenMP directives, resulting in a hybrid-parallelization strategy. Figure 2 shows the partition of the mesh in 500 subdomains and a detail of the surface mesh.

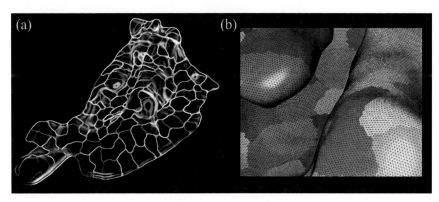

Figure 2: Domain decomposition: (a) partition of the domain into 500 sub-domains, and (b) enlargement showing the partition and mesh resolution.

Two tests are carried out in order to see the impact of the CG solver on the speedup. In the first one, labeled CG(Free), we let both the CG and the GMRES solvers converge to a tolerance of 10^{-5}. In the second test, referred to as CG(200), we perform a fixed number of CG iterations (200). The convergence the CG(Free) solver is very slow (2572 iterations in average) which represents 75% of the total CPU time for the sequential run as shown in Figure 3a. The speed-up for this problem is illustrated in Figure 3b, which shows an increased efficiency by reducing the number of CG iterations.

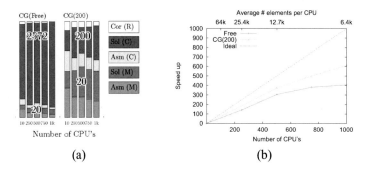

Figure 3: Performance assessment of the parallel implementation: (a) percentage CPU time; and (b) speed-up.

Figure 4 shows the comparisons of the distribution of wall shear stress obtained with Alya and Fluent: a very similar distribution of wall shear stresses was obtained. These results reveal how the complex internal anatomy of the nasal airways directs and controls the airflow to achieve the physiological functions of the nose. Visualisation of the results allows the high shear stress (and thus the high heat and mass transfer zones) on the turbinates to be identified, and reveals complex recirculation regions in the flow.

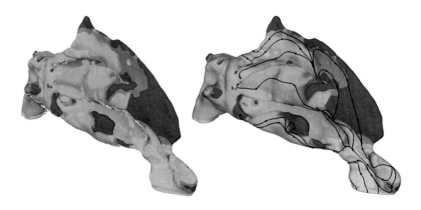

Figure 4: Surface distribution of wall shear stress calculated using the codes: Alya (left) and Fluent (right).

3   CONCLUSIONS

We have presented patient-specific simulations of the flow in the nasal cavity, under restful breathing conditions, obtained using the commercial code Fluent and the research parallel code Alya. The distribution of wall shear stresses calculated by both codes is very similar, but the significant performance gain of the parallel implementation is of interest here. This indicates that the use of high-performance computing will enable the high-scale simulations required to undertake the scientific challenges that improved resolution and speed of MR and CT scans will bring about. Amongst others, we could mention post-surgical follow up and the possibility of non-invasive determination of physiological responses, the assessment of modes of flow control accounting for variations in regional airflow and deposition, the incorporation of deposition and tissue uptake in the simulations, the analysis of inter-species variation in morphology and flow, and the engineering of delivery devices.

REFERENCES

[1]   S.E. Churchill, L.L. Shacklford, J.N. Georgi and M.T. Black, Morphological variation and airflow dynamics in the human nose. *American Journal of Human Biology* 2004; **16**:625-638.

[2]   Amira. *www.amiravis.com*

[3]   Fluent (Flow modeling software) and TGrid (Unstructured volume meshing). Fluent Inc. (Lebanon, USA), *www.fluent.com*.

[4]   D.J. Taylor. Experimental and computational analysis of human nasal inspiration. PhD Thesis, Department of Aeronautics, Imperial College London, 2009.

[5]   G. Houzeaux, M. Vázquez and R. Aubry. A parallel fractional incompressible Navier-Stokes solver for large scale supercomputers. Accepted for publication in *Journal of Computational Physics* 2009.

UNSTEADY FLOW THROUGH A REALISTIC HUMAN AIRWAY GEOMETRY

Prihambodo H. Saksono
Civil and Computational Engineering Center
School of Engineering, Swansea University Singleton Park, Swansea SA2 8PP, U.K.
p.h.saksono@swansea.ac.uk

Igor Sazonov
Civil and Computational Engineering Center
School of Engineering, Swansea University Singleton Park, Swansea SA2 8PP, U.K.
i.sazonov@swansea.ac.uk

Perumal Nithiarasu
Civil and Computational Engineering Center
School of Engineering, Swansea University Singleton Park, Swansea SA2 8PP, U.K.
p.nithiarasu@swansea.ac.uk

ABSTRACT

A three-dimensional unsteady flow in a human airway has been studied numerically. The geometry was derived from a 3D reconstructed geometry of a series of 2D CT-scan images. The flow was considered to be a turbulent one and governed by Reynolds averaged Navier-Stokes equations along with one-equation Spalart-Allmaras (SA) to model the evolution of eddy viscosity. These equations was solved numerically using fully explicit characteristic-based split (CBS) scheme on an unstructured mesh.

Key Words: *airway, respiration, turbulent flow, CBS-scheme, finite element.*

1 INTRODUCTION

The function of airway down to the terminal bronchioles are primarily air conduction, humidification and warming. Many pathophysiological condition affecting any part of human airway or any interventional treatments of human airway disorder are, either directly or indirectly, associated with the changes in the airway geometry. These changes in turn affecting the flow characteristics [1]. Therefore, the ability to predict air flow in a patient-specific airway geometry as the diseases progress will help medical professionals to decide the right treatment or predict the outcome of a chosen treatment. The majority of study on flow in the human airway are related to particle transport especially particles deposition for drug delivery system [2]. In recent years there has been a growing interest in obstructive sleep apnoea and the understanding of upper airway closure [3]. However, most of previous works, if not all, focus on either upper part or central part of the airway. In this study, the flow simulation is carried out starting from the nasal cavities down to the second generation of the tracheobronchial tree.

This study is intended to provide a framework for computational fluid dynamics to be used as one of the pre-operative assessment tools in interventional treatments of human airway disorder.

2 GEOMETRY RECONSTRUCTION AND MESH GENERATION

The geometry of human airway employed in this study is reconstructed from a standard CT scan of a healthy person. The resolution of the scan is 0.625×0.625 mm in the slice plane and 1 mm between slices. It covers the upper and the middle part of the human airway up to the second generation of the tracheobronchial tree.

To extract the geometry, we used the commercial software AMIRA for region segmentation and generating the initial surface geometry in STL format. Although the initial surface generated by AMIRA is already in unstructured triangulated form, it cannot be used directly to generate a volume mesh due to a significant amount of very short edges and CFD analysis requires a smoother surface to increase accuracy. To make the mesh coarser and smoother, the mesh contraction method described in [4] is applied. In addition, an extra operation needs to be carried out to create inlet and outlet boundary surfaces that are perpendicular tor the centerline of the airway. The volume tetrahedron mesh is then generated using Delaunay triangulation method described in [5]. Details of geometry reconstruction and mesh generation process employed in this work can be found in [6].

3 FLUID DYNAMICS

The Reynolds averaged Navier-Stokes equations, in conservation form, are written as

Mean continuity

$$\frac{1}{\beta^2}\frac{\partial p}{\partial t} + \frac{\partial}{\partial x_i}\,\rho\bar{u}_i = 0 \tag{1}$$

Mean momentum

$$\frac{\partial \bar{u}_i}{\partial t} + \frac{\partial}{\partial x_j}\,\bar{u}_i\bar{u}_j = -\frac{1}{\rho}\frac{\partial p}{\partial x_i} + \frac{\partial \tau_{ij}}{\partial x_j} + \frac{\partial \tau_{ij}^R}{\partial x_j} \tag{2}$$

where β is an artificial compressibility parameter, $\bar{u}_i$ are the mean velocity components, p is the mean pressure and ρ is the density. The mean laminar shear stress tensor is given as

$$\tau_{ij} = \nu\left(\frac{\partial \bar{u}_i}{\partial x_j} + \frac{\partial \bar{u}_j}{\partial x_i} - \frac{2}{3}\frac{\partial \bar{u}_k}{\partial x_k}\delta_{ij}\right)$$

and the Reynold's stress tensor τ_{ij}^R, introduced by Boussinesq's assumption, has the expression

$$\tau_{ij}^R = -\overline{u_i'u_j'} = \nu\ \left(\frac{\partial \bar{u}_i}{\partial x_j} + \frac{\partial \bar{u}_j}{\partial x_i} - \frac{2}{3}\frac{\partial \bar{u}_k}{\partial x_k}\delta_{ij}\right)$$

where ν is the kinematic viscosity of the fluid, ν is the turbulent eddy viscosity and δ_{ij} is the Kronecker delta.

The transport of turbulent viscosity $\hat{\nu}$ is govern by

$$\frac{\partial \hat{\nu}}{\partial t} + \frac{\partial}{\partial x_j}\hat{u}_j\hat{\nu} = c_1\hat{\nu} + \frac{1}{\sigma}\left[\frac{\partial}{\partial x_i}\hat{\nu} + \hat{\nu}\frac{\partial \hat{\nu}}{\partial x_i} + c_2\left(\frac{\partial \hat{\nu}}{\partial x_i}\right)^2\right] - c_{w1}f_{w1}\left(\frac{\hat{\nu}}{y}\right)^2 \tag{3}$$

Here, $\hat{}$ and f_2 is defined, respectively, as

$$\hat{} = + \left(\frac{\hat{\nu}}{2y^2}\right) f_2 \quad \text{and} \quad f_2 = 1 - \frac{X}{1 + Xf_1}$$

where $\quad$ is the magnitude of vorticity. The eddy viscosity is given by $\nu = \hat{\nu} f_1$ in which

$$f_1 = \frac{X^3}{X^3 + c_1^3} \quad \text{and} \quad X = \frac{\hat{\nu}}{\nu}.$$

The parameter f_w and the constant c_{w1} are, respectively, given by

$$f_w = g \left[\frac{1 + c_{w3}^6}{g^6 + c_{w3}^3}\right]^{\frac{1}{6}} \quad \text{and} \quad c_{w1} = \frac{c_1}{2} + \frac{\hat{}1 + c_2\hat{}}{\sigma},$$

where $g = + c_{w2}\hat{}^6 - \hat{}$ and

$$= \frac{\hat{\nu}}{\hat{} \, 2y^2}.$$

The constants are $c_1 = 0.1355$, $\sigma = 2/3$, $c_2 = 0.\hat{}22$, $= 0.41$, $c_{w1} =$, $c_{w2} = 0.3$, $c_{w3} = 2$ and $c_1 = 7.1$.

The CFD algorithm used to solve equations 1–3 is based on CBS algorithm [1,7]. The algorithm solves the incompressible Navier-Stokes equations in three steps. In the first step, an intermediate velocity field is obtained, followed by the second step where pressure field is computed and, finally, the velocity field is corrected and true transient term is added in the third step. The one equation SA turbulence model is added as a fourth step. The steps of the AC-CBS scheme in its semi-discrete form can be summarised as

Step 1: intermediate momentum

$$\Delta \tilde{U}_i = \tilde{U}_i - U_i^n = \Delta t \left[-\frac{\partial}{\partial x_j}\hat{}u_j U_i\hat{} + \frac{\partial \tau_{ij}}{\partial x_j} + \frac{\partial \tau_{ij}^R}{\partial x_j} + \frac{\Delta t}{2} u_k \frac{\partial}{\partial x_k}\left(\frac{\partial}{\partial x_j}\hat{}u_j U_i\hat{} +\right)\right]^n \quad (4)$$

Step 2: pressure

$$\left(\frac{1}{\beta^2}\right)^n p^{n+1} = \left(\frac{1}{\beta^2}\right)^n p^n - \Delta t \left[\frac{\partial U_i^n}{\partial x_i} + \theta_1 \frac{\Delta \tilde{U}_i}{\partial x_i} - \Delta t \theta_1 \frac{\partial}{\partial x_i}\frac{\partial p^n}{\partial x_i}\right] \quad (5)$$

Step 3: momentum correction

$$\Delta U_i = U_i^{n+1} - U_i^n = \Delta \tilde{U}_i - \Delta t \frac{\partial p^n}{\partial x_i} + \Delta t \frac{\Delta U_i^\tau}{\partial \tau} \quad (6)$$

where $\Delta \tau$ is the real time step and the true transient term ΔU_i^τ is approximated as

$$\Delta U_i^\tau = \frac{3U_i^{n+1} - 4U_i^n + U_i^{n-1}}{2}$$

Step 4: transport of turbulence variable

$$\hat{\nu}^{n+1} = \hat{\nu}^n + \Delta t \left[-\frac{\partial}{\partial x_i}\hat{}\hat{\nu}\bar{u}_i\hat{} + c_1 \hat{} \hat{\nu} + \frac{1}{\sigma}\left(\frac{\partial}{\partial x_i}\hat{}\nu + \hat{\nu}\hat{}\frac{\partial \hat{\nu}}{\partial x_i} + c_2 \frac{\partial \hat{\nu}}{\partial x_i}\frac{\partial \hat{\nu}}{\partial x_i}\right) - c_{w1}f_{w1}\left(\frac{\hat{\nu}}{y}\right)^2\right] +$$

$$\frac{\Delta t^2}{2}\bar{u}_j \frac{\partial}{\partial x_j}\frac{\partial}{\partial x_i}\hat{}\bar{u}_i\hat{\nu}\hat{} \quad (7)$$

4 NUMERICAL SIMULATIONS

The transient fluid dynamic analysis was carried out on a mesh of more than 2.4 million tetrahedral elements. The boundary conditions used are no-slip condition on the wall, parabolic velocity profiles at the inlets and constant pressure conditions at all outflow boundaries. For normal quiet breathing, tidal volume of $0.5\,l$ is assumed and the simulation is carried out for one breathing cycle. The properties of air are assumed to be constant. A kinematic viscosity of $1.\hat{}9 \times 10^{-5}\,m^2/s$ and density of $1.2\,kg/m^3$ were used in the calculation.

5 CONCLUSIONS

A three dimensional unsteady flow simulation through a realistic human airway has been carried out. The geometry is derived from a three dimensional reconstruction of a series of two dimensional images obtained *in vivo* using CT-scan imaging. An unstructured mesh is generated from the upper airway, including nasal cavity, down to the second generation of the tracheobronchial tree. The simulation clearly shows that the flow acquires complex velocity profile once it passes the nasal cavity. Therefore, the inclusion of the nasal cavity is necessary to precisely model the flow in human airway. In addition to the mesh generation inside the nasal cavity, imposing realistic boundary conditions still poses a serious challenge for the flow simulation in a complete airway. Currently, work on the interaction between the flow and the airway wall is in progress for us to be able to include wall compliance in the simulation.

REFERENCES

[1] P. Nithiarasu, O. Hassan, K. Morgan N.P. Weatherill, C. Fielder, H. Whittet, P. Ebden and K.R. Lewis, Steady flow through a realistic human upper airway geometry, *International Journal for Numerical Methods in Fluids*, 57, 631-651, 2008.

[2] T.B. Martonen, Z. Zhang, G. Yue and C.J. Musante, 3-D particle transport within the human upper respiratory tract, *Journal of Aerosol Science*, 33, 1095-1110, 2002.

[3] S.J. Jeong, W.S. Kim and S.J. Sung, Numerical investigation on the flow characteristics and aerodynamic force of the upper airway of patient with sleep apnea using computational fluid dynamics, *Medical Engineering and Physics*, 29, 637-651, 2007.

[4] D. Wang, O. Hassan, K. Morgan and N. Weatherill. EQSM: an effective high quality surface grid generation method based on remeshing. *Computer Methods in Applied Mechanics and Engineering*, 195, 5621-5633, 2006.

[5] N.P. Weatherill and O. Hassan. Efficient three-dimensional Delaunay triangulation with automatic point creation and imposed boundary constraints. *International Journal for Numerical Methods in Engineering*, 37, 2005-2040, 1994.

[6] I. Sazonov, P.H. Saksono, P. Nithiarasu, R. van Loon, H. Luckraz and S. Ashraf, Patient-specific blood flow simulation through an aneurysimal thoracic aorta with a folded neck. *Communications in Numerical Methods in Engineering*, submitted for publication.

[7] P. Nithiarasu, C.B. Liu and N. Massarotti, Laminar and turbulent flow calculation through a model human upper airway using unstructured meshes, *Communications in Numerical Methods in Engineering*, 23, 1057-1069, 2007.

1st International Conference on Mathematical and Computational Biomedical Engineering – CMBE2009
June 29 – July 1, 2009, Swansea, UK
P. Nithiarasu and R. Löhner (eds)

Investigation of the effects of tensile and compressive loading on the fracture of trabecular bone at the microscale

V.L. Kidgell, Y. Feng, O. Hassan
Civil and Computational Engineering Centre, School of Engineering
Swansea University, Swansea, SA2 8PP, UK
*Corresponding author. Email: y.feng@swansea.ac.uk

ABSTRACT

The failure of trabecular bone is a complex process dependent on many factors. In order to more accurately assess fracture risk for patients with diseases such as osteoporosis, it is necessary to develop an accurate macroscopic model of bone structure. This can be achieved through the use of material properties acquired from microscale models. This study investigates the behaviour of ten trabecular bone models with nonlinear anisotropic material properties subjected to tensile and compressive loading. Trabecular bone is found to be optimally designed to resist compressive loading. The results also indicate that microstructural configuration also plays an important part in the fracture resistance properties, since those models with thinner trabeculae offer lower fracture resistance than those with thicker trabeculae, despite having the same overall volume fraction.

Key Words: *Bone, femur, trabecular bone, osteoporosis, microscale, fracture.*

1. INTRODUCTION

Diseases of the bone, including osteoporosis, affect the architecture and bone density "such that the load bearing capacity of the hip is reduced and the risk for pathologic fracture is increased."[1] It is necessary to create an accurate macroscopic model of bone structure in order to assess this risk. It is often not possible to generate an explicit macroscale model which is valid everywhere, but instead have a microscopic model which describes the microscale variables. In order to accurately numerically approximate the macroscopic state of the system, it is possible to relate the two models using a homogenization procedure, often referred to as multi-scale modelling. Katz et al. (1984) [2] distinguished five levels of hierarchical organization to bone which include the macrostructure, the microstructure, and the nanoscale, This work investigates the behaviour of bone at the microscale.

Although the microstructure of trabecular bone appears to be random, it is an anisotropic material with the plates and struts of its architecture generally assumed to be aligned according the stresses it is subjected to [3]. Many of the microscale finite element models that have been used in the past to investigate the yield behaviour of trabecular bone do not include fracture of the material. It is important to include micro-crack based failure mechanisms in order to investigate the response of trabecular bone to loading before failure due to fracture.

2. ANISOTROPIC FRACTURE MODELS

The present work uses 2D non-linear finite element (FE) models to evaluate the mechanical properties of bone at the microscale when subjected to both compressive and tensile loading. Ten different microstructural configurations were used, all with a bone tissue volume fraction of approximately 43.5%, with varying thickness of trabecular struts.

2.1 Explicit Dynamic Analysis

Explicit dynamic analysis is used to model the fracture failure mechanism in the bone model. The analysis in the present work is run using the finite element software Elfen. The time integration approach used by Elfen is the central difference scheme, since it is ideal for modelling problems with small time scales. The Mohr-Coulomb yield criterion is used in this work, with the rotating crack strain plasticity model used to model the post yield behaviour of the bone tissue material. It was suggested in previous work [4, 5, 6, 7] that this model is appropriate to bone.

2.2 Material Properties

Brozovsky and Pankaj (2007) [8] created anisotropic 3D FE models of the microstructure of bone. This study was used as a basis for this investigation, using the material properties in the models created in this analysis, shown in figure 1. The bone tissue was assigned a yield stress of $\sigma_Y = 1 \times 10^8$ Pa.

Property	Bone Tissue	Holes (Soft Tissue)
Young's modulus (GPa)	6	0.006
Poisson's ratio	0.3	0.3

Figure 1: Material properties of tissue materials

Figure 2 shows the various microstructural configurations used in the analysis. In all cases, the blue colour indicates bone tissue material and the red colour indicates soft tissue material.

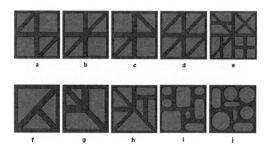

Figure 2: Nonlinear isotropic microstructural configurations

3. RESULTS AND CONCLUSIONS

Figure 3 shows the stress-strain curves produced for all models when loaded in tension. All microstructures behave elastically until they reach a peak stress, which is followed by fracture of the specimen. Following initial failure of one trabecula, the models continue to undergo further fracture.

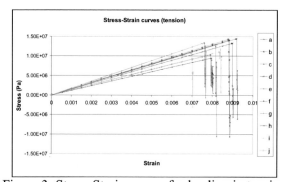

Figure 3: Stress-Strain curves for loading in tension

Figure 4 shows the stress-strain curves produced for all models when loaded in compression. It can be seen that again, the models show different responses for different microstructural configurations. All models show an elastic region followed by an elasto-plastic region and then plastic deformation.

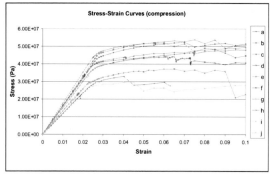

Figure 4: Stress-Strain curves for loading in compression

The results indicate that trabecular architecture is optimally designed to resist compressive loading. Under tensile loading, initial failure of a single trabecular leads to sudden failure of the microstructure immediately after. However, under compressive loading, the initial fracture of one trabecula does not lead to the immediate failure of the entire microstructure. The results also indicate that microstructural configuration also plays an important part in the fracture resistance properties, since those models with thinner trabeculae offer lower fracture resistance than those with thicker trabeculae, despite having the same overall volume fraction.

4. CONCLUSIONS AND FURTHER WORK

The failure of trabecular bone has been the subject of many studies in recent years. It is important to analyse this failure in order to more accurately assess fracture risk in elderly patients with diseases such as osteoporosis. The presented work uses 2D finite element models to investigate the links between volume fraction and trabecular configuration on the strength of bone and its ability to withstand loading. Direct experimental validation has not been possible owing to the non-availability of the corresponding experiments.

Further work includes the development of three dimensional finite element models to analyse the material properties of bone at the microscale when subjected to various loading conditions. This data will then be used in the full 3D model of [7] to more accurately simulate a fractured osteoporotic femur subjected to a fall to the side. Further developments also include the use of CT scan data of osteoporotic bone at the microscale to create a more accurate and realistic bone model.

REFERENCES

[1]   Nazarian, A., et al. Densiometric, morphometric and mechanical distributions in the human proximal femur. *Journal of Biomechanics*, 40, 2573-2579, 2007.

[2]   Katz, J., et al. The effects of remodelling on the elastic properties of bone. *Calcified Tissue Int.*, 36, S31-S36, 1984.

[3]   J. Wolff. *Das Gesetz der Transformation der Knochen (The Law of the Transformation of the Bones)*. 1892, Berlin: Hirschwald.

[4]   C.A. Pridham. Tetrahedral finite element (FE) meshes to model femoral fractures generated from CT scans from the Visible Human Project. MRes Thesis, University of Wales, Swansea, 2004.

[5]   T.D. Fawcett. Creating and validating heterogeneous tetrahedral finite element models of the femur from Computed Tomography (CT) images. MRes Thesis, University of Wales, Swansea, 2004.

[6]   M. Barclay. Bone fracture in the femur: Numerical model with the inclusion of a gamma nail implant. MRes Thesis, University of Wales, Swansea, 2006.

[7]   V.L. Kidgell. Investigation of implant for the treatment of the fracture of cortical and trabecular bones. MRes Thesis, Swansea University, 2006.

[8]   J. Brozovsky and P. Pankaj. Towards modelling of a trabecular bone. Computers and Structures, 2007. 85: pp. 512-517.

1st International Conference on Mathematical and Computational Biomedical Engineering – CMBE2009
June 29 – July 1, 2009, Swansea, UK
P. Nithiarasu and R. Löhner (eds)

Computational Requirements of the Virtual Patient

Nigel W. John
School of Computer Science, Bangor University, n.w.john@bangor.ac.uk
Chris J Hughes
School of Computer Science, Bangor University
Serban R. Pop
School of Computer Science, Bangor University
Franck P. Vidal
APIS, INRIA Saclay Research Centre
Oliver Buckley
School of Technology, Oxford Brookes University

ABSRACT

Medical visualization in a hospital can be used to aid training, diagnosis, and pre- and intra-operative planning. In such an application, a virtual representation of a patient is needed that is interactive, can be viewed in three dimensions (3D), and simulates physiological processes that change over time. This paper highlights some of the computational challenges of implementing a real time simulation of a virtual patient, when accuracy can be traded-off against speed. Illustrations are provided using projects from our research based on Grid-based visualization, through to use of the Graphics Processing Unit (GPU).

Key Words: *Medical visualization, virtual environment, Grid, GPU*

1. INTRODUCTION

The medical domain provides excellent opportunities for communication and teaching of healthcare issues using computer graphics, visualization techniques, and virtual environments. Possible applications include anatomical educational tools; patient education; diagnostic aids; virtual autopsies; planning and guidance aids; skills training; and computer augmented reality. Both clinicians and patients can benefit from the appropriate use of tools that make use of these technologies.

The ability to render and manipulate medical data in 3D is one of the core requirements of a medical virtual environment, but traditionally volume and surface rendering algorithms have been expensive to compute. The ray casting algorithm, for example, is a $O(N^3)$ problem, where N is the dimension of the voxel data set. Despite the use of optimisation techniques, volume rendering on a single CPU is not an option for real time performance. A virtual patient must also simulate soft tissues and so the computer graphics rendering must also deform naturally during interaction with a tool, or as a consequence of physiological processes such as respiration. Finite Element Modelling is a popular choice for achieving soft tissue deformation, but is also too slow for real time. Mass spring models can be in real time, but produce lower fidelity results. Cutting of tissues is another challenge, which often needs a high resolution mesh-based model and the ability to change the topology of that mesh. Fluid dynamics may also be employed for blood flow. In some applications, the operator and instruments being used will need to be tracked. This can be achieved with dedicated hardware (such as optical or magnetic tracking), robotic joystick, or by image processing techniques. This paper examines how the computational demands of all of these requirements can be met so as to deliver an interactive medical virtual environment. Often accuracy of the model used has to be sacrificed to achieve the required speed, but even so we can achieve a suitable fidelity of simulation. Examples are provided below from our research projects and a detailed survey of the principles and applications of computer graphics in medicine can be found in [1].

2. COMPUTING THE VIRTUAL PATIENT

The computational infrastructure that can be deployed within a hospital continues to evolve and benefit from recent technology advances. This section contains several examples from our research where we have taken advantage of and contributed to the state-of-the-art in the field.

2.1 Medical Visualization using the Computational Grid

Grid computing is designed to allow end users transparent access to a wide variety of high performance computing facilities and data acquisition devices. An excellent example of the Grid being deployed for visualization tasks is the RAVE system [2], which is now in production release. Our own first experiment with Grid-based visualization in a hospital setting, however, consisted of a remote visualization application, where a graphics server processes the patient data and the results are delivered in real time across the computer network to a client workstation. This can be achieved by streaming the contents of the frame buffer on the server (where the graphics primitives are rendered) in a similar fashion to how MPEG movie files are streamed across the Internet. OpenGL Vizserver [3] from SGI was the first product to support remote visualization, and we used this software for an intra-operative application to aid with hepato-pancreatic surgery [4]. A volume rendering of the patient's CT data was delivered to a laptop client in the operating theatre where it could be interrogated by the surgeon with an easy to use joystick driven interface. At the time, the CT data sets being used (700 slices at 512 x 512 pixel resolution, with a pixel size of 0.78 mm and an interslice distance of 1 mm.) were too large to be processed on a local PC. Through this approach, however, real time rendering was achieved across a 100baseT network link, with a physical distance of one mile from the server to the operating room. Grid middleware software provided support for scheduling computer time to coincide with the operation and for security of the patient data.

The lessons learnt from the above were invaluable in the e-Viz project [5] that explored the development of autonomic visualization and designed a generic adaptive infrastructure for Grid-based visualization. A particular application that was built on this infrastructure was an augmented reality (AR) interface for a procedure called transcranium magnetic stimulation (TMS) [6]. TMS requires an electro magnetic coil to be accurately positioned against a subject's head. Using AR, a 3D rendering of a subject's brain can be overlayed and registered onto a video stream of their head so helping the clinician to position the coil. A markerless interface was developed to achieve this, in which repeatable feature points are extracted from known views and then we match the best stored view to the user's viewpoint using the matched feature points to estimate the objects pose. Our research has shown that whilst an average desktop PC struggles to carry out the pose estimation, using remote resources can ensure real-time performance. Provided the visualization server is appropriate for the rendering task and network latency is low, then the e-Viz framework is able to return the rendered artefact to the user at a reliable 15 frames/second. On congested networks e-Viz uses stricter compression algorithms at a cost to the image quality to try and maintain these usable frame rates.

2.2 The GPU Age

A well known hardware acceleration technique for volume rendering is to use texture mapping hardware [7] and this method lends itself well for implementation on the Graphics Processing Unit (GPU) found on all modern PC graphics cards, and is often combined with use of per pixel, or fragment, shaders [8]. The latest PCI Express architecture allows efficient fetching of texture data from the main memory of the PC via the graphics bus. Special purpose hardware has also been designed for PCs, for example, the VolumePro 2000 (TereRecon, USA) implements shear warp rendering and supports memory capacities ranging from 512MB to 16GB, which can handle up to 30000 CT slices. This performance can now often be matched by the GPU on a high-end graphics card, and even an inexpensive PC can achieve real time for a 256 cubed voxel data set.

In our simulator for ultrasound guided needle puncture [9], two haptic devices are used: one to manipulate a virtual ultrasound probe; one to represent the virtual needle. Ultrasound-like images are generated from the original patient CT data by transforming the appearance using GPU operations via the OpenGL Shading Language. A 2D multi-planar reconstruction (MPR) image is extracted from the CT voxel data based on the position and orientation of the virtual ultrasound probe being moved across the skin of the virtual patient. This can be efficiently achieved using the OpenGL frame buffer object (FBO) architecture. All voxels that have been penetrated by the virtual needle are assigned a high value corresponding to the metallic material of the needle shaft, which reflects ultrasound. Acoustic shadowing effects are simulated by post-processing the MPR image to compute a shadow mask, and high frequency noise is also added. Bright reflections may occur in ultrasound images at interfaces such as with bone, gas, and fat/tissue. This effect can be produced in the final image by detecting and enhancing horizontal edges in the MPR image using a Sobel filter. Finally, the MPR image, the shadow mask and the noise data are blended using multi-texturing. In an interventional procedure, the needle can then be used as a portal for the entry of other tools such as a guidewire and catheter. Fluoroscopy images are used in the operating room to keep track of these tools. To maintain real time performance we have also developed fluoroscopy simulation on the GPU from voxel data [10] or a polygon mesh [11]. In the latter case, this produces X-ray images using a three pass algorithm through the OpenGL pipeline. For each X-ray pixel, the first pass computes tissue penetration, the second computes an intermediary result required in the final pass to compute the cumulative attenuation using the Beer-Lambert law. This approach is extremely efficient. For example, using full floating point precision, our results show that the GPU is over 60 times faster than a CPU implementation when computing a 1024 x 768 pixel X-Ray image of a test object made up of 871,414 triangles, with no significant loss of accuracy (differences smaller than 0.3%).

2.3 Software Techniques
There has been a great deal of research into optimisation of computer graphics algorithms to gain speed increases – for an overview, refer to [1]. Taking soft tissue deformation as an example, the Chain Mail algorithm [12] has proved to be a popular alternative to FEM and mass-spring models. With this algorithm materials are modelled by adjusting deformation limits for individual elements. For a medical simulator, however, the requirement is not only for rendering speed – often you want to models forces too so that a haptics interface can be used. Haptics devices require a refresh rate of 1000 Hz to provide a smooth response and this must be run in parallel with the graphics rendering. In exploring this problem, we have developed a method based on particle systems, called the Charged Particle Model [13]. The soft tissue is considered as being composed of a large number of particles that are each assigned a virtual electrical charge. The haptic interface point is also assigned a virtual charge and forces are then simulated using the rules of electro-magnetic interaction. Using this approach we have demonstrated that real time performance for deformation with haptics can be achieved, typically using around 6000 charged particles surrounded by a Bezier surface of 250,000 points.

Current work at Bangor is looking at other ways of gaining speed through novel use of particle systems. There is a need to introduce blood flow into our simulators, for example, particularly for vascular intervention. Our model [14] is based on the idea that each layer of fluid behaves as a flock, interconnected by the parameters that govern the flow dynamics. At the macroscopic level blood can be considered as a Newtonian fluid and represented using an underlying particle system. Many similarities with existing particle dynamics systems for fluids are kept (e.g., the kernel function in smooth particle hydrodynamics (SPH) is replaced by the flock neighbourhood rule; however the search for nearby particles is still performed in the usual way). To conserve the mass of the system, we keep the number of particles inside the domain constant during the entire simulation. Each particle carries its own physical quantities such as mass, speed and position, which means that control is maintained over the main physical parameters of the fluid. The result is a real time visualization of blood flow with comparable results to commercial fluid dynamic software that takes 10-20 seconds to produce a single image.

3. CONCLUSIONS

The research projects described above have demonstrated that it is possible to compute a virtual patient for a real time graphics application. Visualization on the Grid is one possibility and provides the opportunity to combine 3D visualization with complex simulation algorithms in real time. However, the ever increasing computational power and very modest cost of desktop PCs make them the ideal platform for running many of the applications discussed in this paper. There remains a trade off between accuracy and speed with the latter taking precedence in a medical virtual environment. Despite this, validation studies that we are actively carrying out with our clinical collaborators show that a sufficient fidelity of simulation can be obtained for training and educational purposes.

REFERENCES

[1]   F.P. Vidal, F. Bello, K.W. Brodlie, D.A. Gould, N.W. John, R. Phillips, and N.J. Avis, Principles and Applications of Computer Graphics in Medicine, *Computer Graphics Forum, Vol. 25 Issue 1*, pp113-137, 2006

[2]   I.J. Grimstead, N.J. Avis, and D.W. Walker, RAVE: Resource-Aware Visualization Environment, *in Proc. of the UK e-Science All Hands Meeting*, Nottingham, UK, 2004

[3]   C. Ohazama, OpenGL Vizserver White Paper, *White Paper*, Silicon Graphics, Inc, 1999

[4]   N.W. John, R.F. McCloy, and S.Herrman, Interrogation of Patient Data delivered to the Operating Theatre during Hepato-Pancreatic Surgery using High Performance Computing, *Computer Aided Surgery 9(6)*, pp235-242, 2004

[5]   K.W. Brodlie, J. Brooke, M. Chen, D. Chisnall, C. Hughes, N.W. John, M.W. Jones, M. Riding, N. Roard, M. Turner, and J.D.Wood, Adaptive Infrastructure for Visual Computing, *Proc. of Theory and Practice of Computer Graphics*, Eurographics, pp. 147-156, 2007

[6]   C. J. Hughes and N. W. John, A Flexible Approach to High Performance Visualization Enabled Augmented Reality, *Proc. of Theory and Practice of Computer Graphics* 2007, Eurographics, pp181-186, 2007

[7]   T.J. Cullip and U. Neumann, Accelerating Volume Reconstruction with 3D Texture Hardware. *Tech. rep.*, University of North Carolina, Chapel Hill, NC, USA, 1994.

[8]   K. Engel, M. Hadwiger, J. M. Kniss, A. E. Lefohn, C. Rezk Salama and D. Weiskopf, Real-time volume graphics. *Tutorial 28 in SIGGRAPH* 2004.

[9]   F.P. Vidal, N.W. John, A.E.Healey, and D.A. Gould, Simulation of Ultrasound Guided Needle Puncture using Patient Specific Data with 3D Textures and Volume Haptics, *Computer Animation and Virtual Worlds. Vol. 19, Issue 2*, pp111-127, 2008

[10]   F.P. Vidal and N.W. John, Interactive Physically-Based X-Ray Simulation: CPU or GPU?, *Stud Health Technol Inform 125*, pp 479-481, 2007

[11]   P.F. Villard, F. Bello, F.P. Vidal, N.W. John, C. Hunt, S. Johnson, D. Gould, Percutaneous transhepatic cholangiography training simulator with real-time breathing motion, *23rd International Congress of CARS - Computer Assisted Radiology and Surgery*, Berlin 2009

[12]   S. Gibson, 3D Chainmail: A Fast Algorithm for Deforming Volumetric Objects, *Proc. Symposium on Interactive 3D Graphics*, pp 149--154, 1997

[13]   O. Buckley and N.W. John, Efficient Soft Tissue Modelling Using Charged Particle Control Points, *Eurographics 2008 Short Paper*, Crete, ISSN 1017-4656, 191-194, 2008

[14]   C.J. Hughes, S.R. Pop, and N.W. John, Macroscopic Blood Flow Visualization using Boids, *23rd International Congress of CARS - Computer Assisted Radiology and Surgery*, Berlin 2009

1st International Conference on Mathematical and Computational Biomedical Engineering – CMBE2009
June 29 – July 1, 2009, Swansea, UK
P. Nithiarasu and R. Löhner (eds)

PARTICLE METHODS FOR A VIRTUAL PATIENT

Oli Buckley
Bangor University, Oliver.Buckley@nominet.org.uk
Chris Hughes
Bangor University, c.j.hughes@bangor.ac.uk
Nigel W. John
Bangor University, n.w.john@bangor.ac.uk
Serban Pop[*]
Bangor University, serban@bangor.ac.uk

ABSTRACT

The particle systems approach is a well known technique in computer graphics for modelling fuzzy objects such as fire and clouds. The algorithm has also been applied to different biomedical applications and this paper presents two such methods: a charged particle method for soft tissue deformation with integrated haptics; and a blood flow visualization technique based on boids. The goal is real time performance with high fidelity results.

Key Words: *Particle systems, boids, blood flow, soft tissue, virtual environments.*

1. INTRODUCTION

There is a growing trend to develop simulators for training a variety of medical procedures as there are obvious advantages to be gained from enabling training on a virtual patient instead of on real patients. Mistakes can be made without risk, different patient physiologies can be used, a variety of pathologies can be modelled and the trainee can practice as many times as they need. The challenge of a medical simulator is therefore to provide real time interaction (with 3D graphics and haptics interfaces) whilst maintaining a fidelity that is high enough to ensure that face, content and construct validity can be achieved in the training process. The Medical Graphics group at Bangor has been developing solutions to address this challenge, with a particular focus on interventional radiology (IR) procedures. This paper presents two novel ways in which we are using the well known particle systems algorithm in this work.

A particle system is a technique used in computer graphics to create certain fuzzy phenomena that are otherwise difficult to model [1]. Particle systems have been used to great effect in a wide variety of applications to model fire, water, clouds, etc. The technique has also been extended to model large collections of *boids* that exhibit emergent behaviour as a result of each boid following a simple set of rules, e.g. a flock of birds or a school of fish [2]. Within medical simulation, blood flowing from wounds, smoke and other effects have already been modelled with particle systems, e.g. [3, 4]. The algorithm has also been adapted for surface reconstruction and so applied to construct skeletal surfaces and organ interaction [5]. For the modelling of muscles, oriented particles were introduced to simulate elastic surfaces by using attraction-repulsion forces or virtual springs to model interactions between particles [6, 7]. However, the

---

[*] The authors are listed in alphabetical order.

integration of realistic tissue properties into particle models is not a trivial task. Previous work with particles has not included support for a force model that can be used with haptic feedback devices, which is an important requirement in a simulation of an IR procedure. In addition, we need to be able to accurately visualise the blood flow within an artery, e.g. for the dissipation of an injected contrast agent into the blood stream. The use of particle systems for modelling blood has not addressed blood flow within this context.

2. MODELLING PHYSIOLOGY WITH PARTICLE SYSTEMS

The hypothesis of this research is that particle systems techniques can be used and adapted to provide an effective real time implementation for some of the key physiological processes that we need to model in a virtual patient. We demonstrate this by focussing on two important areas required in an IR procedure simulation: soft tissue deformation of skin and internal organs; and blood flow through a (possibly diseased) artery.

2.1 Charged Particle Method for Tissue Deformation with Haptics

Traditional soft tissue deformation methods are based on Finite Element Modelling (FEM) or a Mass Spring Model (MSM). A typical FEM solution e.g. [8], usually offers a deformation model that provides high levels of realism but at a high computational cost. This means that the simulation will either not provide real time interaction, particularly with haptics, or will require an expensive pre-processing step. Conversely a soft tissue model that uses a MSM [9] will trade off the quality of results attained for real time interaction. MSM and FEM are both mesh-based approaches, and the resolution of the mesh will also have an implication on the performance of any simulation. Cutting or re-structuring of soft tissue will require new elements to be created and the mesh to re-calculated, both of which are costly to implement.

Our Charged Particle Model (CPM) [10] provides a visually and haptically realistic simulation that runs on a standard desktop machine, and also provides the ability to both deform and restructure soft tissue. Each particle within a CPM surface is given a notional electro-magnetic charge, and the haptic interaction point (HIP) is also given the same charge. Then the charged particles and the HIP are governed by the rules of electro-magnetic interaction i.e. like charges will repel and opposite charges will attract. As the charged particles and HIP have a like charge, once the HIP is within is a given distance of the particle surface, the surface will then deform accordingly (see **Figure 1**) with neighbouring particles moving to take up stress and slack within the surface in a method similar to that used in the ChainMail Model [11]. Multiple HIPs are also supported in the CPM, which provides support for different shaped tools. A Bezier surface can then be rendered to provide the visual representation, using the charged particles as control points for the surface.

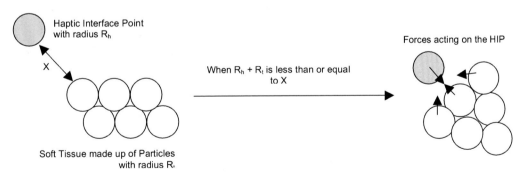

Figure 1: *As the HIP, the shaded disc, moves closer to the particles which represent the soft tissue to be deformed then under the rules of electromagnetic interaction the particles are repelled accordingly*

Results achieved using the CPM demonstrates that real time deformation with haptics can be achieved. We typically use around 6000 charged particles and 250,000 points in a Bezier surface, and run at over 30 frames per second.

2.2 Blood Flow Visualization using Boids

Simulation of blood flow is essential to interventional radiology simulators, such as the injection of contrast medium whilst using fluoroscopy. However, the blood flow generally plays a supporting role and must appear to behave realistically in real time. The flow does not need to be accurately computed in this case, which due to its complexity represents a challenge for conventional methods of simulation, even at a macroscopic scale (flow in arteries, veins). We therefore propose a new computer simulated model to visualize blood flow in arteries using boids [12].

The boids individual properties (separation, alignment, cohesion) cannot be used to describe individual particles of fluid; however their group behaviour, flocking, matches the characteristics of laminar flow (collision avoidance, velocity matching, flock centering) and it is suitable for modelling channel flows. Due to their nature, a model based on boids algorithm can be used for visualization purposes only; hence our method is compared with existing fluid particle based simulation, only qualitatively not quantitatively. Our model is based on the idea the each layer of fluid behaves as a flock, interconnected by the parameters which govern the flow dynamics. At the macroscopic level blood is seen as a Newtonian fluid and can be represented with a particle system. Many similarities with existing particle dynamics systems for fluids are kept (kernel function in SPH is replaced by the flock neighbourhood; however the search for nearby particles is done in the same way). In order to conserve mass properly we keep constant the number of particles inside the domain during the entire simulation. Each particle carry its own physical quantity as mass, speed, position, which means that we have control over the entire fluid's main physical parameters.

The results are compares with many existing benchmarks (non-uniform channel flows, with or without obstacles). The following benchmark comparisons (Figures 2 and 3) have been generated to compare our results with commercial software. In all figures the red colour emphasizes the layer of fluid with the highest velocity, with blue representing the lowest velocity. The boids-based visualization is on the right hand side.

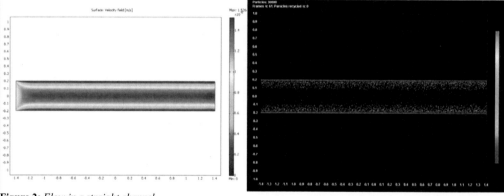

Figure 2: *Flow in a straight channel*

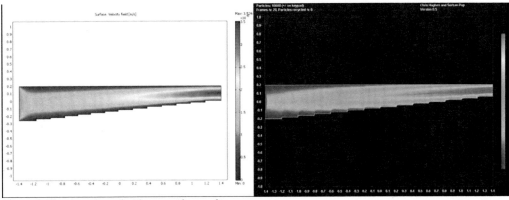

Figure 3: *Flow in a channel with non-uniform radius*

3. CONCLUSIONS

In this paper we have shown that we are able to deform and restructure a Charged Particle Model, that is both visually and haptically realistic and able to be run in real time on a standard desktop machine. We have also shown a particle model which enables the visualization of fluids flow in tubes with non-uniform radius considering also fluid interactions with stationary objects. In our simulations the trade of is accuracy for speed. The method can be successfully use in complex haptic simulators where the "real-time" aspect of the model is essential.

The research hypothesis is shown to be true for the above examples and particle systems techniques can indeed be used and adapted to provide an effective real time implementation for some of the key physiological processes that we need to model in a virtual patient. We are now working on further applications based on these techniques, for example, the simulation of Doppler ultrasound visualization effects.

REFERENCES

[1]   W.T. Reeves, Particle Systems—a Technique for Modeling a Class of Fuzzy Objects. *ACM Trans. Graph.* 2, 2 (Apr. 1983), 91-108. 1983

[2]   C.W. Reynolds, Flocks, Herds, and Schools: A Distributed Behavioral Model, *Computer Graphics*, 21(4), 25-34, 1987

[3]   J. Brown, S. Sorkin, J.-C. Latombe, and K. Montgomery, Algorithmic Tools for Real-Time Microsurgery Simulation, *Medical Image Analysis,* vol. 6, no. 3, 289 – 300, 2002

[4]   M. Agus, A. Giachetti, E. Gobbetti, G. Zanetti, and A. Zorcolo, Adaptive techniques for real time haptic and visual simulation of bone dissection, *IEEE Virtual Reality Conference*, 102 – 109, 2003

[5]   M. Amrani, B. Crespin, and B. Shariat, Skeletal implicit surface reconstruction and particle system for organ's interactions simulation, *Geometric modeling: techniques, applications, systems and tools*, 172–192, 2004

[6]   R. Szelinski and D. Tonnesen, Surface Modeling with Oriented Particle Systems, *Computer Graphics*, 26(2), 185-194, 1992.

[7]   L.P. Nedel, D. Thalmann, Real Time Muscle Deformations using Mass-Spring Systems, *Computer Graphics International (CGI'98)*, 156-165, 1998

[8]   M. Bro Nielsen and S. Cotin, Real-time Volumetric Deformable Models for Surgery Simulation using Finite Elements and Condensation, Computer Graphics Forum, Volume 15 Issue 3, pp 57-66, 1996

[9]   Nedel L. P., Thalmann D.: Real Time Muscle Deformations using Mass-Spring Systems, p. 156, Computer Graphics International 1998 (CGI'98), 1998

[10]   O. Buckley and N.W. John, Efficient Soft Tissue Modelling Using Charged Particle Control Points, *Eurographics 2008 Short Paper*, Crete, ISSN 1017-4656, 191-194, 2008

[11]   Gibson S. F.: 3D ChainMail: A Fast Algorithm for Deforming Volumetric Objects, Proceedings of Symposium on Interactive 3D Graphics, pp 149 – 154, 1997

[12]   C.J. Hughes, S.R. Pop, and N.W. John, Macroscopic blood flow visualization using boids, *23rd International Congress of CARS - Computer Assisted Radiology and Surgery*, Berlin, Germany, June 2009

1st International Conference on Mathematical and Computational Biomedical Engineering - CMBE2009
June 29 - July 1, 2009, Swansea, UK
P.Nithiarasu and R.Löhner (Eds.)

LATTICE BOLTZMANN METHODS FOR NON-NEWTONIAN FLUIDS

G. W. Roberts
School of Computer Science, Cardiff University, Cardiff, CF24 3AA.
g.w.roberts@cs.cardiff.ac.uk

D. W. Walker
School of Computer Science, Cardiff University, Cardiff, CF24 3AA.
David.W.Walker@cs.cardiff.ac.uk

ABSTRACT

Key Words: *lattice Boltzmann methods, numerical simulation, non-Newtonian fluids, blood flow.*

1 INTRODUCTION

A general framework for the simulation of non-Newtonian fluids is presented. The kernel of the software uses lattice-based methods and incorporates Newtonian, generalised Newtonian, viscoplastic and viscoelastic behaviour. Its application to blood flow is demonstrated.

2 MAIN BODY

The lattice Boltzmann method has become established as an alternative to other numerical techniques for the solution of problems in fluid dynamics. Its mesoscopic kinetic approach has the potential to describe a diverse range of physical fluid models and its local lattice computation is ideally suited to parallelisation.

We have developed a generic code based on lattice Boltzmann type theory which could potentially model a wide range of different physical flows including nanoscale fluids, multiphase and/or multicomponent flows and porous media etc.

In this work we demonstrate the application of the code to the flow of blood modelled as a non-Newtonian fluid, compare different rheological models and describe phenomena arising in steady, oscillatory and pulsatile conditions.

We also discuss the prospects for using more sophisticated models of blood rheology within a lattice based framework.

3 CONCLUSIONS

Lattice Boltzmann type methods are shown to be useful for simulating non-Newtonian fluids and facilitate the study of different models of blood flow under a variety of forcing conditions.

REFERENCES

[1] R. Ouared and B. Chopard, Lattice Boltzmann simulations of blood flow: non-Newtonian rheology and clotting processes, *Journal of Statistical Physics*, 121(1/2), 209-221, 2005.

[2] J. Boyd and J. M. Buick, Three-dimensional modelling of the human carotid artery using the lattice Boltzmann method: I. Model and velocity analysis, *Phys. Med. Biol.* 53, 5767-5779, 2008.

1st International Conference on Mathematical and Computational Biomedical Engineering - CMBE2009
June 29 - July 1, 2009, Swansea, UK
P.Nithiarasu and R.Löhner (Eds.)

EXACT SOLUTION TO A REFINED CONTACT PROBLEM FOR BIPHASIC CARTILAGE LAYERS

G. Mishuris

Wales Institute of Mathematical and Computational Sciences, Institute of Mathematics and Physics, Aberystwyth University, Ceredigion, SY23 3BZ, Wales, UK, ggm@aber.ac.uk

I. Argatov

Laboratory of Friction and Wear, Research Institute of Mechanical Engineering Problems, V.O., Bolshoy pr., 61, 199178 St. Petersburg, Russia, argatov@home.ru

ABSTRACT

We revisit the axisymmetric contact problem for a biphasic cartilage layer and consider a refined formulation taking into account the both normal and tangential displacements at the contact interface. The obtained analytical solution is valid for arbitrary time and increasing loading conditions. We compare it with the classic result and indicate cases where the difference could be pronounced.

Key Words: *contact problem, biphasic cartilage layer, tangential displacement, analytical solution.*

1 INTRODUCTION

Solution to biomechanical contact problems for biological joints are of great importance for medical applications, especially in analysing different stages of osteoarthitis. As the cartilage layers are extremely thin in comparison with the characteristic size of the bones while the physics of the problem is rather complicated, direct computations can meet with serious numerical difficulties [1]. This explains those several attempts which have been made to take advantage from existence of the small dimensionless parameter in the problem by employing asymptotic analysis [2, 3]. Few solutions are available [2–4] for monotonic loading where the latter [4] has been extended for the case of an arbitrary time dependent load in [5]. All these solutions are based on the simplified kinematic relationship in contact zone when the tangential displacement can be negligible in the analysis.

In real joints, the structural and biomechanical properties of the cartilage layer may change dramatically in the pathologic stage [5]. Therefore, the refined kinetic relationship which takes into account the tangential displacements of the boundary points of a biphasic cartilage layer should be rather imposed for correct predictions of biomechanical parameters in the contact region of the articular cartilage instead of the classic kinetic relationship.

We revisit the original asymptotic formulation of the contact problem and improve it by taking into account the tangential displacements at the contact interface. Namely, using the well-known asymptotic relationships for biomechanical parameters valid inside the biphasic cartilage layer [2], we construct a new more accurate solution which is also capable to represent the limit situation when the biomechanical properties of the contacting cartilage layers differ drastically. We restrict ourself a monotonic load and essentially use in our analysis the approach proposed earlier in [6] for the case of the classic static mechanical contact problem. For the details of the original problem formulation, we refer prospective reader to the paper [2] where, from our best knowledge, the asymptotical approach to the contact problem for the biphasic cartilage layer has been developed.

2 PROBLEM FORMULATION AND MAIN RESULTS

We consider a thin linear biphasic cartilage layer indented by a spherical punch. The refined linearized kinetic relationship which takes into account the both normal $w(r,t)$ and tangential $u(r,t)$ displacements of the boundary points of the cartilage layer can be written as follows [6] (see Fig. 1a):

$$-w(r,t) + \frac{r}{R_0}u(r,t) = \delta_0(t) - \frac{r^2}{2R_0}, \quad r \le a(t). \tag{1}$$

Here, $\delta_0(t)$ is the punch displacement, R_0 is the radius of the punch surface, $a(t)$ is the contact radius.

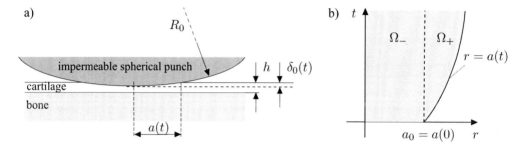

Figure 1: a) - geometry of the problem; b) - support of the solution of Eq. (2).

Expressing the displacements $w(r,t)$ and $u(r,t)$ in terms of the contact pressure $P(r,t)$ by means of formulas [2], we reduce Eq. (1) to the following integro-differential equation (we assume that $r \le a(t)$):

$$\frac{1}{r}\frac{\partial}{\partial r}\left(r\frac{\partial P(r,t)}{\partial r}\right) + \chi \int_0^t \frac{1}{r}\frac{\partial}{\partial r}\left(r\frac{\partial P(r,\tau)}{\partial r}\right)d\tau + \kappa r\frac{\partial P(r,t)}{\partial r} = m(Cr^2 - \delta_0(t)). \tag{2}$$

Here we used the notation $\chi = 3\mu_s k/h^2$, $\kappa = 3/(2hR_0)$, $m = 3\mu_s/h^3$, $C = 1/2R_0$.

The radius of the contact area $a(t)$ is determined from the boundary conditions [2,4]:

$$P(a(t),t) = 0, \quad \partial_r P(r,t)\big|_{r=a(t)} = 0, \quad \partial_r P(r,t)\big|_{r=0} = 0. \tag{3}$$

Denoting a non-decreasing external load by $F(t)$, we will have the following equilibrium equation:

$$2\pi \int_0^{a(t)} P(\rho,t)\rho\,d\rho = F(t). \tag{4}$$

Notice that because the load $F(t)$ is non-decreasing, the contact radius $a(t)$ increases monotonously. Notice also that in case $\kappa = 0$ the contact problem (2) – (4) coincides with that studied in [2,4].

The following exact equation connects the the unknown punch displacement $\delta_0(t)$ and the contact load $F(t)$:

$$\delta_0(t) = C\frac{a^2(t)}{2} + \frac{2\kappa}{m}\frac{F(t)}{\pi a^2(t)}, \tag{5}$$

while the radius $a(t)$ of the contact area and the contact load $F(t)$ satisfy the equation:

$$\frac{\pi m}{48}Ca^6(t) = F(t) + \chi \int_0^t F(\tau)\,d\tau + \kappa\left\{\frac{a^2(t)}{4}F(t) + \frac{\pi}{2}\int_0^{a(t)} \rho^4 \partial_\rho P(\rho,t)\,d\rho\right\}. \tag{6}$$

The contact pressure, $P(r,t)$, will be considered separately in the domains Ω_- and Ω_+ (see Figure 1b)). If we denote by $a^{-1}(r)$ the unknown inverse to the function $a(t)$ then

$$b(r) = 0, \; r \le a_0, \quad b(r) = a^{-1}(r), \; a_0 \le r. \tag{7}$$

In the domain Ω_-, integrating Eq. (2) leads to the following result:

$$\frac{\kappa}{m}\frac{\partial P_-(r,t)}{\partial r} = Cr + C_0 M(t,r)e^{-\kappa r^2/2} + \frac{e^{-\kappa r^2/2}}{r}\int_0^t M(t-\tau,r)(2C\chi\kappa^{-1}+\delta_0'(\tau))d\tau. \quad (8)$$

Here we introduced the notation $C_0 = 2C\kappa^{-1} + \delta_0(0)$, η is an arbitrary value $0 < \eta < \chi$ and

$$M(t,r) = \frac{1}{2\pi i}\int_{-i\infty-\eta}^{i\infty-\eta}\frac{1}{s}\left(\exp\left\{\frac{\kappa\chi r^2}{2(s+\chi)}\right\}-1\right)e^{st}ds. \quad (9)$$

In the domain Ω_+, we have

$$
\begin{aligned}
\frac{\kappa}{m}\frac{\partial P_+(r,t)}{\partial r} =\ & \frac{C}{r}a_0^2 + \frac{1}{r}e^{-\kappa\frac{r^2}{2}}\left\{C_0 M(t,r) + \frac{1}{r}\int_0^t M(t-\tau,r)\left[\frac{2C\chi}{\kappa}+\delta_0'(\tau)\right]d\tau\right\}\\
& -\frac{2C}{\kappa r}e^{-\kappa\frac{r^2-a_0^2}{2}}\left\{M(t,\sqrt{r^2-a_0^2}) + \chi\int_0^t M(t-\tau,\sqrt{r^2-a_0^2})d\tau\right\}\\
& -\frac{2C}{r}\int_{a_0}^r e^{-\kappa\frac{r^2-\xi^2}{2}}\xi M(t-b(\xi),\sqrt{r^2-\xi^2})d\xi\\
& +\frac{1}{r}\int_{a_0}^r e^{-\kappa\frac{r^2-\xi^2}{2}}\partial_t M(t-b(\xi),\sqrt{r^2-\xi^2})b'(\xi)(C\xi^2-\delta_0(b(\xi)))d\xi. \quad (10)
\end{aligned}
$$

3 NUMERICAL EXAMPLES AND CONCLUSIONS

In order to illustrate the constructed solution of the refined biomechanical contact problem and compare it with that from [4], we will adopt for the computations the same material properties and geometrical parameters of a typical human cartilage reported in [2,4]. Namely we assume that $\mu_s = 0.25$ MPa, $k = 2 \cdot 10^{-3}$ mm^{4}N^{-1}s^{-1}, $h = 1$ mm, $R_0 = 400$ mm. In the sequel we also consider some variation of this set to analyze the sensitivity of the solution to the variation of material characteristics. In all the numerical tests, a constant contact load $F(t) = F_0 = 100$ N is applied. The respective results for the main contact parameters are presented in Fig. 2.

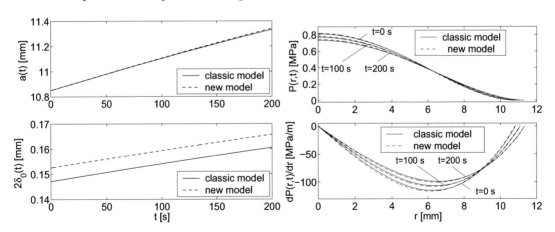

Figure 2: Comparison of the radius of the contact zone, $a(t)$, the indentation parameter $\delta_0(t)$, the contact pressure $P(r,t)$ and its derivative with respect to the radial coordinate r for times $t = 0, 100, 200$ [s] computed in accordance with the model from [4] and the present one for the set of parameters from [2]

The difference between the obtained solution and the classic one [4] is very small and increases with time though. Thus, for the contact zone radius, $a(t)$, the maximal discrepancy between the solutions is of 0.074% for $t = 200$ s. The punch indentation, $\delta_0(t)$, differs for these two models on 3.5% and does not practically change in time. (We depict the doubled punch indentation, $2\delta_0(t)$, for easy comparison with the results from [4]). Finally, the maximal pressure difference between the models appears at point $r = 0$ and increases from 0.85% and 3.57% with time.

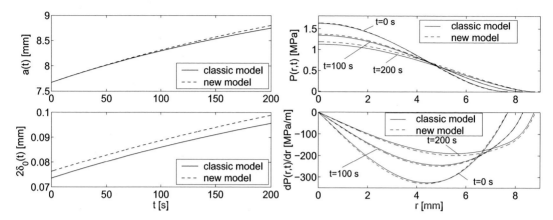

Figure 3: Comparison of the contact zone radius, $a(t)$, the indentation parameter $\delta_0(t)$, the contact pressure $P(r,t)$ and its derivative, $\partial_r P(r,t)$, for moments $t = 0, 100, 200$ [s] computed in accordance with the model [4] and the present one for $h' = h/2$ while others parameters are the same as above.

The second set of the biomechanical parameters chosen for the numerical simulation defers from the previous one only by the thickness of the cartilage layer $h' = h/2$, while all others stay the same. Now the aforementioned discrepancy between the solution becomes more pronounced (Fig. 3). Thus, the difference between the contact zone takes its maximal value of 0.6% for $t = 200$ s. The punch indentation, $\delta_0(t)$, differs even further on to reach its maximum 9% for $t = 0$. Finally, the maximum pressure difference between the models lies in range between 0.8% and 5% increasing with time.

Summarizing, for the set of parameters discussed above, the difference between the classic solution and the refined one is not essential, but for the punch indentation and the contact pressure should be important in some cases though. These cases may include inverse problems of determining biomechanical and the geometrical parameters of the cartilage layer from experiments. Note also, that the refined contact model always yields higher contact pressure maximum with the longest contact zone and, as a direct consequence, to a higher pressure gradient.

REFERENCES

[1] W. Wilson, C.C. van Donkelaar, R. van Rietbergen, R. Huiskes, The role of computational models in the search for the mechanical behaviour and damage mechanisms of articular cartilage. *Medical Engng & Physics*, 27, 810-826, 2005.

[2] G.A. Ateshian, W.M. Lai, W.B. Zhu, V.C. Mow, An asymptotic solution for the contact of two biphasic cartilage layers. *J. Biomechanics*, 27, 1347-1360, 1994.

[3] J.Z. Wu, W. Herzog, J. Ronsky, Modeling axi-symmetrical joint contact with biphasic cartilage layers – An asymptotic solution. *J. Biomechanics*, 29, 1263-1281, 1996.

[4] J.Z. Wu, W. Herzog, M. Epstein, An improved solution for the contact of two biphasic cartilage layers. *J. Biomechanics*, 30, 371-375, 1997.

[5] J.Z. Wu, W. Herzog, M. Epstein, Joint contact mechanics in the early stages of osteoarthritis. *Medical Engng & Physics*, 22, 1-12, 2000.

[6] I.I. Argatov, Approximate solution of an axisymmetric contact problem with allowance for tangential displacements on the contact surface. *J. Appl. Mech. and Techn. Physics*, 45, 118-123, 2004.

Influence of internal carotid artery geometry on aneurysms location and orientation

Marina Piccinelli
Math&CS Department, Emory University, Atlanta, GA, USA, marina@mathcs.emory.edu
Susanna Bacigaluppi
Universita' degli Studi di Milano, Neurosurgery, Ospedale Policlinico Fondazione IRCCS,
Milano, Italy, susannabacigaluppi@yahoo.it
Alessandro Veneziani
Math&CS Department, Emory University, Atlanta, GA, USA, ale@mathcs.emory.edu
Andrea Remuzzi
Biomedical Engineering Department, Mario Negri Institute, BG, Italy,
aremuzzi@marionegri.it
Luca Antiga
Biomedical Engineering Department, Mario Negri Institute, BG, Italy, antiga@marionegri.it

ABSTRACT

Key Words: cerebral aneurysms, computational geometry, 3D geometric characterization

1. INTRODUCTION

Cerebral aneurysm formation is thought to be the results of an interplay between changes in biomechanical properties of the vascular wall and local hemodynamics factors. This hypothesis is strengthened by the well documented evidence that aneurysms preferentially arise in areas subjected to altered hemodynamic forces, such as arterial bifurcations and sharp bends. On the other hand, given the major impact of vessel geometry on blood dynamics, the study of the three-dimensional (3D) geometry of cerebral aneurysms in relation to their parent vasculature may shed some light on the mechanisms involving hemodynamics into the initiation and progression of the disease.

Many authors have indeed underlined the importance of characterizing the parent vasculature in order to identify recurrent geometric patterns between aneurysms and hosting vessels, study intra-aneurysmal hemodynamics, plan and evaluate surgical procedures[1,2].

In this work we applied robust and semi-automatic computational geometry techniques[3,4] to quantitatively characterize the geometry of aneurysms and their parent vasculature in a population of lateral aneurysms developing along the internal carotid artery (ICA). In particular, the geometry of the ICA siphons as well as the position and the orientation of the aneurysm necks with respect to the parent artery are investigated. Medical images were obtained in the context of the ANEURISK project, a collaborative research project aimed at assessing the role of geometry and hemodynamics in the development and rupture of cerebral aneurysms.

2. MAIN BODY

Materials and Methods - Three-dimensional rotational angiography (3D RA) performed in 50 patients with lateral aneurysms along the ICA were collected at the Neuroradiology Division of the Niguarda Ca' Grande Hospital in Milan following clinical routine for assessment of cerebral aneurysms, for a total number of 54 aneurysms. Clinical data on the patients was available, including aneurysm rupture status.

Three-dimensional reconstruction of the luminal surface and the geometric characterization of the vascular segments and the aneurysms were performed by means of the Vascular Modeling Toolkit (VMTK)[5], an open source framework specifically developed for the analysis of vascular structures. The segmentation technique is based on a gradient-driven level-set approach, while all the geometric evaluations depend on computation of centerlines and identification of bifurcations.

As detailed in a previous work[3,4], the algorithm for the extraction of centerlines robustly relies on the Voronoi diagram of the model surface and needs a minimum user interaction for the interactive placement of seeds at the end of the branches and on the dome of the aneurysm. After the computation of the centerlines, two bifurcations were automatically detected on each 3D network: the bifurcation of the ICA into middle cerebral (MCA) and anterior cerebral (ACA) arteries, and *the aneurysm bifurcation*, which identifies the area where the aneurysm dome depart from the parent vessel at the aneurysm neck (Figure 1); each set of centerlines was then split into branches, namely the ICA siphon and the aneurysm sac.

The following geometric quantities were retrieved: the curvilinear abscissa was computed along the siphon and the zero abscissa location was set at the bifurcation of the ICA into MCA and ACA, this location provided a stable reference point for all the models; the ICA siphon geometry was characterized in terms of curvature and torsion following their classical differential geometry expressions, while to describe its local 3D geometry the Frenet frame (composed of tangent t_{ff}, normal n_{ff} and binormal b_{ff} unit vectors) was built along the its centerline; at the aneurysm bifurcation the following features were automatically computed[3,4]: the origin o_{an} of the aneurysm neck, which accounted for the position of the lesion along the siphon; the normal n_{an} of the plane where the two centerlines lie while departing from each other which described the orientation of the aneurysm neck, and the aneurysm vector v_{an}, which described the direction of the aneurysm sac immediately after the bifurcation (Figure 2).

The following operations were performed in order to investigate common geometric patterns in the development of the aneurysms: the ICA centerline was subdivided in major bends on the basis of its curvature and torsion, each bend being identified by a curvature maximum and its two closest torsion peaks. The aneurysm neck position was investigated in terms of position of the neck origin o_{an} along the ICA centerline, distance between the neck origin and the curvature maximum of the hosting bend and distribution of aneurysms on the siphon bends. Comparing the direction of the neck vector v_{an} with the n_{ff} at the neck origin, the aneurysms were classified as developing along the inner or the outer wall of the parent vessel; the orientation of the neck with respect to the parent artery was also evaluated as the angle between the neck plane identified by n_{an} and the osculating plane defined by b_{ff} which described the ICA local geometry (Figure 3). To characterize the influence of the upstream ICA geometry, the *parallel transport* technique[3,4] was applied: the normal n_{an} was transported along the siphon centerline and the orientation of the neck plane was compared with the ICA osculating planes at different positions in the upstream portion of the artery.

Statistical analysis of the previously introduced quantities was performed with R statistical package.

Results From the analysis of curvature and torsion profiles of the ICA, the siphon could be described as a sequence of near-planar bends concatenated in a non-planar fashion: these results highlight the relevance of non-planarity in the siphon geometry and provides a guide for future studies that aim at investigating the role of non-planarity in hemodynamics. The extent and shape of bends were highly heterogeneous, but the curvature of all ICAs showed similar patterns; for example a high curvature peak corresponding to a sudden sharp bend was always identifiable: anatomically this bend corresponds to the final bend of the cavernous segment of the ICA, where anatomical constraints force the artery to follow a path similar to an italic s, before entering the intra-cerebral space.

The aneurysms were located in the distal upper portion of the ICA, at a mean distance of 12.5 mm from the ICA bifurcation with the ruptured group appearing to be positioned more distally than the unruptured (t-test, $p < 0.05$). The analysis of the distribution of lesions on the siphon bends showed a predominance of aneurysms to develop on distal ones, on or after the sharp bend of the ICA cavernous segment previously identified; a significant difference was found between aneurysm distributions in the ruptured and unruptured groups (Fisher's test, $p < 0.05$); these findings may result in the classification of aneurysms in the intra-cerebral space at a higher risk of rupture. Last, the majority of aneurysms developed within the hosting bend at the site of the curvature maximum or within one diameter from it, where the region of flow impingement is expected. Moreover, as far as the geometry of the hosting bend was considered, the ruptured group showed a less pronounced peak of curvature than the unruptured one, a geometric feature of the parent artery that may have an impact on intra-aneurysmal flow structures, as well as wall shear stress distribution and washout mechanisms.

The analysis of the necks orientation showed that the aneurysms were as expected predominantly located along the outer wall of the hosting bends, where the action of hemodynamics forces are stronger. As for the orientation with respect to the ICA local geometry, we could not find any particular preferential orientation of the necks at the site of the lesion. However, the angle distributions upstream the aneurysm neck showed a gradual tendency to orientate orthogonally to the local osculating plane. Angle distributions were tested for uniformity with a chi-square test: all distributions were not significantly different from uniform except at -4mm from the neck origin. A deeper analysis showed that for abrupt changes in the orientation of ICA planes of curvature, the neck predominantly orientates within the local plane of curvature, while for smaller changes the orientation of the neck with respect to the parent artery is more variable. This link between the location of the aneurysm neck and the upstream geometry of the parent artery hints a possible role for hemodynamics in the determination of the site of lesion and suggests further characterization of the hemodynamics arising from non-planar concatenation of bends.

3. CONCLUSIONS

In the present work, we quantitatively investigated the geometric relationship between ICA lateral aneurysms and their parent vasculature through the use of robust and objective criteria. The results here presented provide evidence for an association between geometry and aneurysm development, supporting the hypothesis of a role of hemodynamics in aneurysmal disease.

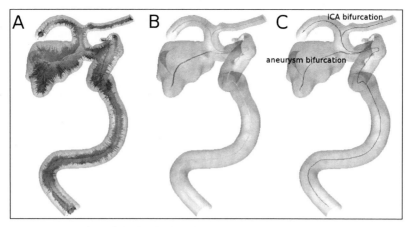

Figure 1. A. 3D reconstruction of the luminal surface of an ICA hosting an aneurysm and its bifurcation into MCA and ACA; the computed Voronoi diagram is shown inside the model; B. centerlines of all the branches and the aneurysm sac; C. identification of the ICA and the aneurysm bifurcations.

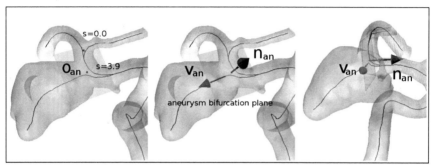

Figure 2. Determination of the location and the orientation of the aneurysm neck by means of the neck origin o_{an}, the bifurcation aneurysm normal n_{an} and the aneurysm vector v_{an}.

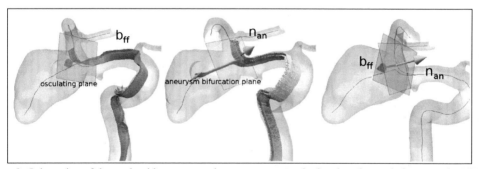

Figure 3. Orientation of the neck with respect to the parent artery calculated as the angle between the ICA local osculating plane and the aneurysm bifurcation plane.

REFERENCES

1. Castro MA, Putman CM, Cebral JR. Computational fluid dynamics modeling of intracranial aneurysms: effects of parent artery segmentation on intra-aneurysmal hemodynamics. AJNR Am J Neuroradiol 2006; 27(8):1703-9.

2. Sato K, Imai Y, Ishikawa T, Matsuki N, Yamaguchi T. The importance of parent artery in intra-aneurysmal hemodynamics. *Med Eng Phys,* 2008; 30(6):774-82.

3. Antiga L, Steinman DA. Robust and objective decomposition and mapping of bifurcating vessels. *IEEE Transactions on Medical Imaging,*23(6):704-13,2004.

4. Piccinelli M, Veneziani A, Steinman DA, Remuzzi A, Antiga L. A framework for geometric analysis of vascular structures: applications to cerebral aneurysm. *IEEE Transactions on Medical Imaging* - Submitted.

5. Antiga L, Steinman DA. The Vascular Modeling Toolkit http://www.vmtk.org. Last access Mar 13, 2009.

1st International Conference on Mathematical and Computational Biomedical Engineering - CMBE2009
June 29 - July 1, 2009, Swansea, UK
P.Nithiarasu and R.Löhner (Eds.)

SENSITIVITY OF FLOW PATTERNS IN CEREBRAL ANEURYSMS

Jens-D. Müller, Maki Jitsumura
Dept. of Engineering, Queen Mary, University of London, Mile End Road, London, UK,
j.mueller@qmul.ac.uk, ex04148@qmul.ac.uk

Nils H. F. Müller-Kronast
Fort Wayne Neurological Center, Fort Wayne IN, USA,

ABSTRACT

The sensitivity of the flow pattern in a patient-specific cerebral aneurysm on the ACoA is assessed with respect to uncertain parameters. Outflow balance and segmentation parameters such as smoothing level and threshold are shown to have a significant effect on the flow pattern. A novel methodology based on sensitivity analysis is proposed as a potential predictor for rupture.

Key Words: *cerebral aneurysm, flow stability, sensitivity analysis.*

1 INTRODUCTION

Patient-specific simulations of cerebral aneurysms [8,2] have been presented over the past years. They bear the potential to reproduce the patient's haemodynamics accurately and a large number of such studies have been presented. However simple correlations with peak pressures or wall shear stress have so far not been shown to have a statistically significant link to aneurysmal rupture.

More recently, Cebral et al. have proposed an approach based on characterising the pulsatile changes in the flow pattern [4]. Their study shows a significant link of rupture with impingement size, and a near significant link with the existence unstable flow patterns that undergo strong changes during the cycle. Considering the temporal stability allows to include more realistic haemodynamic effects than time-averaged or peak-value indicators can offer.

A small number of studies have considered the sensitivity of the flow simulation with respect to numerical discretisation, mesh size [5], variations in mean flow [7] flow division, waveform, effect of small vessels, mesh size and non-Newtonian viscosity [3]. In general it was found that these parameters resulted only in relatively proportional, linear changes. On the other hand, in the particular case of aneurysms on the anterior communicating artery (ACoA), the flow did show strong sensitivity to changes in inflow-balance, inflow geometry, phase shifts in the waveform, or altering the waveforms between left and right inlets [2].

While one could assess the inflow velocity and waveform in the A1 segments with transcranial Doppler with reasonable accuracy, the A2 outflow vessels are not accessible to TCD. MRI velocity measurements could be performed, but their accuracy is very limited as the vessel will only be resolved with 2-3 pixels with the current hardware. Moreover, even if we were to accurately measure a phase shift or waveform difference in the inlet waveform, it is by no means certain that this difference is a constant feature of the patient's haemodynamics. This puts in doubt the expectations of many authors in the field that with increased imaging resolution, a truly accurate patient-specific flow simulation can be conducted which would then be indicative for likelihood of aneurysmal rupture.

Here we propose to expand from the viewpoint of temporal stability [4] to a more general concept of analysing the stability of the aneurysmal flow pattern with respect to a range of relevant parameters. Our hypothesis is twofold. Firstly, changing flow patterns can be linked to rupture, whether the changes arise from the pulsatile flow or from changes in the patient's state, resulting e.g. in changes in the flow rate, the flow balance or the vessel geometry. Secondly, by assessing the sensitivity of the flow pattern with respect to a range of relevant parameters, we can simulate the stability of the flow pattern in response to a range of haemodynamic parameters as experienced over the long period of growth of the aneurysm.

2 Method and Results

A ruptured 5mm saccular ACoA aneurysm of a 55 year old female was imaged using CT-scan (0.5 mm pixel size). The image has been segmented with MIMICS (Version 11.11, Materialise BV, Belgium). The geometry of the aneurysm including the supplying and draining vessels has been isolated and meshed uniformly with tetrahedra using GAMBIT (Fluent Inc.).

Flow simulations have been conducted in FLUENT (Fluent Inc.) using the incompressible laminar flow equations. Boundary conditions at the inflow of the A1 segments were imposed as velocity inlet based on transcranial Dopper (TCD) measurements of a normal sex-matched patient with ACA-A1 with peak velocities of 0.45m/s and 0.57 m/s on the right (inlet 1) and left side (inlet 2), respectively. A typical waveform for the common carotid artery has been used [6] and results were analysed for the third cycle. A steady-state mesh convergence analysis demonstrated that for this case a mesh with a mesh width of 0.175mm and 600k tetrahedra was very nearly mesh converged.

Unsteady flow computations were performed for variations in outflow split and smoothing parameter. Changes in outlet mass flow split over physiological range alter the flow balance between the left and right branch and reverse the flow in the ACoA. This has a significant effect on the aneurysmal flow pattern as the flow direction reverses in the ACoA, depending on outflow balance.

Smoothing of the extracted geometry is required to remove artefacts from the voxel-grid of the medical image. Fig. 1 shows the resulting surface geometry using three smoothing values, the lower segmentation threshold is kept constant at 180 HU.

Figure 1: Effect of smoothing parameter on the geometry. Left model 1: $\sigma = 0.9$, middle model 2 $\sigma = 0.5$, right model 3 $\sigma = 0.0$.

In the case with strong smoothing $\sigma = 0.9$ the surface of the geometry is smooth and no imaging artefacts are visible. There is a bulge at the sharp bend of the right A1 segment distal to the anastomoses with the ACoA. In the case without smoothing $\sigma = 0.0$ one can clearly identify imaging artefacts which should have been smoothened out: distinct triangular facets on the ACoA, as well as on both A1 segments. There is also a pronounced ridge across the dome of the aneurysm which may be a feature, but may also be due to alignment with imaging planes. The sharp bend on the right A1 segment in this case shows a pronounced bulge which may be a small aneurysm. As has been shown by Castro et al. [1] inflow geometry has a strong effect on aneurysm flow and is to be expected that the resolution of this geometry detail is very relevant.

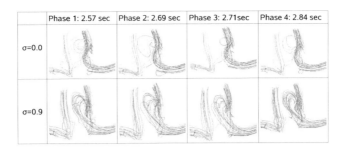

Figure 2: Pathlines coloured by particle numbers in different smoothing factors in pulsatile flow.

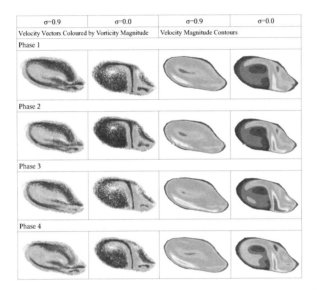

Figure 3: Velocity vectors coloured by vorticity magnitude and velocity magnitude contours with different smoothing factors – Plane B

For the case of an outflow velocity in the left A2 segment of 0.84 m/s, the pathline patterns (Fig. 2) are shown for the two geometry variations resulting from $\sigma = 0.9$ and $\sigma = 0.0$. There are two major differences in the flow upstream to the aneurysm which can be seen to interact with the aneurysm flow. resulting in a distinctly different flow pattern in the aneurysm.

Firstly, one can observe a helical vortex originating from the bulge in the right A1 segment. This vortex persists, is swept into the aneurysm and interacts with the aneurysmal flow. Without smoothing, $\sigma = 0.0$, the surface geometry has a much more pronounced bulge (Fig. 1). This results in a much more pronounced helical vortex as compared to the case with high smoothing, $\sigma = 0.9$. However, the bulge is still present in that case which would suggest that the bulge is not a visualisation artifact but a genuine geometric feature. The smaller bulge in the high smoothing case is less strong compared to the case without smoothing, but it still results in a clearly observable helical vortex. This vortex is weaker as compared to without smoothing, but does interact with aneurysmal flow.

As a second difference, the flow for $\sigma = 0.0$ exhibits a stronger left-to-right flow through the ACoA. One might expect that the flow rate in the ACoA would remain unchanged since both cases have the same left outlet velocity profile with $u_{left,max} = 0.84$m/s. If the inlet and outlet cross-sectional areas were unaffected by smoothing, then this outlet boundary condition would fix the mass-flow split in the two outlets and hence also fix the balancing flow-rate in the ACoA. However, the cross-sectional areas throughout the model will be affected by smoothing, the algorithm used by MIMICS results in a slight reduction which is more significant for smaller cross sections. As a consequence we can observe an increase in mass-flow from left to right through the ACoA.

The velocity field in the cutting plane B (Fig. 2) confirms these findings, the flow fields are completely different. It is remarkable however, that there are no major differences in flow pattern observable in the various phases of the flow. While this flow is very sensitive to variations in geometry smoothing, there appears to be little sensitivity to the large variations in flow rate through the pulsatile cycle.

3 CONCLUSIONS

We have demonstrated that uncertain parameters such as outflow split, geometric smoothing value and threshold level can have a significant effect on the flow pattern. In the presented case reasonable choices of smoothing value lead to slight variations in geometry which in turn lead to completely different flow patterns. On the other hand, this flow pattern appears to be insensitive to pulsatile flow rate variations.

We therefore propose to widen the characterisation of Cebral et al. [4] to analyse flow pattern stability not only with respect to pulsatile flow variations, but also to other relevant parameters, in particular those affecting the geometry.

REFERENCES

[1] M.A. Castro, C.M. Putman CM, and J.R. Cebral, Computational fluid dynamics modeling of intracranial aneurysms: Effects of parent artery segmentation on intra-aneurysmal hemody-namics, *Am. J Neuroradiology*, 27:1703 – 1709, Nov 2006.

[2] M.A. Castro, C.M. Putman CM, and J.R. Cebral, Patient-specific computational fluid dynamics modeling of anterior communicating artery aneurysms: A study of the sensitivity of intra-aneurysmal flow patterns to flow conditions in the carotid arteries, *Am. J Neuroradiology*, 27:2061 – 2068, Nov 2006.

[3] J.R. Cebral, M.A. Castro, S. Appanaboyina, et al., Efficient pipeline for image-based patient-specific analysis of cerebral aneurysm hemodynamics: Technique and sensitivity, *IEEE Transactions on Medical Imaging*, 24:457–467, 2005.

[4] J.R. Cebral, M.A. Castro, M.A. Burgess et al., Characterization of cerebral aneurysms for assessing risk of rupture by using patient-specific computational hemodynamics models, *Am. J Neuroradiology*, 26:2550 – 2559, Sep 2005.

[5] A.G. Radaelli et al, Reproducibility of haemodynamical simulations in a subject-specific stented aneurysm model - a report on the virtual intracranial stenting challenge 2007, *J. Biomech.*, 41:2069–2081, 2008.

[6] D.W. Holdsworth, C.J.D. Norley, R. Fraynek, et al., Characterization of common carotid artery blood-flow waveforms in normal human subjects, *Physiol. Meas.*, 20(219-240), 1999.

[7] P. Venugopal, D. Valentino, H. Schmitt et al., Sensitivity of patient-specific numerical simulation of cerebal aneurysm hemodynamics to inflow boundary conditions, *J. Neurosurgery*, 106(6):1051–1060, 2007.

[8] D.A. Steinman, J.S. Milner, and C.J. Norley CJ et al, Image-based computational simulation of flow dynamics in a giant intracranial aneurysm, *AJNR Am J Neuroradiol*, 24:559–66, 2003.

1st International Conference on Mathematical and Computational Biomedical Engineering - CMBE2009
June 29 - July 1, 2009, Swansea, UK
P.Nithiarasu and R.Löhner (Eds.)

Wall shear stress in the Internal Carotid Artery and its relation to aneurysm location

Tiziano Passerini
Alessandro Veneziani
Department of Mathematics and Computer Science, Emory University, 400 Dowman Dr., W401
Atlanta, GA 30322, tiziano@mathcs.emory.edu, ale@mathcs.emory.edu

Laura M. Sangalli
Piercesare Secchi
Simone Vantini
MOX, Department of Mathematics, Politecnico di Milano, via Bonardi 9, 20133 Milano,
laura.sangalli@polimi.it, piercesare.secchi@polimi.it, simone.vantini@polimi.it

ABSTRACT

In the framework of the Aneurisk project, an extensive statistical investigation has been conducted on the geometrical features of the Internal Carotid Artery, finding that certain spatial patterns of radius and curvature are associated to the presence and to the position of an aneurysm in the cerebral vasculature. Starting from this observation, a classification strategy for vascular geometries has been devised. In the present work, blood flow has been simulated in the patient-specific vascular geometries reconstructed in the context of the Aneurisk project, and an index of the mechanical load exerted by the blood on the vascular wall near the aneurysm has been defined. Finally, it has been shown that certain values of the mechanical load are associated to the presence and the location of an aneurysm in the cerebral circulation.

Key Words: *blood flow, wall shear stress, aneurysm, statistical classification.*

1 INTRODUCTION

The Aneurisk research project (2005-2008, *http://www2.mate.polimi.it:9080/aneurisk*) was developed by a joint venture of different subjects: academic and non academic research centers (MOX - Department of Mathematics, Politecnico di Milano; LaBS - Department of Structural Engineering, Politecnico di Milano; "M. Negri" Institute for Farmacological Research, Bergamo), medical centers (Dipartimento di Neurochirurgia, Università degli Studi di Milano; Ospedale Niguarda Ca' Granda di Milano; Ospedale Maggiore Policlinico di Milano), industrial partners (Siemens Medical Solutions Italy; Fondazione Politecnico di Milano). The main goal of Aneurisk project was to develop a framework for the analysis of cerebral vascular geometries. The project was based on the idea of a stream of information starting from the medical image and passing through a series of steps, each one adding a layer of knowledge to the overall process. The first step is image segmentation, together with geometry reconstruction and morphology characterization. It is followed by a modeling step for the simulation of blood flow in realistic geometries and the characterization of the wall mechanics. Statistical analyses represent the explanatory step, for the organization and the extraction of information from the complete data set. The final product of this process is intended to be an "enhanced" medical image, analysed in its more significant features which are then synthetized in a diagnostic (and possibly prognostic) perspective.

The analyses conducted within the Aneurisk project have focused on the Internal Carotid Artery (ICA), a preferential site for cerebral aneurysm development [2]. A conjecture formulated by neuroradiologists at Ospedale Niguarda Ca' Granda was tested, namely that some geometrical features of ICA are different according to the presence and the location of an aneurysm. The idea was confirmed by a classification of Aneurisk data set, proposed by Sangalli et al. [3]. They considered two groups of patients. The first (which we will refer to as the *blue* group) is composed of patients with an aneurysm located at or after the terminal bifurcation of the ICA; the second group (*red* group) is composed by patients having an aneurysm before the terminal bifurcation or healthy. Radius and curvature profiles were studied in the last tract of ICA prior to the bifurcation [4], and patients in the *blue* group were found to have significantly wider, more tapered and less curved ICA's. Moreover within the latter group there is a lower variability of radius and curvature of the ICA. A *similarity index* was defined to measure how the geometrical features of each vessel compare to those of the representatives of the morphological classes [3].

It is well known that blood flow features strongly depend on the vascular morphology: therefore we believe that the differences in the geometry of ICA of patients belonging to the described groups induce different hemodynamic features and that these may trigger the pathologic response of the arterial wall. We then propose a CFD analysis over the Aneurisk dataset, in order to study the blood flow features in the last tract of ICA. Moreover, we look for parameters able to synthetically describe the effects of blood flow on the vessel wall, such as the spatial average of wall shear stress. This information could be used to have a better understanding of the mechanisms of aneurysm development in the vascular district at hand; on the other hand, it could be used to enhance the classification proposed in [3] by combining the mechanical and the morphological characterization of the vessels.

2 HEMODYNAMICS OF THE INTERNAL CAROTID ARTERY

We chose 21 ICA geometry models, based on their score in the morphological classification [3]. In particular, we selected seven geometries of the *red* group having features that strongly distinguish them from the *blue* group, and likewise we selected seven geometries of the *blue* group with features strongly different from those of the *red* group; the remaining seven geometries were chosen among the cases (*red* or *blue*) with features intermediate between the *red* and *blue* group. Following what has been done in [3], we focused our attention on the last tract of the Internal Carotid Artery, prior to its terminal bifurcation. In facts, this location is particularly interesting, since it is a preferential site for aneurysm development [2]. The hemodynamic quantity of main interest was wall shear stress (WSS): we computed the integral average of WSS on a specific region of the vascular wall, corresponding to an interval of curvilinear abscissas on the vessel centerline spanning the last ICA bend and the last tract prior to the bifurcation.

For each one of these geometrical models we obtained a tetrahedral grid, refined on the basis of the surface curvature. The computational domain was assumed to be fixed, corresponding to the hypothesis of rigid vascular walls. We further assumed that blood can be modeled as a continuous incompressible Newtonian fluid, so that the blood flow problem can be described by the incompressible Navier-Stokes equations. Cylindrical prolongations were added to each extremity of the surface, in such a way that the geometrical model presents circular inlet and outlet sections, corresponding to the proximal and the distal boundaries respectively. The length of these cylindrical extensions was adaptively selected as 10 times the clipped section radius. We imposed as inflow boundary condition on the inlet section a realistic flow rate wave form, the amplitude being scaled in order to give the same flow regime in all the computational domains (corresponding to a time-averaged Reynolds number of 350, computed on the inlet section). A zero-stress condition was prescribed on the outlet sections through homogeneous Neumann boundary conditions. For each vascular geometry, three cardiac cycles were simulated, in

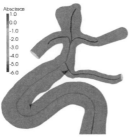

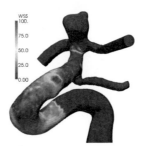

(a) Curvilinear reference system in a vessel bifurcation: the origin is placed in the center of the main bifurcation (where the aneurysm is located). Abscissas in cm.

(b) Wall shear stress (in dyn / cm^2) values in the region of interest.

Figure 1: Evaluation of wall shear stress on a region of interest selected on the vessel surface and corresponding to an interval of curvilinear abscissas on the centerline. Undesired branches are excluded from the analysis.

order to dump the effects of the initial conditions and obtain the periodic solution in the last simulated heartbeat. The spatial discretization was based on the Galerkin finite element method, and was carried out with a P1 approximation for both the pressure and the velocity. The adopted time advancing scheme is a BDF of order 1, with a time step of 10^{-3} s.

The spatial integral average of WSS was computed on the arterial wall, after the removal of possible branching vessels and aneurysms. An example of the considered portion of the ICA surface is shown in Fig. 1. All the fluid dynamics simulations and the WSS computations were carried out with a software specifically realized for Aneurisk project and based on LifeV (*www.lifev.org*), a C++ implementation of algorithms and data structures for the numerical solution of partial differential equations. The treatment of vascular geometries (addition of flow extensions, splitting in branches, identification of regions of interest) has been performed by using the software VMTK (*www.vmtk.org*) [1].

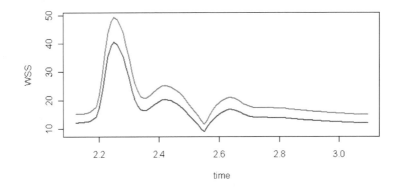

Figure 2: Spatial integral average of wall shear stress (in dyn / cm^2), over the last portion of ICA prior to the bifurcation: median time patterns for the *red* and *blue* groups.

For each geometry we computed the spatial integral average WSS, in the region of interest, as a function of time. Fig. 2 shows the median time patterns for the *red* and *blue* groups. Moreover, we computed the average over time of each of the WSS patterns, getting 21 space-time integral average WSS. We took the space-time integral average WSS as an index of the *mechanical load*. Fig. 3 shows the distribution of

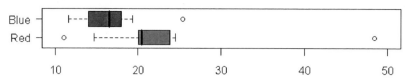

Figure 3: Boxplots of space-time integral average WSS for the *red* and *blue* groups.

the mechanical load for the *red* and *blue* groups. This analysis shows that arteries of patients belonging to the *red* group (that is, with narrower, less tapered and more curved vessels) typically undergo a higher mechanical load, with respect to geometries belonging to the *blue* group, in the same flow regime. This preliminary result strongly supports the existence of a dependence between hemodynamic features and the aneurysm location. A similar result, if observed on a larger number of geometries, would also allow for a characterization of the *red* and the *blue* groups in terms of the mechanical load.

3 CONCLUSIONS

The results of this work suggest that high WSS is associated to the presence of aneurysms in the Internal Carotid Artery. Starting from this observation, based on the presented data set, it may be conjectured that a high-WSS environment, induced by geometrical features, predisposes to the development of the pathology. The *in-silico* setup here presented, and its further improvements, stand as a candidate tool to give a synthetic description of the mechanical solicitation exerted by blood flow on the vascular wall. More than that, our results show that it might be used to characterize cerebral vascular geometries which feature the presence of an aneurysm. In particular, once the fluid dynamical analysis will be completed on the entire Aneurisk dataset of geometries, we shall also quantify to what extent the hemodynamic features help in characterizing different aneurysmal locations with respect to the sole morphological features. In this respect, it is worth noting that the information provided by CFD could have a prognostic value, helping to assess the evolution trend of the studied vessels: geometries featuring high WSS in the region near the bifurcation could be more prone to the development of an aneurysm in ICA.

Further application and improvement of this twofold approach, morphological and hemodynamic, is likely to give a greater insight and comprehension of cerebral aneurysms.

REFERENCES

[1] L. Antiga, B. Ene-Iordache, L. Caverni, G. P. Cornalba, and A. Remuzzi, Geometric reconstruction for computational mesh generation of arterial bifurcations from CT angiography, *Computerized medical imaging and graphics*, 26, 227-35, 2002.

[2] M. Piccinelli, S. Bacigaluppi, E. Boccardi, B. Ene-Iordache, A. Remuzzi, A. Veneziani, and L. Antiga, Influence of Internal Carotid Artery geometry on aneurysm location and orientation: a computational geometry study, Emory University, Technical report, 2008.

[3] L. M. Sangalli, P. Secchi, S. Vantini, and A. Veneziani, A Case Study in Exploratory Functional Data Analysis: Geometrical Features of the Internal Carotid Artery, *Journal of the American Statistical Association*, Vol. 104, No. 485: 3748, 2009.

[4] L. M. Sangalli, P. Secchi, S. Vantini, and A. Veneziani, Efficient estimation of three-dimensional curves and their derivatives by free-knot regression splines, applied to the analysis of inner carotid artery centrelines, *Journal of the Royal Statistical Society, Ser. C*, Vol. 58, part 3, 2009.

Large-scale CFD in Cerebral Hemodynamics: Characterizing Arterial Flow

G. Houzeaux, R. Aubry, M. Vázquez, and H. Calmet
Barcelona SuperComputing Center, Nexus I, Campus Nord UPC, Barcelona, Spain,
mariano.vazquez@bsc.es

F. Mut, S. Wright, G. Ascoli, J. Cebral
George Mason University, Fairfax, Virginia, USA, jcebral@gmu.edu

ABSTRACT

The objective of this work is to characterize the hemodynamics in normal cerebral arteries and establish normal baseline values of blood flow variables along normal arteries such as wall shear stress, velocity magnitudes, secondary or swirling flows, etc. This information is highly valuable to compare with pathological values in diseased vessels in order to better understand the role of hemodynamics in the processes responsible for the initiation, progression and outcome of cerebrovascular diseases. In order to achieve this goal, a massive use of computational resources becomes a must, being efficiency a premise as important as accuracy. In this paper we present the Computational Fluid Dynamics (CFD) background of the project, which is a parallel incompressible flow solver. The numerical scheme is FEM-based, stabilized by means of Variational Multi Scales. The solution strategy is a fractional formulation, based on an preconditioned Orthomin(1) iteration for the pressure Schur complement. The momentum equations are solved with a BiCGSTAB/GMRES solver and the preconditioned Schur complement system with a Deflated Conjugate Gradient solver.

Key Words: *Computational Hemodynamics, Cerebrovascular Diseases, CFD, Parallelization, Variational Multi Scale*

1 INTRODUCTION

Stroke or brain infarct is the third cause of death after heart disease and cancer in industrialized countries and the leading cause of long term disability. There are two types of strokes: ischemic and hemorrhagic. Ischemic strokes are caused by a diminution of blood flow to a part of the brain, typically caused by atherosclerotic occlusion of the main arteries supplying the brain (e.g. the carotid arteries). Hemorrhagic strokes are most commonly caused by the rupture of an intracranial aneurysm and bleeding into the subarachnoid space [1, 2]. The mechanisms responsible for the initiation, progression and rupture of intracranial aneurysms are not well understood. Previous studies have identified the hemodynamics, wall biomechanics and peri-aneurysmal (extravascular) environment as key players [3]. Although the relative importance, interaction and exact function of these factors remains poorly understood, hemodynamics is though to play an important role. The hemodynamics in cerebral aneurysms has been studied using experimental and computational models using the patient-specific vascular geometry obtained from anatomical images [4-9]. These studies have characterized the complex hemodynamics inside cerebral aneurysms. However, there is a lack of information regarding the normal hemodynamic conditions at the location of these aneurysms. This information is extremely valuable in order to quantify the local differences in hemodynamic variables such as the wall shear stress between normal and diseased arteries. This is important to establish thresholds below or above which the hemodynamic variables can be considered "abnormal". Therefore, the final goal of this project is to characterize the hemodynamics in the cerebral arteries of normal subjects.

This paper is an introduction to the larger research project to be carried on and deals with the Computational Mechanics side of the problem. In it, it is described the numerical formulation and its implementation, focusing in what is central when solving such large scale problems: both the numerical and computational efficiency of the simulation process. We also show how performance analysis tools can help developers to improve the parallel behaviour of their codes. As a second main issue, we introduce some particularities of Biomechanics' grand challenge cases, like this one. The paper ends with numerical examples.

2   THE METHOD

2.1   General Description

In order to characterize the normal brain hemodynamics, we propose to construct subject-specific models of healthy brain arteries from magnetic resonance angiography (MRA) images of normal subjects. A series of 60 high resolution MRA datasets covering the entire brain obtained using a 3T scanner has been collected though our collaboration with the UCLA Center for Computational Biology. To date, more than 40 of these datasets have been segmented using semi-automatic tools. These tools provide a hierarchical representation of the brain vascular trees covering several arterial generations. We propose to use these detailed vascular reconstructions to build 3D subject-specific computational fluid dynamics (CFD) models. For this purpose, a cylindrical surface is created along each arterial branch, and all branches are subsequently fused to form a watertight surface model of the brain vasculature. This geometry is then meshed using an advancing front method with local element sizes prescribed using adaptive background grids and sources [10, 11]. Typical computational grids contain between 20 and 100 million tetrahedral elements for over 100 arterial branches. The blood flow is modeled by the 3D unsteady Navier-Stokes equations. As a first approximation, blood is assumed Newtonian and the vessel walls rigid. Since subject-specific physiologic flow information is not available, boundary conditions are derived form blood flow measurements obtained using phase-contrast magnetic resonance techniques on normal volunteers. The example shown in this paper has constant flow prescribed at the inlets, leaving the transient boundary conditions' example to be presented at the conference.

In summary, we propose to construct a series of subject-specific brain arterial models from MRA datasets, and for each model perform a number of CFD calculations corresponding to different heart rates in order to characterize the hemodynamics in normal subjects under the range of normal physiologic flow conditions.

2.2   The Computational Model

The governing equations are the Navier-Stokes set for incompressible flow. The space discretization is done over a non-structured grid using the Variational Multiscale Finite Element Method. The solution strategy is based on a fractional scheme converging to the monolithic solution. It consists of a preconditioned Orthomin(1) iteration for the pressure Schur complement, exhibiting much higher convergence rates than the classical Richardson iteration which is the core of common fractional step techniques. The momentum equation is solved with a BiCGSTAB/GMRES solver and the preconditioned Schur complement system with a Deflated Conjugate Gradient solver, a keypoint for the efficiency of the algorithm.

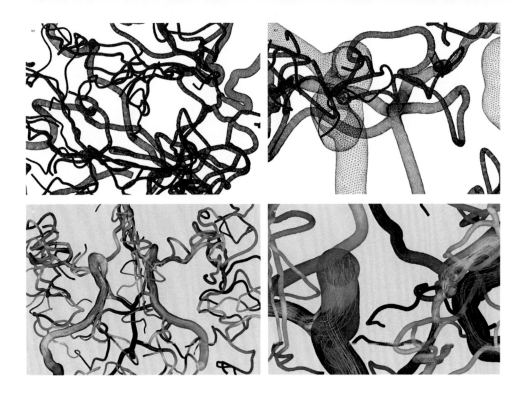

Figure 1: Details of the mesh and results.

The resulting scheme is programmed in the Alya System [14, 15], the in-house High Performance Computational Mechanics code of BSC-CNS. The code is parallelized using a hybrid OpenMP-MPI strategy. The MPI strategy is based in a mesh partition performed firstly, that divides the computational domain in equilibrated pieces that are distributed among the processors available. The automatic mesh partitioner used is Metis [16]. Metis balances the load based on two premises: sub-domains of approximatedly the same load but keeping the minimal surface for the inter domain boundaries to optimize communications. Although this is a useful strategy, when blindly applied it can lead to a large imbalance, like in this particular case, where the extremely elongated and branchy domains with meeting points degrades Metis partition. The mesh as well as some results are shown in Figure 1.

3 CONCLUSIONS AND FUTURE LINES

This paper presents the simulation kernel of a large-scale Computational Biomechanics project, a project that consists in characterizing the normal arterial flow of the brain. We describe the project and present the numerical scheme and the strategy to improve the code efficiency, attacking two different aspects: the algorithm (improving convergence) and the code (improving parallel efficiency). The target geometry is a typical case out of the subject-specific models database. At the moment of writting the paper, more models are being analyzed. To complete this task is the first horizon.

REFERENCES

[1]   W.E. Stehbens Intracranial aneurysms, *Pathology of the Cerebral Blood Vessels*. 1972.

[2]   B. Weir, Unruptured intracranial aneurysms: a review. *Journal of Neurosurgery*. 96: p. 3-42. 2002.

[3]   D. Sforza, C.M. Putman, and J.R. Cebral, Hemodynamics of Cerebral Aneurysms. *Ann Rev Fluid Mechanics, 2009*. 41: p. 91-107. 2009.

[4]   S. Tateshima, Y. Murayama, J.P. Villablanca, T. Morino, K. Nomura, K. Tanishita, and F. Vinuela, In vitro measurement of fluid-induced wall shear stress in unruptured cerebral aneurysms harboring blebs. *Stroke*. 34(1): p. 187-192. 2003.

[5]   M. Shojima, M. Oshima, K. Takagi, R. Torii, M. Hayakawa, K. Katada, A. Morita, and T. Kirino, Magnitude and role of wall shear stress on cerebral aneurysm: computational fluid dynamic study of 20 middle cerebral artery aneurysms. *Stroke*. 35(11): p. 2500-2505. 2004.

[6]   J.R. Cebral, M.A. Castro, J.E. Burgess, R. Pergolizzi, M.J. Sheridan, and C.M. Putman, Characterization of cerebral aneurysm for assessing risk of rupture using patient-specific computational hemodynamics models. *AJNR American Journal of Neuroradiology*. 26: p. 2550-2559. 2005.

[7]   D.A. Steinman, J.S. Milner, C.J. Norley, S.P. Lownie, and D.W. Holdworth, Image-based computational simulation of flow dynamics in a giant intracranial aneurysm. *AJNR American Journal of Neuroradiology*. 24(4): p. 559-566. 2003.

[8]   L.D. Jou, C.M. Quick, W.L. Young, M.T. Lawton, R. Higashida, A. Martin, and D. Saloner, Computational approach to quantifying hemodynamic forces in giant cerebral aneurysms. *AJNR American Journal of Neuroradiology*. 24(9): p. 1804-1810. 2003.

[9]   J.R. Cebral, M.A. Castro, S. Appanaboyina, C.M. Putman, and D. Millan, Efficient pipeline for image-based patient-specific analysis of cerebral aneurysm hemodynamics: Technique and sensitivity. *IEEE Transactions in Medical Imaging*. 24(1): p. 457-467. 2005.

[10]   R. Löhner, Automatic unstructured grid generators. *Finite Elements in Analysis and Design*. 25: p. 111-134. 1995.

[11]   R. Löhner, Regridding surface triangulations. *Journal of Computational Physics*. 126: p. 1-10. 1996.

[12]   T.R. Sherman, On connecting large vessels to small. The meaning of Murray's law. *J Gen Physiol*. 78: p. 431-453. 1981.

[13]   R. Aubry, F. Mut, R. Löhner, and J.R. Cebral, Deflated preconditioned conjugate gradients solvers for the pressure Poisson equation. *J Comp Phys*. 227(24): p. 10196-10208, 2008.

[14]   G. Houzeaux, M. Vázquez and R. Aubry, A Parallel Fractional Incompressible Navier-Stokes Solver for Large Scale Supercomputers. Submitted to *J. Comput. Phys.*. 2008.

[15]   G. Houzeaux, R. Aubry, M. Vázquez, A pressure Schur complement solver for incompressible Flows: the Orthomin(1) iteration as an extension of classical fractional step techniques. In peparation. 2008.

[16]   METIS, Family of Multilevel Partitioning Algorithms http:// glaros.dtc.umn.edu / gkhome / views / metis

1st International Conference on Mathematical and Computational Biomedical Engineering – CMBE2009
June 29 – July 1, 2009, Swansea, UK
P. Nithiarasu and R. Löhner (eds)

HEMODYNAMIC EFFECTS IN VIRTUAL ANEURYSM MODELS WITH STENTING

S. Seshadhri[1], G. Janiga[1], G. Rose[2], B. Preim[3], M. Skalej[4], D. Thévenin[1]

University of Magdeburg "Otto von Guericke", Magdeburg (Germany)
1: Lab. of Fluid Dynamics and Technical Flows
2. Medical Telematics & Medical Engineering Group
3: Visualization Research Group
4: Institute for Neuro-Radiology, Medical Department

ABSTRACT

Cerebral aneurysms are found in approximately 1-8% of the population and 90% of these cases result in subarachnoid hemorrhage [1]. Nearly half of these cases will result in death and many more will result in severe neurological deficits despite the best possible medical and surgical interventions. In order to prevent this rupture, endovascular stenting is sought as a new and minimally-invasive treatment paradigm. This important medical problem is therefore attracting growing interest. Aneurysm surgery remains dangerous, in particular because surgeons have limited knowledge of blood flow patterns and complex 3D geometry of aneurysms. The placement of a stent across the neck of an aneurysm has the potential to alter the hemodynamic in such a way as to induce self-thrombosis within the aneurysm sac, stopping its further growth and preventing its rupture [2]. Furthermore, the porous nature of a stent will keep the adjacent perforating vessels patent even after the stent is deployed [3]. As a summary, 'intracranial stenting' is a relatively novel, minimally-invasive and promising treatment paradigm for cerebral aneurysms.

Even though stents have been identified as a potential treatment of aneurysm, there is still no quantitative data available yet on optimal stent design parameters and on the resulting effect on hemodynamics. The present project is thus focused on obtaining a complete characterization and understanding of the flow patterns through non-stented and stented aneurysm models using a Computational Fluid Dynamics (CFD) analysis, with companion experimental validation. This information is essential to determine later if a specific aneurysm is suitable for a particular surgical technique.

The growth and rupture of saccular aneurysms are related to body systemic influences, such as blood pressure and pulsatility, as well as to local factors such as arterial wall properties and hemodynamic stress. The mechanism by which blood flow velocity influences aneurysm formation is thought to be through wall shear stress and pressure load, inducing vibrations and secondary endothelial disruption. To obtain the detailed information needed by medical specialists, a Virtual Aneurysm (VA) configuration is considered in the present project.

Key Words: *Blood flow, hemodynamic, wall shear stress, aneurysm, and stent.*

Configuration and Methods: Different VA configurations have been examined, involving different aspect ratios, different curvatures of the parent vessel, and using either Newtonian or non-Newtonian fluid assumptions. The basic geometry of the aneurysm is based on values for a middle cerebral aneurysm as investigated in [4]. The diameter of the artery is 3 mm and the size of the dome to neck ratio (Fig.1) is varied between 1.3 and 1.6.

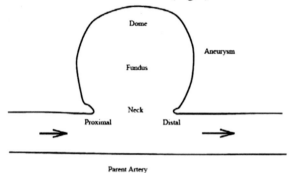

Figure 1: Dome to Neck geometry [4]

Aneurysm geometry, possibly including a stent, is generated using Autodesk Inventor (Fig.2) and later meshed using ICEM-CFD. Prism layers are generated on the walls and tetrahedral layers in the remaining of the model. A standard geometry is considered for the stent in this first study, with wires of diameter 0.2 mm and a spiral with displacement length 3 mm, total length 10 mm. The flow solution is obtained following best-practice guidelines developed specifically for CFD simulations. The simulation procedure has been validated previously by comparing with experimental measurements on an aortic aneurysm model [5,6]. The resulting flow field is computed by considering both, Newtonian and non-Newtonian fluid behavior, since previous studies have demonstrated that this might be an important feature [6].

Figure 2: Example of a geometry with stent

Computational simulations are performed to analyze the intra-aneurysmal flow. The finite-volume package ANSYS-Fluent is used to solve the Navier- Stokes equations. Firstly, the geometry of the artery, aneurysm and stent and the boundary conditions of the flow problem are defined. The intra-aneurysmal inflow, mean absolute velocity, wall shear stress, pressure field and vorticity are then computed and analyzed in order to examine the influence of stent placement.

Results: Various endovascular techniques have been introduced for the treatment of aneurysms. Stenting has been mainly used to treat wide-necked aneurysms. Even though characteristic hemodynamic parameters cannot explain alone the complicated embolization process, they can provide a favorable environment. Therefore, hemodynamic changes caused by the insertion of a stent in both a steady and a pulsatile flow case have been examined in the present study.

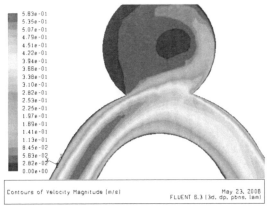

Figure 3: Contours of velocity magnitude without stent

The results from all simulations, as exemplified in Figs. 3 and 4 indicate that the stent indeed induces small but noticeable modifications of the flow patterns. The results without stenting first show an increase in peak flow velocity within the aneurysm for decreasing aspect ratio. The simulations furthermore show in both steady and pulsatile flow cases a noticeable flow penetration along the distal side of the aneurysm neck and a vortex formation within the aneurysm.

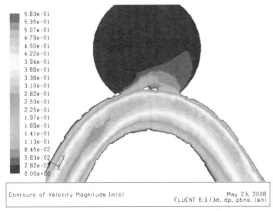

Figure 4: Contours of velocity magnitude with stent (same scale as Fig.3)

This vortex moves towards the distal part of the aneurysm when the inflow velocity increases. Stenting systematically leads to a reduction in flow penetration and peak velocity within the aneurysm (compare Fig.3 to Fig.4). Our results can thus help explain *in vivo* thrombus formation within an aneurysm after placement of a stent, compatible with local hemodynamics. Furthermore, the design and development of optimised stents can be carried out based on CFD, providing a suitable treatment for selected cerebral aneurysms. Further results will be shown at the conference.

References:

1. Chander Sadasivan, B. B. Lieber, M. J. Gounis, D. K. Lopes and L. N. Hopkins.; Angiographic quantification of contrast medium washout from cerebral aneurysms after stent placement, American Journal of Neuroradiology, Vol. 23, 1214- 1221, 2002.
2. Imbesi S., Kerber C.; Analysis of slipstream flow in a wide necked basilar artery aneurysm: Evaluation of potential treatment regimens, American Journal of Neuroradiology, Vol. 22, 721-724, 2001.
3. Issam A. Awad, Daniel L. Barrow; Giant Intracranial Aneurysms, American Association of Neurological Surgeons Publications Committee, 1995. ISBN: 9781879284227 / 9783131347718.
4. Parlea, L., Fahrig, R., Holdsworth, D.W.; An analysis of the geometry of saccular aneurysms. *American Journal of Neuroradiology* 1999;20:1079-1089.
5. B. Wunderlich, R. Bordás, S. Santhosh, T. Bölke, D. Thévenin, M. Skalej; LDA-Messungen in Blutgefäßen mittels Brechungsindex-Anpassung, Proc. 14th GALA Conf., Rostock, Germany, 47/1-47/7, 2007.
6. G. Janiga, S. Seshadhri, R. Bordás, R. Bade, B. Preim, T. Bölke, Ö. Gürvit, M. Skalej, D. Thévenin; Experimental validation of CFD results in the model of an artificial aortic aneurysm, Proc. ANSYS Conference, Dresden, Germany, 2.2.8, 2007.

1st International Conference on Mathematical and Computational Biomedical Engineering – CMBE2009
June 29 – July 1, 2009, Swansea, UK
P. Nithiarasu and R. Löhner (eds)

Impacts of Flow Vortex on a Chorded Mitral valve in the Left Ventricle

Ming Yi
Key Laboratory for Strength and Vibration, Xi'an Jiaotong University, China
yinmin@mail.xjtu.edu.cn
Xiaoyu Luo
Department of Mathematics, University of Glasgow, UK
x.y.luo@maths.gla.ac.uk
Tiejun Wang
MOE Key Laboratory for Strength and Vibration, Xi'an Jiaotong University, China
wangtj@mail.xjtu.edu.cn
Paul Watton
[3]Institute of Biomedical Engineering, Department of Engineering Science,
University of Oxford, UK
p.watton@eng.ox.ac.uk

ABSTRACT

An Immersed Boundary fluid-structure interaction model is developed to investigate the dynamic behaviour of a designed chorded mitral prosthesis inside the left ventricle. In order to simulate more realistic physiological flow conditions, *in vivo* magnetic resonance images of the left ventricle are used to determine the anatomical structure and the motion of the left ventricle. The ventricle geometry and its motion are incorporated into the dynamic mitral valve model. This model allows us to investigate the influences of the flow vortex generated by the ventricle motion on the valve dynamics, as well as the impact of the motion of the chordae attachment points. Results are compared with two other cases: (i) a ventricle model with no prescribed motion of the chordae attachment points, (ii) a tube model in which the ventricle is replaced by a tube, although the motion of the chordae is incorporated. These special cases enable the influence of the chordae motion and the vortex on the behaviour of the valve to be analysed independently. It is found that the vortex flow helps to reduce the cross valve pressure gradient; however, it can significantly increase the chordae and the valve stretch in the commissural region and make the flow field strongly asymmetric. Surprisingly, we observe that the presence of the flow vortex does not necessarily aid the valve closure.

Key Words: *mitral valve, left ventricle, fluid-structure interactions, prosthetic heart valve, vortex, left ventricle, chordae, 3D dynamic modelling*

1. INTRODUCTION

Compared with the aortic valves, mitral valve (MV) has been understudied due to its complex anatomical structure consisting of two geometrically distinct flexible leaflets; a mitral annulus and chordae tendinae that connect the valve leaflets to the papillary muscles [1] which are located in the walls of the ventricle. The chordae act to reinforce the leaflet structure and prevent prolapse of the leaflets when the valve closes. In addition, they also assist in maintaining the geometry and functionality of the ventricle.

Both experimental and computational analysis can guide prosthesis design; however the advantage of computational analysis is that material and geometric parameters can be easily changed to determine an optimum design. The focus of our research is to evaluate the optimal design of prosthetic mitral valves and guide experimental analysis and design. Computational modelling of the native mitral valve is highly difficult: the geometry of the chordae and leaflets is complex; the dynamic motion of the left ventricle causes a displacement of the papillary muscle base relative to the mitral annulus; the papillary muscles contract and relax during the cardiac cycle; the geometry of the mitral annulus is dynamic and so on. Furthermore, large deformation fluid-structure interactions are present during opening and closing phases.

Recently, the dynamic performance of a bioprosthetic mitral valve has been studied by the present author (Watton et al. 2007, 2008). In these studies, the dynamic behaviour of a chorded mitral prosthesis was modelled using the immersed boundary (IB) method, which accounts for the coupled fluid-structure interactions of the blood flow and the mitral valve leaflets.

In this paper, the MV model is extended to include the effect of the dynamic motion of the whole LV. The IB method is used to describe the fluid-structure interactions between the blood flow and the mitral valve leaflets. The motion of LV is extracted from the in vivo MRI data of a healthy subject. The simulation shows that the vortex has a strong influence on the mechanical behaviour of the valve. The results are compared with the two other cases: the Tube model, in which the LV is replaced by a tube, and the LV Fixed CAP model, in which the chordae positions are fixed in space, although the MV is still placed in a moving ventricle. The main observation is that the presence of the ventricle model changes the flow significantly; it introduces a strong vortex and makes the valve deformation greater and highly asymmetric. It also helps to reduce the valve opening pressure gradient by almost half compared with that of the Tube model. However, the simulation suggests that the vortex flow induced by the left ventricle does not necessarily help with the valve closure.

2. METHODS AND RESULTS

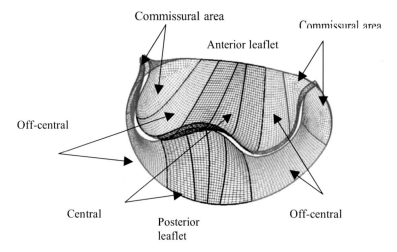

Fig.1 The MV model with posterior and anterior leaflets, and is divided into central, off central and commissural areas.

The geometry of the MV is generated using the software SOLIDWORKS, and for the IB simulation it is represented as a surface constructed from one-dimensional elastic fibre segments, see Fig.1. Following Watton et al. (2007, 2008), we generate the MV model from the IGES file of the designed valve, which was imported to Gambit to create quadrilateral finite element mesh. The nodal coordinate data and the connectivity are then used to create the IB fibre model. For the anterior leaflet, 3718 elements are used to generate 22308 fibre ends, and for the posterior leaflet, 4269 elements are used, leading to 25614 fibre ends. The requirement for the fibre grid is that the maximum grid density should be at least twice as much as the fluid grid.

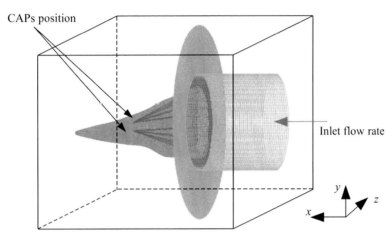

Fig.2 The whole computational model, with the fluid box of size 0.08*0.08*0.08 m³.

The imaging software CMRTOOLS (www.cmrtools.com, Imperial College, UK) is used to analyse high resolution MRI data of the dynamic motion of the ventricle (32 phases per cardiac cycle of about 0.75 sec) from a healthy subject. This software enables the user to interactively define the geometry of the ventricle and the directional axes of the papillary muscles at each time step, which is used to set the boundary of the MV model, see Fig.2.

A periodic velocity profile based on a pulsatile flow rate is exerted on the input fluid of the fluid domain. The pulsatile flow rate has to be calculated according to the change of the volume of the left ventricle due to mass conservation. The immersed boundary method code is used to solve this 3D fluid-structure interaction problem (Watton et al. 2007, 2008). A total of 20,000 time steps (at step size of $0.25*10^{-4}$ sec), is required for each cardiac cycle (0-0.5sec) which took about 35 hours on a Dell Precision T5400 Workstation with 16GB DDR2 667 Quad Channel FBD Memory, and 2330MHz. TECPLOT software was used for graphical post-processing.

Three simulation models are considered: (i) the LV model: MV inserted in LV with chordae attachments points embedded in the wall of the ventricle; (ii) the LV Fixed CAP model: MV inserted in LV with fixed chordae attachment points relative to mitral annulus; (iii) the Tube model: MV inserted in a tube with dynamic chordae attachment points – with same relative motion as in (i).

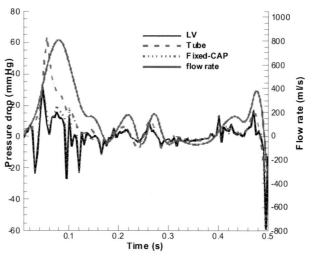

Fig.3 The pressure gradients across the prosthesis MV of the three models. There are more spikes in the pressure drop curve due to the vortex impacts on the LV wall. The flow rate curve is also overlapped to show the correspondence events.

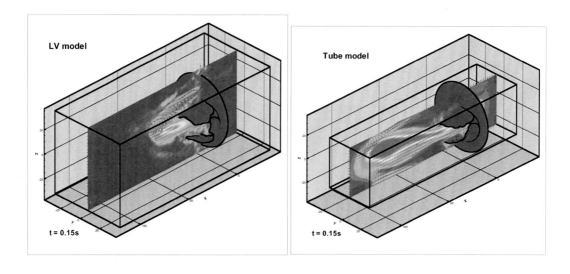

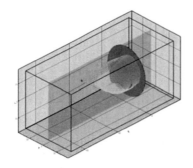

Fig.4 Velocity vector plots of the LV model at t=0.15 sec for the LV and the Tube model. Note although the moving LV is included in the simulation, as indicated by the insert (at t=0), it is not plotted for graphic clarity.

3. CONCLUSIONS

The effect of the vortex flow induced by the left ventricle model on the MV mechanics has been assessed in a three dimensional dynamic fluid-structure interaction simulation using the immersed boundary method. Three models are considered; the LV model in which the chordae run through the mitral valves are fully attached onto the ventricle wall, the LV Fixed CAP model in which the mitral valve is placed inside a moving LV, but the chordae attachment points are fixed in space during the cardiac cycle, and the Tube model in which chordae are moving as in the LV model, but the LV is replaced by a tube. Results show that the LV motion and the induced vortex flow can reduce the opening pressure gradient significantly. On the other hand, these also make the valve motion more asymmetric and increase the valve stretch in the commissural areas. The impact of the chordae attachment motion is also assessed and the results show that although the LV and the LV Fixed CAP models yield very similar results in the flow field, the LV Fixed CAP model has much smaller stretch in the chordae and the posterior leaflet. This suggests that if the papillary muscle can be kept to function (i.e. to compensate the chordae motion) in the MV implantation, it will reduce the valve and chordae stretch significantly.

ACKNOWLEDGEMENTS

We are grateful for the funding provided by the British Heart Foundation, the Royal Society, and the Royal Academy of Engineering.

REFERENCES

[1] Watton PN, Luo XY, Wang X, Bernacca GM, Molloy P, Wheatley DJ. Dynamic modelling of prosthetic chorded mitral valves using the immersed boundary method. *Journal of Biomechanics* 2007; **40**: 613-626.
[2]. Watton PN, Luo XY, Yin M, Bernacca GM, Wheatley DJ. Effect of ventricle motion on the dynamic behaviour of chorded mitral valves. *Journal of Fluids and Structures* 2008; **24**: 58-74.

1st International Conference on Mathematical and Computational Biomedical Engineering – CMBE2009
June 29 – July 1, 2009, Swansea, UK
P. Nithiarasu and R. Löhner (eds)

The analysis of a mechanical heart valve prosthesis and a native venous valve using commercial fluid-structure interaction codes

A J Narracott
Academic Unit of Medical Physics, School of Medicine and Biomedical Sciences, University of Sheffield, Beech Hill Road, Sheffield, S10 2RX. a.j.narracott@sheffield.ac.uk
V Diaz
Department of Mechanical Engineering, University College London, UK. v.diaz@ucl.ac.uk
D Rafiroiu
Department of Electrical Engineering, Technical University of Cluj-Napoca, Romania
dan.rafiroiu@et.utcluj.ro
C Zervides
Department of Mechanical Engineering, University College London, UK. c.zervides@hotmail.co.uk
P V Lawford
Academic Unit of Medical Physics, University of Sheffield, UK. p.lawford@sheffield.ac.uk
D R Hose
Academic Unit of Medical Physics, University of Sheffield, UK. d.r.hose@sheffield.ac.uk

ABSTRACT

This paper reports the application of two commercial codes to the study of distinct cardiovascular problems: dynamics of a mechanical heart valve prosthesis, using ANSYS-CFX, and function of a native venous valve, using LS-DYNA. The mechanical valve dynamics remain consistent for a range of mesh densities and residual criteria but begin to vary once the solution timestep is increased above 0.2ms. A reduction of venous valve orifice area is observed as a result of gravitational loading. Both approaches show promise for further study of these biomedical systems.

Key Words: *Heart valve, venous valve, fluid-structure interaction.*

1. INTRODUCTION

Advances in computational power have allowed numerical simulation of problems which have traditionally been difficult to address. Of particular interest is the behaviour and fluid dynamic performance of both native and prosthetic (replacement) valves within the cardiovascular system. Native valves are formed by soft tissues with complex properties which provide optimum valve performance under normal conditions, whilst prosthetic valves have been designed using either soft tissue or mechanical components. For all valves there is strong interaction between fluid dynamics and solid mechanics, requiring a fluid-structure interaction (FSI) approach to determine equilibrium between solid and fluid physical systems.

In this paper we describe the application of two commercial codes with FSI capabilities to the study of distinct valve conditions: a mechanical heart valve prosthesis and a native venous valve. The applications are distinguished by the relative flexibility of the valve leaflet.

- Mechanical valve: ANSYS-CFX is used to resolve valve motion with an implicit time integration method. The valve leaflet is a rigid body which undergoes large rotations under the fluid loading.
- Native venous valve: LS-DYNA is used with explicit time integration to capture the dynamic response of the highly flexible venous valve leaflets.

2. METHODS

The geometry and boundary conditions of the mechanical mitral valve are shown in figure 1. An idealized single leaflet valve is studied. The leaflet has a single rotational degree of freedom about the hinge point and symmetry is exploited to model half the valve geometry. A non-slip boundary condition is applied at the walls, a constant rate of change of pressure (dp/dt) at the inlet of 13.3kPa/s (100 mmHg/s), generated by the left ventricle, and a constant atrial pressure of 1.995KPa (15 mmHg) at the outlet.

The volume within the chambers and the valve housing is meshed, excluding the solid valve leaflet from the fluid model. The ANSYS-CFX finite volume code was employed with an ALE approach to incorporate mesh deformation effects during transient solutions and an implicit time integration method. The fluid is defined with density 1000kgm^{-3}, viscosity 0.004 Pa s to approximate blood-like behaviour. Solution convergence is monitored based on the RMS value of the normalized residuals at each timestep.

To couple the motion of the fluid and the valve leaflet we compute the rigid body motion of the valve under the action of the fluid forces. This is achieved using internal routines within the software to calculate the total moment, M, about the axis of rotation of the valve leaflet, given by equation 1.

$$M = r_G \left[\vec{F}_G^z \sin\theta + \left(\vec{F}_G^y - G + A \right) \cos\theta \right]$$

(1)

Where r_G is the distance between the axis of rotation and the centroid and θ is the angle between the leaflet and the y axis. The dynamic equation for the leaflet, given by equation 2, is then solved.

$$d\theta = \omega_{old} dt + \frac{M}{2I} dt^2$$

(2)

Where $d\theta$ is the increment of leaflet angle θ, dt is the time increment, ω_{old} is the angular velocity at the beginning of the current time step and M is the moment about the axis of rotation of the leaflet. The moment of inertia of the leaflet, $I = 6.6E-8$ kgm^2. The motion of the leaflet results in a displacement of the fluid mesh at the boundary with the leaflet geometry. Mesh movement is applied at the start of each timestep based on the fluid forces calculated at the previous timestep. This constitutes an explicit approach, which may result in a sensitivity of results to the timestep size chosen for solution.

	Coarse	Ref	Fine	Large Δt	Small Δt	Large RMS	Small RMS
Mesh elements	**33,739**	53,055	**88,600**	53,055	53,055	53,055	53,055
Timestep	0.2ms	0.2ms	0.2ms	**2ms**	**0.05ms**	0.2ms	0.2ms
RMS criteria	1e-5	1e-5	1e-5	1e-5	1e-5	**1e-4**	**1e-6**

Table 1: Parameters used for numerical sensitivity study

The sensitivity of the leaflet dynamics was investigated with variation of mesh density, timestep size and RMS convergence criteria as shown in Table 1. These sensitivity tests were undertaken during the early phase of the valve motion, before remeshing of the fluid volume is required. Manual remeshing of the fluid domain to obtain results through to valve closure is reported elsewhere [1].

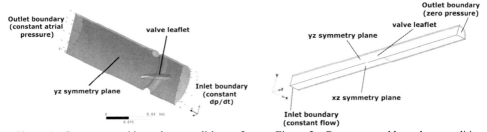

Figure 1: Geometry and boundary conditions of mechanical valve model

Figure 2: Geometry and boundary conditions of native venous valve model

The venous valve geometry and boundary conditions are shown in figure 2, half a single valve leaflet is modeled in a quarter of the vessel, which is represented by a cylinder of diameter 1.19 cm (representative of the femoral vein [2]). The valve is located between z = 0.1 m and 0.112 m of a 0.2m vessel length. Leaflet geometry is defined based on qualitative superficial valve geometry obtained during a previous study [3] with an axial length twice that of the vessel radius and radius of curvature 17.73 mm (150% of the leaflet axial length). The solid domain (vein wall and valve leaflet) is meshed with four node shell elements and the fluid domain is meshed with hexahedral eight node elements. The boundary between fluid and void is co-located with the vessel wall.

The inlet fluid condition is a parabolic velocity profile which represents the flow into the vein from the distal (ankle) end of the vessel at a constant flow rate of 15.1 ml s-1 [2]. An initial parabolic velocity profile is applied throughout the vessel, assuming developed flow. Zero pressure is applied at the outlet to represent the low resistance outflow as blood drains into the larger veins towards the heart. All degrees of freedom are constrained in the solid domain at both the inlet and outlet. After a short period of 0.15 seconds an instantaneous gravitational body force is applied to simulate the effects of a sudden change in posture from supine to standing. The initial boundary conditions are maintained throughout the simulation.

The methods used to model the fluid and solid components are similar to those described by other authors [4]. An elastic modulus of 1MPa is specified for the vein wall, with a wall thickness of

1.182mm. Leaflet thickness and leaflet stiffness are specified as 0.05mm and 0.25MPa respectively. The fluid is modeled as a compressible, Newtonian fluid with density of 1000 kg m-3 and dynamic viscosity 0.004 Pa.s. A value of bulk modulus K = 1.27E+7 Pa was used in the current study, which represents a fluid with wavespeed of 112 ms^{-1} and requires an explicit timestep of the order 1e-6 seconds. It is assumed that compressibility effects will be negligible until the wavespeed of the fluid approaches that of the wavespeed associated with the elasticity of the vessel wall, determined from the Moens-Korteweg equation:

$$c = \left(Eh/2R\rho\left(1-v^2\right)\right)^{\frac{1}{2}}$$

(3)

which gives a value of c = 11.5ms-1, ten times lower than the wavespeed associated with the fluid alone.

An Arbitrary Lagrangian Eulerian (ALE) approach is adopted for the fluid domain in LS-DYNA with acceleration and velocity coupling between the fluid and solid components.

3. RESULTS

Mechanical prosthetic valve dynamics (sensitivity analysis) Valve dynamics was observed to be consistent with variation of most parameters described in Table 1, with less than 0.4 degrees difference in the leaflet opening angle at a solution time 0.08 seconds. The exception to this was when the timestep was reduced to 0.002 seconds, where there was a 2.4 degree difference in the calculated leaflet angle from the reference parameter analysis. A comparison of the leaflet position and local velocity vectors between the reference parameter analysis and the 0.002 second timestep analysis is shown in figure 3a. Figure 3b shows the difference in the time history of the leaflet angle for these two analyses.

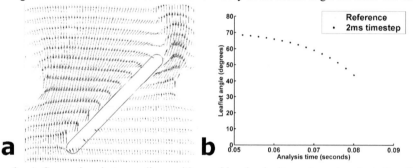

Figure 3: a) Comparison between disc position and local velocity vectors at analysis time 0.08 seconds between the reference parameter analysis (black) and the increased timestep (0.002 seconds) analysis (grey) b) Comparison of the time history of leaflet angle between the reference and reduced timestep analyses.

Native venous valve function Figure 4 shows the velocity vectors local to the venous valve at a number of time points throughout the simulation. A reduction of valve orifice area of 5% is observed between 0.15 seconds, the instant at which the gravitational load is applied and 0.178 seconds, the maximum initial valve closure after gravitational loading.

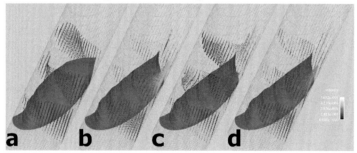

Figure 4: Valve deformation and local velocity vectors at a) 0.048 seconds, during initial valve opening phase b) 0.15 seconds, the instant at which the gravitational body force is applied c) 0.166 seconds, peak reverse flow behind the valve leaflet d) 0.178, maximum initial valve closure after gravitational loading

4. DISCUSSION

In the case of the mechanical valve, the consistency of the results with variation in the solution parameters provides confidence in the stability of the numerical scheme used to update the leaflet position as a result of the imposed fluid forces. The noted exception occurs when the timestep size is significantly reduced, this is likely to arise from the adoption of an explicit scheme to impose the leaflet displacements based on the fluid forces calculated at the previous timestep. Such a limitation is unlikely to present significant issues as we have observed during other studies [1] that a small timestep size is required to allow resolution of valve dynamics through to valve closure as the leaflet accelerates. The analysis of venous valve function is of particular interest after the application of the gravitational body force at 0.15 seconds. The valve initially begins to close as the gravitational force acts. The response after the initial closure becomes more complex as a result of the propagation of pressure waves within the fluid domain and the reflection of these at the domain boundaries. It is acknowledged that the oscillations present in the response of the system are determined by artificial wave reflection effects due to the imposed boundary conditions. It is suggested that wave reflection will be experienced *in vivo* due to a number of factors including: changes in vessel compliance, bifurcations upstream of the valve and additional valves in the vein which are not represented in this model. The results of the current study can be compared with experimental observations of valve function reported by Lurie et. al [5]. The opening area of the valve appears to be underestimated and the velocity increase through the valve overestimated in the current study, as Lurie reports reduction in valvular area of 35% and a velocity increase of approximately 200%. A significant limitation of this study which may account for these differences is the simplification of the vessel geometry which neglects the valve sinuses.

5. CONCLUSIONS

Alternate methods of FSI analysis using the commercial codes ANSYS-CFX and LS-DYNA have been presented. Results from the ANSYS-CFX analysis have shown that the dynamics of the mechanical valve remain consistent for a range of mesh densities and residual criteria but are particularly sensitive to the solution timestep. The LS-DYNA study of venous valve function demonstrates that a reduction of venous valve orifice area is observed after the application of a gravitational body.

Both approaches are well-suited to the individual applications and show promise for further study of these biomedical systems. Examination of the cavitation and thrombotic potential of mechanical valves and the local residence of blood constituents close to venous valve sinuses will form the basis of future work.

Acknowledgements

The authors thank Dr Ian Jones and Dr Justin Penrose (ANSYS-CFX) for advice and training and Dr. Brian Walker (ARUP) for support with LS-DYNA software. The work presented here has developed from a number of projects funded under the FP6 EU funded Marie Curie project C-CARES, Romanian University Research Council funding, British Heart Foundation (BHF) PhD studentship FS/05/086/19462 and Engineering and Physical Sciences Research Council (EPSRC) project GR/S86464/01.

REFERENCES

[1]   Diaz-Zuccarini, V., et al., Multiphysics and multiscale simulation: Application to a coupled model of the left ventricle and a mechanical heart valve, *International Journal for Multiscale Computational Engineering*, 6(1), 65-76. 2008.

[2]   Fronek, A., et al., Common femoral vein dimensions and hemodynamics including Valsalva response as a function of sex, age, and ethnicity in a population study, *J Vasc Surg*, 33, 1050-1056, 2001.

[3]   Narracott, A., et al., A validated model of calf compression and deep vessel collapse during external cuff inflation, *IEEE Transactions on Biomedical Engineering*, 56(2), 273 – 280, 2009.

[4]   Carmody, C.J., et al., An approach to the simulation of fluid-structure interaction in the aortic valve, *Journal of Biomechanics*, 39(1), 158-169, 2006.

[5]   Lurie, F., et al., Mechanism of venous valve closure and role of the valve in circulation: a new concept, *J Vasc Surg,* **38**(5), 955-61, 2003.

Realistic Blood Flow Through the Aortic Valve: Simulation and Analysis

M. Astorino
INRIA Paris-Rocquencourt
78153 Le Chesnay Cedex, France
matteo.astorino@inria.fr

J.-F. Gerbeau
INRIA Paris-Rocquencourt
78153 Le Chesnay Cedex, France
jean-frederic.gerbeau@inria.fr

S. Shadden
Departement of Bioengineering
Stanford University, Stanford, USA
sshadden@gmail.com

I.E. Vignon-Clementel
INRIA Paris-Rocquencourt
78153 Le Chesnay Cedex, France
irene.vignon-clementel@inria.fr

ABSTRACT

The purpose of this work is to investigate the fluid mechanics downstream of the aortic valve. Some of the main difficulties in modeling and simulating flow near the aortic valve arise from modeling the fluid-structure interaction, modeling the contact amongst the valve's leaflets, and handling the intense unsteadiness and velocity gradients present in the fluid. The ultimate goal of such modeling is to better understand the flow physics to help clinical decision making and the understanding of pathophysiology.

In this work, computational models are brought together to investigate the pulsatile flow downstream of the aortic valve in a three-dimensional aortic root geometry with realistic hemodynamic conditions. Numerical simulations are performed by means of a partitioned procedure for fluid-structure interaction (FSI) problems in which contacts amongst different deformable bodies can occur. Blood flow kinematics downstream of the valve is analyzed by computing Lagrangian coherent structures (LCS) from the blood flow velocity.

Key Words: *aortic valve, fluid-structure interaction, contact, finite-time Lyapunov exponents, Lagrangian coherent structures.*

1 INTRODUCTION

Heart disease is amongst the major causes of death in the world. According to the World Health Organization, heart disease is responsible for more than 15 million deaths every year [1]. Part of these cases involve disorders of the aortic valve. Valve malfunctions (e.g. valvular stenosis) dramatically modify the normal physiological blood flow, affecting the hemodynamic performance and the efficiency of the heart. Numerical simulations give a deeper insight into the fluid mechanics in the neighborhood of the valve, providing a useful tool to better understand how flow conditions relate to health and disease, or to evaluate interventions that affect blood flow mechanics.

The modeling and the numerical simulation of the interaction between the blood and the valve are challenging due to complex moving geometries, possible contact amongst the valve's leaflets, intrinsic flow unsteadiness and very intense velocity gradients. In this work, two aspects are mainly considered: the FSI between the blood and the valve and the contact that could happen amongst the leaflets of the valve during closure. Both problems are automatically handled by a partitioned procedure introduced in [2]. The scheme is applied here to obtain a three-dimensional realistic simulation of the pulsatile blood flow through the aortic valve.

The rapid movement of the valve and the intense velocity gradients (both in space and time) lead to complex downstream flow, which is often difficult to characterize but nevertheless extremely important from a clinical point of view. Here we propose to compute LCS to better characterize blood flow kinematics downstream of the valve. Lagrangian coherent structures have already been successfully applied to the study of flow in large vessels in [7], to characterize flow stagnation, flow separation, partitioning of the fluid and mechanisms governing stirring and mixing in vascular model. Preliminary but promising results are here briefly reported.

2 SIMULATION AND ANALYSIS OF THE FLOW THROUGH THE AORTIC VALVE

2.1 Fluid and Structure Models

In this study, both the fluid and the structure problems are approximated by means of the finite element method. The fluid is governed by the incompressible Navier-Stokes equations. At the inflow boundary, Γ_{in}, a time dependent velocity profile is imposed. At the outflow, Γ_{out}, the original two-element windkessel model (RC) is used to represent the exponential decay of pressure in the ascending aorta during diastole (when the input flow is zero). For the structure, in view of the ratio thickness/size of the leaflets, we consider the MITC4 general shell element. This approximation is known to be reliable and effective in the two asymptotic states (membrane and bending) and can handle large displacements [3].

2.2 Fluid-Structure Interaction and Multi-Body Contact

Here we briefly recall the main aspects of the partitioned procedure used to solve the coupled FSI and multi-body contact problems. We refer to [2] for more details. The FSI problem is based on a Fictitious Domain formulation. The fluid and structure meshes are independent and the continuity of the displacement of the fluid and the structure is enforced through Lagrange multipliers, as in [4]. The FSI problem is implemented in a partitioned scheme, as proposed in [2] and [5]. Fluid and structure solvers are considered as independent "black-boxes" that exchange forces and displacements. A strong coupling is enforced by means of an Aitken accelerated fixed point algorithm.

At the closure of the valve, the contact of the leaflets is handled with a contact algorithm. The hypothesis of non-penetration of the solid objects defines a non-convex optimization problem, which is solved using the internal approximation algorithm proposed by O. Pantz [6]. This algorithm is able to directly manage the cases of thin structures and self-contact. Moreover, the dual approach used in this algorithm allows us to add the contact problem in the partitioned scheme without modifying any part of the structure solver, thus preserving the modularity of the solvers. This algorithm has been applied to the simulation of a three-dimensional aortic valve, and the result evaluated through different physiological parameters: the rapid valve opening and closing times, the total ejection time and the peak velocity.

2.3 Characterization of Coherent Structures

To understand the transport of fluid from the valve, Lagrangian coherent structures are computed from the velocity field data. We utilized the finite-time Lyapunov exponent (FTLE) approach described in [8]. As shown in [7], LCS can be used to determine the boundary of separated flow, even when the flow is highly transient, as for the data analyzed here. Figure 1 shows four sections of the backward-time FTLE field downstream of the valve at four times during early systole. The sections are obtained by computing the fully 3D FTLE field and then sectioning the field. A distinct attracting LCS is observed in each section. These LCS are sections of a LCS that represents the bounding surface between the ejected jet and separated flow. From this figure we can see the propagation of the jet downstream and the evolution of the cross-sectional geometry of the jet over time. At time 0.09 s the jet is fully established and there are three distinct regions of separated flow.

3   CONCLUSIONS

In this work we investigated the pulsatile flow downstream of the aortic valve in a realistic aortic root geometry by means of FSI and contact computational models. We computed LCS to better understand the transport of fluid from the valve. We believe this method may offer a breakthrough in understanding complex flow physics and be a useful tool to better diagnose unfavorable hemodynamics.

REFERENCES

[1]   http://www.who.int/cardiovascular_diseases/en/

[2]   M. Astorino, J.-F. Gerbeau, O. Pantz and K.-F. Traoré. "Fluid-Structure Interaction and multi-body contact. Application to the aortic valves", *Comp. Meth. Appl. Mech. Engng.*, doi:10.1016/j.cma.2008.09.012, 2008.

[3]   D. Chapelle, K. Bathe, The Finite Element Analysis of Shells - Fundamentals, Springer Verlag, 2003.

[4]   J. de Hart, G. Peters, P. Schreurs, F. Baaijens, "A three-dimensional computational analysis of fluid-structure interaction in the aortic valve", *J. Biomech.* 36 (2003) 103112.

[5]   N. Diniz dos Santos, J.-F. Gerbeau and J.-F. Bourgat. "A partitioned fluid-structure algorithm for elastic thin valves with contact". *Comp. Meth. Appl. Mech. Engng.*, Vol. 197, pp. 1750-1761, 2008.

[6]   O. Panz. "A frictionless contact algorithm for deformable bodies", To appear.

[7]   S.C. Shadden and C. A. Taylor, "Characterization of coherent structures in the cardiovascular system", *Annals of Biomedical Engineering* 36(7), 1152-1162, 2008.

[8]   S.C. Shadden, F. Lekien and J.E. Marsden, Definition and properties of Lagrangian coherent structures from finite-time Lyapunov exponents in two-dimensional aperiodic flows, *Physica D* 212(3-4), 271-304, 2005.

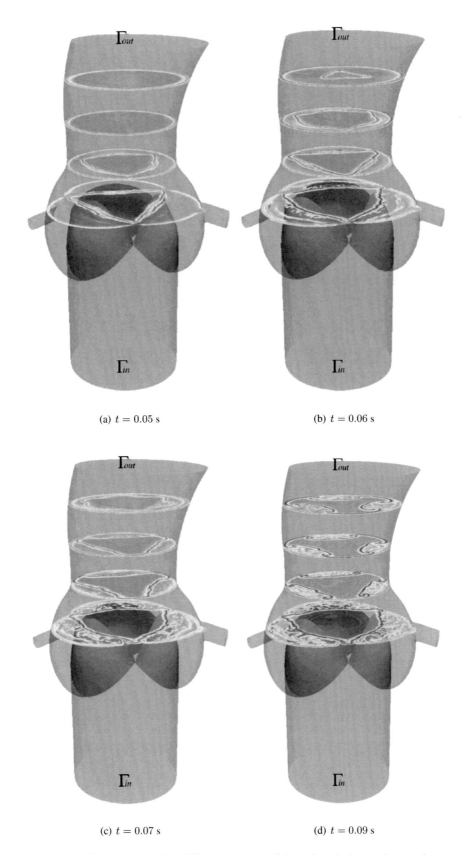

(a) $t = 0.05$ s

(b) $t = 0.06$ s

(c) $t = 0.07$ s

(d) $t = 0.09$ s

Figure 1: Evolution of the LCS downstream of the valve during early systole.

HEART VALVE FLUID-STRUCTURE INTERACTION USING WEAK COUPLING

Jens-D. Müller
Dept. of Engineering, Queen Mary, University of London, Mile End Road, London, UK,
j.mueller@qmul.ac.uk

Key Words: *valve simulation, fluid-structure interaction, weak coupling, artificial compressibility, remeshing.*

1 ABSTRACT

The flow through heart valves and the aortic valve in particular involves the strongly coupled interaction of incompressible blood flow ejected through the valve into the aortic arch. This strong coupling with incompressible flow gives rise to instabilities in simple coupling strategies. Many of the occurring phenomena are not fully understood such as e.g. the thrombus formation in mechanical heart valves or the localised calcification of bio-prosthetic valves. Being able to fully understand, characterise and quantify the flow is essential for the improvement of replacement valve designs. This is of vital importance as every year 250000 aortic valves are replaced [9].

A number of numerical approaches to solving heart valve flows has been proposed. The earliest methods were immersed boundary or ficticious domain methods [5] where the moving valve mesh sweeps over the fixed fluid mesh and the valve boundary is represented through Lagrange multipliers. While this circumvents the need for a modification of the fluid mesh, the the valve surface is not represented in the mesh and accurate prediction of the flow field next to the leaflets is difficult leading to low accuracy of wall shear stresses and local bending.

An ALE formulation is used here to deform the fluid mesh along with the embedded valve mesh. This approach allows the imposition of physical and accurate boundary conditions at the valve surface, however it requires a strategy to modify the mesh under large valve displacements. As an alternative, the fluid mesh deforms along with the embedded valve mesh using an ALE formulation. This approach does allow to impose physical and accurate boundary conditions at the valve surface, however it does require a strategy to modify the mesh under large valve displacements.

Global remeshing onto a new mesh [7] introduces excessive diffusion during the interpolation from old to new mesh. Regional remeshing of poor quality regions [2] improves this, but the most deformed regions tend to be the regions of interest near the moving valve surface which will still suffer from excessive diffusive errors.

This study is based on previous work [4] which proposes two novel approaches to simulating heart valves. The method uses local remeshing where only a cell and its immediate edge-neighbours or face-neighbours are affected by a topological operation such as edge-deletion, node-insertion and edge- or face-swaps. A simple second-order non-conservative interpolation is used, owing to the locality of the topology change diffusive artefacts are minimised. Computational overheads for remeshing are negligible compared to the CFD solver time by the use of a combined node-to-face and node-to-boundary face data-structure.

The second novel aspect is the approach coupling of fluid and structure. Commonly, biological FSI simulations use a projection-type solver for the incompressible flow which requires the use of a strong coupling method where the equations and compatibility conditions at the fluid-structure interface are converged using a fixed-point iteration, typically some 10 subiterations are needed per time-step [6]

The method uses an artificial compressibility formulation for the incompressible Navier-Stokes equations, which allows to use the linearly stable midpoint rule algorithms [3]. In particular the ISS scheme is chosen which satisfies velocity continuity and the geometric conservation law by solving fluid and structure at staggered half time-steps.

The method was validated for mechanical heart valves on a simplified experiment [8] and has been shown to provide very good accuracy for velocities and opening angle at very low mesh resolution.

The original work of [4] used a preconditioning approach based on the Lax-Wendroff scheme requiring only a single flow iteration per timestep to achieve second-order accuracy. However, while the preconditioning kept compressible effects small, they were still present.

This paper presents an implementation method based on Chorin's original formulation [1] embedded in a dual-timestepping loop. The paper will compare the results of the preconditioning formulation of [4] with Chorin's [1] in terms of the effects of compressibility on the FSI, the wall shear stress and the numerical efficiency.

REFERENCES

[1]   A. Chorin, A numerical method for solving incompressible viscous flow problems, *Journal of Computational Physics*, 2(1):12–26, 1967

[2]   K. Dumont, J. M. A. Stijnen, J. Vierendeels, F. N. van de Vosse, and P. R. Verdonck. Validation of a fluid-structure interaction model of a heart valve using the dynamic mesh method in Fluent. *Computer Methods in Biomechanics and Biomedical Engineering.*, 7(3):139–146, 2004.

[3]   C. Farhat and M. Lesoinne. Two efficient staggered algorithms for the serial and parallel solution of three-dimensional nonlinear transient aeroelastic problems. *Computer Methods in Applied Mechanics and Engineering*, 182(3-4):499–515, 2000.

[4]   N. Forsythe. *A partitioned approach to fluid-structure interaction for artificial heart valves.* PhD thesis, School of Mechanical and Aero. Eng., Queen's University Belfast, Belfast, UK, November 2006.

[5]   J. De Hart, G. W. Peters, P. J. Schreurs, and F. P. Baaijens. A three-dimensional computational analysis of fluid-structure interaction in the aortic valve. *Journal of Biomechanics*, 36(1):103–112, 2003.

[6]   D. P. Mok, W. A. Wall, and E. Ramm. Accelerated iterative substructuring schemes for instationary fluid-structure interaction. In K. J Bathe, editor, *Conference on computational fluid and solid mechanics*, pages 1325–1328. Amsterdam; London; Elsevier, 2001; Jun 2001.

[7]   J. M. T. Penrose and C. J. Staples. Implicit fluid-structure coupling for simulation of cardiovascular problems. *International Journal for Numerical Methods in Fluids*, 40(1-4):467–478, 2002.

[8]   J. M. Stijnen, J. de Hart, P. H. Bovendeerd, and F. N. van de Vosse. Evaluation of a fictitious domain method for predicting dynamic response of mechanical heart valves. *Journal of Fluids and Structures*, 19(6):835–850, 2004.

[9]   A.P. Yoganathan, Z. He, and S.C. Jones. Fluid mechanics of heart valves. *Annu. Rev. Biomed. Eng*, 6:331–62, 2004.

1st International Conference on Mathematical and Computational Biomedical Engineering – CMBE2009
June 29 – July 1, 2009, Swansea, UK
P. Nithiarasu and R. Löhner (eds)

TOWARDS THE DEVELOPMENT OF A NUMERICAL METHOD TO STUDY FSI OF HEART VALVES

Akram Joda
John Fisher
Sotirios Korossis
Zhongmin Jin
Institute of Medical and Biological Engineering, University of Leeds
Leeds, LS2 9JT, United Kingdom.
A.A.O.Joda@leeds.ac.uk

ABSRACT

Fluid-solid-interaction (FSI) simulation of heart valves can provide valuable information regarding their deformation and fluid dynamics, which can be used to optimize the culturing/conditioning of tissue-engineered heart valves in bioreactors. The aim of this preliminary work was to develop and validate a coupled 3D FSI model of a bileaflet mechanical valve using the finite element software LS-DYNA (LSTC, Livermore). In parallel to the numerical simulation, pulsatile flow experiments were carried out with a 19 mm St Jude bileaflet valve (St Jude Medical Inc.) for model validation purposes. The FSI method developed during the course of this work can be easily adapted to model tissue valves by using appropriate valvular material properties and geometry. In general, good agreement was found between the 3D FSI model of the bileaflet valve and the pulsatile flow experiments. Future work will focus on applying the developed FSI methodology to investigate the effect of the mechanical properties of different heart valve scaffolds and cultivating conditions on the stress distribution and fluid dynamics of tissue-engineered heart valves and, subsequently, on seeded cell function and tissue remodeling and regeneration.

Key Words: *Fluid-structure interaction, bileaflet valve, tissue engineering*

1. INTRODUCTION

The interest on fluid-structure interaction (FSI) has been grown rapidly in the last decade, especially in the field of biomedical engineering, due to the advancement in computer resources and computational techniques. FSI modelling can play an important role in designing and developing artificial and tissue engineered organs, such as heart valves. FSI models of valves can provide advanced knowledge of valvular dynamics and stress-strain distributions. In general, two methods have been adopted to couple the fluid and solid domains. In the first method, a conforming dynamic mesh is used for the fluid domain by means of the Arbitrary Lagrangian Eulerian (ALE) technique [1], where the fluid nodes on the interface boundary move with the solid structure. This method has been implemented in many commercial and in-house FSI codes. Although this method works adequately for simple problems with small/moderate deformations, it has shown limitations in handling complex fluid geometries. In the second method the fluid mesh remains fixed during the computation, whereas an interpolation method is used to calculate pressure and fluid stresses on the structure boundaries, as in the Immersed Boundary Method (IBM) [2].

Mechanical heart valves are now widely used to replace diseased native valves. About 50% of all implanted mechanical valves are bileaflet valves. This valve has two semicircular leaflets which produce more uniform central flow patterns and reduced pressure gradients and turbulence, overcoming the problems associated with the early caged-ball and monostrut valves [3]. Since the introduction of the bileaflet valves, numerous studies have been conducted to understand the flow patterns around the valve and to improve its performance. Earlier studies have focused on steady or pulsatile flow around fixed leaflets [4], whereas more recently, blood/fluid-leaflets interaction has been targeted [5-7].

In this work, a method to simulate the FSI of a St Jude bileaflet mechanical valve using the commercially available finite element software LS-DYNA was developed.

2. METHODS

2.1. EXPERIMENTAL METHOD

The experimental validation utilized a pulsatile flow duplicator (Fig. 1) developed at the Institute of Medical and Biological Engineering at the University of Leeds. The duplicator was able to replicate the function of the right or the left side of the heart, for testing tricuspid/mitral and pulmonary/aortic valves under physiological conditions. During the course of this work, the duplicator was used to model the left side of the heart for testing the aortic valve. The rig consisted of a linear actuator for the generation of pulsatile flow, a viscoelastic impedance adapter, ventricle and aortic chambers, an atrial reservoir, a compliance chamber, a peripheral resistance tap, peripheral circulation, and measuring instrumentation connected to a PC for data acquisition and analysis. Saline (0.9% NaCl) with density of 1000 kg/m^3 and viscosity of 10^{-3} Pa·s was used as the blood substitute. The ventricle was designed as a cylindrical and rigid Perspex chamber with a diameter 60 mm. Upstream the aortic valve, the ventricle was tapered to 30 mm in 20 mm distance. A high-speed camera was used to capture the motion of the leaflets, which was used to extract the radial leaflet displacement using an image processing software (Image-Pro Plus v4.5). A 27 mm Bjork-Shiley tilting disk monostrut valve was mounted in the mitral position and a 19 mm St Jude bileaflet valve was used in the aortic position. Testing in the pulsatile duplicator was conducted at a cycling rate of 72 beats/min and a stroke volume of 70 ml, whereas the aortic pressure was set to fluctuate between 80 and 120 mmHg (diastolic/systolic).

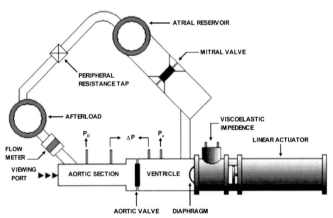

Fig. 1: The pulsatile flow duplicator

2.2. NUMERICAL METHOD

The test rig geometry was generated in LS-DYNA and a quarter of the domain was meshed in the numerical study to reduce the computational time (Fig. 2). The domain downstream of the valve was extended further than in the test rig to insure a uniform flow at the outlet. The finite element software LS-DYNA is a general-purpose explicit, transient dynamic finite element package that can be used to solve the dynamics and deformations of structures, fluid dynamics, and fluid-structure interactions. The package has limited implicit capabilities and a wide range of constitutive material models. This package was chosen in this work because of its ability to handle FSI of complex geometries, such as heart valves, by using a fixed fluid mesh throughout the computation; hence no re-meshing was required. LS-DYNA uses operator-split method to solve the coupled problem. This method divides FSI computation into two steps in each time step [8]. At first a Lagrangian step is performed where the mesh moves with the material and then the advection step is performed to remap the mesh back to its original Eulerian mesh. Although LS-DYNA has been used to study FSI in tissue valves [9,10], this is the first study, to the author's knowledge, to employ LS-DYNA in the FSI simulation of a mechanical valve. The leaflet was modelled as a rigid body with one degree of freedom (x-rotation). In order to simplify the model, the hinges of the valve were ignored and the leaflet were assumed to rotate around two nodes located parallel to the x-axis. The governing equation for the leaflet motion was given by:

$$\mathrm{I}\frac{d^2\theta}{dt^2} = M \tag{1}$$

where I represents the moment of inertia of the leaflet, θ the rotation angle, and M the sum of moments acting on the leaflet surfaces. No constrain was applied to the leaflet at fully open position. The same fluid properties as in the experiment were used in the computation. Two independent meshes were created for the fluid and the solid domains. With regards to the inlet boundary condition, two cases were considered. In the first case, the pressure difference between the ventricle and the aorta obtained experimentally was used at the inlet (FSI_Pin). In the second case, the axial velocity was used as input boundary condition (FSI_Vin). No-slip boundary condition was specified on the walls and the normal velocity was assumed zero in the planes of symmetry.

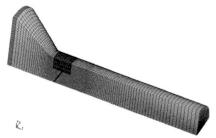

Fig. 2: The computational mesh

3. RESULTS

The leaflet displacement at two instances during opening is shown in Fig. 3. The radial displacements (y-axis) of the experimental and numerical models for a point at the middle of the top leaflet during opening are shown in Fig. 4. The computation of the model with the axial velocity inlet boundary condition (FSI_Vin) is currently in progress, and therefore, the results for FSI_Vin presented in Fig.4 correspond to the interval between the fully closed and fully open valve positions. In general, good agreement was found between the numerical and experimental results, although some differences could be noticed especially at the beginning of opening phase as reported previously [5,6].

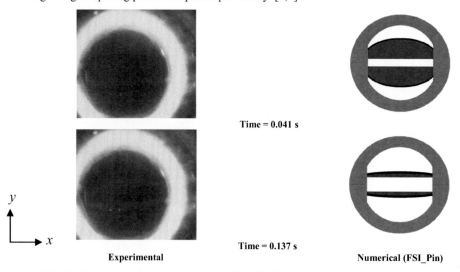

Fig. 3: Experimental and numerical leaflets displacement at two instants during opening phase

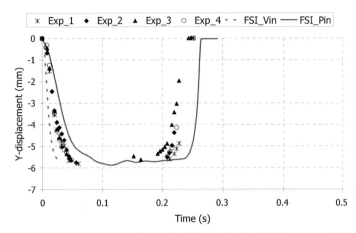

Fig. 4: Comparison between experimental and numerical y-displacement of the leaflet.

4. CONCLUSIONS

This work developed a FSI model of a bileaflet heart valve and validated the numerical results by comparison to experimental pulsatile flow experiments. Two physiological input boundary conditions were tested; the differential pressure and the axial velocity. Applying a differential pressure inlet boundary condition seemed to delay the opening process and overestimated leaflet closure. On the other hand, application of the axial velocity at the inlet caused rapid opening of the leaflet.

The developed methodology can be applied to model the FSI in tissue valves by utilizing appropriate valvular material properties and geometry. Future work will focus on the application of the developed methodology to valvular scaffolds seeded with cells and cultured in pulsatile flow bioreactors, with a view to optimizing the bioreactor culturing conditions.

REFERENCES

[1]   J. Donea, A. Huerta, J. Ponthot, A. Rodrguez-Ferran, Arbitrary Lagrangian–Eulerian methods in *Encylopaedia of Computational Mechanics*. E. Stein, R. de Brost and T.J.R. Hughes, Editors. John Wiley & Sons: Chichester, 2004.

[2]   C.S. Peskin, Flow patterns around heart valves: a numerical method. *J. Comp. Phy.*, 10, 252-271, 1972.

[3]   S.A. Korossis, J. Fisher, E. Ingham, Cardiac valve replacement: A bioengineering approach. *Bio-Med. Mat. Eng.* 10, 83 – 124, 2000.

[4]   M.J. King, T. David, J. Fisher, Three-dimensional study of the effect of two leaflet opening angles on the time-dependent flow through a bileaflet mechanical heart valve. *Med. Eng. & Phy.*, 19, 235-241, 1997.

[5]   Y.B. Shi, Y. Zhao, J.H. Yeo, NH. Hwang, Numerical simulation of opening process in a bi-leaflet mechanical heart valve under pulsatile flow condition. *J. Heart Valve Dis.*, 12, 245-256, 2003.

[6]   A. Redaelli, H. Bothorel, E. Votta, M. Soncini, U. Morbiducci, C. Del Gaudio, A. Balducci, M. Grigioni, 3-D simulation of the SJM bileaflet valve opening process: fluid–structure interaction study and experimental validation. *J. Heart Valve Dis.* 13, 804-813, 2004.

[7]   G.H. Xia, Y. Zhao, J.H. Yeo, Parallel unstructured multigrid simulation of 3D unsteady flows and fluid–structure interaction in mechanical heart valve using immersed membrane method. *Computers & Fluids* 38, 71–79, 2009.

[8]   D.J. Benson, Computational methods in Lagrangian and Eulerian hydrocodes. *Comp. Meth. App. Mech. Eng.*, 99, 235-394, 1992.

[9]   C.J. Carmody, G. Burriesci, I.C. Howard, E.A. Patterson, An approach to the simulation of fluid–structure interaction in the aortic valve. *J. Biomech.*, 39, 158-169, 2006.

[10]   E.J. Weinberg, K.R. Mofrad, Transient, three-dimensional, multiscale simulations of the human aortic valve. *Cardiovas. Eng.*, 7, 140-155, 2007.

1st International Conference on Mathematical and Computational Biomedical Engineering – CMBE2009
June 29 – July 1, 2009, Swansea, UK
P. Nithiarasu and R. Löhner (eds)

FINITE ELEMENT TESTING IN PATIENTS' IMPLANTATION SITE OF NEW PERCUTANEOUS PULMONARY VALVE DEVICE

Claudio Capelli
UCL Institute of Child Health & GOSH, 30 Guilford Street, London WC1N 1EH
c.capelli@ucl.ac.uk
Francesco Migliavacca
LaBS, Politecnico di Milano, P.zza Leonardo da Vinci,32 - 20133 Milan, Ita
francesco.migliavacca@polimi.it
Andrew M. Taylor
UCL Institute of Child Health & GOSH, 30 Guilford Street, London WC1N 1EH
a.taylor@ich.ucl.ac.uk
Philipp Bonhoeffer
UCL Institute of Child Health & GOSH, 30 Guilford Street, London WC1N 1EH
BonhoP@gosh.nhs.uk
Silvia Schievano
UCL Institute of Child Health & GOSH, 30 Guilford Street, London WC1N 1EH
s.schievano@ich.ucl.ac.uk

ABSTRACT

A new stent for percutaneous pulmonary valve implantation has been designed in collaboration with industry, and recently implanted for the first time in man. This new device should guarantee greater adaptability to different right ventricular outflow tract (RVOT) morphologies. The aim of this study was to verify this by mimicking the implantation of the device in 67 selected patients using computer simulation. Magnetic resonance images of patients who underwent surgical treatment were elaborated to reconstruct a 3D volume of each patient's RVOT. The volumes were imported into finite element software where the implant of the stent was simulated. The stent expanded diameters and the areas of contact were measured. The methodology described in this study allowed us to estimate the number of patients suitable for the new device (approximately 40%), to help the clinician in the decision making process and to study potential changes of this device design.

Key Words: *Pulmonary Valve Device, Patient Specific, Finite element*

1. INTRODUCTION

Since 2000, percutaneous pulmonary valve implantation (PPVI) has become a reality [Bonhoeffer, 2000], with over 800 patients already treated worldwide. This technique was based on the concept that a heart valve sewn inside a stent could be reduced in size by crimping it into a catheter, and then introduced through a peripheral vessel to the desired implantation site in the heart. However, due to morphological limitations [Schievano, 2007], the current device is suitable for only 13% of patients requiring treatment. A new device, which would potentially increase the number of patients who could benefit from this minimally-invasive procedure, has recently been designed in collaboration with industry (Medtronic Inc., Minneapolis, USA). The main novelties of this device are an hourglass geometry and the use of self-expanding wires (Nitinol) interwoven with a polymeric graft (Dacron) that should guarantee a greater adaptability of the device to different right ventricular outflow tract (RVOT) morphologies. The aim of this study was to mimic the implantation of this device in 67 selected patients using finite element (FE) modelling, in order to study the stent geometrical conformability and anchoring to the different implantation sites.

2. METHODS AND RESULTS

We retrospectively selected 67 consecutive patients with RVOT dysfunction and dimensions of the pulmonary trunk which would preclude the PPVI with the current device. The study involved 3 phases (Figure 1), which were repeated for all 67 patients: 1) Magnetic resonance (MR) scan – 3D images of the patients' RVOT anatomies were acquired; 2) Imaging post-processing – MR data were elaborated to reconstruct a 3D shell of the patients' RVOT; 3) FE analysis– Patients' reconstructed RVOTs were imported into the FE software (Abaqus/Explicit, Simulia, USA) where they were discretized with rigid elements.

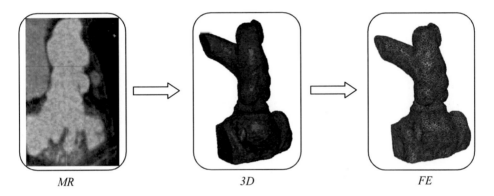

Figure 1. Process of RVOT modelling: left) acquisition of MR images; centre) reconstruction of 3D volume; right) discretization of the FE model

Furthermore, a model of the new stent was designed and discretized with beam and membrane elements (Figure 2a). The analysis consisted of 2 steps. First, the stent was crimped inside the RVOT by radial displacements. Second, these constraints were removed but allowing the stent to recover its original shape (super-elasticity behaviour). In this step, a contact algorithm was activated to allow the interaction between the device and the selected RVOT.

The stent, during the recovery of its super-elastic deformation and whilst in contact with the RVOT wall, adapted its shape to the patients' implantation site morphologies (Figure 2b).

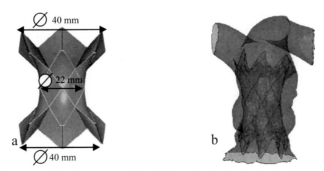

Figure 2. a) Model of the stent and its dimensions. b) Simulation of the implant inside the RVOT

Expanded diameters were measured at the distal, central and proximal section of the stent and an average diameter was calculated for each section. In order to both establish a correct functioning of the valve and to guarantee a safe anchoring of the device to the implantation site wall, the central portion of the stent, holding the valve, has to be deployed at diameters >18mm, whilst the distal and proximal portion cannot exceed 32mm.

Moreover, contact areas with the RVOT wall were identified in the distal and proximal struts of the stent for all patients (Figure 3).

■ Contact Areas
■ Free from Contact

Figure 3. Map of the stent-RVOT contact areas.

The central portion of the stent was fully deployed in 87% of the patients but most of them (48%) did not satisfy the distal and proximal dimension criteria. Therefore, this device could be potentially suitable and implanted safely in only 39% of the patients.

Furthermore, a geometrical modification has been tested using the presented FE methodology. An increase of the proximal and distal diameters of 4mm would enable to guarantee a good stability of the device in approximately 59% of the patients, thus significantly increasing the applicability of this minimally-invasive technique.

3. CONCLUSIONS

The methodology developed in this study allowed us to estimate the number of patients suitable for the proposed new device. Patient morphological reconstructions from MR images combined with FE analyses may help optimise a new device for PPVI. Furthermore, FE analysis of stent implantation may help clinicians to assess the RVOT morphological suitability and to evaluate the stability of the device in each individual patient, before the actual procedure is performed.

REFERENCES

[1]   Bonhoeffer P, Boudjemline Y, Saliba Z, Merckx J, Aggoun Y, Bonnet D, Acar P, Le Bidois J, Sidi D, Kachaner J., *Percutaneous replacement of pulmonary valve in a right-ventricle to pulmonary-artery prosthetic conduit with valve dysfunction.* Lancet. 2000.

[2]   Schievano S, Coats L, Migliavacca F, Norman W, Frigiola A, Deanfield J, Bonhoeffer P, Taylor AM., *Variations in right ventricular outflow tract morphology following repair of congenital heart disease: implications for percutaneous pulmonary valve implantation.* J Cardiovasc Magn Reson. 2007.

COMPUTATIONAL MODELLING OF THE BEATING HEART: BLOOD FLOW THROUGH AN ARTIFICIAL HEART VALVE

C. Wood
Civil and Computational Engineering Centre, Swansea University, c.wood@swansea.ac.uk

A. Gil
Civil and Computational Engineering Centre, Swansea University, a.j.gil@swansea.ac.uk

O. Hassan
Civil and Computational Engineering Centre, Swansea University, o.hassan@swansea.ac.uk

S. Ashraf
Cardiac Centre, Morriston Hospital, Swansea, saeed.ashraf@swansea-tr.wales.nhs.uk

ABSTRACT

A fully coupled three-dimensional solver is presented for the analysis of time-dependent fluid-structure interaction in biomedicine. A partitioned time marching algorithm is employed for the solution of the time-dependent coupled discretised problem, enabling the use of highly developed, robust and well-tested solvers for both the fluid and the structure field problems. Coupling of the fields is achieved through the two-way transfer of information at the fluid-structure interface. Implicit coupling is achieved when the solutions of the fluid and structure subproblems are sub-cycled at each time-step until convergence. A number of examples are presented to benchmark the scheme and to demonstrate the potential applications of this approach in cardiovascular modelling. Specifically, a geometrically accurate three-dimensional model of a beating heart is used to demonstrate realistic blood flow behaviour through a bileaflet mechanical heart valve.

Key Words: *mechanical heart valve, beating heart model, cardiovascular simulation.*

1 INTRODUCTION

Computational engineering techniques that were first developed over thirty years ago have now become fundamental to all aspects of engineering analysis worldwide. In aerospace and other complex engineering applications, expensive experimental testing has now all but been replaced by computational numerical simulation. In cardiovascular medicine in particular, it is believed that a computational engineering analysis approach would enable an extremely detailed understanding of the fluid and structural dynamics processes at work in the cardiovascular system to be built up, enabling a level of understanding well beyond that attainable through conventional experimental methods.

Cardiovascular Disease (CVD) is one of the main causes of premature death in the UK, with over 198,000 deaths occurring per year. Over 10,000 patients per year undergo open heart surgery to replace a diseased native heart valve with a highly-engineered mechanical or biological heart valve. This paper will present a computational modelling approach for the geometrically accurate simulation of blood flow through the beating heart and an artificial heart valve. The resulting fluid-structure interaction

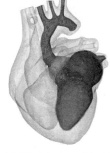

(a) Biological and mechanical heart valves (b) Streamlines through bileaflet heart valve model (c) Whole heart model with interior and exterior surfaces (d) Left heart surface triangulation (e) Streamlines of atrium-ventricular flow

Figure 1: Computational modelling of cardiovascular fluid-structure interaction.

analysis will be used to consider the effects of such surgical interventions on both patients and artificial devices.

2 METHODOLOGY

A fully coupled three-dimensional solver is presented for the analysis of time-dependent fluid-structure interaction in biomedicine [1]. A partitioned time marching algorithm is employed for the solution of the time-dependent coupled discretised problem, enabling the use of highly developed, robust and well-tested solvers for both the fluid and the structure field problems. Coupling of the fields is achieved through the two-way transfer of information at the fluid-structure interface. An implicit coupling is achieved when the solutions of the fluid and structure subproblems are sub-cycled at each time-step until convergence is reached [2].

The boundary-fitted three-dimensional fluid domain is discretised into a tetrahedral or hybrid mesh using in-house mesh generation software [3]. Mesh-moving and adaptive mesh procedures are also implemented to ensure that mesh quality is maintained throughout the simulation.

Unsteady fluid flow over moving boundaries is modelled using an interface-tracking ALE approach. The governing time-dependent incompressible Navier-Stokes equations are solved using a cell vertex finite volume algorithm with a dual time stepping scheme based on the artificial compressibility approach. The computational performance is enhanced by multigrid acceleration and parallelisation [4].

Nonlinear dynamic analysis of highly deformable structures is achieved by using an implicit dynamic scheme which combines the implicit Newmark time integration algorithm with a Newton-Raphson second order optimisation within a finite element structure solver [5].

A number of examples are presented to benchmark the scheme and to demonstrate the potential applications of this approach in cardiovascular modelling, as shown in Figure 1. Specifically, a geometrically accurate three-dimensional model of a beating heart will be used to demonstrate realistic blood flow behaviour through a bileaflet mechanical heart valve. A thorough and detailed understanding of such flows could have great impact on both patient wellbeing and the longevity and performance of such artificial devices.

3   CONCLUSIONS

It is now widely acknowledged that within cardiovascular medicine in particular, there is increasing need for patient-specific computational modelling in many aspects of the diagnostic and pre-operative planning stages of cardiovascular surgical intervention[6]. This work aims to shed light on the complex fluid-structure interaction processes which are fundamental to the successful functioning of devices such as artificial heart valves, and demonstrate a computational approach which enables a level of detailed analysis which has hitherto been impossible using conventional experimental techniques.

REFERENCES

[1] C. Wood, A.J. Gil, O. Hassan, J. Bonet, "A partitioned coupling approach for dynamic fluid-structure interaction with applications to biological membranes", *International Journal of Numerical Methods in Fluids*, 2008. DOI: 10.1002/fld.1815

[2] C. Farhat, M. Lesoinne, and N. Maman, "Mixed explicit/implicit time integration of coupled aeroelastic problems: three-field formulation, geometric conservation and distributed solution" *International Journal of Numerical Methods in Fluids*, v. 21, p. 807-835, 1995.

[3] O. Hassan, E.J. Probert, K. Morgan, and J. Peraire, "Mesh generation and adaptivity for the solution of compressible viscous high speed flows", *International Journal of Numerical Methods in Engineering* **38**, 1123–1148, 1995.

[4] A.J. Gil, Z. Zhang, O. Hassan and K. Morgan, "Parallel multigrid detached eddy simulation algorithm for three dimensional unsteady incompressible flows on unstructured meshes,". *Journal of Aerospace Engineering*, v. 19, p. 271-280, 2006.

[5] C. Wood, A.J. Gil, O. Hassan, J. Bonet, "Partitioned block Gauss-Seidel coupling for dynamic fluid-structure interaction", *Computers and Structures*, 2008. DOI: 10.1016/j.compstruc.2008.08.005

[6] C.A. Taylor, "Predictive Medicine: Computational Techniques in Therapeutic Decision-Making", *Computer Aided Surgery* **4**, 231-247, 1999.

1st International Conference on Mathematical and Computational Biomedical Engineering – CMBE2009
June 29 – July 1, 2009, Swansea, UK
P. Nithiarasu and R. Löhner (eds)

MODELLING AORTIC STENOSIS

Raoul van Loon
School of Engineering, Swansea University, Singleton Park, Swansea, SA2 8PP,
r.vanloon@swansea.ac.uk
Adrian Ionescu
Cardiac Centre, Morriston Hospital, Swansea NHS Trust, Swansea, SA6 6NL,
adrian.ionescu@swansea-tr.wales.nhs.uk

ABSTRACT

This work investigates the assessment of aortic stenosis severity using computational models of the aortic heart valve. Clinically aortic stenosis is assessed using geometric orifice area (GOA), pressure gradient (PG) and effective orifice area (EOA). Three-dimensional fluid-structure interaction models are developed to mimic clinical scenarios such as variable stroke volumes, different valve shapes or different material properties. The assessment criteria are used to assess stenosis severity of these computational models.

Key Words: *Aortic stenosis, Aortic valve, CFD, Fluid-structure interaction*

1. INTRODUCTION

The aortic valve ensures uni-directional flow during the cardiac cycle, by allowing the stroke volume to be ejected from the left ventricle into the aorta during systole, and by preventing backflow from the aorta into the left ventricle in diastole. There are two main reasons for valve malfunction, 1) regurgitation (retrograde flow) and 2) stenosis (flow obstruction), which are often combined to different extents in patients. Degenerative (age-related) aortic stenosis (AS) is the most prevalent cardiovascular disease in developed countries after coronary artery disease and hypertension and is curable by open heart surgery (aortic valve replacement or, more rarely, repair).

The accuracy with which the severity of AS is assessed in clinical practice, is particularly important. From a fluid dynamics perspective, the ideal method for quantifying AS would be to measure the energy 'loss' caused by the high-velocity flow jet across a narrow, irregular orifice and in particular by the turbulent area downstream where the jet expands. However, accurate measurement of the energy 'loss' and correlating this with clinical outcomes is fraught with difficulties. Clinicians therefore rely on two well-tested [2], but nevertheless imperfect, measures of AS severity: pressure gradients (PG) and aortic valve area (AVA).

1) PG is a good measure for the energy loss and can be measured invasively, by passing across the aortic valve using a catheter connected to a pressure gauge (**Fig 1**). The drawbacks of PG is that the procedure is invasive and that PG is flow-dependent, which requires it to be indexed when used as an assessment criteria.

2) AVA is less flow dependent than PG and can be subdivided in 2 types: Geometric Orifice Area, GOA, and Effective Orifice Area, EOA (**Fig 1**). The GOA is the aortic valve orifice from a frontal view and it is routinely measured by echocardiography. The aortic valve has a 3D shape, which makes 2D visualization problematic for certain valve geometries. Furthermore, the geometric area does not distinguish between a smooth and sharp constriction, something that has a large impact on the flow and therefore on the pressure field.

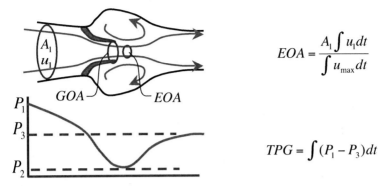

$$EOA = \frac{A_1 \int u_1 dt}{\int u_{max} dt}$$

$$TPG = \int (P_1 - P_3) dt$$

Fig1: *Clinical assessment of aortic stenosis: Geometric Orifice Area (GOA), Effective Orifice Area EOA and transvalvular Pressure Gradients (PG)*

The EOA is an alternative measure for AS severity that distinguishes between smooth and sharp constrictions. It represents the cross-sectional area of the vena contracta just downstream of the valve. The EOA is less flow dependent than PGs and considered a good measure for the energy loss caused by the stenosis. Furthermore, non-invasive fast Doppler measurements are used to determine EOA, which makes this quantity the preferred one in clinical practice.

However, some major assumptions are made for the calculation of EOA, i.e. the flow jet is axisymmetric with a uniform profile and is considered flow independent. These assumptions can be questioned for the distinct three-dimensional geometry of the aortic valve, the asymmetry of many diseased valves and the incompressible turbulent flow. Hence, the aim of this work is to elucidate the effect of these assumptions using computational models. It should also be noted that the EOA is calculated as a time integral and therefore, time-transients are currently not considered in the assessment of AS severity. However, clinical research suggests that these time-transients (during opening and closing) could play a role in the progression of AS. Hence, this work also seeks to investigate the time-transient behaviour of the valve.

2. METHODS

Three-dimensional finite element models of the aortic heart valve are created to investigate the behaviour of the fluid jet as a function of the material properties and geometry. An idealised geometry is chosen based on 5 characteristic dimensions of an aortic valve. The reason for not (yet) using a scan-derived patient specific geometry is that these are difficult to obtain at a high enough resolution due to their relatively small size, large motion and complex geometry. Also from a clinical point of view it would be interesting to understand the influence of each of these characteristic dimensions that could be measured based on echocardiography.

Three different geometries of the valve are shown in **Fig 2**. The shown a change in radial curvature and free edge length.

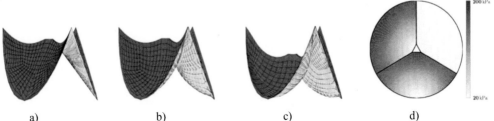

a)   b)   c)   d)

Fig. 2: a)b)c) *Idealised valve geometries with different dimensions. d) Distribution of shear modulus value across the valve in 3 distinct cases.*

The models consist of a Lagrangian solid, described by a Neo-Hookean material law, and an Eulerian Fluid, described by the incompressible, unsteady Navier-Stokes equation with a Newtonian material law. To capture the fluid-structure interaction between the valve and blood a fictitious domain method is employed, which links the solid to the fluid by means of a Lagrange multiplier that is distributed across the solid boundary [4,5]. Second order polynomials are used for the velocities, first order polynomials for the pressure variables and constant polynomials for the Lagrange multipliers.

3. RESULTS

Combining the 3 geometries in **Fig 2** with the 3 different distributions for the shear modulus gives 9 models that are being evaluated during the systolic part of the cardiac cycle. A pulsatile velocity wave is prescribed at the upstream of the valve, which causes the valve to open. The GOA can be measured for each of these models as a function of time and the results are shown in **Fig 3**.

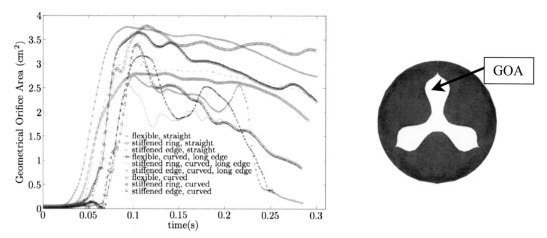

Fig3: a) The Geometric Orifice Area (GOA) plotted as a function of time during systole.
b) Although the valve is distinctly three-dimensional, the GOA is defined as the orifice area observed from a frontal view.

From **Fig 3** a change in geometry or material properties seems to have a large effect on the GOA and therefore indirectly on the EOA. The valves without radial curvature **Fig 2a)** show much less flutter behaviour than the geometries with radial curvature **Fig 2b)** and **2c)**. In clinical practice the time averaged values for these criteria are taken to assess the severity of the stenosis. Curvature of the leaflets also seems to decrease the time averaged values due to later opening and a lower GOA during peak systole. We believe that the time transients might actually provide a better assessment if the underlying fluid dynamics is understood.

4. CONCLUSIONS

A first investigation is performed regarding the assessment of aortic stenosis. Three-dimensional models are created to study the behaviour of valves with different shapes and properties. The results suggested that radial curvature has an influence on the opening behaviour of the valve. This can be interesting for clinicians from a diagnostic point of view, but also for valve design in the prosthetic industry. However, further study on the flow details and valve mechanics is necessary.

REFERENCES

[1] C.W. Akins, B. Travis, and A.P. Yoganathan. Energy loss for evaluating heart valve performance. *J. Thorac. Cardiovasc. Surg.*, 136(1):820–833, 2008.

[2] J.G. Dumesnil, P. Pibarot, and C. Akins. New approaches to quantifying aortic stenosis severity. *Current Cardiology Reports*, 10:91–97, 2008.

[3] D. Garcia, P. Pibarot, J. Dumesnil, F. Sakr, and L. Durand. Assessment of aortic valve stenosis severity. *Circulation*, 101:765–771, 2000.

[4] R. Van Loon, P.D. Anderson, F.N Van de Vosse, and S.J. Sherwin. Comparison of various fluid-structure methods for deformable bodies. *Comput. and Struct.*, 85:833–843, 2007.

[5] J. De Hart, G.W.M. Peters, P.J.G. Schreurs, and F.P.T Baaijens. A three-dimensional computational analysis of fluid-structure interaction in the aortic valve. J. Biomech., 36:103-112, 2003

[6] R. Van Loon, Towards computational modelling of aortic stenosis. Comm. Num. Meth. Eng., DOI: 10.1002/cnm.1270, 2009

IMAGE AND SURFACE ANALYSIS VIA GEOMETRIC EVOLUTION EQUATIONS

Guo-Wei Wei
Department of Mathematics & Department of Electrical and Computer Engineering
Michigan State University
East Lansing, MI 48824, USA

Key Words: *image analysis, surface formation, partial differential equations, geometric flows.*

PROPOSAL

We report high order geometric evolution equations and new geometric flow equations for the analysis of biomedical images and theoretical modeling biomolecular surfaces. We introduce a family of high-order geometric partial differential equations (PDEs) to enhance the biomedical images. Appropriate selections or combinations of diffusion coefficients can lead to desirable image processing effects. First, the hyper-diffusion term can be used to provide an efficient algorithm for image denoising. Additionally, the balance of the second order forward diffusion and the fourth order backward diffusion can be used for image enhancement. Finally, unlike other geometric evolution equations, our method provides a gradient depending production term for image analysis. Such a term can be used to balance the intrinsic geometric (force) terms with extrinsic potential (force) terms to achieve special effects. Image edge detection is an elementary process in image analysis. The edge detection of texture images is challenging issue. We introduce coupled geometric evolution equations for the edge detection. Our algorithm works best for texture images.

We propose potential driving geometric flows, which balance the intrinsic geometric forces with the potential forces induced by the interactions, to account for the local hydrodynamical variations near the biological interfaces due to interactions between solvent molecules and solvent-solute molecules. Stochastic geometric flows are introduced to account for the random fluctuation and dissipation in density and pressure near the solvent-solute interface. Physical properties, such as free energy minimization (area decreasing) and incompressibility (volume preserving), are realized in new geometric flow equations. The proposed approach for geometric and potential driving formation and evolution of biological surfaces is illustrated by extensive numerical experiments and compared with established minimal molecular surfaces and molecular surfaces. Local modification of biomolecular surfaces is demonstrated with potential driving geometric flows. High order geometric flows are also considered and tested in the present work. Biological surfaces generated by the proposed approaches are typically free of geometric singularities.

References

[1] G.W. Wei. "Generalized Perona-Malik equation for Image Restoration" *IEEE Signal Processing Lett.* Vol. **6**, 165-167, 1999.

[2] G. W. Wei and Y. Q. Jia. "Synchronization based image edge detection'" *Europhys. Lett.* Vol **59**, 814-819, 2002.

[3] P. Bates, G.W. Wei and S. Zhao. "Minimal molecular surfaces and their application" *J. Comput. Chem.*, Vol. **29**, 380-391, 2008.

[4] P. Bates, Z. Chen, Y.H. Sun, G.W. Wei and S. Zhao. "Geometric and potential driving formation and evolution of biomolecular surfaces" *J. Math. Biol.*, in press, 2008.

HIGH QUALITY MESHING BASED ON HARMONIC MAPPINGS FOR BIOMEDICAL SIMULATION

E. Marchandise, J.-F. Remacle, M. Willemet
institute of Mechanics, Materials and Civil Engineering (iMMC), Université catholique de Louvain, 1348 Louvain-la-Neuve, Belgium.

C. Geuzaine
Department of Electrical Engineering and Computer Science, Université de Liège, Belgium.

ABSTRACT

This work describes an approach based on harmonic mappings to recover a high quality surface mesh from low-quality oversampled inputs obtained from medical imaging through classical segmentation techniques. Different examples will be presented that show a quality improvement of the surface mesh by using harmonic maps to parametrize the initial STL triangulation of low quality.

Key Words: *surface mapping, surface meshing, parametrization.*

1 INTRODUCTION

Creating high quality meshes is an essential feature for obtaining accurate and efficient numerical solutions of partial differential equations. For manufactured objects (designed using a CAD system) that are often described by constructive solide geometry (CGS) or non-uniform rational B-spline (NURBS), automatic volume meshing methods render high quality meshes [1]. In the biomedical field, the geometrical data is often a triangulation created from imaging techniques (CT or MRI) through a segmentation procedure. A straightforward meshing of the triangulation is generally of very low quality and oversampled. This is also problematic for the volume meshing since the surface meshing serves as input to volume meshing algorithms. In this work, we propose to recover a high quality surface mesh from low-quality oversampled inputs obtained via 3D acquisition systems by using a harmonic map onto the unit disk.

2 METHOD AND RESULTS

The key feature of our remeshing algorithm is to construct a parametrization [2,3] of a surface $\mathcal{S} \in \mathcal{R}^3$ onto a unit disk $D \in \mathcal{R}^2$. The parametrization should be a bijective fonction $\mathbf{x}(u,v)$ such that:

$$\mathbf{u} = (u,v) \in \mathcal{D} \mapsto \mathbf{x}(u,v) \in \mathcal{S}.$$

In this work, we have chosen harmonics maps [4,5] for the parametrization. Harmonic maps satisfy the two Laplace equations:

$$\nabla^2 u = 0, \ \ \nabla^2 v = 0. \tag{1}$$

The advantage of harmonic maps over conformal maps is the ease with which they can be computed, at least approximatively. We subsequently chose a suitable Dirichlet boundary condition for one closed boundary $\partial \mathcal{S}_i$ of the surface $\mathcal{S}$,

$$u_i = \cos(2\pi l_i/L) \quad , \quad v_i = \sin(2\pi l_i/L), \tag{2}$$

where l_i is the curvilinear abcissa of a point along the the boundary $\partial \mathcal{S}_i$ of total length L, and impose Neumann boundary conditions on the other boundaries.

After the resolution of the two linear elliptic partial differential equations (approximated by finite elements) (1) with the appropriate boundary conditions (2), we have the mapping completed: each internal vertex of the original triangulation $\mathbf{x}$ has its local coordinates u and v. Harmonic maps have nice properties, the most important one of which being that they are guaranteed to be one-to-one for convex regions.

Figure 1 shows both an initial triangular mesh of $\mathcal{S}$ and its map onto the unit circle. The surface $\mathcal{S}$ results from the segmentation of an anastomosis site in the lower limbs, more precisely a bypass of an occluded femoral artery realized with the patient's saphenous vein. The unit disk D contains two holes that correspond to the boundary of the femoral artery $\partial \mathcal{S}_2$ and the saphenous vein $\partial \mathcal{S}_3$ on which we have imposed Neumann boundary conditions.

Once the parametrization is computed, we can easily perform a high quality mesh of the surface $\mathcal{S}$ by remeshing in the parametric unit disk D.

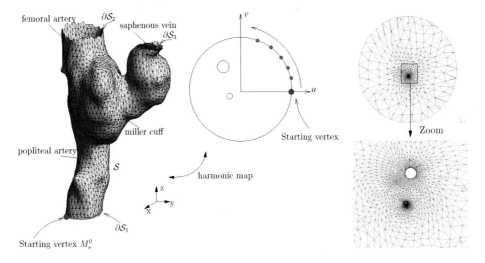

Figure 1: STL triangulation and its map onto the unit circle (left) and mapped mesh on the unit circle (right).

Figure 2 shows the quality histogram (ratio between the inscribed radius and the circumscribed radius) for the initial STL triangulation presented in Fig.1 and the remeshed geometry. We can see that with the remeshing procedure, we greatly enhance the quality of the mesh.

3   CONCLUSIONS

Harmonic mappings provide an elegant and efficient tool for the parametrization of triangulations. With such a parametrization, we can generate high quality meshes that will improve the convergence of

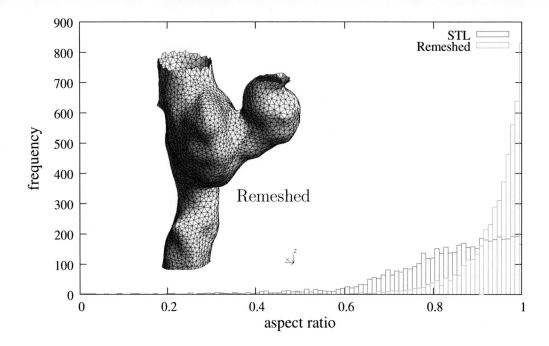

Figure 2: Plot of the quality histogram of both the STL triangulation and the remeshed part.

numerical simulations. Another important outcome is the ability with such a parametrization to perform boolean operations with other geometrical entities such as cylinders, or parallelepipeds to take into account for example the placement of a synthetic bypass in an artery or the placement of screws or plates in a fractured bone.

REFERENCES

[1] C. Geuzaine and J.-F. Remacle, Gmsh: a three-dimensional finite element mesh generator with built-in pre- and post-processing facilities. *International Journal for Numerical Methods in Engineering*, Accepted for publication, 2009

[2] M. S. Floater and K. Hormann, Surface Parameterization: a Tutorial and Survey, *Advances in Multiresolution for Geometric Modelling*, 157-186, Springer 2005.

[3] A. Sheffer, E. Praun, K. Rose, Mesh Parameterization Methods and Their Applications, *Computer Graphics and Vision*, 2(2), 2006.

[4] Marcum, David L. and Adam Gaither, Unstructured Surface Grid Generation Using Global Mapping and Physical Space Approximation, *Proceedings, 8th International Meshing Roundtable*, 1South Lake Tahoe, CA, U.S.A., pp.397-406, October 1999

1st International Conference on Mathematical and Computational Biomedical Engineering – CMBE2009
June 29 – July 1, 2009, Swansea, UK
P. Nithiarasu and R. Löhner (eds)

3D RECONSTRUCTION OF A REALISTIC ARTERIOVENOUS FISTULA FROM 2D MRI IMAGES: A GEOMETRICAL REMODELLING AND COMPUTATIONAL HAEMODYNAMIC INVESTIGATION

Gráinne T. Carroll
Centre for Applied Biomedical Engineering Research (CABER), Department of Mechanical and Aeronautical Engineering, and the Materials and Surface Science Institute, University of Limerick, Limerick, Ireland, grainne.carroll@ul.ie

Timothy M. McGloughlin
Centre for Applied Biomedical Engineering Research (CABER), Department of Mechanical and Aeronautical Engineering, and the Materials and Surface Science Institute, University of Limerick, Limerick, Ireland

Michael T. Walsh
Centre for Applied Biomedical Engineering Research (CABER), Department of Mechanical and Aeronautical Engineering, and the Materials and Surface Science Institute, University of Limerick, Limerick, Ireland

ABSRACT

Key Words: *Geometry Reconstruction, Vascular Access, Wall Shear Stress, Computational Fluid Dynamics.*

1. INTRODUCTION

Haemodialysis involves the non-physiological removal of waste products from the body through an extracorporeal artificial kidney and is the primary treatment modality available to patients with end stage renal disease (ESRD). Successful and efficient haemodialysis requires the construction of a vascular access (VA) site, which induces elevated blood flow rates in the local vasculature. Although the VA method of choice is an arteriovenous fistula (AVF), primary patency rates have been reported to be as low as 56% and 39% at one and two years, respectively[1-3].

The primary cause of VA dysfunction is the development of thrombosis and over 90% of VA thrombosis originates from venous neointimal hyperplasia (VNH)[4,5]. This lesion formation tends to occur in specific regions within the AVF, the venous "floor" of the VA junction (49%) and proximally, within the efferent vein (44%)[6]. Many theories have been put forward as to the potential risk factors that influence VA patency and the initiating stimuli of VNH in the dialysis population including compliance mismatch, surgical technique, haemodynamic environment, veni-puncture and systemic uremia. In an attempt to elucidate the contributing factors of VA VNH, magnetic resonance (MR) images of a healthy vein geometry and a patient-specific AVF were obtained. The corresponding patient-specific velocity profiles were measured *in vivo* using Doppler ultrasound. These MRI images were reconstructed into a three-dimensional flow field using the commercially available software Mimics 10.01. The geometrical characteristics of each model were quantified and the haemodynamics within the realistic healthy vein geometry and the patient-specific radiocephalic AVF were then evaluated and characterized using computational fluid dynamics (CFD) software Fluent 6.3.26. The blood flow patterns and wall shear stress (WSS) distributions within these geometries are quantified, compared and contrasted with specific attention paid to the local haemodynamic environment of potentially pathological sections of the AVF.

2. MATERIAL AND METHODS

Computational Geometries and Reconstruction
Two realistic, patient-specific geometries were modelled: (a) the realistic healthy vein geometry from a non dialysis patient and (b) a functioning realistic End Vein-to-Side Artery radiocephalic AVF geometry. The images of both geometries were acquired from magnetic resonance imaging (MRI) scans taken in the Mid-Western Regional Hospital, Limerick, Ireland. The data sheets acquired from MRI scans provide a series of 2-D cross-sectional images, which are imported into the software package Mimics 10.01 (Materialise,

Belgium). The Hounsfield unit (HU) thresholding technique is employed to segment the regions of interest, and allows for edge detection and lumen cross-section contour creation. Polylines are then generated at the segmented regions of interest throughout the series and a curve fit is fitted to each polyline. These curve fit polylines can be exported as wire-frame geometries allowing for the creation of a 3-D reconstructed geometry in Gambit 2.3 *(Fluent Inc. Lebanon, NH, USA).*

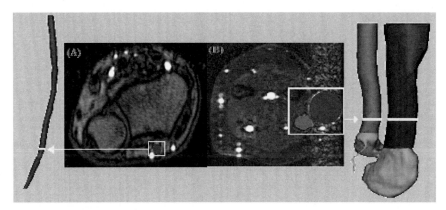

Figure 1: 2-D Images acquired from MRI Scans. The series of 2-D slices create 3-D images: (A) Healthy Vein 2-D slice and 3-D image, (B) Realistic Radiocephalic AV Fistula 2-D slice and 3-D image.

Computational Modelling

The CFD code Fluent 6.3.2 *(Fluent Inc. Lebanon, NH, USA)* was employed as the finite volume solver to determine the haemodynamics within each geometry analysed. Patient specific flow waveforms were obtained for the realistic vein and realistic AV fistula models, using ultrasound technology, from the Mid-Western Regional Hospital, Limerick. Steady flow analysis was carried out on the healthy vein realistic geometry with an inlet velocity magnitude of 0.0314m/s, while pulsatile flow analysis was performed on the realistic AVF geometry. The inlet velocity flow waveforms employed in the time-dependent analysis is represented as a 12th order fourier series in a user subroutine. The blood was assumed to be a Newtonian, incompressible and homogenous fluid of viscosity 0.00345Pas[7] and density 1050kg/m[8]. Grid independence was established for WSS, and was specified to within ±2%. The steady flow Reynolds number for the healthy vein was 20 and the AVF time-dependent peak Reynolds number was 1950. WSS measurements within the AVF geometry were found to be periodic in nature over repeated pulse cycles, demonstrating a laminar flow field.

3. RESULTS AND DISCUSSION

Blood Flow Patterns and Wall Shear Stress

The realistic vein has an inlet diameter of 2.13mm which over the length of the vein geometry graduates to an outlet diameter of 3.58mm, with a mean diameter of 2.96mm. The blood flows from left to right, figure 2(a) and slight out of plane curvature is illustrated in the x-z plane, with a maximum angle of curvature of 20°. It is important to note that as this is a healthy vein, this out of plane curvature is a natural movement of the cephalic vein around the radius bone of the arm; from the wrist to the mid-arm region.

The flow within the realistic healthy vein geometry is minimally skewed toward the outer wall in areas of plane curvature with minor flow vortices observed. Within the straight sections of the vein model the flow is close to parabolic and secondary flows are absent. Minor spatial WSS variations are evident both in the circumferential and longitudinal directions, particularly in regions of plane curvature. Minor spatial WSS gradients are also evident in the straight section of the vein model and are primarily a consequence of natural variations in vein diameter. WSS magnitudes are reduced near the outlet section of the vein due to an increase in vessel diameter. A quantitative overview of the WSS within the healthy vein model is graphed in figure 2(B). The WSS values at each circumferential position for the entire length of the vein range from 0.0325Pa to 0.355Ps with a mean WSS magnitude of 0.141Pa, which is within documented WSS magnitudes present in the venous system.

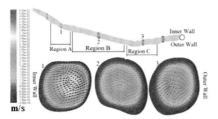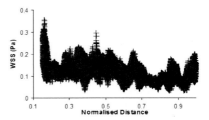

Figure 2: (A)Velocity contours and in-plane secondary flow vectors of the healthy vein geometry within the three regions of interest. (B) Overview of all WSS magnitudes at each circumferential point along the length of the realistic vein geometry.

The realistic radiocephalic AV fistula consists of the end of a vein sutured to the side of an artery, figure 3 (A). The artery has an inlet diameter of 8.52mm with a venous outlet diameter of 21.2mm. The blood flows from the artery into the vein at an angle of 120° and continues proximally through the vein. Out of plane curvature can be seen in both the x-y and x-z planes, particularly in the x-y plane with a maximum angle of curvature of 30°, figure 3(A). Neither the artery nor the vein have a constant, circular cross-section, with the diameter of the artery increasing from 8.52mm at the inlet to 15.2mm at the artery-vein junction and the diameter of the vein ranging from 17.22mm and 23.28mm (mean vein diameter = 21.11mm).

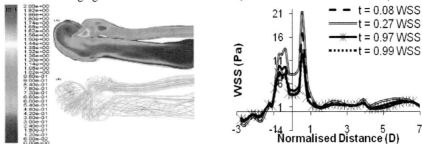

Figure 3: (A) Velocity Contours in the EA-SV AV fistula geometry, (B) Velocity Path-lines in the realistic AV fistula geometry, (C) The axial direction venous floor centre-line WSS.

Due to the construction of the AV fistula, very high flow velocities enter the VA junction of the realistic AVF. The out of plane curvature, high flow velocities, large diameter ratio and angle of blood flow from the artery to the vein (120°) result in a highly disturbed haemodynamic environment in the AVF VA junction. These complex flow patterns in the artery-vein junction are demonstrated by the velocity contours and path-lines reported in figure 3(A) and 3(B). The path-lines highlight skewed blood flow towards the vein floor, with flow impingement, separation, recirculation and flow reversal phenomena present within the VAJ. The bulbous shape of the VAJ and the large vein diameter allows for significant flow velocity reduction but secondary flow vortices continue downstream of the VA junction in the efferent vein. Significantly different WSS patterns are found within the VAJ and efferent vein of the AVF to those reported in the healthy vein venous environment. Highly elevated shear forces are present at the joining of the artery and vein, and on the venous floor of the VAJ in comparison to the roof, from where the blood flow is directed away. The sWSS plot, figure 3(C), demonstrates the presence of elevated WSS magnitudes and spatial WSS gradients on the floor of the VAJ and vein. A peak WSS magnitude of 21.4Pa is located opposite the toe of the junction and a second, less dominant peak in WSS of 7.5Pa is seen within the VAJ. Downstream of the heel slight secondary flow vortices are still present and the WSS magnitudes have reduced significantly but are still greater than the reported physiological venous WSS values as shown in figure 2(b).

The significant geometrical and haemodynamic changes within the local venous system upon creation of a VAJ, as demonstrated in this study, have significant implications for the long-term patency of the AVFs. Initially, increases in fluid volume within the vein allows for vessel dilation and remodelling. In theory this would result in the reduction of the WSS magnitudes within the vein, in an attempt to return to pre-anastomosis shear stress magnitudes. However, although increases in diameter were observed in the AVF examined in this study, complex haemodynamics and significantly elevated WSS magnitudes persist within the geometry. VNH has been described as a maladaptive response to vessel wall injury that leads to stenotic formation and a narrowing of the lumen. It is proposed that endothelial cell exposure to the non-physiological haemodynamics observed in this patient-specific AVF investigation may contribute to the initiating events that lead to VNH development. VNH is characterised by the degradation of the ECM, the abnormal and rapid migration and proliferation of SMCs from the media to the intima with subsequent leukocyte, monocyte and macrophage infiltration and finally abundant ECM deposition. The EC activation, IEL degradation and SMC migration that occur during the initial stages of vessel remodelling, with the formation of gaps within the IEL and the degradation of elastic fibres and the subsequent SMC proliferation, migration and reorientation during vessel dilation may contribute to the maladaptive response previously mentioned. It is theorised that the extensive vessel remodelling triggers these chain of events which would finish upon a return of physiological WSS within the venous system. However, as seen in this computational study, this does not occur and thus the continued presence of high WSS magnitudes and elevated WSSGs within the venous conduit of the AVF compound to result in VNH development and subsequent VA morbidity.

4. CONCLUSIONS

The 3-D reconstruction of the realistic healthy vein and AV fistula geometries allows for direct comparisons to be made between the geometrical characteristics and haemodynamic environment within the local venous vasculature prior to and after the construction of a vascular access site. Although MRI imaging of an AV fistula is not standard procedure for haemodialysis patients, it is a non-invasive method of obtaining a series of 2-D images that can then be reconstructed into 3-D geometries and further employed in computational investigations.

Through this methodology, measurement of the degree of geometrical remodelling within the local venous system following VA site creation and quantification of the complex haemodynamics that develop due to the decreased peripheral resistance were possible. Considerable geometrical changes and significant haemodynamic alterations were observed. A 7-fold increase in mean diameter, a 1.5-fold increase in vessel curvature and a dramatic increase in the angle of blood flow entering the vein (120°). Complex haemodynamics and significantly elevated WSS magnitudes were present within the AV fistula geometry when compared to the healthy venous haemodynamic environment. The maximum and mean WSS magnitudes in the AV fistula are approximately 250 times and 25 times greater than those in the healthy vein, respectively. Elevated WSSGs were also seen within the AV fistula geometry with a peak WSSG of 12,000Pa/m. The two primary locations of lesion development within AV fistulae, the VA junction and efferent vein, experienced elevated WSS magnitudes, WSS gradients and negative flow, all of which may play an initiating role or contributing factor to VNH development. Thus it is theorized that the extensive geometrical remodelling and the non-physiological haemodynamic environment compound to result in VNH development and subsequently VA dysfunction.

REFERENCES

1) Albayrak, R., Yuksel, S., Colbay, Mehmet., Degirmenci, B., Acarturk, Gursel., Haktanir, A., Karaman, O. 'Hemodynamic changes in the Cephalic Vein of Patients with Hemodialysis Arteriovenous Fistula'. *Journal of Clinical Ultrasound*, 35: 3, 133-139, 2007.

2) Ates, A., Özyazicioglu, A., Yekeler, I., Ceviz, M., Erkut, B., Karapolat, S., Koçogullari C. U., Kocak, H. 'Primary and Secondary Patency Rates and Complications of Upper Extremity Arteriovenous Fistulae Created for Hemodialysis'. *The Tohoku Journal of Experimental Medicine*, 210: 91-97, 2006.

3) Gibson, K. D., Gillen, D. L., Caps, M. T., Kohler, T. R., Sherrard, D. J., Stehman-Breen, C. O. 'Vascular access survival and incidence of revisions: A comparison of prosthetic grafts, simple autogenous fistulas, and venous transposition fistulas from the United States Renal Data System Dialysis morbidity and mortality study'. *Journal of Vascular Surgery*, 34: 694-700, 2001.

4) Albers, F. J. 'Causes of hemodialysis access failure'. *Advances in Renal Replacement Therapy*, 1: 107-18, 1994.

5) Roy-Chaudhury P, McKee L, Miller M, Reaves A, Armstrong J, Duncan H, Munda R, Kelly B, Heffelfinger S. 'Hemodialysis vascular access dysfunction: From pathophysiology to novel therapies'. *Blood Purification*, 21: 99-110, 2003.

6) Roy-Chaudhury, P., Sukhatme, V. P., Cheung, A. K. 'Hemodialysis vascular access dysfunction: a cellular and molecular viewpoint'. *Journal of the American Society of Nephrology*, 17: 1112-1127, 2006.

7) Cho, Y.I. and Kensey K.R. "Effect of the non- Newtonian viscosity of blood on flows in a diseased arterial vessel. Part1: Steady flows." *Biorheology*, 28, 241-262, 1991.

8) Cole J.S., Watterson, J.K. and O Reilly, M.J.G. 'Numerical Investigation of the haemodynamics at a patched arterial bypass anastomosis', *Medical Engineering and Physics*, 24, 393-401, 2002.

1st International Conference on Mathematical and Computational Biomedical Engineering - CMBE2009
June 29 - July 1, 2009, Swansea, UK
P.Nithiarasu and R.Löhner (Eds.)

PROTEIN MECHANICS

Alex Macdonald
Cambridge University Engineering Department
Inglis Building, Trumpington St., Cambridge, CP2 1PZ
adm59@cam.ac.uk

Simon Guest
Cambridge University Engineering Department
Inglis Building, Trumpington St., Cambridge, CP2 1PZ
sdg@eng.cam.ac.uk

ABSTRACT

Key Words: *protein rigidity analysis, kinematics, elastic normal mode analysis*

1 INTRODUCTION

Protein function (and hence malfunction) is closely linked to conformational changes within the protein, but identifying these configuration changes is conceptually and computationally demanding. State of the art molecular dynamics approaches often cannot be used due to restrictive time step limitations. Various non-dynamic methods of analysing protein rigidity and kinematics have been developed in recent years with some success. We propose a new non-dynamic technique for analysing individual protein structures wherein we identify rigid regions, small kinematic changes and elastic normal modes. Large scale protein conformational changes can be identified over thousands of iterations. Our methodology is developed from structural engineering principles and provides a more unified approach to protein statics and kinematics than existing non-dynamic methods.

2 METHODOLOGY

RIGIDITY ANALYSIS

The protein is initially discretised into rigid bar, joint and hinge elements. It is then possible to write linear compatibility equations relating atomic displacements, $\mathbf{d}$, to generalised strains, $\mathbf{e}$, in the idealised components.

$$\mathbf{Cd} = \mathbf{e}$$

The nullspace of the compatibility matrix, $\mathbf{C}$, can be utilised to do two things. Firstly, we can identify *rigid* regions within the protein. To do this we:

1. Find displacement vectors that span the nullspace of the compatibility matrix, $\mathbf{C}$

2. Displace the complete protein using combinations of these vectors

3. Return a peptide unit to its original position using translations and linearised rotations

4. Map adjacent areas as rigid or flexible depending on whether or not they have internal mechanisms

Rigid regions will overlap their original positions but flexible regions will not, see figure 1.

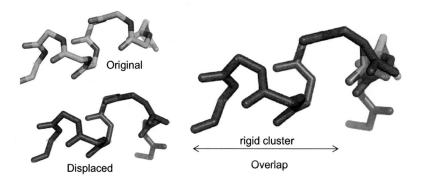

Figure 1: Rigidity Decomposition

This rigidity decomposition reduces the size of subsequent compatibility matrices resulting in a reduction in computational demand.

KINEMATIC ANALYSIS

The second use of the compatibility matrix nullspace is to provide atomic displacement directions that do not (to the first order) strain the constraints described above. The constraints are not linear and therefore errors occur after each kinematic step. An objective function minimises any errors and may also take account of steric clashes, hydrophobic interactions and any other function that may be desired. For instance, it may be desirable to limit the radius of gyration of a protein to model the confinement lipid bilayers provide to membrane proteins.

Using a virtual work argument it can be shown that the compatibility matrix can be used to form the first order stiffness matrix, $\mathbf{K}$, of the protein.

$$\mathbf{K} = \mathbf{C}^T \mathbf{G} \mathbf{C}$$

Where $\mathbf{C}$ is the compatibility matrix defined above and $\mathbf{G}$ is a matrix with scalar stiffness parameters along the main diagonal. The atomic displacements contained in the compatibility matrix nullspace have zero energy and do not identify large scale collective deformations, but the low frequency normal modes contain low energy collective deformations. Therefore, mapping out the low frequency conformation space of the protein is possible by iteratively finding low energy paths and minimising the protein's potential energy (using a similar objective function to the one detailed above) after each displacement step.

3   RESULTS AND DISCUSSION

Our method is reviewed in figure 2. It can be summarised as infinitesimal rigidity analysis followed by kinematic analysis using a geometric and/or elastic based method for conformer generation.

We present rigidity analysis results for various proteins that correlate exactly with existing graph theoretical methods[1]. This is as expected and highlights the generic properties of protein graphs.

The kinematic analysis is more problematic due to considerations such as having a large conformation space to map. Currently our research is focused on applying the method to the ATP/ADP carrier (AAC) through the inner mitochondrial membrane (PDB ID: 1OKC[2]). The rigidity map for the AAC is shown in the top panel of figure 2. It can be seen that the secondary structure elements can be assumed to be rigid. A torsional mechanism has been proposed for the operation of the AAC, but it has not been validated. We will use our methodology to attempt to develop this and other possible mechanisms.

4   CONCLUSIONS

While the rigidity analysis is slower than graph methods, the ability to get linearised motions from the compatibility or stiffness matrices provides a distinct advantage over other methods. This method can also be applied to atypical structures such as zeolites, minerals that are used as adsorbents in the medical and petrochemical industries, whereas graph theory (specifically the pebble game) cannot.

Another attraction of our method is the ability to easily customise the level of abstraction of the analysis. For instance, we can choose to simply model the main chain or we may alternatively include non-hydrophobic side chains in our computation. Easy alteration of the level of coarse graining is inherent to our methodology. We can also see the effect individual bond alterations have on the rigidity map and kinematics.

In summary, this novel method provides a unified method of undertaking rigidity and kinematic analysis where in the past it was necessary to combine graph theoretical and elastic methods, such as in the rigid cluster normal mode analysis method[3]. Further development is required to fully realise the potential of this method.

References

[1]   S. Wells, S. Menor, B. M. Hespenheide, M. F. Thorpe, Constrained geometric simulation of diffusive motions in proteins. Phys Biol 2, 1-10, 2005.

[2]   E. Pebay-Peyroula, C. Dahout-Gonzalez, R. Kahn, V. Trezeguet, G.J.-M. Lauquin, G. Brandolin, Structure of Mitochondrial ADP/ATP Carrier in Complex with Carboxyatractyloside. Nature 426, 39-44, 2003

[3]   A. Ahmed, H. Gohlke, Multi-scale modeling of macromolecular conformational changes combining concepts from rigidity and elastic network theory. Proteins 63, 1038-1051, 2006.

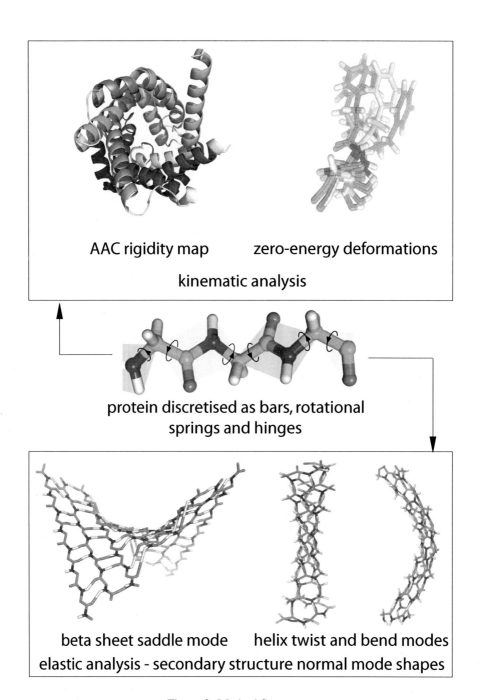

AAC rigidity map   zero-energy deformations

kinematic analysis

protein discretised as bars, rotational
springs and hinges

beta sheet saddle mode   helix twist and bend modes
elastic analysis - secondary structure normal mode shapes

Figure 2: Method Summary

1st International Conference on Mathematical and Computational Biomedical Engineering – CMBE2009
June 29 – July 1, 2009, Swansea, UK
P. Nithiarasu and R. Löhner (eds)

DynDom3D: A Method for the Analysis of Domain Movements in Large Biomolecular Complexes

S. Hayward
School of Computing Sciences and School of Biological Sciences, University of East Anglia, Norwich, UK, sjh@cmp.uea.ac.uk

G. Poornam
Department of Biochemistry and Molecular Biophysics, University of Arizona, Arizona, USA, guru@email.arizona.edu

A. Matsumoto
Center for Computational Science and Engineering, Japan Atomic Energy Agency, Kyoto 619-0215, Japan, matsumoto.atsushi@jaea.go.jp

H. Ishida
Center for Computational Science and Engineering, Japan Atomic Energy Agency, Kyoto 619-0215, Japan, ishida.hisashi@jaea.go.jp

ABSRACT

Key Words: *Hinge Bending, Allosteric Mechanism, Molecular Machine, Supramolecule.*

1. INTRODUCTION

It is now accepted wisdom that biomolecular function involves a change in the shape of the biomolecule. This change in shape, or more precisely conformation, is often not merely an unimportant side effect of function but is integral to it. This is certainly true for allosteric mechanism where the binding of a ligand at one site affects binding affinities at distant sites. It is also true for domain enzymes where the binding of a substrate causes domain closure, isolating the substrate from the solvent. The mechanisms of some very large biomolecular complexes are beginning to be understood and for these in particular it is apparent that conformational change and function are intimately linked. For example, in F_1F_0-ATPase, the conformational change which involves rotation of a central γ-subunit and domain movements in the surrounding β-subunits is an integral part of ATP synthesis from ADP. Another example, is the 70S ribosome in which a so-called "ratchet" like movement between the 30S and 50S subunits is thought to occur during translocation of tRNA.

Conformational change involving protein domains represents a significant proportion of all the possible types of conformational change seen in proteins. In fact an exhaustive analysis of the X-ray structures in the Protein Data Bank (PDB) [1] has indicated that in families that showed an appreciable conformational change, approximately half involve a domain movement as determined by the program DynDom [2,3]. The DynDom program is able to determine dynamics domains, hinge axes and hinge-bending residues from two protein structures representing the conformational change. However, it has a limitation in being applicable only to single protein chains and cannot be applied to large multimolecular complexes. The new method overcomes this limitation.

2. METHODS

At the heart of the method is the use of blocks located at grid points spanning the whole molecule. The rotation vector for the rotation of atoms from each block between the two conformations is calculated. Treating components of these vectors as coordinates means that each block is associated with a point in a "rotation space" and that blocks with atoms that rotate together, perhaps as part of the same rigid domain, will have co-located points. Thus a domain can be identified from the clustering of points from blocks that span it. The relative movements of domains are described by use of screw axes. A crucial advantage of this approach is that it is blind to atomic bonding and atom type allowing it to be applied to multichained biomolecules comprising protein, RNA, DNA, etc. The methodology has been implemented in the program, DynDom3D.

3. RESULTS

The methodology has been applied to five biomolecules spanning a considerable size range: hemoglobin, liver alcohol dehydrogenase, *S*- Adenosylhomocysteine hydrolase, aspartate transcarbamylase and the 70S ribosome. Results indicate a considerable robustness of the results against variation of the five main parameters. Figure 1 shows the result on *S*- Adenosylhomocysteine hydrolase, a homotetramer which has five domains. First indications suggest that common subunit and domain boundaries may be good regions to focus on for understanding allosteric mechanism. In addition using a combined DynDom and DynDom3D approach has shown that in some cases these common boundary regions coincide with the hinge bending regions of an individual subunit.

4. CONCLUSIONS

A new method has been developed for the analysis of domain movements in large, multi-chain, biomolecular complexes. The method is applicable to any molecule for which two atomic structures are available that represent a conformational change indicating a possible domain movement. It has been shown that it can depict the conformational change in a way that is easily understood, that is, as the relative screw movement of a small number of domain pairs. The method has proved to be robust and is fast enough to run on a standard desktop computer within a few minutes on all but the largest biomolecule. A beta-test version is available from: http://www.cmp.uea.ac.uk/dyndom/3D/ .

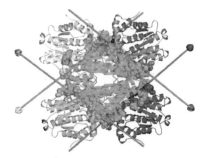

Figure 1 DynDom3D result on the homotetramer S-adenosylhomocysteine

REFERENCES

[1]   Qi G, Lee RA, Hayward S. A comprehensive and non-redundant database of protein domain movements. Bioinformatics 2005;21(12):2832-2838.

[2]   Hayward S, Berendsen HJC. Systematic analysis of domain motions in proteins from conformational change: New results on citrate synthase and T4 lysozyme. Proteins 1998;30:144-154.

[3]   Hayward S, Lee RA. Improvements in the analysis of domain motions in proteins from conformational change: DynDom version 1.50. J Mol Graph Model 2002;21(3):181-183.

1st International Conference on Mathematical and Computational Biomedical Engineering – CMBE2009
June 29 – July 1, 2009, Swansea, UK
P. Nithiarasu and R. Löhner (eds)

MULTI-SCALE MODELING OF MACROMOLECULAR CONFORMATIONAL CHANGES

Aqeel Ahmed
Institut für Pharmazeutische und Medizinische Chemie, Heinrich-Heine-Universität,
Düsseldorf, Germany, aqeel@bioinformatik.uni-frankfurt.de
Holger Gohlke
Institut für Pharmazeutische und Medizinische Chemie, Heinrich-Heine-Universität,
Düsseldorf, Germany, gohlke@uni-duesseldorf.de

ABSTRACT

Key Words: *Constrained geometric simulation, rigid cluster normal mode analysis.*

1. INTRODUCTION

Specific functions of biological systems often require conformational transitions of macromolecules. Such changes range from movements of single side-chains and loop rearrangements to large scale domain motions. In binding events involving macromolecules, molecular motions provide the origin of plasticity of the binding partners, enabling them to conformational adapt to each other.[1,2] Thus, being able to describe and predict conformational changes of biological macromolecules is not only important for understanding their impact on biological function, but will also have implications for the modeling of (macro)molecular complex formation [3] and in structure-based drug design approaches.[4] Modelling conformational transitions of macromolecules is computationally challenging. Hence, coarse-grained approaches have emerged as efficient alternatives for investigating large-scale conformational changes.[5] Here, we introduce a three-step approach for multi-scale modeling of macromolecular conformational changes (Figure 1).

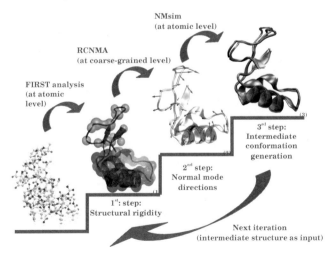

Figure 1: Three-step approach for multi-scale modeling of macromolecular conformational changes

2. RESULTS AND DISCUSSION

The first two steps are based on recent developments in rigidity and elastic network theory.[6] Initially, *static* properties of the macromolecule are determined by decomposing the macromolecule into rigid clusters using the graph-theoretical approach FIRST [7] and an all-atom representation of the protein. That way, the rigid cluster decomposition is not limited to consist of residues adjacent in sequence or secondary structure elements as in previous studies.[8] Furthermore, flexible links between rigid clusters are identified and can be modeled as such subsequently. In a second step, *dynamical* properties of the molecule are revealed by the rotations-translations of blocks approach (RTB) [9] using an elastic network model representation of the coarse-grained protein (termed **R**igid **C**luster **N**ormal **M**ode **A**nalysis). I.e., in this step, only rigid body motions are allowed for rigid clusters while links between them are treated as fully flexible.

In the final step, the recently introduced idea of constrained geometric simulations of diffusive motions in proteins [10] is extended. New macromolecule conformers are generated by deforming the structure along low-energy normal mode directions predicted by RCNMA plus random direction components. The generated structures are then iteratively corrected regarding steric clashes or constraint violations. This module is termed NMsim. Constraints to be satisfied include torsions of the main-chain and side-chains, distances and angles due to noncovalent interactions such as hydrogen bonds or hydrophobic interactions, and bond, angle, and planarity constraints. In total, when applied repetitively over all three steps, the procedure generates efficiently series of conformations that lie preferentially in the low energy subspace of normal modes.

The RCNMA approach was initially tested on a data set of 10 proteins that show conformational changes upon ligand binding.[6] In terms of efficiency, coarse-graining the protein results in a remarkable reduction of memory requirements and computational times by factors of 9 and 27 on average and up to 25 and 125, respectively. In terms of accuracy, directions and magnitudes of motions predicted by our approach agree well with experimentally determined ones (Figure 2), despite embracing in extreme cases more than 50 % of the protein into one rigid cluster. In fact, the results of our method are in general comparable to if no or a uniform coarse-graining is applied and become superior if the movement is dominated by loop or fragment motions (Figure 2b). This indicates that explicitly distinguishing between flexible and rigid regions is advantageous when using a simplified protein representation in the second step. Finally, motions of atoms in rigid clusters are also well predicted by our approach, which points to the need to consider *mobile* protein regions in addition to *flexible* ones when modeling correlated motions.

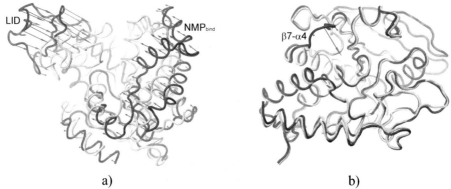

a)   b)

Figure 2: Superimposition of open (blue) and closed (green) conformations of adenylate kinase (panel a) and tyrosine phosphatase (panel b). In addition, the amplitudes and directions of motions as predicted by RCNMA modes most involved in the conformational changes, respectively, are depicted as red arrows. In both cases, the amplitudes of the motions were scaled for best graphical representation.

The NMsim approach was tested on hen egg white lysozyme (HEWL), a well-investigated protein consisting of 129 residues, in terms of exploration of the conformational space, residue fluctuations, and quality of the generated structures. Experimental structures and conformations from state of the art molecular dynamics simulations [11] were compared with conformations obtained from the constrained geometric simulation-based approach FRODA,[10] the distance geometry-based approach CONCOORD,[12] and NMsim.

In the case of constrained geometric simulations, the progression of a series of conformers is usually measured in terms of the root means square deviation (RMSD) from a reference conformer. Figure 3a) shows RMSD values of backbone atoms with respect to the HEWL starting structure for the different methods. Except FRODA, all other methods show considerable RMSD predominantly in the range of 1 to 2 Å. While FRODA apparently underestimates the conformational variability of HEWL, CONCOORD provides the broadest sampling. NMSim explores conformations in a similar range as CONCOORD, with higher RMSD values and more frequent peaks compared to MD. An analysis in terms of the "essential dynamics" [13] of HEWL confirms this finding: CONCOORD and NMsim broadly sample the space spanned by the first two principal components obtained from the MD trajectory (data not shown).

Regarding residue fluctuations, i.e., mass-weighted averages of heavy-atom fluctuations for each residue, NMsim and CONCOORD results are strongly correlated with MD results with correlation coefficients of 0.79, respectively. Encouragingly, for the residue fluctuations obtained from NMsim and CONCOORD a good correlation with fluctuations obtained from 130 experimental HEWL structures is found, too, with correlation coefficients of ~0.70. Residue fluctuations from NMsim, MD, and experiment are given in Figure 3b). Qualitatively and quantitatively, the NMsim results are in good agreement with those from MD and experiment, with the C-terminal region being the exception.

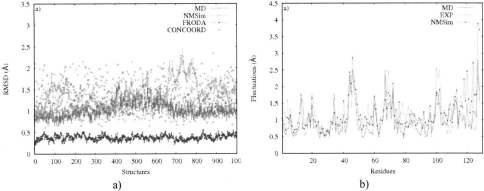

a)   b)

Figure 3: Panel a: Backbone RMSD between the starting structure and the conformations generated by MD (red), NMSim (green), FRODA (blue), and CONCOORD (magenta). Panel b: Residue fluctuations obtained from MD (red), 130 experimental structures (green), and NMSim (blue).

Finally, the stereochemical quality of structures obtained from NMsim was analyzed using Procheck.[14] For comparison, 100 high resolution crystal structures from Richardson's lab [15] were analysed, as were 130 experimental HEWL structures. Table 1 summarizes the results. Procheck divides the Ramachandran map into four types: most favored or core, additionally allowed, generously allowed, and disallowed. NMsim shows a good Ramachandran plot distribution with almost no structures in generously allowed and disallowed regions and with a highly populated core region (92 %) due to the specific modeling of phi/psi constraints. These results are in remarkable agreement with the characteristics of 100 high resolution experimental structures. The G-factor provides a measure of how likely a stereochemical property is. In Procheck it is computed for torsions and covalent geometry. A low G-factor indicates that the property corresponds to a low-probability conformation. Ideally, the G-factor should be above -0.5. Values below -1.0 indicate that a re-investigation of the structure is necessary. Table 1 shows that for NMsim the overall G-factor is -0.3. This value is comparable to the other geometry-based simulation methods CONCOORD and FRODA (data not shown). Regarding the planarity of, e.g., aromatic rings, NMsim succeeds in all cases.

3. CONCLUSIONS

In summary, the multi-scale approach introduced here provides an efficient means for sampling macromolecular conformational changes. In this respect, a computational time of ~30 h in the HEWL case compares favorably to days or weeks of computational time required by FRODA or MD, respectively. At the same time, the sampling is exhaustive and provides protein conformations of good stereochemical quality. At present, the scope and limitations of the approach are further tested regarding a hierarchy of movements, including domain, loop, and side-chain motions.

Table 1: Stereochemical quality of NMsim generated and experimental structures

Dataset	Ramachandran plot [a]				G-factor [b]			Planar [c]
	Core	Allow	Gen.	Disal.	Dihe.	Cova.	Overall	
NMSim [d]	92.55	7.42	0.01	0.00	-0.26	-0.36	-0.30	100.0
EXP [e]	81.31	17.62	0.89	0.18	-0.07	0.24	0.06	98.34
EXPTOP [f]	91.26	8.30	0.28	0.14	0.06	-0.28	-0.05	92.82

a) Percentages of phi/psi values found in different regions (i.e. core, allowed, generously allowed, and disallowed) of the Ramachandran map. b) Procheck-derived G-factor. Procheck computes G-factors for torsions, covalent geometry and overall. c) Percentages of side-chain planarity. d) NMsim generated conformations. e) 130 experimental HEWL structures. f) 100 high resolution structures taken from ref. [15].

REFERENCES

[1]   C.-S. Goh, D. Milburn and M. Gerstein, M., Conformational changes associated with protein-protein interactions. *Curr Opin Struct Biol* 14, 104-109, 2004.
[2]   S. J. Teague, Implications of Protein Flexibility for Drug Discovery. *Nat Rev Drug Discov* 2, 527-541, 2003.
[3]   H. A. Carlson, Protein flexibility and drug design: How to hit a moving target. *Curr Opin Chem Biol* 6, 447-452, 2002.
[4]   A. Ahmed, S. Kazemi, H. Gohlke, Protein flexibility and mobility in structure-based drug design. *Frontiers Drug Des Discov* 3, 455-476, 2007.
[5]   V. Tozzini, Coarse-grained models for proteins. *Curr Opin Struct Biol* 15, 144-150, 2005.
[6]   A. Ahmed, H. Gohlke, Multi-scale modeling of macromolecular conformational changes combining concepts from rigidity and elastic network theory. *Proteins* 63, 1038-1051, 2006.
[7]   D. J. Jacobs, A. J. Rader, L. A. Kuhn, M. F. Thorpe, Protein flexibility predictions using graph theory. *Proteins* 44, 150-65, 2001.
[8]   F. Tama, F. X. Gadea, O. Marques, Y.-H. Sanejouand, Building-Block Approach for Determining Low-Frequency Normal Modes of Macromolecules. *Proteins* 41, 1-7, 2000.
[9]   P. Durand, G. Trinquier, Y.-H. Sanejouand, A New Approach for Determining Low-Frequency Normal Modes in Macromolecules. *Biopolymers* 34, 759-771, 1994.
[10]   S. Wells, S. Menor, B. M. Hespenheide, M. F. Thorpe, Constrained geometric simulation of diffusive motions in proteins. *Phys Biol* 2, 1-10, 2005.
[11]   A. N. Koller, H. Schwalbe, H. Gohlke, Starting structure dependence of NMR order parameters derived from MD simulations. *Biophys J* 95, L04-6, 2008.
[12]   B. L. de Groot, G. Vriend, H. J. Berendsen, Conformational changes in the chaperonin GroEL: new insights into the allosteric mechanism. *J Mol Biol* 286, 1241-9, 1999.
[13]   A. Amadei, A. B. Linssen, H. J. Berendsen, Essential dynamics of proteins. *Proteins* 17, 412-25, 1993.
[14]   R. A. Laskowski, M. W. MacArthur, D. S. Moss, J. M. Thornton, PROCHECK: A program to check the stereochemical quality of protein structures. *J Appl Cryst* 26, 283-291, 1993.
[15]   J. M. Word, S. C. Lovell, T. H. LaBean, H. C. Taylor, M. E. Zalis, B. K. Presley, J. S. Richardson, D. C. Richardson, Visualizing and quantifying molecular goodness-of-fit: small-probe contact dots with explicit hydrogen atoms. *J Mol Biol* 285, 1711-33, 1999.

Geometric modeling of flexible motion in proteins

Stephen A. Wells

Department of Physics and Centre for Scientific Computing, University of Warwick,

s.a.wells@warwick.ac.uk

ABSTRACT

Key Words: *protein structure, flexible motion, modeling.*

1 INTRODUCTION

I will discuss the development of the method of "geometric simulation" of the flexible motion of proteins, as implemented in the FRODA module of the FIRST software package [1]. I will review some cases where the method has been used to study protein flexibility and conformational change [2,3]. The method is not yet widely known in the biophysics community and I will discuss its potential usefulness and its synergies with other methods such as molecular dynamics (MD) and elastic network modelling [4].

2 MAIN BODY

It is a common goal in biophysics to represent the flexibility of a protein and study its large-scale motion without incurring the full computational cost of molecular dynamics (MD) simulations, particularly as large-scale conformational change typically occurs on timescales much longer than the nanosecond scales that are generally accessible in MD. For example, one popular family of approaches is based on normal-mode analysis applied to a full or simplified representation of the protein structure in an "elastic network" model [4] whose low-frequency modes should represent natural pathways for conformational change in the biomolecule.

Another approach is to divide up the protein structure into relatively rigid sections or domains, connected together by flexible regions or "hinges". Here we concern ourselves with the "pebble game", an integer algorithm for rigidity analysis. By matching degrees of freedom against constraints, it can rapidly divide a network into rigid regions and floppy "hinges" with excess degrees of freedom. The algorithm is applicable to protein crystal structures if these are treated as molecular frameworks in which bond lengths and angles are constant but dihedral angles may vary; this application, and the program "FIRST" which implements the algorithm, have been described in the literature [5]. The rigid units in a protein structure may be as small as individual methyl groups or large enough to include entire protein domains containing multiple secondary-structure units. Rigidity analysis thus generates a natural multiscale coarse graining of a protein structure [6]. The division of a structure into rigid units is referred to as a Rigid Cluster Decomposition (RCD).

This coarse graining has been used as the basis of simulation methods aiming to explore the large-amplitude flexible motion of proteins, first in the ROCK algorithm [7] based on ring closure, and more recently in the "FRODA" geometric simulation algorithm [1]. I originally developed geometric simulation as a highly simplified model of mineral framework structures, in particular the framework silicates and aluminosilicate zeolites. A great deal of the behaviour of these frameworks can be interpreted using a model in which the constituent SiO_4 tetrahedra remain rigid while pivoting freely at their linked corners; in geometric simulation, such "rigid units" are maintained as rigid shapes and steric exclusion of atoms is maintained using hard-sphere interactions, while longer-range interactions are neglected. This highly simplified modeling approach, by abandoning much detail and retaining only the most essential geometry and physics of the system, has provided insights into the behaviour of complex, flexible mineral framework structures [8, 9, 10].

The "FRODA" algorithm for biomolecules is a geometric simulation in which the "rigid units", rather than being the small units defined by local chemistry in minerals, are the rigid units identified in proteins by FIRST's rigidity analysis. Invocation of the FRODA module when using FIRST leads to the simulation of a random walk through the flexible motion allowed to the protein by its rigidity. The undirected walk has been used to compare the inherent mobility of a crystal structure to that seen experimentally in an NMR ensemble [1] and to examine the relation between protein flexibility and function in enzymes such as IDO [11] and myosin [12]. For studies of conformational change, the walk can be biased to model the desired change. This method has been applied to study possible mechanisms of assembly of a photosynthetic protein complex [2] and to fit the structure of the bacterial chaperonin GroEL to low-resolution cryo-EM data [3]. FRODA is capable of exploring motions of several Ångstroms RMSD for a protein of some hundreds of residues in a few CPU-minutes.

Thanks to recent development, the algorithm is now able to take input from ENM modeling (so as to explore motion along the direction of ENM eigenmodes) and has been made even faster and more stable (unpublished work, Thorpe group). I will discuss these improvements and some current applications in research.

3 CONCLUSIONS

Geometric modeling using the FIRST/FRODA software is computationally very inexpensive and can provide valuable insight into the inherent flexible motion of protein structures. I believe that wider use of the method in parallel to other modeling and simulation techniques including MD and ENM will be profitable to the biophysical modeling community.

REFERENCES

[1]   S.A. Wells, S. Menor, B.M. Hespenheide and M.F. Thorpe, Constrained geometric simulation of diffusive motion in proteins, *Physical Biology* , 2, S127–S136, 2005.

[2]   C.C. Jolley, S.A. Wells, B.M. Hespenheide, M.F. Thorpe and P. Fromme, Docking of Photosystem I subunit C using a constrained geometric simulation, *JACS* , 128, 8803–8812, 2006.

[3]   C.C. Jolley, S.A. Wells, P. Fromme and M.F. Thorpe, Fitting low-resolution cryo-EM maps of proteins using constrained geometric simulations, *Biophysical Journal* , 94, 1613–1621, 2008.

[4]   F. Tama and Y.H. Sanejouand, Conformational change of proteins arising from normal mode calculations, *Protein Engineering* , 14, 1—6, 2001.

[5]   D.J. Jacobs, A.J. Rader, L.A. Kuhn and M.F. Thorpe, Protein flexibility predictions using graph theory, *PROTEINS: Struct., Func. and Gen.* , 44, 150–165, 2001.

[6]   H. Gohlke and M.F. Thorpe, A natural coarse graining for simulating large biomolecular motion, *Biophys. J.* , 91, 2115–2120, 2006.

[7]   M.F. Thorpe, M. Lei, A.J. Rader, D.J. Jacobs and L.A. Kuhn, Protein flexibility and dynamics using constraint theory, *J. Mol. Graph. & Model.* , 19, 60–69, 2001.

[8]   GD Gatta and SA Wells, Rigid Unit Modes at high pressure: an explorative study of a fibrous zeolite-like framework with EDI topology, *Phys. Chem. Minerals* , 31, 465–474, 2004.

[9]   GD Gatta and SA Wells, Structural evolution of zeolite levyne under hydrostatic and non-hydrostatic pressure: geometric modelling, *Phys. Chem. Minerals* , 33, 243–255, 2006.

[10]   A Sartbaeva, SA Wells, MMJ Treacy and MF Thorpe, The flexibility window in zeolites, *Nature Materials* , 5, 962–965, 2006.

[11]   A. Macchiarulo, R. Nuti, D. Bellochi, E. Camaioni, and R. Pellicciari, Molecular docking and spatial coarse graining simulations as tools to investigate substrate recognition, enhancer binding and conformational transitions in indoleamine-2,3-dioxygenase (ido), *Biochim. et Biophys. Acta- Proteins and Proteomics* , 1774, 1058–1068, 2007.

[12]   M. Sun, M.B. Rose, S.K. Ananthanarayanan, D.J. Jacobs and C.M. Yengo, Characterisation of the pre-force-generation state in the actomyosin cross-bridge cycle, *PNAS* , 105, 8631–8636, 2008.

FFT-Based Conjugate Gradient strategies for numerical simulation of GVF-Snakes

Panganai Gomo

Digital Systems and Vision Processing, Electronic, Electrical and Computer Engineering, The University of Birmingham Birmingham, B15 2TT, United Kingdom, pxg132@engmail.bham.ac.uk

Mike Spann

Digital Systems and Vision Processing, Electronic, Electrical and Computer Engineering, The University of Birmingham Birmingham, B15 2TT, United Kingdom, M.Spann@bham.ac.uk

ABSTRACT

In imaging applications near realtime performance of the image segmentation is required. The nature of this paper is to provide a storage and computationally efficient strategy for simulating the GVF-snakes. In particular this approach is based upon Fourier approximations of Circulant matrices [7],[6], [8], fast Toeplitz solvers [2] and an implict-explicit (IMEX) time marching method for the GVF simulation. **Key Words:** *GVF, active contour, Toeplitz, conjugate gradient, FFT, IMEX, Multigrid, Krylov*

1 Introduction

Active contours also known as snakes were introduced in [3] as a model for image segmentation. They are based upon a variational principle that minimizes an energy functional associated with the elasticity and rigidity of a parametric spline function. The parametric spline functional can be expressed as

$$J(C) = \frac{1}{2} \int_0^1 \alpha |C'(s)|^2 + \beta |C''(s)|^2 ds. \tag{1}$$

Here C is a closed curve parametric spline parameterized by s and $'$ denotes a partial derivative such as $C'' = \frac{\partial^2 C}{\partial s^2}$. An external forcing function is used to drive this spline function towards image boundaries. Note this model can only be used to extract closed curves. In cases where multiple objects are to be segmented or significant topological change of the initial snake is expected a related state of the art method is presented in [4]. The complete model results in minimizing a functional

$$P(C) = J(C(s)) + F_{ext}(C(s)), \tag{2}$$

where $P(C)$ is an energy term and $F_{ext}C(s)$ is an external forcing function to drive the parametric spline model. This force is calculated as a function of image gradients. We will introduce a fast parametric active contour based on the realization that the matrices arising from the finite difference discretization of the Euler-Lagrange equations that minimize the parametric spline function are circulant. We then recall that circulant matrices can be diagonalized by the Fourier matrix. Secondly we introduce a fast strategy for computation of the gradient vector flow (GVF) field [10] a popular method in medical imaging for generating an external forcing function. The GVF is defined as the vector field $\mathbf{v} = (u(x,y), v(x,y))$ that minimizes the functional

$$\int_\Omega \mu(u_x^2 + u_y^2 + v_x^2 + v_y^2) + |\nabla f|^2 |\mathbf{v} - \nabla f|^2 dxdy \tag{3}$$

where μ is a regularization parameter, f is the image data and Ω is the image domain.

1.1 Euler-Lagrange Minimizer

The Euler-Lagrange equation that minimizes the functional $J(C)$ is

$$-\alpha(C''(s)) + \beta(C''''(s))$$

and we prescribe periodic boundary conditions as this is a closed curve spline. The Euler-Lagrange minimizer for the gradient vector flow (3) is

$$\mu\nabla^2 u - (u - f_x)(f_x^2 + f_y^2) = 0$$
$$\mu\nabla^2 v - (v - f_y)(f_x^2 + f_y^2) = 0.$$

and for our experiments we prescribe Dirichlet boundary conditions. The GVF-Snake is then defined as

$$C(s) = -\alpha(C''(s)) + \beta(C''''(s)) + \mathbf{v}. \tag{4}$$

After finite difference discretization of (4) a linear system is formed

$$A\mathbf{u} = \mathbf{b} \tag{5}$$

where the vector $\mathbf{u}$ is the parametric curve, $\mathbf{b} = \mathbf{v}(x, y)$ is the data resulting from discretization of the forcing function and A is a discrete state matrix. A has a circulant structure due to the periodic boundary conditions. A is square and has a symmetric positive definite structure and in general is Toeplitz. This linear system invites solvers based upon the circulant approximation of A. Solvers based upon a Fourier approximation such as Toeplitz solvers are extremely efficient for solving such systems. They are $O(n\log(n))$ complexity as opposed to the $O(n^2)$ or $O(n^{3/2})$ complexity of direct solvers.

A popular technique for simulating this system is to introduce an artificial time parameter and use a time marching method;

$$\frac{\mathbf{u}^{n+1} - \mathbf{u}^n}{\tau} + A\mathbf{u} = \mathbf{b}$$

then we can solve iteratively

$$K\mathbf{u}^{n+1} = \mathbf{u}^n + \tau\mathbf{b} \tag{6}$$

where

$$K = [I + \tau A]$$

and retains the same matrix properties as A, namely Toeplitz and symmetric. In general we note that A is not positive definite.

1.2 Parametric Active Contour

We use the following implicit finite difference scheme to discretize the Euler-Lagrange equations

$$\frac{u_i^{n+1} - u_i^n}{\tau} = -\frac{\alpha}{h^2}(u_{i-1}^{n+1} - 2u_i^{n+1} + u_{i+1}^{n+1}) + \frac{\beta}{h^4}(u_{i-2}^{n+1} - 4u_{i-1}^{n+1} + 6u_i^{n+1} - 4u_{i+1}^{n+1} + u_{i+2}^{n+1})$$

where τ is a temporal time step and h is a spatial time step. This is a typical interior row of a matrix with a circulant structure.

Denoting this matrix as A the Fourier matrix diagonalizes this matrix

$$A = F^*\Delta F$$

where F^* is the Hermitian transpose of the fourier matrix and Δ is matrix of eigenvalues of A.

1.3 IMEX-GVF

The implicit-explicit (IMEX) finite difference scheme for the GVF can be written as

$$\frac{\mathbf{v}_{i,j}^{n+1} - \mathbf{v}_{i,j}^n}{\Delta t} + \frac{\mu}{h_1^2}(\mathbf{v}_{i-1,j}^{n+1} - 2\mathbf{v}_{i,j}^{n+1} + \mathbf{v}_{i+1,j}^{n+1}) + \frac{\mu}{h_1^2}(\mathbf{v}_{i,j-1}^{n+1} - 2\mathbf{v}_{i,j}^{n+1} + \mathbf{v}_{i,j+1}^{n+1}) - \nabla f_{i,j}\mathbf{v}^n = \tag{7}$$

$$\nabla f_{i,j}(f_{x,i,j}^2 + f_{x,i,j}^2)$$

leading to a linear system

$$\left[\frac{1}{\Delta t}I + \mu M\right]\mathbf{v}^{n+1} = \left[\frac{1}{\Delta t}I + D\right]\mathbf{v}^n + f, \tag{8}$$

where $\left[\frac{1}{\Delta t}I + \mu M\right]$ is a BTTB (block Toeplitz with Toeplitz blocks) matrix and $\left[\frac{1}{\Delta t}I + D\right]$ is diagonal matrix.

1.4 Implementation and Results

The numerical scheme to solve the finite difference discretization of the parametric active contour is given by the time marching method of equation (6). We propose to solve this system by Fourier methods. Recalling that K is circulant then

$$\mathbf{u}^{n+1} = K^{-1}(\mathbf{u}^n + \tau\mathbf{b}) = F^*\Lambda^{-1}F(\mathbf{u}^n + \tau\mathbf{b})$$

and algorithmically

$$\text{u=iFFT(FFT}(\mathbf{u}^n + \tau\mathbf{b})./\text{evs)};$$

where evs are the eigenvalues of the matrix K and ./ denotes an element wise division. FFT is a fast fourier transform. The eigenvalues of K are obtained by taking a Fourier transform of the first row of K hence we only need to generate and store the first row of K. Although this aspect of the GVF-snake algorithm is storage efficient experimentally it did not offer faster convergence of the snake. Further experiments are required to ascertain it's utility in a 3D finite elements implementation of GVF-snakes.

To simulate the GVF fields we compare two strategies. Firstly simulating the IMEX Scheme (8) using a multigrid strategy. Secondly we use FFT-based preconditioned conjugate gradients algorithm to solve the elliptic system (5) . We refer to [9] and [5] for detailed discussion of the preconditioned conjugate gradient algorithm, to [7] for FFT-based preconditioned conjugate gradients extension to Toeplitz solvers and to [2] for the BTTB case. A detailed discussion of multigrid methods can be found in [1]. In our experiments we use a Gauss-Seidel relaxation scheme with full-weighting injection for the restriction and prolongations operators. The parameters of the multigrid iteration (ν_0, ν_1, ν_2) refer to number of number of "v" cycles, pre-smoothing and post-smoothing iterations respectively. Best parameters can only be determined empirically. Table (1.4) presents comparative results for simulation of the GVF fields. MG and FMG refer to multigrid and full-multigrid schemes. The values in the parentheses refer to the parameters used in the simulation. MGCG and FMGCG refer to FFT-based preconditioned conjugate gradients initialised by a particular multigrid scheme. IMEX refers to the scheme being used as a solver in the time marching IMEX method. Experiments are terminated when the solution is smaller than a residual $\rho = 1 \times 10^{-6}$. The codes were written in Matlab and run on an AMD Athlon 64X2 without any multicore optimisations.

Algorithm	63 × 63 Time, s	Speed gain	127 × 127 Time, s	Speed gain	255 × 255 Time, s	Speed gain
Original	0.453	1	3.625	1	30.109	1
IMEX-MG(1,2,2)	0.234	2	0.937	4	5.172	6
IMEX-FMG(1,2,2)	0.422	1	1.562	2	8.594	4
MG(2,4,4)	0.234	2	0.812	4	3.109	10
FMG(1,2,2)	0.234	2	0.627	5	2.734	11
MGCG(1,1,1)	0.235	2	0.984	4	3.625	8
FMGCG(1,1,1)	0.218	2	1.031	4	4.563	7

Table 1: Comparison of computational speed in 2D

2 Conclusion

In this paper we have presented a fast storage efficient implementation of GVF-Snakes. We have shown strategies that significantly improve the computational efficiency of GVF. Particularly strategies such as FMGCG are powerful as they do not require one to experimentally ascertain the parameters for the multigrid scheme. These schemes are shown to have more utility as the size of the images increases. Further work is required so that the algorithms not only reduce operations count but take advantage of modern computer architectures which are becoming more parallel and exhibit ever deeper levels of caching.

References

[1] W. L. Briggs, V. E. Henson, and S. F. McCormick. *A multigrid tutorial*. SIAM, 2000.

[2] R.H. Chan and X.Q Jin. *An Introduction to Iterative Toeplitz Solvers*. SIAM, 2007.

[3] M. Kass, A. Witkin, and D. Terzopoulos. Snakes: Active contour models. *International Journal of Computer Vision*, 1:321–331, 1988.

[4] G. Papandreou and P. Maragos. Multigrid geometric active contour models. *IEEE Transactions on Image Processing*, 16:229–240, 2007.

[5] Y. Saad. *Iterative Methods for Sparse Linear Systems*. SIAM, 2003.

[6] G. Strang. *Introduction to Applied Mathematics*. 1986.

[7] G. Strang. A proposal for toeplitz matrix calculations. *Studies in Applied Mathematics*, 2:171–176, 1986.

[8] G. Strang. The discrete cosine transform. *SIAM Review*, 41:135–147, 1999.

[9] L.N. Trefethen and D. Bau. *Numerical Linear Algebra*. SIAM, 1997.

[10] C. Xu and J. L. Prince. Snakes, shapes, and gradient vector flow. *IEEE Transactions on Image Processing*, 7:359–369, 1998.

Using Shape Entropy as a Feature to Lesion Boundary Segmentation with Level Sets

Elizabeth M.Massey
University of Lincoln, Brayford Pool, Lincoln LN6 7TS UK, bmassey@lincoln.ac.uk

Andrew Hunter
University of Lincoln, Brayford Pool, Lincoln LN6 7TS UK, ahunter@lincoln.ac.uk

James A. Lowell
Foster Findlay Associates Limited, Newcastle Technopole Kings Manor, Newcastle Upon Tyne NE1 6PA UK, james.lowell@gmail.com

David Steel
Consultant Ophthalmologist, Sunderland Eye Infirmary, Queen Alexandra Road, Sunderland SR2 9HP UK, David.Steel@chs.northy.nhs.uk

ABSTRACT

Accurate lesion segmentation in retinal imagery is an area of vast research. Of the many segmentation methods available very few are insensitive to topological changes on noisy surfaces. This paper presents an extension to earlier work on a novel stopping mechanism for level sets. The elementary features scheme (ELS) in [5] is extended to include shape entropy as a feature used to 'look back in time' and find the point at which the curve best fits the real object. We compare the proposed extension against the original algorithm for timing and accuracy using 50 randomly selected images of exudates with a database of clinician demarcated boundaries as ground truth. While this work is presented applied to medical imagery, it can be used for any application involving the segmentation of bright or dark blobs on noisy images.

Key Words: *Shape Special Session, Exudate Segmentation, Level Sets, Medical Image Processing.*

1 INTRODUCTION

The diagnosis of diabetic retinopathy is based upon visually recognizing various clinical features. Retinal lesions are among the first visual indicators suggestive of diabetic retinopathy. The threat to visual loss increases with the frequency of retinal lesions combined with their encroachment into the macula. To enable early diagnosis, it is necessary to identify both frequency and position of retinal lesions in relation to the fovea and other major structures (such as the optic nerve). In [5] a *lesionness* measure was introduced and defined as a combination of perimeter size constancy shp and compactness $c = p^2/a$, where p is the perimeter and a is the area [3]. The *lesionness* measure was the core of the stopping mechanism and upon further analysis we discovered a more direct approach by tracking the entropy of the shape of the region of interest (roi). In this work we introduce the notion of using a multivariate histogram to describe the changing shape of the roi and track the shape entropy to determine the best fit. The correlation between the change in shape entropy and the perimeter size constancy indicates the point where the curve best fits the lesion (or region of interest).

2 BACKGROUND

Retinal exudates are an interesting challenge for segmentation algorithms as they vary in appearance, conforming to one of three structures: dot exudates, fluffy exudates and circumscribed plaques of exudate. Dot exudates consist of round yellow spots lying superficially or deep in the sensory retina [9]. Exudates are usually reflective and may appear to have a rigid, multifaceted contour, ranging in color from white to yellow [1]. With varying shapes, sizes, patterns and contrast, exudate segmentation is a demanding problem, complicated by lighting variation over the image, natural pigmentation, the intrinsic color of the lesion, and decreasing color saturation at lesion boundaries [2].

We compare our current work to the novel scheme presented in [5], along with three other well known segmentation algorithms. Sinthanayothin et al., [11], Wang et al., [12] and Osareh et al.,[6].

3 PROPOSED MODEL

3.1 Curve Propagation

For our work in lesion segmentation, level set methods provide the capability to determine not just the coarse shape of an object, but are extremely useful to tease out the fine delicate boundary fissures and curves that give a deeper look into the overall shape of a lesion candidate. From the well known definition of level sets [7]:

$$\phi_t + F_0 \, |\nabla\phi| + \vec{U}(x,y,t)\vec{\nabla}\phi = \varepsilon K \, |\nabla\phi| \tag{1}$$

where: ϕ_t is the propagating function at time t, $F_0 \, |\nabla\phi|$ is the motion of the curve in the direction normal to the front, $\vec{U}(x,y,t)\vec{\nabla}\phi$ is the term that moves the curve across the surface and $\varepsilon K \, |\nabla\phi|$ is the speed term dependent upon curvature. $\vec{U}(x,y,t)\vec{\nabla}\phi$ is the gradient map, described in section 3.2 and $\varepsilon K \, |\nabla\phi|$ is approximated using a central differencing scheme.

Our numerical implementation takes insights from [10]. Let ϕ_i^n be the value of ϕ at a point (pixel) i at time n. The curve evolves over a given time step thus:

$$\phi_{ij}^{n+1} = \phi_{ij}^n - \triangle t[max(-\beta_{ij},0) \, \triangle^+ + min(-\beta_{ij},0)\triangle^-] \tag{2}$$

where: $\beta(k) = 1 + \epsilon k$ is the velocity function, u_{ij}^n is the 'current' level set zero, $\triangle t$ is the time step (or scaling factor) and the [max...min] describes the *normal* component, and where:

$$\triangle^+ = [max(D_x^-,0)^2 + min(D_x^+,0)^2 + max(D_y^-,0)^2 + min(D_y^+,0)^2]^{1/2} \tag{3}$$
$$\triangle^- = [max(D_x^+,0)^2 + min(D_x^-,0)^2 + max(D_y^+,0)^2 + min(D_y^-,0)^2]^{1/2}$$

and $D_x^-, D_x^+, D_y^-, D_y^+$ are the forward and backward difference approximations in the **x** and the **y** directions, respectively.

3.2 Gradient Map

The boundary of a lesion can be characterized by the point of strongest intensity contrast between itself and the background retina. Since retinal images are inherently noisy and the lesion edge pixels can look very much like background pixels, we want a mechanism that smooths out the noise but preserves the edges in our gradient map. Anisotropic filters address the issue of edge preservation [8]. We build our gradient map thus: $g_I(x,y) = \frac{2*(I_n)}{(2-(I_n)^2)}$ where: I_n is a histogram equalized, normalized gray-scale (green channel) image $I(x,y)$ and $\sigma = 1$.

3.3 Stopping Mechanism

A traditional use of level sets is to track a curve to an object's boundary and then stop. In our case, it is more interesting to 'peek ahead' by allowing the curve to move past the optimal boundary and then 'look back' and measure how well-formed the accumulated region is as a lesion. We have found that when the curve begins to hold its shape, or position in time, this is a potential boundary point. The curve may slow down and then subsequently speed up as its moves over a surface. It is for this reason we use the shape entropy information from one iteration to another to correlate the best stopping point with the slowing down of the curve.

3.3.1 Histogram

Our histogram model is from [4] in which the third (skewness) and fourth (kurtosis) order moments are defined for multi-dimensional surfaces. Mardia [4] defines a measure of skewness corresponding to: $\beta_{1,p} = \Sigma\Sigma\Sigma S^{rr'}S^{ss'}S^{tt'}M_{111}^{(rst)}M_{111}^{(r's't')}$ where:

$S^{-1} = S^{ij}$ and $M_{111}^{(r's't')} = \frac{1}{n}\Sigma_{i=1}^{n}(X_{ri} - \bar{X}_r)(X_{si} - \bar{X}_s)(X_{ti} - \bar{X}_t)$. We modify the $M_{111}^{(r's't')}$ term to address location of pixel intensities relative to the grid to retain the true shape of the bounded object thus, $M_{111}^{(r's't')} = \frac{1}{\Sigma w}\Sigma_{i=1}^{n}\Sigma w_i(X_{ri} - \bar{X}_r)(X_{si} - \bar{X}_s)(X_{ti} - \bar{X}_t)$, where: X is a vector of x,y values, and $\bar{X}$ is a vector of the means; p is the number of dimensions ($p = 2$), w_i is the intensities at value i, $\sum w$ is the sum of all the intensities in the region of interest, and S^{-1} is the Covariance Matrix (inverted).

The measure of kurtosis corresponding to $B_{2,p}$ is, with our modifications:

$$b_{2,p} = \frac{(\sum w)+2}{(\sum w^2)p}\sum_{i=1}^{n}w_i\{(X_i - \bar{X})'S^{-1}(X_i - \bar{X})\}^2.$$

Although we do not use the values of these moments during this portion of the work, we do employ the full covariance matrix from the output of the histogram generation, and apply it to calculate entropy $H(X) = \frac{1}{2}\ln\left[(2\pi e)^n |det(S)|\right]$ where: n is the number of observations in the region of interest and S is the covariance matrix. When no discernible change is detected from one iteration to another, the curve has found its 'most informative' boundary point.

3.3.2 Best Fit Features

From the original work in [5] we are looking for measurements that can give indicators of how well-formed a region is as a candidate lesion. Thus, elementary features include 1) the number of iterations the curve held its perimeter size: shp; 2) the minimum compactness value: c; 3) the number of iterations the curve held that compactness value: chp; and 4) the gradient contrast: gc. After the curve has moved for a number of iterations (we use $P = 180$) it is possible that the curve has evolved past the optimal point describing the object boundary. Because of this possibility, the gathered measurement values are then used to 'look back in time' to find the point at which the curve best fit the object boundary.

3.3.3 Correlation

Let q be the iteration number and $h(q)$ be the count of the number of iterations for which the feature values have held up to and including q. Let q_{shp} be the iteration point where the perimeter holds its size for a $h(q) > 2$, and q_{ent} the entropy value at each successive iteration. Let q_c be the iteration with the smallest value of c, q_{gc} be the iteration with the largest contrast and q_{chp} be the iteration where c held its value the longest. Let q_μ and q_σ be the mean and standard deviation, respectively, of the iteration values for the gathered features. Let $q_{ub} = q_\mu + q_\sigma$ be the upper bound and let $q_{lb} = q_\mu - q_\sigma$ be the lower bound. Then let Z^* be the collection of features that fall within the $(one)\sigma$ boundary. Those features that fall within $(one)\sigma$ of q_μ are used to calculate the best fit point. $SV = \frac{\Sigma_{q \in Z^*} q}{\#Z^*}$ is the average of these bounded features, where: q is a bounded feature and $\#Z*$ is the number of bounded features. To determine the best fit point we use Pearson's product-moment coefficient correlated between the q_{shp} feature and the shape entropy q_{ent} features. $\rho_{q_{shp},q_{ent}} = \frac{E((q_{shp} - \mu_{q_{shp}})(q_{ent} - \mu_{q_{ent}}))}{\sigma_{q_{shp}}\sigma_{q_{ent}}}$ where: E is the expected value, and $\mu_{q_{ent}}$, $\sigma_{q_{shp}}$ and $\mu_{q_{shp}}$, $\sigma_{q_{ent}}$ are the first and second moments for perimeter size constancy and entropy, respectively. The images with high correlation of entropy $H(X)$ to perimeter size constancy shp use the $max(shp)$ value - the iteration where the perimeter held its size the longest. Lower correlation values require the SV calculation.

4 CONCLUSIONS

Table 1 shows the final segmentation result compared with other algorithms, and shows an increase in accuracy and decrease in error rate for the proposed model. Sensitivity values can be increased with developments to the gradient map generation. Algorithm names are as follows: ELSwE - Elementary Features Scheme w/Entropy

Correlation; ELS - Elementary Features Scheme (orig); Fuzzy - Fuzzy C-means; RRG - Recursive Region Grow; DC - Color Discriminant.

Table 1: Algorithm Performance Metrics.

Model	Sens.	Spec.	Accuracy	Error
ELSwE	96.53	99.28	99.13	22.38
ELS	96.94	98.97	98.87	29.35
Fuzzy	88.29	94.18	93.89	158.95
RRG	47.72	90.99	88.85	290.1
DC	64.67	75.77	75.21	644.75

A novel idea for automated segmentation and classification of candidate lesions using a new level set stopping mechanism has been presented. Experimental comparisons have been conducted on five segmentation approaches. All algorithms were evaluated against a randomly-selected image set with ophthalmic lesion boundary demarcation. The results shown in Table 1 demonstrate the advantage of allowing the curve propagation (region growing) to run past the optimal boundary point, thus providing a 'peek ahead' to adjacent areas. Then using gathered elementary features and correlating the strongest to shape entropy to 'look back in time' determines the best fitting curve.

REFERENCES

[1] Hean-Choon Chen. *Vascular Complications of Diabetes; current issues in pathogenesis and treatment*, chapter 10, pages 97–108. Blackwell Publishing, 2002.

[2] M.H. Goldbaum, N.P. Katz, M.R. Nelson, and L.R. Haff. The discrimination of similarly colored objects in computer images of the ocular fundus. *Investigative Ophthalmology & Visual Science*, 31:617–623, 1990.

[3] Rafael C. Gonzalez and Richard E. Woods. *Digital Image Processing*. Prentice Hall, Upper Saddle River, NJ, 2001.

[4] K.V. Mardia. Measures of multivariate skewness and kurtosis with applications. *Biometrika*, 57(3):519–530, March 1970.

[5] E. M. Massey, J. A. Lowell, A. Hunter, and D. Steel. Lesion boundary segmentation using level set methods. In *Advances in Computer Graphics and Computer Vision*, 2009. To be published.

[6] A. Osareh, M. Mirmehdi, B. Thomas, and Richard Markham. Automatic recognition of exudative maculopathy using fuzzy c-means clustering and neural networks. In E Claridge and J Bamber, editors, *Medical Image Understanding and Analysis*, pages 49–52. BMVA Press, July 2001.

[7] Stanley Osher and James A Sethian. Fronts propagating with curvature-dependent speed: Algorithms based on Hamilton-Jacobi formulations. *Journal of Computational Physics*, 79:12–49, 1988.

[8] P. Perona and J. Malik. Scale-space and edge detection using anisotropic diffusion. *IEEE Transactions on Pattern Analysis and Machine Intelligence*, 12(7):629–639, July 1990.

[9] M. Porta and F. Bandello. Diabetic retinopathy a clinical update. *Diabetologia*, 45(12):1617–1634, December 2002.

[10] G. Sapiro. *Geometric Partial Differential Equations and Image Analysis*. Cambridge University Press, 2001.

[11] C. Sinthanayothin, J.F. Boyce, T.H. Williamson, H.L. Cook, E. Mensah, and D. Lal, S. andUsher. Automated detection of diabetic retinopathy on digital fundus images. *Diabetic Medicine*, 19:105–112, 2002.

[12] H. Wang, W. Hsu, K.G. Goh, and M.L. Lee. An effective approach to detect lesions in color retinal images. In *Proceedings IEEE Conference on Computer Vision and Pattern Recognition*, volume 2, pages 181–186, 2000.

A ROBUST ACTIVE CONTOUR APPROACH FOR STUDYING CELL DEFORMATION FROM NOISY IMAGES

Angelo Cenedese
Department of Engineering and Management, University of Padova, Stradella S.Nicola 3, Vicenza, Italy, angelo.cenedese@unipd.it

Alberto Silletti
Department of Information Engineering, University of Padova, Via Gradenigo 6A, Padova, Italy, silletti@dei.unipd.it

ABSTRACT

This work presents a generalized formulation of the Snake model defining new terms for the internal and the external energy functionals. These modifications conjugate features of the object contour as well as the inside of the shape. The obtained model is significantly more accurate spatially on the image plane and temporally on the frame sequence. In particular, the application to single cell analysis is in focus: In this context, we show how to cast the specific problem into the extended framework we propose. Shape descriptors and suitable metrics are then derived from the curve representation. The boundary identification produced through the classic formulation shows a poor and imprecise segmentation and leads to misleading metrics. The new model instead represents the boundary and the derived shape parameters in a way more consistent with the visual perception of shape evolution and deformation.

Key Words: *deformable models, snake, shape analysis, stem cells.*

1   INTRODUCTION

In the past few decades, the fast advances in computer science have revolutionized our ability of obtaining and analyzing medical and biological data, with impact on a wide range of applications in research and therapy. Computer vision has become a strong ally for the biomedical researcher and clinical operator, becoming a supporting technology for the medical staff [1]. In particular, researchers in the fields of stem cell research express the necessity of methodologies and procedures to quantify cell and tissue modifications after specific stimuli or along the natural growth. Even if the skills of biomedical staff in reading and interpreting the analysis data are beyond reach for nonmedical researcher, considering a set of medical or biological images, it is easy to note that, roughly speaking, the level of "noise" heavily affects the interpretation of the represented data: These images often exhibit poor contrast, non-uniform background illumination, resulting in boundaries that are not sufficiently sharp to be segmented. Very few works address this problem [2], and the majority focus on image enhancement or derive enhancement [3] to highlight edges. In some contexts these solutions show their insufficiency, missing a key point of the problem, namely the possibility of getting information not relying on edges.

In this perspective we propose a Snake framework that contributes with an improved yet agile new formulation. The model is able to cope with high level of noise, corrupted images, and to embed a model of the object of interest. The approach, close in spirit to the work in [4], combines synergically a number of ingredients, resorting to classical computer vision techniques, a priori biomedical information, mathematical modeling and bio-inspired modeling.

2 GENERALIZED SNAKE MODEL

In the context described in the Introduction it is of paramount importance to formulate a model accurate in the dynamic representation of the deformation and able to yield accurate shape metrics. The purpose of this section is thus to present a Generalized Active Contour framework and show how to specialize it to the analysis of single cell shape (object A in the following).

To begin with, we introduce Snakes as parametric models obtained as an energy minimizing curves. In the original formulation by Kass and coworkers [5], an acceptable solution C is characterized by an energy functional:

$$\mathcal{E}(C) = S(C) + \mathcal{P}(C) = \int_{\partial A} \alpha(s) \left|\frac{\partial C}{\partial s}\right|^2 + \beta(s) \left|\frac{\partial^2 C}{\partial s^2}\right|^2 ds + \int_{\partial A} \mathcal{F}\left[I(C(s))\right] ds \qquad (1)$$

where the two terms $S(C)$ and $\mathcal{P}(C)$ are respectively the *internal energy*, computed directly on the geometric model of the curve, and the *external energy*, a term accounting for the image I according to a transformation $\mathcal{F}(I) : \mathbb{R}^2 \to \mathbb{R}$.

The Generalized Active Contour we propose takes the form

$$S(A, C) = S\left(\left|\frac{\partial C}{\partial s}\right|, \left|\frac{\partial^2 C}{\partial s^2}\right|, S_i(A, C)\right) \qquad \mathcal{P}(A, C) = \mathcal{P}(I(A), \mathcal{P}_j(A, C)) \qquad (2)$$

where the extended energy functionals show a suitable combination of S_i and $\mathcal{P}_j$ terms. Each term tackles a specific aspect of A such as metrics of the shape, color or texture properties, or time evolution.

The rationale behind this approach is in the following statement [6]: *A plane shape $A \in \mathbb{R}^2$ has a 1-dimensional side given by features of its boundary $C = \partial A$; and a 2-dimensional side given by its interior. No successful theory of shape description can ignore one or the other.* In this sense, we extend the energy functional terms by integrating any other relevant aspect such as the geometric model, physical properties and even non video data. Generalized Active Contours provides a standard and manageable framework to do this. Hereafter, we specialize the discussion to suit the cell application, providing directions to build the terms S_i and $\mathcal{P}_j$ using linear probability density. This section gives a brief mathematical explanation, more examples and a more theoretical discussion are reserved for the full paper. As a general guideline, given a metric τ for A (computed on A, ∂A or outside A) a probability density $\Phi(\tau)$ can be derived via a learning phase, analytically, or inferred empirically. It is then possible to define an energy term $E_i(A, C)$, both for S_i and $\mathcal{P}_i$, as a function of $\Phi(\tau)$, whose minima correspond to high probability behaviors. The Energy term drives the Snakes towards a configuration compatible with $\Phi(\tau)$, still allowing some degree of freedom in the same way the probability density does.

Cells evolve in time undergoing a continuous change in shape appearance by protruding appendages that adhere to the culture surface (1D-side of the shape). In this sense, the smoothness imposed in the Snake's standard formulation counteracts this behavior: Conversely a curvature term allowing the boundary curvature κ to assume negative values enforces a spiky appearance. A simple energy term capturing this feature can use a piecewise linear probability density with maximum curvature value τ_{max}:

$$S_{spike}(C) = -2\frac{\tau_{max} - \tau_{spike}(C)}{\tau_{max}} \qquad \text{where} \quad \tau_{spike}(C) = \int_{\partial A} \kappa(s) ds \quad \text{and} \quad \kappa(s) = \frac{\partial^2 C(s)}{\partial s^2}. \qquad (3)$$

Similarly, the presence of a rest shape for the cell can also be exploited:

$$\max_{\tau} \left(\Phi(\tau) - \Phi(\tau_{rest})\right)^2 \qquad \text{where} \quad \tau_{rest} \text{ is measured w.r.t. the rest shape.} \qquad (4)$$

Cells viewed from a microscope often show a bright halo, due to the scattering properties of the living material enhanced by the thinness of the cells at the border. These optical phenomena are common in back-lit organic materials. This information is related to the inside cell texture (f_W defined in A) and neighborhood features (f_b defined in ΔA). The related contributions (2D shape descriptors) are:

$$\tau_W(C) = \int_A [I_W(\omega) - f_W(\omega)]^2 \, d\omega \qquad f_W(\omega) = \text{inner texture prototype} \qquad (5)$$

$$\tau_b(C) = \int_{\Delta A} [I_b(\omega) - f_b(\omega)]^2 \, d\omega \qquad f_b(\omega) = \text{neighborhood prototype} \qquad (6)$$

This kind of measures maps directly into energy terms and drives the snake towards a suitable interior and a suitable neighbor background, a-priori defined (details here omitted). Hence, for the specific cell application, the Active Contour is based on the following global functionals, whose terms are linearly combined:

$$S(A,C) = S\left(\left|\frac{\partial C}{\partial s}\right|, \left|\frac{\partial^2 C}{\partial s^2}\right|, \kappa(C), \Phi(A), A_{rest}\right) \qquad P(A,C) = P(I(A), f_W(A), f_b(A)) \qquad (7)$$

We present in Fig. 1 the results of the application of the proposed model in some frames from a video sequence of a cell deformation. The standard Active Contour formulation is not able to correctly detect the cell shape: Errors accumulate over frames and end up with a general failure of the tracking algorithm. Nonetheless, even in the first frames of the sequence, the Active Contour fails in capturing all the fine details, such as protein spikes and ridges, yielding erroneous statistics.

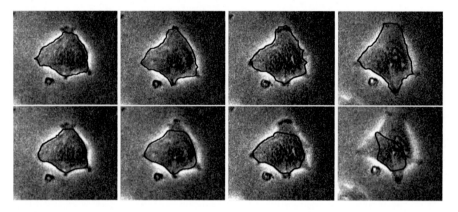

Figure 1: Cell dynamic detection. The first row is obtained using the proposed Snake model, while the second row is produced with the original formulation.

3   THE MEASURE OF SHAPE

The measure of shape mainly serves two purposes: on the one side there is a *control purpose*, namely the translation of the distance between two objects in the shape space, on the other there is a *classification purpose*, aiming at learning the shape representation. Several approaches can be exploited, among which we recall a statistical shape analysis approach based on landmarks and a functional approach relying on curve representations. The latter naturally exploits the accurate reconstruction of the shape provided by the Active contour: Given a planar shape $A \subset \mathbb{R}^2$ a simple way to derive a measurement $f(A) \in \mathbb{R}^n$ is to refer to linear filters: $f(A) = \int \psi(A) dA$, with $\psi(\bullet)$ suitable base functions. A polynomial set of functions ($\psi(x,y) = x^p y^q$) in the filter formulation produces the order $(p+q)$ curve moments $m_{p,q}(C)$. Although the moment description captures various levels of the shape distribution, single moments (especially the high order ones) link poorly to perceivable principal deformation, thus failing in supporting the perception with actual measurements. To provide a complete set of shape descriptor able to describe the continuous evolution while keeping consistency with the perception, we instead introduce the concept of *sphericity* as a scaled ratio between shape area $\Phi(A)$ and perimeter $\Lambda(A)$, refer to the definition of *ellipticity* and *ellipticity variance* given in [7], and to the classical definition of total and average *curvature* κ_{tot} and κ_{avg}. We also complete the set of shape parameters by defining two additional quantities *spikeness* Σ and *boundary activity* Γ, which we consider strongly coupled with the visual activity of the cells:

$$\Sigma(C) = \oint_C \left| \frac{\partial^2 C(s)}{\partial s^2} - \kappa_{avg}(C) \right| ds \qquad \Gamma(C) = \left(\Lambda(C) - \frac{1}{n} \cdot \sum_{j=t-n}^{t-1} \Lambda(C_j) \right)^2 \qquad (8)$$

where C_j refers to the shape C at time step j and n controls the temporal averaging. The computation of these quantities benefits from the underlying proposed Snake model, in that it is more accurate and conveys more information about the dynamics of the shape and the deformation process (Fig. 2).

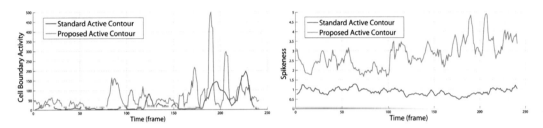

Figure 2: Shape metrics. Evolution of spikeness and boundary activity, according to the proposed and original snake model.

4 CONCLUSIONS

The development of the proposed Active Contour model is an element in a framework of study of wider perspective, where the measurement of the shape and its deformation is a central issue. In this regard, this model presents appealing properties of robustness and accuracy in the detection, validated with several cells in different experimental conditions. For the sake's of brevity, insights and many technical details have been omitted, and also references to the more general picture of the whole shape problem.

REFERENCES

[1] J. Duncan and N. Ayache, Medical image analysis: Progress over two decades and the challenges ahead, *IEEE Trans. on Pattern Analysis and Machine Intelligence*, 22, 85-106, 2000.

[2] C. Xu and J.L. Prince, Generalized gradient vector flow external forces for active contours, *Signal Processing, An International Journal*, 71, 131-139, 1998.

[3] A. Steiner, R. Kimmel, and A.M. Bruckstein, Planar Shape Enhancement and Exaggeration, *Technion Israel Institute of Technology, Internal Report*, 1995.

[4] T.F. Chan and L.A. Vese, Active contours without edges, *IEEE Trans. on Image Processing*, 10(2), 266-277, 2001.

[5] M. Kass, A. Witkin, and D. Terzopoulus, Snakes: Active contour models, *International Journal of Computer Vision*, 1, 321-331, 1987.

[6] D. Mumford, Mathematical Theories of Shape: Do they model perception?, *Proc. Geometric Methods in Computer Vision Conference, SPIE*, 1570, 2-10, 1991.

[7] P.L. Rosin, Measuring shape: ellipticity, rectangularity, and triangularity, *Machine Vision and Applications*, 14(3), 172-184, 2003.

1st International Conference on Mathematical and Computational Biomedical Engineering - CMBE2009

June 29 - July 1, 2009, Swansea, UK

P.Nithiarasu and R.Löhner (Eds.)

Mammographic Image Segmentation using Edge Based Deformable Contour Models

Xianghua Xie

Department of Computer Science, University of Swansea, Swansea, UK

`x.xie@swansea.ac.uk`

ABSTRACT

Deformable contour models, also known as snakes, are commonly used in image processing and computer vision due to their natural handling of shape variation and independence of operation (once initialized), which make them highly appropriate to segment mass lesions in digital (or digitized) mammographic images. The extracted shape and texture information through contour based segmentation are useful in determining benignancy or malignancy. In this paper, we present a preliminary sudy on comparative analysis of four edge based active contour models in segmenting mass lesions in mammogram images. Two of them are widely used, classic active contour models and the other two are most recent advances in active contouring. Experiments are carried out to compare their accuracy, as well as the ability in handling weak edges and difficult initializations.

Key Words: *Digital mammography, computer-aided diagnosis, lesion segmentation, mass segmentation, active contours, deformable model, object segmentation.*

1 INTRODUCTION

Breast cancer is one of the leading cause of cancer deaths in women and the risk of developing breast cancer in life time for women is very high, from eight to twelve percent [14]. Mammography has been proved effective in examining abnormalities for early detection which is the key to improve breast cancer prognosis. Analyzing mammogram using computer vision has been widely reported in the literature, e.g. [4, 10, 8]. Segmenting mass lesions is a critical step in automatic or computed aided detecting abnormalities and diagnosis. Masses are space occupying lesions, characterized by their shape, margin and density. A benign neoplasm is smoothly marginated, while a malignancy often has an indistinct border with low contrast which appears more spiculated over time. Some example mass lesions are shown in Figs. 1 and 2. Potential lesion sites can be automatically or semi-automatically detected and located, e.g. [4]. These regions will be closely examined. Thus lesion segmentation is useful to delineate them from surrounding tissues. Various techniques have been developed to carry out this task, including Markov random field modeling [6], region growing [2], SOM [5], fuzzy sets [9], morphological process [3], and watershed segmentation [10].

Active contour models are highly appropriate to segment mass lesions in mammographic images, e.g. [11]. In this paper, we present a preliminary study on comparative analysis of four edge based active contour models in segmenting mass lesions in mammogram images. Two of them are widely used, classic active contour models and the other two are most recent advances in active contouring. Experiments are carried out to compare their segmentation accuracy, as well as the ability in handling weak edges and difficult initializations.

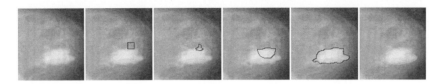

Figure 1: Mass lesion segmentation - from left: mass lesion image, initial MAC snake, its evolution, MAC final result, and the hand labeled segmentation. None of the other methods can achieve reasonable results with such difficult initialization.

2   EDGE BASED ACTIVE CONTOURING

We conduct an applied comparative study of four edge based active contour models, namely geodesic [1], GGVF [13], GeoGGVF [7] and MAC [12], in mammogram mass lesion segmentation. Due to lack of space, we only provide an overview of the more recent MAC model. Interested readers can refer to the references for more details.

The MAC model [12] is one of the most recent advances in edge based active contouring. It has shown significant improvements over other edge based models and comparable performances against more sophisticated region based methods. It is based on hypothesized magnetic interactions between the object boundary and the active contour. We hypothesize charged particles flowing through the edges. These flows of charges will then generate a magnetic field. The snake, carrying similar flow of charges, will be attracted towards the edges under this magnetic influence. Without losing generality, let us consider the image plane as a 2D plane in a 3D space whose origin coincides with the origin of the image coordinates. Additionally, the third dimension of this 3D space is considered perpendicular to the image plane.

The direction of the currents, flows of charges, running through object boundary can be estimated based on edge orientation, which can be conveniently obtained by a $90°$ rotation in the image plane of the normalized gradient vectors $\hat{\Phi}_x$, $\hat{}_y\Phi$ where $\quad$ denotes an image. Let $\mathbf{x}$ denote point in the image domain. Thus, the object boundary current direction, $\mathbf{O}(\mathbf{x})$ can be estimated as: $\mathbf{O}(\mathbf{x}) = (-1)^{\Phi}(\hat{}_y(\mathbf{x}), \hat{}_x(\mathbf{x}), 0)$ where $\lambda = 1$ gives an anti-clockwise rotation in the image coordinates, and $\lambda = 2$ provides a clockwise rotation. Since the snake is embedded in a signed distance function, the direction of current for the snake, denoted as Υ, can be similarly obtained by rotating the gradient vector $\nabla\Phi$ of the level set function.

Let $f(\mathbf{x})$ be the magnitude of edge pixel and the magnitude of boundary current be proportional to edge strength, that is, the electric current on object boundary is defined as $f(\mathbf{x})\mathbf{O}(\mathbf{x})$. The magnetic flux $\mathbf{B}(\mathbf{x})$ generated by gradient vectors at each pixel position $\mathbf{x}$ can then be computed as: $\mathbf{B}(\mathbf{x}) \propto \sum_{s\in S} f(\mathbf{s})\mathbf{O}(\mathbf{s}) \times \frac{\hat{\mathbf{R}}_{\mathbf{xs}}}{R_{\mathbf{xs}}^2}$, where $\mathbf{s}$ denotes an edge pixel position, $\mathbf{S}$ is the set containing all the edge pixel positions, $\hat{\mathbf{R}}_{\mathbf{xs}}$ denotes a 3D unit vector from $\mathbf{x}$ to $\mathbf{s}$ in the image plane, and $R_{\mathbf{xs}}$ is the distance between them. The snake is assigned with unit magnitude of electric current. The force imposed on it can be derived as: $\mathbf{F}(\mathbf{x}) \propto \Upsilon(\mathbf{x}) \times \mathbf{B}(\mathbf{x})$. We can see that $\mathbf{B}$ intersects the image plane perpendicularly and $\mathbf{F}$ is always perpendicular to both Υ and $\mathbf{B}$. Thus, $\mathbf{F}$ also lies in the image domain and its third element equals to zero. For simplicity, we shall ignore its third dimensional component and denote $\mathbf{F}(\mathbf{x})$ as a 2D vector field in the image domain. The basic MAC model can then be formulated as: $C_t = \alpha g(\mathbf{x})\kappa\hat{\mathbf{N}} + (1 - \alpha)(\mathbf{F}(\mathbf{x}) \cdot \hat{\mathbf{N}})\hat{\mathbf{N}}$, where $g(\mathbf{x}) = 1/(1 + f(\mathbf{x}))$, κ denotes the curvature, and $\hat{\mathbf{N}}$ is inward unit normal. Its level set representation then takes this form: $\Phi_t = \alpha g(\mathbf{x})\nabla \cdot \left(\frac{\nabla\Phi}{|\nabla\Phi|}\right)|\nabla\Phi| - (1 - \alpha)\mathbf{F}(\mathbf{x}) \cdot \nabla\Phi$. Nonlinear diffusion of the magnetic field can be applied in order to overcome noise interference if necessary. More details can be found in [12].

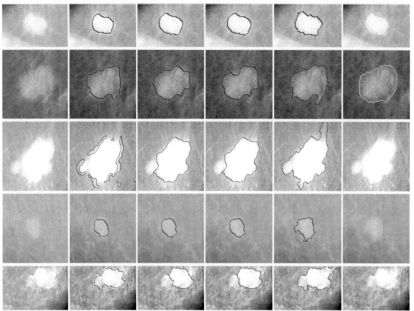

Figure 2: Mass lesion segmentation - Row (a): original mass lesion images row (b): geodesic results; row (c): GGVF results; row (d): GeoGGVF results; row (e): MAC results; row (f): hand labeled segmentations. Note the initialization conditions for the MAC model are much more challenging than those for the rest models.

Table 1: Segmentation Comparison.

Test No.		1	2	3	4	5	6	7	8	Overall
Geodesic	spec.	100	99.98	4.04	99.96	0	99.96	0.02	99.63	62.95
	sens.	76.40	70.75	91.25	79.65	93.14	75.72	94.38	81.25	82.82
	accu.	96.34	97.35	28.52	95.02	3.14	98.56	7.68	96.23	65.36
GGVF	spec.	100	99.98	99.19	99.84	100	99.97	99.89	99.38	99.78
	sens.	88.05	85.14	82.58	80.14	64.38	83.85	69.44	65.89	77.43
	accu.	98.14	98.65	94.53	95.04	98.80	99.04	97.42	93.19	96.85
GeoGGVF	spec.	100	100	99.26	99.96	100	99.98	99.59	99.15	99.74
	sens.	87.17	81.24	81.97	78.51	62.93	82.60	86.80	71.38	79.08
	accu.	98.01	98.31	**98.41**	94.74	98.75	**98.98**	**98.55**	94.02	97.47
MAC	spec.	98.59	99.26	95.03	98.01	99.94	98.92	96.37	96.40	97.82
	sens.	97.78	95.17	96.73	92.89	89.31	97.50	98.78	98.22	95.80
	accu.	**98.47**	**98.89**	95.51	**96.76**	**99.58**	98.84	96.56	**96.74**	**97.67**

3 MASS LESION SEGMENTATION

We test these four edge based active contour models to segment lesions in a set of mammogram images. These mass lesion images are also hand labeled so that quantitative analysis can be carried out. Fig. 1 provides an example of mass lesion segmentation using the MAC model. The lesion boundaries are largely diffused. Note the initial contour crosses the region boundary and only sits on the edge of the lesion boundary, which can happen when using automatic lesion detection. This kind of initialization is very challenging for edge based active contour models. The MAC contour did not collapse itself but converged reasonably. None of the other techniques can achieve such result with this difficult initialization. This initialization independence ability of the MAC model makes it particularly suitable for automatic lesion detection and segmentation. Lesion detection algorithms may not be able to find the center of the lesion and often have little knowledge of the shape of the lesion region which makes it very difficult to place the initial contours in the way that is necessary for GGVF or GeoGGVF to successfully converge. MAC, on the hand, provides great flexibility and robustness.

More examples are given in Fig. 2. The geodesic, GGVF and GeoGGVF had to be carefully initialized, whileas the MAC achieved slightly better results even without dedicated initialization. The quantitative results are shown in Table 1. GGVF, GeoGGVF and MAC all performed reasonably well, except the geodesic snake. MAC generally outperformed the rest.

Overall, we found that MAC's ability to handle difficult initialization provided superior performance. The MAC model showed great potential in automatic lesion detection and segmentation. The shape information and other feature extracted from the segmentation can be passed on for further automatic analysis. This means the whole lesion analysis process can be automated without human intervention, which can improve throughput and may reduce the possibility of false negative since more data can be processed.

4 CONCLUSION

We compared four important edge based active contour model for mass lesion segmentation. This preliminary study on real world mass lesion mammogram image data showed significant improvement in initialization invariancy and convergence capability of the MAC model compared to other advanced edges based methods.

References

[1] V. Caselles, F. Catte, T. Coll, and F. Dibos. A geometric model for active contours. *Numerische Mathematik*, 66(1):1–31, 1993.

[2] D. Guliato, R. Rangayyan, and W. Carnielli. Segmentation of breast tumors in mammograms by fuzzy region growing. In *EMBC*, pages 1002–1005, 2005.

[3] M. Hejaz and Y. Ho. Automated detection of tumors in mammograms using two segments for classification. In *Pacific-Rim Conference on Multimedia*, pages 910–921, 2005.

[4] M. Kupinski and M. Giger. Automated seeded lesion segmentation on digital mammograms. *IEEE T-MI*, 17(4):510–517, 1998.

[5] K. Lee. Segmentation of mammography images using kohonen self-organizing feature maps. In *Midwest Artificial Intelligence and Cognitive Science Conference*, pages 41–46, 1997.

[6] H. Li, M. Kallergi, L. Clarke, and V. Jain. Markov random field for tumor detection in digital mammography. *IEEE T-MI*, 14:565–576, 1995.

[7] N. Paragios, O. Mellina-Gottardo, and V. Ramesh. Gradient vector flow geometric active contours. *IEEE T-PAMI*, 26(3):402–407, 2004.

[8] G. Rad and M. Kashanian. Extraction of the breast cancer tumor in mammograms using genetic active contour. In *Biomed. and Pharmac. Eng.*, pages 30–33, 2006.

[9] M. Sameti and R. Ward. A fuzzy segmentation algorithm for mammogram partitioning. In K. Doi, editor, *Digital Mammography*, pages 471–474. Elsevier, Amsterdam, the Netherlands, 1996.

[10] V. Santos, H. Schiabel, C. Góes, and Benatti. A segmentation technique to detect masses in dense breast digitized mammograms. *J. Digital Imaging*, 15(1):210–213, 2002.

[11] M. Xiao, S. Xia, and S. Wang. Geometric active contour model with color and intensity priors for medical image segmentation. In *EMBC*, pages 6496–6499, 2005.

[12] X. Xie and M. Mirmehdi. MAC: Magnetostatic active contour. *IEEE T-PAMI*, 30(4):636–646, 2008.

[13] C. Xu and J. Prince. Generalized gradient vector flow external forces for active contours. *Signal Processing*, 71(2):131–139, 1998.

[14] R. Yapa and K. Harada. Breast skin-line estimation and breast segmentation in mammograms using fast-marching method. *J. Bio., Biomed., Med. Scis.*, 3(1):54–62, 2008.

Level Set Based Automatic Segmentation of Human Aorta

S. Y. Yeo

School of Engineering, Swansea University, Swansea SA2 8PP, U.K., 465186@swansea.ac.uk

I. Sazonov

School of Engineering, Swansea University, Swansea SA2 8PP, U.K., i.sazonov@swansea.ac.uk

X. Xie

Department of Computer Science, Swansea University, Swansea SA2 8PP, U.K. x.xie@swansea.ac.uk

P. Nithiarasu

School of Engineering, Swansea University, Swansea SA2 8PP, U.K., p.nithiarasu@swansea.ac.uk

ABSTRACT

Segmentation of aorta and other blood vessels from standard 3D CT or MRI scans needs a lot of hand work if to do it by a standard segmentation software like Mimimcs and Amira.

In this paper, we present a new level set based deformable model for the segmentation of human aorta from 3D image dataset. Accurate 3D geometrical models are essential for realistic computational fluid analysis of the blood flow in human aortas, which can improve our understanding of flow-related aortic diseases. Segmentation of the human aorta is however difficult, due to its complex topology and intensity inhomogeneity in the image structures. The proposed method uses a hypothesized interaction force between the geometries of the deformable surface and image objects which can greatly improve the performance of the deformable model in extracting complex geometries, deep boundary concavities, and in handling weak image edges. The results show that the new deformable model can be used to efficiently segment complex structures such as the human aorta from medical images.

Key Words: *level set, deformable model, segmentation, human aorta.*

1 INTRODUCTION

Deformable models are highly appropriate in the segmentation of the human aorta since they can naturally adapt to local image structures. However, explicit or parametric models are not suitable in our case since they generally have difficulties in dealing with topological changes and reaching into deep concavities such as tubular structures. Implicit deformable models based on the level set technique are introduced by Caselles et al. [1] and Malladi et al. [4] to address some of the limitations of parametric deformable models. In this approach, the evolution of curves and surfaces are represented implicitly as a level set of a higher-dimensional scalar function and the deformation of the model is based on geometric measures such as the unit normal and curvature. The evolution of the model is therefore independent of the parameterisation, and topological changes can be handled automatically.

Conventional image gradient based methods are generally prone to local minima that often appear in real images. The balloon force [4] can monotonically expand or shrink the contours, but has great difficulties in dealing with weak edges and cross boundary initialisations. The bidirectionality of the gradient vector flow (GVF) model [7] allows more flexible initialisation and its diffused force field handles image noise interference in a much better manner. However, it has serious convergence issues [6]. More recent works, such as [2, 5, 3], showed promising but limited success.

In this paper, we present a new external force field which is based on the relative position and orientation between deformable model and the image object boundaries. The geometrically induced force field can easily deal with arbitrary cross-boundary initializations and weak image edges due to its bidirectionality. In addtion, the dynamic interaction forces between the geometries of the deformable model and image object can greatly improve the performance of the deformable model in acquiring complex geometries and highly concave boundaries.

2 PROPOSED METHOD

The new external force field proposed in this paper is created based on the hypothesized geometrically induced interactions between the relative geometries of the deformable model and the object boundaries (characterized by image gradients). In other words, the magnitude and direction of the interaction forces are based on the relative position and orientation between the geometries of the deformable model and image object boundaries, and hence, it is called the *geometric potential force (GPF)* field.

2.1 Geometric potential force

Consider two area elements A_1 and A_2 on two surfaces, with unit normals $\hat{n}_1$ and $\hat{n}_2$ respectively. The hypothesized interaction force acting on A_1 due to A_2 is defined as

$$\boldsymbol{F} = A_1\hat{n}_1 \ \boldsymbol{G} \tag{1}$$

where dG is the corresponding geometrically induced potential created by element A_1, and is given as

$$\boldsymbol{G} = \frac{|\boldsymbol{n_2}| \ A_2}{3} \ \hat{r}_{12} \cdot \hat{n}_2 \tag{2}$$

Here, $|\boldsymbol{n_2}|$ is the magnitude of the normal at element A_2, is the distance between A_1 and A_2, and $\hat{r}_{12}$ is the unit vector pointing from A_1 to A_2.

The geometric potential G can be seen as a induced scalar field, in which the strength of depends on the relative position of the two elements A_1 and A_2. The magnitude and direction of the geometrically induced vector force F is therefore handled intrinsically by the relative postion and orientation between the geometries of the deformable model and object boundary.

2.2 Deformable model based on geometric potential force

Let the 3D image be described by function u x where x is a pixel or voxel location in the image domain, and ∇u be its gradient. Let A_1 belongs to the deformable surface whereas A_2 belongs to the object boundary. To compute the force acting on A_1 from A_2, we substitute $|\boldsymbol{n_2}| = |\nabla u|$, $\hat{n}_2 = \nabla u/|\nabla u|$ into (2) and treat n_2 as a normal to the object boundary. Then we compute the total geometric potential field strength G x at every voxel. Note that only voxels on the object boundary will contribute to the geometric interaction field. Let $\mathcal{S}$ denote the set containing all the edge voxels, and s denote a boundary voxel, the total geometric interaction at x can then be computed as:

$$G \ x \ = V.P. \oiint_{\mathcal{S}} \frac{\hat{r}_{xs}}{r_{xs}^3} \cdot \hat{n}_2 \ s \ |\boldsymbol{n_2}| \ s \ A_s \tag{3}$$

where $\hat{r}_{xs}$ is the unit vector from x to s, and $_{xs}$ is the distance between them. Computation of ((??)) can be performed efficiently using fast fourier transform (FFT).

The force acting due to the geometrically induced potential field on the deformable surface $\mathcal{C}$ at the position $x \in \mathcal{C}$ can then be given as:

$$F\ x\ =\ A_x n\ x\ G\ x \tag{4}$$

Given the force field $F\ x$ derived from the hypothesized interactions based on the relative geometries of the deformable model and object boundary, the evolution of the deformable model $C\ x, t$ under this force field can be given as:

$$C_t = (F \cdot n)\ n \tag{5}$$

Since contour or surface smoothing is usually desirable, the mean curvature flow is added and the complete geometric potential deformable model evolution can be formulated as:

$$C_t = \alpha g\ x\ \kappa n - \ 1 - \alpha\ \ F \cdot n\ n \tag{6}$$

where $g\ x\ =\ \dfrac{1}{1 + |\nabla u\ x\ \Phi|}$ is the edge stopping function. Its level set representation can then be given as:

$$\Phi_t = \alpha g \kappa |\nabla \Phi| - \ 1 - \alpha\ F \cdot |\nabla \Phi| \Phi \tag{7}$$

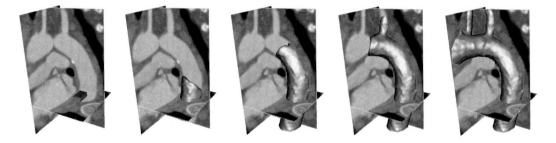

Figure 1: Segmentation process of the human aorta using the GPF deformable model.

3 RESULTS

The new deformable model based on the geometric potential force is applied in the segmentation of the human aorta from a 3D image dataset acquired using computed tomography (CT) imaging. The image dataset is cropped to obtained the region of interest. This is done so as to reduce the computational expenses in using the level set method. Figure 1 portrays the results of the segmentation process using the proposed method. The different views of the segmented aorta model is then shown in Figure 2.

As shown in Figure 1, an initial level set surface is used for the segmentation process. In particular, the level set surface is initialised across object boundaries (i.e. across different structures) in the image to demonstrate the capability of the new deformable model to deal with arbitrary cross-boundary initialisations. The evolution process of the level set surface and the converged deformable model is also shown in the figure.

The example demonstrates that the proposed deformable model can efficiently segment complex geometries such as the human aorta. In addition, it can resolve intensity inhomogeneity in image structures such as those of the human aorta.

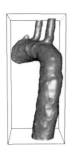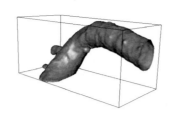

Figure 2: Three different views of the segmented human aorta.

4   CONCLUSIONS

In this paper, we presented a new external force field for image segmentation which is based on hypothesized geometrically induced interactions between the deformable surface and the image object boundary. The proposed deformable model is applied in the segmention of the human aorta from a 3D image dataset. It is shown that by using this approach, complex topologies such as those of the human aorta can be efficiently reconstructed. Accordingly, the new external force is dynamic in nature as it changes according to the relative position and orientation between the evolving deformable model and object boundary. It can thus be used to attract the deformable model into deep boundary concavities that exists in some image objects. In addition, the new deformable model can handle arbitrary cross-initialisation which is a desirable feature to have, especially in the segmentation of complex geometries. Quantitative analysis and comparison to other gradient based methods are necessary to further study the performance of the proposed model. However,this preliminary work illustrates the efficiency of this approach in resolving intensity inhomogeneity and in handling complex 3D geometries, which are often found in biomedical image datasets.

References

[1] V. Caselles, F. Catte, T. Coll, and F. Dibos. A geometric model for active contours. *Numerische Mathematik*, 66:1–31, 1993.

[2] Debora Gil and Petia Radeva. Curvature vector flow to assure convergent deformable models for shape modelling. In *Energy Minimization Methods in Computer Vision and Pattern Recognition*, pages 357–372, 2003.

[3] C. Li, J. Liu, and M. Fox. Segmentation of edge preserving gradient vector flow: an approach toward automatically initializing and splitting of snakes. In *IEEE Conference on Computer Vision Pattern Recognition*, pages 162–167, 2005.

[4] R. Malladi, J. A. Sethian, and B. C. Vemuri. Shape modelling with front propagation: A level set approach. *IEEE Transations on Pattern Analysis and Machine Intelligence*, 17(2):158–175, 1995.

[5] N. Paragios, O. Mellina-Gottardo, and V. Ramesh. Gradient vector flow geometric active contours. *IEEE Transations on Pattern Analysis and Machine Intelligence*, 26(3):402–407, 2004.

[6] Xianghua Xie and Majid Mirmehdi. MAC: Magnetostatic active contour model. *IEEE Transations on Pattern Analysis and Machine Intelligence*, 30(4):632–647, 2008.

[7] C. Xu and J. L. Prince. Snakes, shapes, and gradient vector flow. *IEEE Transations on Image Processing*, 7(3):359–369, 1998.

1st International Conference on Mathematical and Computational Biomedical Engineering – CMBE2009
June 29 – July 1, 2009, Swansea, UK
P. Nithiarasu and R. Löhner (eds)

INVESTIGATIONS OF STEADY AND UNSTEADY FLOWS IN AN AORTIC ANEURYSM

S. Seshadhri[1], G. Janiga[1], G. Rose[2], B. Preim[3], M. Skalej[4], D. Thévenin[1]

University of Magdeburg "Otto von Guericke", Magdeburg (Germany)
1: Lab. of Fluid Dynamics and Technical Flows
2. Medical Telematics & Medical Engineering Group
3: Visualization Research Group
4: Institute for Neuro-Radiology, Medical Department

ABSTRACT

The aortic aneurysm (AA) is a dilatation of the aortic wall, which can occur in the saccular and fusiform types. These aneurysms are localized, balloon-shaped expansions commonly found in the infrarenal segment of the aorta, between the renal arteries and the iliac bifurcation. Aortic aneurysms can rupture, if left untreated. While the cause of AAs is still an important matter of debate, it is essential to identify treatment options, since aortic aneurysm rupture is the 15th leading cause of death in the developed countries, affecting mostly patients over 55 years of age, typically 2–4 percent of elderly males. As the overall mortality rate following aneurysm rupture may exceed 90 percent [1], determining the risk factors that may have an important role in aneurysm growth and rupture has become a major, multidisciplinary task; it is vital to obtain soon a thorough understanding concerning the pathogenesis and evolution of AAs.

There have been many attempts to analyze blood flows in vivo [2, 3]. However, since accurate in vivo measurements are barely possible and extremely complex, the precision and generality of the obtained results is unclear.

In the present project, flow characteristics in an Ascending Aortic Aneurysm have been investigated using Computational Fluid Dynamics (CFD). Both steady and pulsatile flow simulations have been conducted. Validation is realized by comparison with companion experimental measurements in a silicon phantom model with exactly the same vessel geometry. The developed numerical tool will offer a fast possibility to assess quantitatively flow conditions and possible flow alterations for a specific patient's geometry.

Key Words: *Blood flow, Computational Fluid Dynamics, pulsatile flow, wall shear stress, aneurysm*

<u>Configuration and Methods:</u> The ultimate purpose of this project is to deliver accurate, CFD-based information concerning the blood flow in aortic and cerebral aneurysms found on patients. The full procedure involves 5 different research groups of the university and is shown in Fig.1.

To validate the procedure, the generic geometry of an aortic aneurysm is first considered. A silicon model of a commercially available aortic arch phantom (Elastrat, T-R-N-001) is employed for this purpose and is used identically for experiments and simulations. The exact geometry of the inverse model used for the experiments has been obtained from high-resolution 3D rotational angiographic measurements (Siemens AXIOM Artis dBA Twin).

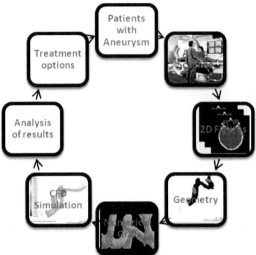

Figure 1: Overview of the flow estimation procedure

The raw data coming from this system are written in DICOM format. After obtaining the geometry from the 3D-RA measurements, an extensive post-processing takes place before the flow simulation. Accurate, in-house 3D vessel segmentation is realized [4], the misleading information is suppressed from the data, the quality of the underlying mesh is checked and improved, leading finally to a high-quality surface mesh; the resulting geometry/surface mesh is then exported as a standard STL-file.

The corresponding data (Fig.2, left) can now be readily imported into a further commercial software (either Tgrid or ICEM-CFD), used for volume grid generation. In the present configuration, an unstructured grid based on tetrahedrons (extract: Fig.2, right) and containing about 1.3 million elements has been generated. A grid-independence study has proved that this high resolution is necessary for resolving the complex geometry and the resulting flow structures in a satisfactory manner. All CFD simulations rely on the software FLUENT 6.3.

The experimental measurements employ non-intrusive, laser-based diagnostics (Laser-Doppler Velocimetry, LDV) to measure the instantaneous velocity field. For this purpose, a blood-mimicking transparent fluid („artificial blood") has been first developed in our group. It has physical properties (density: 1094 kg/m^3; viscosity: 0.0043 Pa.s; non-Newtonian behavior) very close to blood but shows exactly the same refraction index as the silicon phantom model, allowing very accurate optical measurements. After a very long study, the developed fluid contains now a mixture of water, glycerin, Xanthan gum (to match viscosity/behavior), and sodium chloride (to match the refractive index). In previous studies sodium thiocyanate was used [5] but due to its high toxicity it has been now advantageously replaced by non-toxic sodium chloride. The properties of the artificial blood are also employed in the CFD, allowing a direct comparison.

The flow solution is obtained following the ERCOFTAC Best-Practice Guidelines developed specifically for CFD simulations. Both steady and unsteady flow conditions are considered. For the pulsatile flow, a sinusoidal inlet flow velocity is employed. The vessel walls are assumed to be rigid in all simulations; the no-slip condition is applied there.

Figure 2: Geometry with inflow (left), detail of the tetrahedral volume mesh (right)

Results:
Only some representative results are shown here due to lack of space.
Steady flow
As boundary conditions a constant flow-rate of 20 ml/s, as given by LDV measurements has been used at the inflow and outflow boundaries. An example of the results from CFD simulations is presented in Fig. 3, showing chosen streamlines and a color coding of the flow velocity along these streamlines.

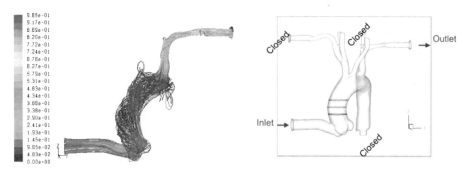

Figure 3. Results from CFD simulations: streamlines and color-coded flow velocity (left) regions of comparison with experimental measurements (right)

The full CFD procedure has been validated successfully under steady conditions by comparing the numerical predictions with experimental measurements of the full velocity field on the regions marked in ascending aorta as shown in fig. 3. Corresponding results are detailed in [5]. Similar LDV measurements are presently carried out for pulsatile conditions, while unsteady CFD results are already available.

Pulsatile flow:

The systolic flow was found to be forward-directed throughout the bulge in the phantom model. Vortices appeared first in the bulge during deceleration from systole (Fig.4), then expanded during the retrograde flow phase. Numerical tests have shown that the structure of the corresponding vortex field depends strongly on bulge diameter.

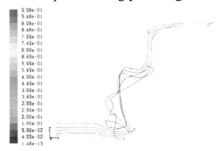

Figure 4. Selected streamlines showing the influence of vortical structures

Conclusions:

The possibility of an accurate validation of CFD results for flows in aneurysms has been demonstrated. For this purpose, great attention must be paid to the employed artificial blood and to the measurement accuracy. The validation is now finished for steady flow conditions, experimental measurements in the pulsatile regime are presently carried out. After finishing this second validation step, the next developments will consider cerebral aneurysms, which are even more difficult to deal with. Post-processing the results in order to understand the link between shear stress, pressure, residence time, blood flow patterns and aneurysm development and treatment will constitute the last step of this project.

References:

1. K. S. Rhode, T. Lambrou, D. J. Hawkes, A. M. Seifalian, "Novel approaches to the measurement of arterial blood flow from dynamic digital X-ray images". IEEE Transactions on Medical Imaging, vol.24, no. 4, pp. 500-513, April 2005.
2. S. D. Shpilfoygel, R. A. Close, D. J. Valentino, G. R. Duckwiler, "X-ray videodensitometric methods for blood flow and velocity measurement: A critical review of literature", Medical Physics 27(9), Sept. 2000.
3. G. J. Hademenos, T. F. Massoud: "Physics of cerebrovascular diseases – Biophysical mechanisms of development, diagnosis and therapy" Springer-Verlag New York Berlin Heidelberg, 1998.
4. M. Neugebauer, G. Janiga, S. Zachow, M. Skalej, B. Preim: ,''Generierung qualitativ hochwertiger Modelle für die Simulation von Blutfluss in zerebralen Aneurysmen''. In: Proc. Simulation and Visualization SimVis (2008) 221-236 [www.simvis.org].
5. S. Seshadhri, G. Janiga, B. Preim, G. Rose, M. Skalej, D. Thévenin: "Numerical simulation and experimental validation in an exact aortic arch aneurysm model", 4th European Conference of the International Federation for Medical and Biological Engineering ECIFMBE 2008, November 2008 Antwerp, Belgium, 1975-1979.

Blood Flow through Stents in Abdominal Aortic Aneurysms

Alfonso Caiazzo[1]
INRIA Paris-Rocquencourt, Le Chesnay, France, `alfonso.caiazzo@inria.fr`

Miguel A. Fernández
INRIA Paris-Rocquencourt, Le Chesnay, France, `miguel.fernandez@inria.fr`

Jean-Frederic Gerbeau
INRIA Paris-Rocquencourt, Le Chesnay, France, `jean-frederic.gerbeau@inria.fr`

Vincent Martin
University of Technology of Compiègne, France, `vincent.martin@utc.fr`

Irene E. Vignon-Clementel
INRIA Paris-Rocquencourt, Le Chesnay, France, `irene.vignon-clementel@inria.fr`

ABSTRACT

We investigate the effect of porous stents on Abdominal Aortic Aneurysms. The blood flow is modelled by the incompressible Navier-Stokes equations, while the stent is viewed as a resistive porous surface. We show numerical results for an idealized three-dimensional aneurysm geometry, discussing the changes in terms of velocity, pressure, vorticity and shear stresses, which can have a relevant impact on the mechanics of the aneurysm.

Key Words: *blood flow, abdominal aortic aneurysm, finite elements, dissipative stent models*

1 INTRODUCTION

An aneurysm is a localized dilatation or ballooning of a blood vessel, due to a weakening of arterial walls. To prevent ruptures, aneurysms can be surgically removed, or treated by inserting a stent.

Postoperative complications, as well as the link between hydrodynamics, stent and dynamics of aneurysms (regression or progression) are not completely understood. Computational models can provide additional insight into the dynamics of the problem, and become an important tool for technical developments [2,5,6].

We focus on a particular class of stents, developed by Cardiatis [1], characterized by a multilayer structure and very thin wires, originally developed to treat cerebral aneurysms. These stents are immersed in the blood flow, with the purpose of reducing the flow in the aneurysm and stimulate thrombus formation. In some situations, these devices showed favorable clinical outcome also in case of Abdominal Aortic Aneurysms (AAA).

The main motivation of this work is to provide additional insight on these advantages. Using a recently proposed approach for simulating the effect of this type of stents in cerebral aneurysms [4], we model

---

[1]This work was carried out during the tenure of an ERCIM "Alain Bensoussan" fellowship programme.

the multilayer stent as a porous interface immersed in the incompressible fluid. With respect to the case discussed in [4], the application to AAA presents different geometrical characteristics, which yield different flow configurations.

It is known that, especially in case of blood flow, fluid-structure interaction (FSI) might be necessary to describe properly the characteristics of the system (see e.g. [3]). However, in this preliminary investigation we focus on the fluid behavior, analyzing the effect of the porous stent, also in comparison with other numerical experimental studies [6]. The full flow-structure coupling and its numerical treatment is currently a work under development. Preliminary FSI simulations will be presented.

2 AAA-STENT AS POROUS INTERFACE

2.1 Modeling approach

We assume the blood to be a Newtonian fluid, with homogeneous density ρ and viscosity μ, governed by the incompressible Navier-Stokes equations.

The stent, consisting of a finely wired grid immersed in the blood flow, is modeled as a porous interface, as proposed in [4]. The velocity is assumed to be continuous across the stent surface, while the pressure might be discontinuous. In particular, we enforce a jump condition on the stress tensor associated with the fluid, where the size of the discontinuity is proportional to the flux through the stent.

From the mathematical point of view, this yields a resistance term in the fluid equations:

$$\rho \left(\frac{\partial \mathbf{u}}{\partial t} + \mathbf{u} \cdot \nabla \mathbf{u} \right) + \nabla p - \mu \nabla^2 \mathbf{u} + r_\gamma \mathbf{u} \delta_\gamma = \mathbf{f}$$
$$\mathrm{div}\mathbf{u} = 0 \,, \tag{1}$$

where $\mathbf{u}$ is the fluid velocity, p the fluid pressure, γ is the stent surface, δ_γ the Dirac measure on γ and r_γ the stent resistance, which depends on the characteristics of the stent.

Solving numerically system (1) with a Finite Elements formulation allows to include naturally the additional dissipative term in the variational form as

$$\langle r_\gamma \mathbf{u} \delta_\gamma, \mathbf{v} \rangle = \int_\gamma r_\gamma \mathbf{u} \mathbf{v} d\gamma \,. \tag{2}$$

Additionally, the discretization space includes discontinuous pressures at the stent interface [4].

From a practical point of view, in this modeling approach the stent is not meshed as a solid structure, which would be particularly prohibitive in case of stents with thin wires.

Blood Flow Simulation. System (1) is completed with boundary conditions to reach physiologically realistic settings. In particular, a parabolic profile is applied at the inlet, prescribing the flow rate as a function of time. At the outlet, we impose a relationship between the mean pressure and the outgoing flow, using a simplified zero-dimensional model to take into account the effect of the downstream vasculature [7].

2.2 AAA Test Geometry

For the numerical simulations, we consider an analytically constructed AAA geometry, modeling a cylindrical vessel of diameter $D = 1.7$ cm dilated at the middle point of the axis. The maximum diameter of the aneurysm is $D_{\mathrm{max}} = 3.4$ cm. A cylindrical stent is included, following the lateral surface of the cylinder vessel (figure 1).

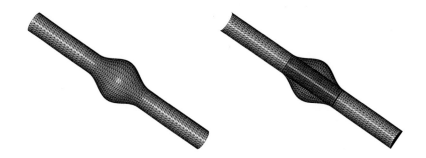

Figure 1: Computational mesh for the test geometry. On the right, the cross section shows the additional interior mesh for the stent.

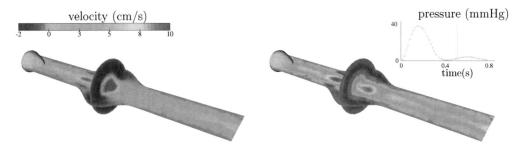

Figure 2: Velocity along the main axis on the middle planes in diastole. Left: flow profile without stent. Right: results with a resistance $r_\gamma = 20\mathrm{g} \cdot \mathrm{s}^{-1} \cdot \mathrm{cm}^{-3}$. The instant in time is indicated in the upper-right plot, showing the pressure pulse (at the outlet) in time.

Regular surface meshes for the aneurysm and for the stent have been designed, which has been used to construct two separate volumes (the vessel and the aneurysm part), meshed in three dimensions using GHS3D[2].

2.3 Results

Different flow setups have been considered. As expected, the presence of the stent reduces flow activity within the aneurysm, redirecting the flow mainly along the vessel axis, throughout the whole cycle.

Moreover, due to the geometrical configuration and to the resulting flow profiles, a small stent resistance results already in a high flow reduction.

As an example, figure 2 show a snapshot of the velocity profile during the cardiac cycle, corresponding to a high-vorticity instant in the stent-free configuration.

We will present detailed comparisons of the two situations, in terms of velocity, pressure, vorticity and shear stress, analyzing also the differences in the oscillatory behaviors.

---

[2]www-c.inria.fr/gamma/ghs3d/ghs.php

3 CONCLUSIONS

The considered aneurysm geometry, though simple, provides already interesting results concerning the effect of the stent and the implications on structural mechanics of the aneurysm.

For further studies, we will consider fluid-structure interaction, allowing the vessel wall to interact with the flow, as well as realistic AAA geometry obtained from medical imaging.

Another important element to be investigated is the presence of *collateral branches* in the aneurysm wall, to understand how the stent implantation modifies the flow.

Among others, one goal is to understand whether the combined stent-flow effect might yield, in particular conditions, a reduction of the aneurysm, driven by changes in mechanical forces.

However, since aneurysm remodeling has a a typical time scale much slower than the time scale of blood flow, a multiscale model could be necessary in order to simulate the long term dynamics.

Acknowledgments

We are grateful to Cardiatis SA for introducing us to this topic. The research of A. Caiazzo is funded by ERCIM (*European Consortium for Informatics and Mathematics*, www.ercim.org).

REFERENCES

[1] Cardiatis SA, http://www.cardiatis.com

[2] B.J. Doyle, A. Callanan, P.E. Burke, P.A. Grace, M.T. Walsch, D.A. Vorp, T.M. McGloughlin, Vessel asymmetry as an additional disgnostic tool in the assessment of abdominal aortic aneurysms, *J. Vasc. Surg.*, 49(2) 443–454, 2009.

[3] M.A. Fernndez, J.-F. Gerbeau, C. Grandmont, A projection semi-implicit scheme for the coupling of an elastic structure with an incompressible fluid *Internat. J. Numer. Methods Engrg.*, 69(4), 794821, 2007.

[4] M.A. Fernández, J.-F. Gerbeau, V. Martin, Numerical simulations of blood flow through porous interface, *Math. Model. Num. Anal. (M2AN)*, 42, 961-990, 2008.

[5] C. Kleinstreurer, Z. Li, M.A. Farber, Fluid-Structure Interaction Analyses of Stented Abdominal Aortic Aneurysms, *Annu. Rev. Biomed. Eng.*, 9, 169–204, 2007.

[6] A.S. Les, S.C. Shadden, C.A. Figueroa, J.M. Park, M.M. Tedesco, R.J. Herfkens, R.L. Dalman, C.A. Taylor, Quantification of Hemodynamics in Abdominal Aortic Aneurysms During Rest and Exercise Using Magnetic Resonance Imaging and Computational Fluid Dynamics, submitted to *Ann. Biomed. Eng.*, 2009.

[7] I. Vignon-Clementel, C. Figueroa, K. Jansen, C. Taylor, Outflow Boundary Conditions for Three-dimensional Finite Element Modeling of Blood Flow and Pressure in Arteries *Comp. Meth. Appl. Mech. and Eng.*, 195, 3776–3796, 2006.

1st International Conference on Mathematical and Computational Biomedical Engineering – CMBE2009
June 29 – July 1, 2009, Swansea, UK
P. Nithiarasu and R. Löhner (eds)

INFLUENCE OF HEMODYNAMICS ON THE FORMATION OF AN INTRALUMINAL THROMBUS IN ABDOMINAL AORTIC ANEURYSMS

Anne-Virginie L.B. Salsac
Biomechanics and Bioengineering Laboratory (CNRS UMR 6600), Université de Technologie de Compiègne, BP 20529, 60205 Compiègne, France, a.salsac@utc.fr
Rubing Tang
Department of Mechanical and Aerospace Engineering, University of California San Diego, 9500 Gilman Drive, La Jolla, CA 92093-0411, USA, r1tang@mae.ucsd.edu
Juan C. Lasheras
Department of Mechanical and Aerospace Engineering, University of California San Diego, 9500 Gilman Drive, La Jolla, CA 92093-0411, USA, lasheras@mae.ucsd.edu

ABSRACT

Thrombosis is typically observed in abdominal aortic aneurysms (AAA). The potential influence of hemodynamic forces on thrombosis has long been recognized, but it has mostly been studied in vessel geometries that induce abnormally high levels of shear stresses (*e.g.* stenoses). The purpose of the study is to investigate the possible mechanism responsible for the thrombus formation in AAAs. We characterize the magnitude of the fluid stresses acting on circulating platelets and the time of exposure in the dilatation. The trajectories of fluid particles are calculated using a Lagrangian particle tracking method applied to previously obtained velocity fields. Results of particle tracking conducted on *in vitro* measurements of velocity fields in AAAs are compared with a numerical simulation. We show that the flow structures within the aneurysm tend to convect platelets towards the wall, which increases their probability of deposition onto the wall. The number of cells convected towards the wall increases with the aneurysm dilatation ratio. These platelets are entrained into regions of slowly recirculating flow, where they experience long residence times and low hemodynamic stresses. The long residence times, low flow conditions and convective patterns towards the wall are hypothesized to be the main factors contributing to the thrombus formation in AAAs. Thrombosis within AAAs is therefore thought be linked to platelet aggregation through fibrinogen polymerization.

Key Words: *Abdominal aortic aneurysms, intraluminal thrombus, Lagrangian particle tracking*

1. INTRODUCTION

An abdominal aortic aneurysm (AAA) is an abnormal local dilatation of the infrarenal aorta. The development of an intraluminal thrombus (ILT) is one of the typical features of AAAs. The ILT, an aggregate of platelets held together by fibrous strands (fibrinogen), has been observed to develop in 30% of AAAs (Al-Barjas *et al.* 2006). It forms inside the aneurysm and obstructs part of the lumen.

When present, the thrombus plays a critical role on the pathology and progression of the vascular disease. It modifies the interaction between the pulsatile blood flow and the vascular wall and therefore changes the stress distribution within the wall. But from a mechanical point of view, the thrombus provides support to the weakened wall. We previously showed that, as the volume of the thrombus increases, the magnitude of the stresses decreases (up to 60%) and the region of maximum stress moves from the inflection point towards the neck of the AAA. However, this gain in structural strength is at the cost of an increase in the inflammatory and degenerative processes inside the aneurysm wall (Gacko & Głowiński 1998).

Preliminary studies conducted under steady-flow conditions suggest that the buildup of the thrombus are impacted by the altered hemodynamic patterns that arise inside the AAA as compared to the flow in a healthy abdominal aorta (Bluestein *et al.* 1996). Blood flow conditions affect thrombosis via their effect on platelets that are the primary cells involved in the mechanism of thrombosis. Studies on platelets have shown that their rate of activation and accumulation depends on the hemodynamic forces and convective flow patterns (Dintenfass 1964).

In this study we investigate how hemodynamics may contribute to the formation of an ILT. By conducting a Lagrangian particle tracking, we analyze the effects of flow patterns on circulating cells as the aneurysm grows in size. We measure the residence time of platelets circulating inside AAAs and the magnitude of the hemodynamic stresses acting on them.

2. MATERIAL AND METHODS

Aneurysm models. The aneurysm is modeled as a rigid axisymmetric expansion, characterized by two parameters, the dilatation ratio D/d and the aspect ratio L/d (figure 1a). The effect of the aneurysm growth is studied by increasing the dilatation ratio from 1.3 to 2.1 for a constant aspect ratio ($L/d = 3$).

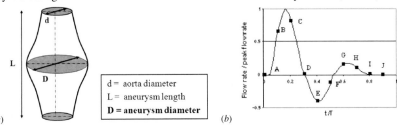

Figure 1 : (a) Aneurysm geometry. (b) Flow waveform imposed at the inlet boundary (from Maier *et al.* 1989).

Velocity fields. Lagrangian tracking is performed on velocity fields obtained both experimentally and numerically.

The same flow conditions have been implemented in the experimental and numerical studies. Blood is supposed to be Newtonian. As inlet boundary condition, we impose a pulsatile blood flow (figure 1b) with a peak Reynolds number of 2700, a mean Reynolds number of 300 and a Womersley number of 10.7, which corresponds to 70 pulses per minute. A constant pressure is set at the outlet.

The instantaneous velocity fields have been measured experimentally by Particle Image Velocimetry (Salsac *et al.* 2006) in the plane of symmetry of the models over six cardiac cycles. The velocity fields are phase-averaged to remove the cycle-to-cycle fluctuations for the particle tracking. They can therefore be assumed to remain axisymmetric, so that particles introduced in the plane of symmetry are supposed to remain within it.

In order to complement and validate the results, a numerical simulation of the three-dimensional flow field is conducted within aneurysm models with similar geometry as those used experimentally. Comsol® is used to solve the Navier-Stokes equations.

Lagrangian 'cell' tracking. Tracking markers are followed in a Lagrangian way both spatially and temporally inside the aneurysm models. The passive point markers are fluid particles that represent individual blood cells. They are entrained passively by the macroscopic blood flow: neither the cell geometry nor the cell interaction with the blood flow is modeled. Ten markers, equally placed along the inlet radius of the aneurysm models, are released with a zero initial velocity at each time step of the cardiac cycle. Their trajectory is calculated as well as the Von Mises stress, used to quantify the magnitude of the hemodynamic stress. It has the advantage of being a scalar and an invariant. It is defined as

$$\sigma = \sqrt{\frac{1}{3}(\sigma_1^2 + \sigma_1^2 + \sigma_1^2 - \sigma_1\sigma_2 - \sigma_2\sigma_3 - \sigma_1\sigma_3)}$$

where σ_i ($i = 1, 2, 3$) are the eigenvalues of the stress tensor $\sigma = (\nabla\vec{u} + \nabla\vec{u}^T)/2$.

A post-processing code has been developed for the cell tracking based on the experimental velocity field. For the numerical simulation, we use the Comsol Lagrangian tracking function. 100 (respectively 450) particles are released in each *in vitro* (respectively *in silico*) model from the 10 different radial locations at times equally spaced within one cardiac cycle. Numerically, the grid mesh has been refined until the trajectories would be independent of it.

3. RESULTS

Flow topology. As the dilatation ratio increases, platelets tend to be diverted from a rectilinear trajectory. This is due to the presence of the vortex rings that form inside the aneurysm (Salsac *et al.* 2006), creating recirculating flow regions along the walls during the diastole. These vortices have the particularity of bringing platelets in the vicinity of the wall. Accumulation of cells on the walls is thus made possible by the convective flow patterns they induce.

Platelet residence time. Experiments have shown that the adhesion of blood cells by fibrinogen is directly proportional to the particle residence time (*PRT*). The post-processing code developed for the *in vitro* results is validated by comparing the platelet residence times with the *in silico* results. A good agreement is found so the *in vitro* residence time is shown in figure 2a. We plot the average of the times of residence of the fluid particles released from each radial position over one cardiac cycle. It is non-dimensionalized by the convective time t_c, which is the typical scale of the residence time in a healthy abdominal aorta ($t_c = L/U$ with U the mean velocity). One can see that the residence time increases with the distance from the centerline. The averaged value of the residence time, calculated for each model, is found to increase with the dilatation ratio: $\overline{PRT}/t_c = 1.9$ ($D/d = 1.3$), 5 ($D/d = 1.5$), 7.2 ($D/d = 1.9$), 7.9 ($D/d = 2.1$).

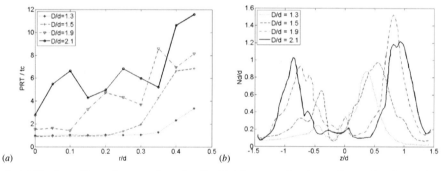

Figure 2 : (*a*) Platelet residence time, non-dimensionalized by the convective time scale as a function of the release position. The residence time is a time-average of the times of residences of the fluid particles released from each radial position. (*b*) Deposition probability along the aneurysm wall.

Deposition probability. Experiments have shown that the adhesion of blood cells through fibrinogen is directly proportional to the time of residence of platelets close to the wall. From the results found on the flow topology, we make the hypothesis that the deposition probability is proportional to the product of the normal velocity to the wall with the near-wall residence time, which is denoted as N_d.

Circulating cells contribute to $N_d(z)$, whenever they enter the near-wall control volume centered on the coordinate z (100 μm in radius) with a wall-normal velocity pointing towards the wall. Their contribution to $N_d(z)$ is the product of the time step with the velocity

$$V_h = \begin{cases} -\vec{u} \cdot \vec{n}_w & \text{if} \quad \vec{u} \cdot \vec{n}_w < 0 \\ 0 & \text{otherwise} \end{cases}$$

where $\vec{n}_w$ is the unit vector normal to the wall.

If the deposition probability can be assumed proportional to N_d, one may conclude from figure 2b that the probability of wall adhesion becomes more significant with increasing dilatation ratios. For small D/d, the deposition of platelets or fibrinogen is more likely in the central region of the aneurysm, where the vortex ring is located. As D/d increases, the peak in the probability of particle deposition moves towards the proximal and distal inflection points.

Platelet activation level (PAL). High levels of hemodynamic stresses (or shear stresses) have been shown to induce platelet activation. Shear stress-activation and aggregation are a function of both the shear stress magnitude and the duration of exposure (Hellums & Hardwick 1981). For each platelet, we evaluate the time integral of the magnitude of the local hemodynamic stress σ that is applied to the platelet as it travels inside the aneurysm. It is called the Platelet Activation Level (*PAL*).

Lower *PAL* values are found inside the aneurysm than in the healthy vessel, even though the platelet residence time is increased. The percentage of platelets having a *PAL* larger than the average value calculated in the healthy abdominal aorta $PAL_{healthy}$ is around 2%. There is no strong correlation found between the number of particles with higher *PAL* value and the dilatation ratio D/d. On the contrary, the number of fluid particles with levels of activation lower than $1/5^{th}$ of $PAL_{healthy}$ is actually found to increase exponentially with the dilatation ratio.

4. DISCUSSION AND CONCLUSION

A Lagrangian particle tracking method is used to compute the trajectories of individual fluid particles (representing platelets) inside aneurysms with increasing dilatation ratios in order to evaluate the effects of the flow field on the formation of the endoluminal thrombus.

We have shown that AAAs have a very strong effect on the trajectories, residence time and stress history of circulating platelets, because of the large vortical structures that develop inside the aneurysm. These grow in size as the dilatation ratio is increased, so that more and more cells are perturbed from their rectilinear trajectory as the aneurysm enlarges. The cell residence time therefore increases drastically with D/d.

The probability for platelet aggregation is enhanced by the convective motion observed inside the aneurysm. The peculiarity of the aneurismal flow topology is to transport the cells towards the wall. We have computed a probability for cell deposition as a function of the normal velocity component for particles located very close to the wall. As the dilatation ratio is increased, we show that the deposition probability becomes larger around the proximal and distal inflection points. The inflection points are located in regions of low hemodynamic stress. Low fluid stresses are known to play a significant role on the fibrin polymerization processes that enable platelet aggregation (Ikeda *et al.* 1991). In low flow conditions, the platelet activity may also be upregulated from the increased time of exposure to subendothelium collagen (Bassiouny *et al.* 1998).

The platelet activation level is found to assume lower values inside AAAs than in the healthy vessels. In the case of AAAs, the observed dramatic decrease in the platelet activation level promotes platelet aggregation. In conclusion, the ILT formation in AAAs appears to be the result of the development of regions with high probability of wall adhesion populated with particles with very small shear-activation level. The long residence times, low magnitude of hemodynamic stresses and convective motion towards the wall are the factors that are expected to contribute to the polymerization of fibrinogen and aggregation of platelets.

REFERENCES

[1]   H.S. Al-Barjas, R. Ariëns, P. Grant and J.A. Scott, Raised plasma fibrinogen concentration in patients with abdominal aortic aneurysm, *Angiology*, 57, 607-614, 2006.

[2]   H.S. Bassiouny, R.H. Song, H. Kocharyan, E. Kins and S. Glagov, Low flow enhances platelet activation after acute experimental arterial injury, *J Vasc Surg*, 27, 910-918 1998.

[3]   D. Bluestein, L. Niu, R.T. Schoephoerster and M.K. Dewanjee, Steady flow in an aneurysm model: correlation between fluid dynamics and blood platelet deposition, *J Biomech Eng*, 118, 280-286, 1996.

[4]   L. Dintenfass, Rheological approach to thrombosis and atherosclerosis, *Angiology*, 15, 333–343, 1964.

[5]   M. Gacko and S. Głowiński, Activities of proteases in parietal thrombus of aortic aneurysm. *Clin Chim Acta*, 271, 171-177, 1998.

[6]   J.D. Hellums and R.A. Hardwick, Response of platelets to shear stress – a review, *The Rheology of blood, blood vessels and associated tissues*, Sijthoff and Noorhoff, 160-183, 1981.

[7]   S.E. Maier, D. Meier, P. Boesinger, U.T. Moser and A. Vieli, Human abdominal aorta: comparative measurements of blood flow with MR imaging and multigated Doppler US, *Radiology*, 171, 487–492, 1989.

[8]   A.V. Salsac, S.R. Sparks, J.M. Chomaz and J.C. Lasheras, Evolution of the wall shear stresses during the progressive enlargement of symmetric abdominal aortic aneurysms, *J Fluid Mech*, 550: 19-51, 2006.

AXISYMMETRIC AND NON-AXISYMMETRIC FLOW AND WALL SHEAR STRESS IN A MODEL FUSIFORM ABDOMINAL AORTIC ANEURYSM

Gregory J. Sheard

Fluids Laboratory for Aeronautical and Industrial Research (FLAIR), Department of Mechanical and Aerospace Engineering, Monash University, VIC 3800, Australia, Greg.Sheard@eng.monash.edu.au

ABSTRACT

Pulsatile flow through a sinusoidal bulge in an otherwise straight circular tube is used to model the fluid mechanics within a fusiform abdominal aortic aneurysm. Three-dimensional flow is computed using a high-order spectral-element/Fourier method, driven by an anatomically realistic heartbeat waveform. Model dimensions and parameters are chosen to describe human abdominal aortic aneurysms considered both low and high risk in terms of their likelihood of rupture. A Reynolds number of 330, a Womersley number of 10.7, and aneurysm length and diameter ranges of 2.9-5.2 and 1.3-2.1 times the vessel diameter, respectively, are investigated. Variation in wall shear stress with both time and as a function of aneurysm dimension is computed. From computations on a bulge with maximum diameter approximately twice the undilated tube diameter, the flow is found to be naturally three-dimensional under conditions consistent with the human abdominal aorta. However, the dominant feature of the flow remains an axisymmetric vortex ring, which is generated at the proximal end of the bulge during systole. Both three-dimensional flow and non-uniformity in azimuthal wall-shear-stress distribution are most pronounced in the vicinity of the distal end of the bulge during the resting phase of the heartbeat. The axial distribution of wall shear stress scales approximately with the length of the bulge. The flow is sensitive to changes in the bulge diameter: a bulge with maximum diameter 1.9 times the vessel diameter invokes significantly more complex dynamics than a modest bulge of 1.3 diameters.

Key Words: *blood flow, wall shear stress, aneurysm, three-dimensional transition, spectral-element method.*

1 INTRODUCTION

Aneurysms present as a localized enlargement of an artery, caused by weakness or degradation in the tissue integrity comprising the artery wall.[1,2] Recent attention has focused on the role of blood flow on aneurysm mechanics, characterizing the fluid mechanics within an aneurysm, and determining the fluid stresses imparted on the artery and aneurysm walls. Recent experiments[3] and axisymmetric simulation[4] have shown that in fusiform aneurysms, the flow is dominated by a strong vortex ring, which develops in the bulge during the systolic phase of the heartbeat waveform. This study employs three-dimensional analysis and simulation to investigate three-dimensional features of this complex flow system.

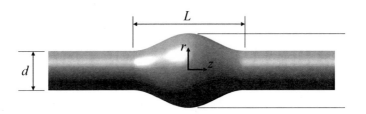

Figure 1: A schematic diagram of the fusiform aneurysm model, with cylindrical r-z coordinate system and dimensions shown.

2 METHODOLOGY

In this study, the aneurysm is modeled as a sinusoidal bulge in an otherwise straight pipe,[4] characterized by a length ratio LR $= L/d$ and a diameter ratio DR $= D/d$, where L is the aneurysm bulge length, d is the undilated tube diameter, and D is the maximum bulge diameter. Flow is driven by a pressure gradient derived to reproduce a physiologically realistic pulse waveform. A Reynolds number based on the time-averaged mean velocity through the model (U) is defined as $Re = Ud/\nu$, where ν is the kinematic viscosity of the fluid. In this study a Reynolds number of $Re = 330$ is chosen consistent with previous studies. Similarly, a Womersley number of $\alpha = 10.7$ is employed ($\alpha = \frac{d}{2}\sqrt{2\pi f/\nu}$, where f is the frequency of the heartbeat). Two-dimensional flow and linear stability analysis were computed using an incompressible Navier–Stokes solver[4,5] based on the spectral-element method.[6] Three-dimensional computations were efficiently calculated using a spectral-element/Fourier algorithm detailed in Blackburn & Sherwin.[7]

3 RESULTS: 3D FLOW DEVELOPMENT

Using a Floquet linear stability analysis technique formulated in cylindrical coordinates,[5] the axisymmetric flow computed and described in Sheard[4] was analysed at a range of Reynolds numbers to determine the stability of the pulsatile flow to non-axisymmetric perturbations. The fastest-growing wavenumber was found to change with Reynolds number: the flow was predicted to first become unstable with a wavenumber $m = 1$ at $Re \approx 270$. Inspection of the perturbation field arising from this analysis demonstrated that the non-axisymmetric flow features evolved in the distal region of the bulge during the resting phase of the hearbeat, before being flushed out of the bulge during the systolic phase. At $Re = 330$, matching Salsac et al.[3] and Sheard[4], who selected parameters relevant hemodynamics within a human abdominal aorta, the fastest-growing wavenumber was $m = 3$, though the location and behaviour of the three-dimensional structures was similar to that at onset of the transition.

Three-dimensional simulations were then conducted to confirm these predictions at $Re = 330$. Figure 2 plots contours of wall shear stress magnitude over single a period from the saturated three-dimensional simulation. The contours indicate that the non-axisymmetric effects are most visible in the resting phase of the pulse cycle (a). During the systolic phase (c), where wall shear stress levels are highest, there is little wall shear stress variation in the azimuthal direction: axisymmetric features dominate.

4 RESULTS: GEOMETRY VARIATION

Consideration was given to the effect of changing the aneurysm geometry on the distribution of wall shear stress magnitude ($|$WSS$|$, taken as the leading eigenvalue of the rate-of-strain tensor: the wall shear

Figure 2: Flooded contours of wall shear stress magnitude (|WSS|) plotted on the surface of the aneurysm model with LR $= 2.9$ and DR $= 1.9$. The model is shown in isometric view with flow from left to right. The frames are taken at equi-spaced times during the pulse cycle: (a-b) displays the resting (diastolic) phase, and (c-d) shows the systolic phase. Contour levels from 0 (blue) through to $40U/d$ (red) are plotted.

stress is recovered by multiplying these dimensionless values by $\mu U/d$). Motivated by the previous observation that |WSS|is predominantly axisymmetric in this model aneurysm, axisymmetric simulations were undertaken to investigate how |WSS|throughout the model varied in time. The plots in figure 3 show contours of |WSS|in t-z space: that is, along any horizontal line the axial |WSS|distribution along the vessel and aneurysm wall is given at that instant in time. A single heartbeat is shown.

In figure 3(a), the length ratio is varied over $2.9 \leq$ LR ≤ 5.2 for a constant diameter ratio DR $= 1.3$. It is notable that the |WSS|is similarly distributed in these plots (peak systole occurs at approximately $t = 0$), and away from the aneurysm bulge, the wall shear stress is axially uniform and consistent irrespective of LR. Within the bulge ($|z|/d < 1.45$, 1.95 and 2.6 for top, middle and bottom, respectively), a high zone of |WSS|is detected in the vicinity of $z/d = 1.5\text{-}2$ at $t \approx 0$, followed by a localized peak of |WSS|which migrates upstream over $0.1 \lesssim t/T \lesssim 0.3$ from just upstream of the centre of the aneurysm bulge ($z \approx 0$). These correspond to the flushing of fluid into the distal artery at systole, and the development of a secondary vortex ring after peak systole (as described in Salsac et al.[3] and Sheard[4]). With increasing length ratio, the magnitude of |WSS|within the bulge decreases, and the distribution appears to scale in the axial direction with the length ratio.

To consider diameter-ratio variation, three models with LR $= 2.9$ and DR $= 1.3$, 1.9 and 2.1 were studied (figure 3(b)). It was found increasing the diameter ratio leads to a marked change in |WSS|distribution. At higher diameter ratios, the regions of highest |WSS|are consistently located in the distal half of the bulge and into the distal artery. In contrast to the smaller diameter ratio DR $= 1.3$, for DR $\gtrsim= 1.9$, the aneurysm bulge experiences |WSS|levels far higher than recorded in the undilated artery segments, and these persist for a majority of the heartbeat cycle. Even during the resting phase, elevated |WSS|levels are detected in the bulge at $z \approx -0.6$. A further striking difference is the appearance of small regions of low |WSS|during systole (e.g. see $t \approx 0$ and 0.2), in contrast to the DR $= 1.3$ cases. This indicates that at larger aneurysm diameters, vessel wall tissue is exposed to greater levels of peak |WSS|, and greater temporal and spatial fluctuations in |WSS|, all of which can erode the integrity of luminal tissue.[1,2]

5 CONCLUSIONS

A stability analysis and high-resolution non-axisymmetric computations of a flow representative of pulsatile flow through a fusiform human abdominal aortic aneurysm have shown that while the flow is non-axisymmetric under these conditions, wall shear stress is predominantly axisymmetric. By systematically varying the length ratio and diameter ratio independently, it has been found that the axial wall-shear-stress distribution scales approximately with the length of the aneurysm bulge, and that increasing the bulge diameter invokes a marked increase in the spatio-temporal fluctuation of wall shear stress throughout the pulse cycle, due to the increased circulation in the vortex ring shed into the bulge during the systolic phase of the heartbeat.

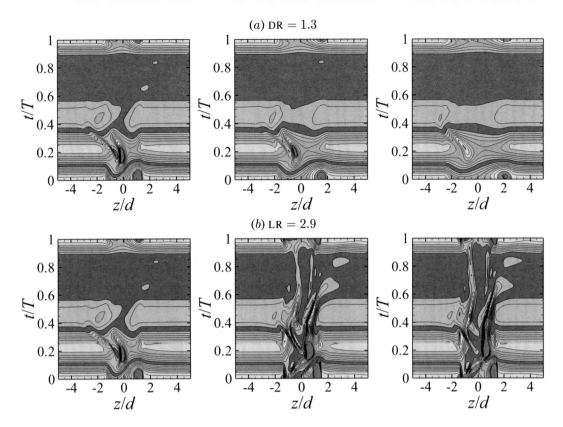

Figure 3: Contours of shear rate plotted on t-z axes to demonstrate the variation in wall shear stress over a single pulse cycle. (a) DR $= 1.3$, and from left to right LR $= 2.9$, 3.9 and 5.2. (b) LR $= 2.9$, and left to right DR $= 1.3$, 1.9 and 2.1. 10 equi-spaced contour levels are plotted between 0 (blue) and $100U/d$ (red).

REFERENCES

[1] J.C. Lasheras, The biomechanics of arterial aneurysms, *Ann. Rev. Fluid Mech.*, **39**, 293-319, 2007.

[2] R.B. Rutherford, Randomized EVAR trials and advent of level I evidence: a paradigm shift in management of large abdominal aortic aneurysms?, *Semin. Vasc. Surg.*, **19**(2), 69-74, 2006.

[3] A.-V. Salsac, S.R. Sparks, J.-M. Chomaz and J.C. Lasheras, Evolution of the wall shear stresses during the progressive enlargement of symmetric abdominal aortic aneurysm, *J. Fluid Mech.*, **560**, 19-51, 2006.

[4] G.J. Sheard, Flow dynamics and wall shear stress variation in a fusiform aneurysm, *J. Eng. Math.*, DOI: 10.1007/h10665-008-9261-z, 2009.

[5] G.J. Sheard and K. Ryan, Pressure-driven flow past spheres moving in a circular tube, *J. Fluid Mech.*, **592**, 233-262, 2007.

[6] G.E. Karniadakis, M. Israeli and S.A. Orszag, High-order splitting methods for the incompressible Navier–Stokes equations, *J. Comput. Phys.*, **97**, 414-443, 1991.

[7] H.M. Blackburn and S.J. Sherwin, Formulation of a Galerkin spectral element-Fourier method for three-dimensional incompressible flow in cylindrical geometries, *J. Comput. Phys.*, **197**, 759-778, 2003.

A PATIENT-SPECIFIC BLOOD FLOW SIMULATION THROUGH AN ANEURYSMAL THORACIC AORTA

Prihambodo H. Saksono
School of Engineering Swansea University, Swansea SA2 8PP, UK, p.h.saksono@swansea.ac.uk

Igor Sazonov
School of Engineering Swansea University, Swansea SA2 8PP, UK, i.sazonov@swansea.ac.uk

Perumal Nithiarasu
School of Engineering Swansea University, Swansea SA2 8PP, UK, p.nithiarasu@swansea.ac.uk

Raoul van Loon
School of Engineering Swansea University, Swansea SA2 8PP, UK, r.vanloon@swansea.ac.uk

Heyman Luckraz
Cardiothoracic Unit The Royal Wolverhampton Hospitals NHS Trust, Wolverhampton WV10 0QP, UK, E-mail address

Saeed Ashraf
Deparment of Cardiothoracic Surgery Moriston Hospital Swansea & School of Medicine Swansea University, Swansea SA2 8PP, UK, s.ashraf@swansea.ac.uk

ABSTRACT

Blood flow simulation through a geometrically patient-specific human aorta with a thoracic aortic aneurysm (TAA) is carried out using a geometry reconstructed from a series of CT-scan images. The fully explicit characteristic-based split (CBS) scheme along with artificial compressibility is used for the flow computations. The temporal and spatial distributions of hemodynamic variables during the cardiac cycle were analysed to study their role in the failure of aorta with aneurysm.

Key Words: *blood flow, wall shear stress, aneurysm, artificial compressibility, CBS scheme.*

1 INTRODUCTION

An aortic aneurysm is a localised weakening and dilation of the aortic wall. The larger the aneurysm becomes, the more likely it will burst with fatal consequences[1]. Based on its location, aortic aneurysms are classified into thoracic aortic aneurysm (TAA) and abdominal aortic aneurysm (AAA). Currently about 2% of deaths in men in England and Wales ($\approx$,000 per year) are caused by the rupture of an aortic aneurysm[2]. Evidence also suggest that the incidence of aortic aneurysm are on the increase[3].

Criteria that are currently in use for the selection of surgical patients are based on the geometrical features of the aneurysm such as maximum aneurysm diameter, aspect ratio and the rate of change of aortic diameter. Studies on AAA have shown that peak internal wall stress is a more reliable parameter for the assessment of the rupture risk. However, the pathogenesis and growth of aneurysm are associated with the flow features, such as recirculation, secondary flows, flow separation, turbulence, as well as fluid dynamics quantities, such as wall shear stress (WSS) and oscillating shear index (OSI).

This work proposes a frame work for geometry reconstruction, mesh generation and flow computation of patient-specific TAA geometry.

2 GEOMETRY RECONSTRUCTION AND MESH GENERATION

The geometry of aorta is restored from standard CT scans without contrast enhancement. The resolution of the scans is 0.877×0.877 mm in horizontal plane and 1 mm between the slices. The AMIRA software is used for region segmentation and initial surface mesh generation. The initial surface mesh produced by AMIRA contains a significant amount of very short edges and is not smooth enough, resulting from the use of standard Marching Cube method for surface mesh generation. To make the mesh coarser and smoother, the mesh contraction method described in [4] is applied.

To increase the accuracy of computed wall shear stress, boundary layer elements are needed to resolve the high near-wall velocity gradient. The process of generating boundary layer mesh starts by creating an inner surface. This surface is obtained by displacing every wall surface point in the opposite direction of its normal vector at a specified distance, that is taken to equal the mean size of surface elements. Additional surfaces are added between the two surfaces to create boundary layers of progressive thickness. The prism formed by the surface triangle of two adjacent surfaces and normals in all the vertices are then split into three tetrahedra.

The regions of inlet and outlets that are not part of boundary layer mesh are 0 by the stitching method [5] which provides a high quality surface mesh. Finally, the volume tetrahedron mesh of the remaining domain is generated by the Delaunay triangulation method described in [6]. Details of geometry reconstruction and mesh generation process employed in this work can be found in [6].

3 THE NAVIER-STOKES EQUATIONS AND NUMERICAL SCHEME

In the aorta the, rheological behavior of blood can be approximated by a Newtonian model with acceptable accuracy. Under this assumption, the unsteady Navier-Stokes equations in three dimensions can be written as follows

$$\frac{\partial \rho}{\partial t} + \frac{\partial}{\partial x_i} U_i = 0 \tag{1}$$

$$\frac{\partial U_i}{\partial t} + \frac{\partial}{\partial x_j} u_j U_i = -\frac{\partial p}{\partial x_i} + \frac{\partial \tau_{ij}}{\partial x_j} \tag{2}$$

where $\mathbf{u}$ is the velocity, p is the pressure and ρ is the density. Here, $\mathbf{U} = \rho \mathbf{u}$ and the deviatoric stress components τ are related to velocity as

$$\tau_{ij} = \mu \left(\frac{\partial u_i}{\partial x_j} + \frac{\partial u_j}{\partial u_i} - \frac{2}{3} \frac{\partial u_k}{\partial x_k} \delta_{ij} \right) \tag{3}$$

where μ is the viscosity and $\mathbf{I}$ is the second order identity tensor. The transient density term in Eq.(2), under isentropic conditions, can be replaced by

$$\frac{\partial \rho}{\partial t} = \frac{1}{c^2} \frac{\partial p}{\partial t} \tag{4}$$

where c is the wave speed. The problem is completed by specifying appropriate initial condition for $\mathbf{u}$ and p together with boundary conditions.

The above equations are solved using fully explicit Artificial Compressibility–CBS scheme (for details, see [7]) along with standard Galerkin finite element for spatial discretisation. The CBS scheme is very similar to the original Chorin split and also has similarities with the projection scheme widely employed in incompressible flow calculations. The scheme essentially contains three steps. In the first step, the intermediate velocity field is established. In the second step, the pressure is obtained from the continuity equation and, finally, the intermediate velocities are corrected and true transient term is added in the third step get the final values. The steps of the AC-CBS scheme in its semi-discrete form can be summarised as

Step 1: intermediate momentum

$$\Delta \tilde{U}_i = \tilde{U}_i - U_i^n = \Delta t \left[-\frac{\partial}{\partial x_j} \tilde{u}_j U_i\tilde{} + \frac{\partial \tau_{ij}}{\partial x_j} + \frac{\partial \tau_{ij}^R}{\partial x_j} + \frac{\Delta t}{2} u_k \frac{\partial}{\partial x_k} \left(\frac{\partial}{\partial x_j} \tilde{u}_j U_i\tilde{} + \right) \right]^n \tag{5}$$

Step 2: pressure

$$\left(\frac{1}{\beta^2} \right)^n p^{n+1} = \left(\frac{1}{\beta^2} \right)^n p^n - \Delta t \left[\frac{\partial U_i^n}{\partial x_i} + \theta_1 \frac{\Delta \tilde{U}_i}{\partial x_i} - \Delta t \theta_1 \frac{\partial}{\partial x_i} \frac{\partial p^n}{\partial x_i} \right] \tag{6}$$

Step 3: momentum correction

$$\Delta U_i = U_i^{n+1} - U_i^n = \Delta \tilde{U}_i - \Delta t \frac{\partial p^n}{\partial x_i} + \Delta t \frac{\Delta U_i^\tau}{\partial \tau} \tag{7}$$

where $\Delta \tau$ is the real time step and the true transient term ΔU_i^τ is approximated as

$$\Delta U_i^\tau = \frac{3 U_i^{n+1} - 4 U_i^n + U_i^{n-1}}{2}$$

4 NUMERICAL SIMULATION

The mesh used in the computation contains just over 1.2 million elements with five boundary mesh layer close to the wall. The boundary conditions used are no-slip conditions on the wall and parabolic velocity profiles at the inlet and all the four exits. The flow rate is divided between the four exits based on the physiology of an average human being. A total flow rate of ~1/m is also assumed to simulate a condition of an average human being. The mechanical properties of the blood are assumed to be constant. A kinematic viscosity of $3.77 \times 10^{-2} \, cm^2/s$ and density of $1.0^-0 \, gram/cm^3$.

5 CONCLUSIONS

This work was undertaken to study the role of geometry of the aorta distal to the arch affecting the WSS and OSI distribution on the descending aorta. The compliance of the aorta is important for estimating the WSS distribution and oscillating shear index (OSI). However, this influence is only of the order 10-15% and is neglected in the present study. The value of WSS is very small at the beginning of the blood flow cycle and rapidly increases as the flow speed increases, reaching a peak WSS value at the peak flow rate. Beyond the peak velocity, the WSS drops rapidly as expected. Before the diastole, the reverse flow velocity and the forward moving waves make the WSS to oscillate before slowly reaching a minimum value. Since the velocity history during diastole consists of very small velocity variations, the WSS never drops to zero. It was found that the WSS reaches maximum value at the folded neck.

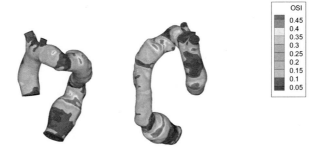

Figure 1: Contour plot of the oscillating shear index (OSI); anterior and posterior views.

However, the dilatation happened distal from the fold location. Nevertheless, the high OSI values occur on the area where the dilatation started as shown in Figure 1.

Work to implement more realistic boundary condition on both inlet and outlets and to include the effects of wall compliance in in progress.

REFERENCES

[1] T. Juvonen, M.A. Ergin, J.D. Galla, S.L. Lansman, K.H. Nguyen, J.N. McCullough, D. Levi, R.A. de Asla, C.A. Bodian and R.B. Griepp. Prospective study of the natural history of thoracic aortic aneurysm.*Annals Thoracic Surgery*, 63, 1533–1545, 1997.

[2] Patient U.K. Ruptured aortic aneurysm.*http://www.patient.co.uk/showdoc/ 40024966/.*

[3] F.G.R. Fowkes, C.A.A. Macintyre and C.V. Ruckley. Increasing incidence of aortic aneurysm in England and Wales. *British Medical Journal*, 298, 33–35,1989.

[4] D. Wang, O. Hassan, K. Morgan and N. Weatherill. EQSM: an effective high quality surface grid generation method based on remeshing. *Computer Methods in Applied Mechanics and Engineering*, 195, 5621–5633, 2006.

[5] I. Sazonov, D. Wang, O. Hassan, K. Morgan and N. Weatherill. A stitching method for the generation of unstructured meshes for use with co-volume solution techniques. *Computer Methods in Applied Mechanics and Engineering*, 195, 1826–1845, 2006.

[6] N.P. Weatherill and O. Hassan. Efficient three-dimensional Delaunay triangulation with automatic point creation and imposed boundary constraints. *International Journal for Numerical Methods in Engineering*, 37, 2005–2040, 1994.

[7] P. Nithiarasu. An efficient Artificial Compressibility (AC) scheme based on Characteristic Based Split (CBS) method for incompressible flows. *International Journal for Numerical Methods in Engineering*, 56, 1815–1845, 2003.

Standard Sessions

A Riemannian Approach to Cardiac Fiber Architecture Modelling

Debora Gil, Jaume Garcia-Barnes
Computer Vision Center, Edifici O, campus UAB, 08193 Barcelona, Spain, debora, jaumegb@cvc.uab.es

Ruth Arís, Guillaume Houzeaux, Mariano Vázquez
Barcelona SuperComputing Center, Nexus I - Campus Nord UPC, Barcelona, Spain

ABSTRACT

There is general consensus that myocardial fiber architecture should be modelled in order to fully understand the electromechanical properties of the Left Ventricle (LV). Diffusion Tensor magnetic resonance Imaging (DTI) is the reference image modality for rapid measurement of fiber orientations by means of the tensor principal eigenvectors.

In this work, we present a mathematical framework for across subject comparison of the local geometry of the LV anatomy including the fiber architecture from the statistical analysis of DTI studies. We use concepts of differential geometry for defining a parametric domain suitable for statistical analysis of a low number of samples. We use Riemannian metrics to define a consistent computation of DTI principal eigenvector modes of variation. Our framework has been applied to build an atlas of the LV fiber architecture from 7 DTI normal canine hearts.

Key Words: *cardiac fiber architecture, diffusion tensor magnetic resonance imaging, differential (Riemannian) geometry.*

1 INTRODUCTION

Cardiologists accept that analysis of myocardium motion, especially the Left Ventricle (LV), provides information about the health of the heart. Since the architecture of myocardial fibers determines LV electromechanical activation pattern, as well as, its mechanics, its thorough knowledge is crucial for defining reliable computational models. Diffusion Tensor Magnetic Resonance Imaging (DTI) has the ability of measuring the diffusion of water molecules along various directions in tissues. This converts DTI volumes in a unique (medical) imaging modality for visualizing the local structure of fibrous tissue. In the particular case of myocardial fibers, it is well established that the primary eigenvector is locally aligned with fiber direction [1].

In this work, we introduce a unifying mathematical framework for computing a statistical atlas of fiber orientations from the analysis of DTI studies. We define differentiable charts [2] parameterizing the LV volume in unitary (radial, longitudinal and circumferential) coordinates (the Normalized Parametric Domain, NPD). In order to ensure registration across subjects, the parametric coordinates are defined according to common anatomic landmarks.

By differential geometry arguments [2] the parametric map defines (local) coordinates on the LV spatial volume and, by means of the Jacobian, on its tangent space. The local reference system given by the

Jacobian describes the geometry of the LV anatomy and it is used to decompose DTI primary eigenvector. The components of the DTI principal eigenvectors in the local reference system are mapped onto the NPD for a PCA analysis of their variability. Riemannian metrics are used to provide a consistent computational framework for variation modes.

2 MAIN BODY

In order to quantify the variability of ventricular geometry and fiber architecture of the LV across subjects, the data volumes of the different subjects should be registered first. Current approaches [3-4] use a non-rigid deformation based on, both, image intensity and anatomical landmarks to register data volumes to the image volume of a reference subject. A common inconvenience is that registration does not provide any geometric description of the LV anatomic shape. Such description is incorporated by a global coordinate change representing (parametrizing) the geometry of an approximate template. Usual coordinate changes (such as cylindrical or prolate spheroidal) model an oversimplified geometry unable to account for the patient-specific (local) anatomic form of the heart.

As suggested in [5], we parameterize the LV volume ($\mathcal{LV}$) in normalized circumferential, longitudinal and radial directions (Fig. 2 (a)) using 3D B-Splines. The parametric coordinates define for each subject a mapping, $\Psi : \Omega^3 = [0,1] \times [0,1] \times [0,1] \longrightarrow \mathcal{LV}$, between the unitary cube and any $\mathcal{LV}$ domain. We call Ω^3 Normalized Parametric Domain (NPD). By taking into account anatomic features common to any LV, we ensure that given anatomic locations in $\mathcal{LV}$ share the same parametric configuration $(u, v, w) \in \Omega^3$. In this manner, we achieve implicit registration among different subjects by means of the inverse of the parametric mapping Ψ^{-1}.

The map Ψ registers $\mathcal{LV}$ to the unitary (cubic) domain Ω^3 "straightening" (unwrapping) $\mathcal{LV}$ geometry. A main advantage over approaches registering volumes to a reference $\mathcal{LV}$ domain in cartesian coordinates is that the NPD domain allows a straightforward definition of neighborhoods adapted to $\mathcal{LV}$ subject-specific anatomy.

The Jacobian, $D\Psi(u, v, w)$, of the parametric map defines at each point $p \in \mathcal{LV}$ a non orthogonal reference of unitary vectors $\{e_u(p), e_w(p), e_w(p)\}$:

$$e_u = \frac{\nabla_u \Psi}{\|\nabla_u \Psi\|_2}, e_v = \frac{\nabla_v \Psi}{\|\nabla_v \Psi\|_2}, e_w = \frac{\nabla_w \Psi}{\|\nabla_w \Psi\|_2} \tag{1}$$

describing the local geometry of the $\mathcal{LV}$ volume. Unlike approaches using a global change of coordinates in the cartesian image volume, our local reference is able to capture the subject-specific $\mathcal{LV}$ geometry (given by the parametrization of the volumetric manifold [2]). Figure 2 shows the description of $\mathcal{LV}$ local geometry given by $D\Psi(u, v, w)$. We observe that the reference vectors (1) are tangent to $\mathcal{LV}$ parametric curves, so that in the NPD they correspond to the axis defined by the parametric coordinates (u, v, w).

The tangent application $D\Psi(u, v, w)$ maps vectors, ξ, expressed in cartesian image volume coordinates into the NPD [2]. By linearity of the tangent application, the mapping is given by the decomposition of ξ in the local reference (1). Such components can be mapped to the NPD for statistical analysis.

The atlas of myocardial anatomy includes a mean geometry of the $\mathcal{LV}$, as well as, exploring the principal modes of variation of the principal eigenvector average orientation. The average $\mathcal{LV}$ template follows from the 3D B-Spline parametrization of the average position of points of different subjects obtained by uniform sampling of the parametric space. Concerning fiber architecture, the computation of an statistical atlas requires statistical measurements (arithmetic mean and covariance matrix) on the values (ξ_u, ξ_v, ξ_w) for all subjects. In order to compensate for the low number of DTI studies, N, for each parametric point (u_i, v_j, w_k), we considered the values (ξ_u, ξ_v, ξ_w) in a 6-connected neighborhood

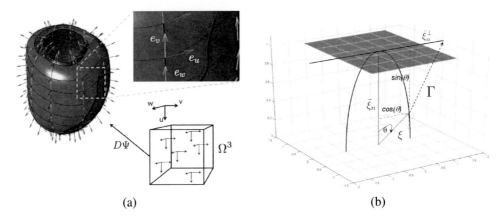

(a)   (b)

Figure 1: Local Reference System given by the Parametric Map Describing $\mathcal{LV}$ Geometry, (a), and sketch of the the definition of the isometry on S^2 for statistical analysis of DTI principal eigenvector.

defined in the NPD. This strategy increases to $7N$ the number of samples for computing the descriptive statistics. We will note the set of samples for each parametric point Ξ.

For an arbitrary vector, (ξ_u, ξ_v, ξ_w) would be a point cloud in $\mathbb{R}^9$. In our particular case, DTI principal eigenvector in cartesian coordinates is unitary (i.e. it belongs to the sphere, S^2). Although the local reference system (1) is non-orthogonal (i.e. the tangent application does not preserve the metric), it does not significantly deviate from orthonormality. This implies that $(\xi_u, \xi_v, \xi_w) \in \Xi$ approximately lie on S^2 and, thus, the statistical analysis should not be done in $\mathbb{R}^3$ but on the Riemmanian manifold S^2 [6].

In the particular case of the sphere, it is possible to construct an isometry mapping S^2 onto a plane such that distances can be measured using the Euclidean metric in the plane. Let $\bar{\xi}$ be the average of all $\xi = (\xi_u, \xi_v, \xi_w) \in \Xi$ and $\bar{\xi}_n = \bar{\xi}/\|\bar{\xi}\|$ the associated unitary vector. The inverse of the exponential map [6] projects maximum circles through $\bar{\xi}$ to its perpendicular vector, $\bar{\xi}_n^\perp$, on the tangent plane (see fig.2 (b)). By general theory of Lie groups the exponential map is a local isometry. In the particular case of spheres [6], it is an isometry between the circle and the vector space generated by $\bar{\xi}_n^\perp$ given by the angle, θ, between $\bar{\xi}_n$ and any point ξ in the maximum circle:

$$\exp^{-1} : \xi \longmapsto \theta \bar{\xi}_n^\perp \qquad (2)$$

By trigonometric arguments $\bar{\xi}_n^\perp$ and θ are given by (see fig.2 (b)):

$$\bar{\xi}_n^\perp = \frac{\xi - \langle \xi, \bar{\xi}_n \rangle}{\|\xi - \langle \xi, \bar{\xi}_n \rangle\|} \qquad \theta = \arctan\left(\frac{\langle \xi, \bar{\xi}_n^\perp \rangle}{\langle \xi, \bar{\xi}_n \rangle}\right) \qquad (3)$$

By definition the map (2) provides three values which correspond to coordinates in the NPD. It follows that their statistical analysis can be still anatomically interpret in terms of the local reference (1). A Principal Component Analysis for $\exp^{-1}(\xi)$, $\xi \in \Xi$, gives the fiber average model and its modes of variation. Regarding the modes of variation, since $\exp^{-1}(\xi)$ are on a plane, the covariance matrix always has a zero eigenvalue corresponding to the direction perpendicular to the plane $\bar{\xi}_n$. The remaining modes are in terms of the local reference (1) and can be anatomically interpreted.

Our mathematical framework has been applied to DTI studies of $N = 7$ normal canine hearts from the Johns Hopkins Hospital public data based (available at http://www.ccbm.jhu.edu/). The NPD has been sampled in $100 \times 50 \times 10$ parametric points uniformly distributed. Figure 2 shows the average fiber model over the average geometry of the $\mathcal{LV}$. Vectors are colored according to the sign of the circumferential component: cyan stands for positive orientation and black for negative one.

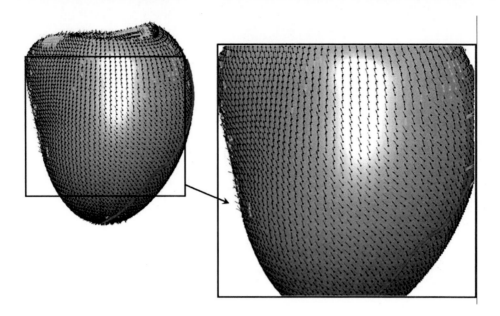

Figure 2: Average fiber architecture over an average geometry of the $\mathcal{LV}$ anatomy.

3   CONCLUSIONS

Modelling the architecture of cardiac fibers is a challenging problem and a milestone for developing consistent models of the heart electromechanical activation. On the grounds of Riemannian theory, we have presented a general mathematical framework for computing consistent statistical models of cardiac fiber architecture from the analysis of DTI images. The average model is suitable for fiber tracking and simulation of heart electromechanical propagation models [7], whereas the modes of variation can be anatomically interpreted.

REFERENCES

[1]   D.F. Scollan, A. Holmes, R.L. Wilson, et al., Histological validation of myocardial microstructure obatined from diffusion tensor imaging, *Am. J. Phys.- Heart and Circ. Phys.*,275, H2308-H2318,1998.

[2]   M. Spivak, *A Comprehensive Introduction to Differential Geometry, vol. 1*, Publish or Perish, Inc, 1999.

[3]   J-M. Peyrat, M. Sermesant, X. Pennec, et al., A computational framework for the statistical analysis of cardiac diffusion tensors: application to a small database of canine hearts, *IEEE Trans. Med. Imag.*, 26(10), 1500-1514, 2007.

[4]   H. Sundar, D. Shen, G. Biros, et al., *Estimating Myocardial fiber orientation by template warping*, 3rd IEEE Int. Symp. Biomed. Imag. (ISBI'06), 73-76, 2006.

[5]   J. Garcia-Barnes, D. Gil, S. Pujades, et al, *A Normalized Parametric Domain for the Analysis of the Left Ventricle Function*, 3rd Int. Conf. Comp. Vis. Theory App., 267-274, 2008

[6]   X. Pennec, Intrinsic Statistics on Riemannian Manifolds: Basic Tools for Geometric Measurements, *J. Math Imag. Vis.*, 25, 127-154, 2006.

[7]   M. Vazquez, R. Aris, A. Rosolen, et al. *A high performance computational electrophysiology model*, 8th.World Congress on Computational Mechanics, 2008.

1st International Conference on Mathematical and Computational Biomedical Engineering - CMBE2009
June 29 - July 1, 2009, Swansea, UK
P.Nithiarasu and R.Löhner (Eds.)

Parallel Computational Electrophysiology in Cell/B.E. Processors

F. Rubio, M. Hanzich, R. Arís, G. Houzeaux and M. Vázquez

Barcelona Supercomputing Center, Campus Nord UPC, Barcelona, Spain, felix.rubio@bsc.es

ABSTRACT

This paper presents an efficient implementation of a Computational Electrophysiology model for heterogeneous processors, namely IBM's Cell/B.E. The Physiological model, that of FitzHugh - Nagumo, includes diffusion and non-linear terms representing the activation potential propagation in excitable media. The numerical discretization is based on the Finite Differences Method, usign a 4-point stencil explicitly advanced in time, and the computational performance of the model is assessed through numerical experiments. The proposed scheme is intended to simulate large-scale problems, hence our efforts have been focused in obtaining the maximum performance.

Key Words: *Computational Electrophysiology, Excitable Media, High Performance Computing, Cell/B.E.*

1 INTRODUCTION

We present an implementation of a Computational Electrophysiology model for Excitable Media in Cell/B.E. processor. Due to its computational capabilities, Cell/B.E. emerges as a promising computational platform for high-performance applications [1]. Its use in high computation demanding applications (Geophysics Seismic Imaging [2]) encourage us to try to get the most performance of it. Moreover, the Cell/B.E. processor is the main building block for the Roadrunner, the current largest supercomputer and the first one to break the Petaflop barrier [1]. This paper represents a first effort to develop a computational simulation tool capable of efficiently running in such architecture. The motivation is double: on one hand, to solve large problems in real time to be used in diagnose. On the second hand, to solve grand challenge problems where complex models can be studied and developed.

2 HPC ELECTROPHYSIOLOGY

In this paper, the Physiological model of the excitable media is based on the Hodgkin-Huxley theory. As a first approach, we implemented the FitzHugh - Nagumo (FHN) [3] model,

$$C_m \frac{\partial \phi}{\partial t} = \frac{\partial}{\partial x_i} \left(\frac{D_{ij}}{S_v} \frac{\partial \phi}{\partial x_j} \right) + I_{\text{ion}}, \tag{1}$$

where C_m and S_v are constants of the model, the membrane capacitance $(\mu F\, cm^{-2})$ and the surface to volume ratio respectively. The total membrane ionic current is I_{ion} $(\mu A\, cm^{-2})$. In this model, to the ionic current definition, a gate potential W equation is added:

---

[1]http://www.lanl.gov/roadrunner/

$$I_{\text{ion}} = c_1\phi(\phi - c_3)(\phi - 1) + c_2 W$$
$$\frac{\partial W}{\partial t} = \varepsilon(\phi - \gamma W). \tag{2}$$

W is called recovery potential. Constants c_1, c_2 and c_3 define the shape of the propagation wave and ε and γ control the recovery potential evolution.

The numerical discretization used for implementing the stated equations, is based on the Finite Differences Method (FDM) [4], explicitly advanced in time. The presented scheme is a proof of concept, based on the following points:

- The computational domain is a paralelepipedal structured mesh.

- The Physiological model is simple: the FHN.

- The model does not includes fiber orientation information.

The pseudo-code shown in Algorithm 1, implement the equations using FDM. The body of the algorithm is a loop in time that applies the equations for each and every point in the input potential model (lines 1 and 2). For each point, the algorithm computes the laplacian (Equation 1), which is the most time consuming part of the algorithm due to the low operation/memory access ratio. This situation encourage us to optimize the laplacian calculation in order to get the maximum efficiency from the algorithm.

Potential propagation

---

input: model, spatial and time discretization, source
output: potential field

```
1: for all time steps do
2:     for all model points do
3:         compute the laplacian
4:         compute the free term
5:         do time integration
6:         compute the coupled equation
7:     end for
8: end for
```

Figure 1: The potential propagation algorithm

Our focus in this work is to map Algorithm 1 on the Cell/B.E. processor (from an IBM QS22 blade), which is one of the emerging HPC technologies. This processor was originally developed for the Sony PS3, but its remarkable floating point throughput (>200 GFlops/s) and main memory bandwidth (25 Gbyte/s) make him a very interesting election as HPC platform. Our analysis shows that the algorithm is memory-bounded, and using 98% of the processor's memory bandwidth we reach 50 Gflops/s. This results are consistent with FDM methods performance in HPC platforms[5].

Figure 2 show the Cell/B.E. internal organization. The Power Processing Element (PPE) is a general-purpose 64 bit PowerPC-type with cache memories. Also, there are 8 Synergistic Processing Elements (SPE) with scratchpad memories called Local Stores (LS). This memories must be explicitly managed by the software developer, so the programming effort outstands other HPC processors. The PPE and the SPEs both have a 128-bit wide Simple Instruction Multiple Data (SIMD or vectorial) instruction set. SPEs SIMD instructions allow to simultaneously process 4 single-precision floating-point operands,

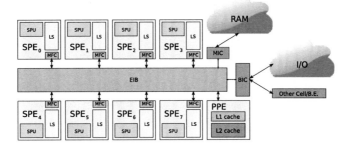

Figure 2: Cell/B.E. processor architecture

so its usage is mandatory if high performance is required. The necessity for manually programming the memory accesses and the development of SIMD code increases the software complexity, but gives outstanding performance. On the energy side, Cell/B.E,'s efficiency outperforms every other HPC platform, considering that the seven most energy-efficient clusters use it as their processing element [2].

3 CONCLUSIONS

The current work presents the FHN equations implemented on Cell/B.E., an HPC platform. Our results show we have obtained 50 Gflops using a FDM numerical schema. Consequently, we can run simulations of sizes that were prohibitive some years ago. In the future we want to enhance the complexity of the model while mantaining the performance. Furthermore, different hardware architectures will be evaluated so as to compare their performance against our Cell/B.E. version.

References

[1] Chen, T., Raghavan, R., Dale, J. N., and Iwata, E. Technical Report 51(5), IBM J. Res. And Devel., (2007).

[2] Araya-Polo, M., Rubio, F., de la Cruz, R., Hanzich, M., Cela, J. M., and Scarpazza, D. P. *ISCA2008 - WCSA2008 (also to be published in SCIENTIFIC PROGRAMMING SPECIAL ISSUE ON HIGH PERFORMANCE COMPUTING ON CELL B.E. PROCESSORS)* , 21–26 June (2008).

[3] Fitzhugh, R. *Biophys. J.* **Vol. 1**, 445–466 (1961).

[4] Cohen, G. C. *Higher-Order Numerical Methods for Transient Wave Equations*. Springer, (2002).

[5] Baker, Z. K., Gokhale, M. B., and Tripp, J. L. In *Field-Programmable Custom Computing Machines, 2007. FCCM 2007. 15th Annual IEEE Symposium on*, 207–218, (2007).

---

[2]http://www.green500.org

Application of novel numerical methods to electrophysiology simulation in real heart geometries

Lucia Mirabella

MOX - Department of Mathematics, Politecnico di Milano, piazza L. Da Vinci 32, 20133 Milano, Italy
and Department of Mathematics and Computer Science, Emory University, 200 Dowman Drive,
Atlanta, GA 30322, USA, lucia.mirabella@mail.polimi.it

Joint work with L. Gerardo-Giorda, M. Perego, M. Piccinelli, A. Veneziani (Emory University) and F. Nobile (Politecnico di Milano)

ABSTRACT

We present a model-based preconditioner for the solution of the Bidomain system governing the propagation of action potentials in the myocardial tissue. It is based on a suitable adaptation of the Monodomain model, a simplified version of the Bidomain one, which is simpler to solve, but unable to capture significant features of the physical phenomenon. This strategy allows to save about half the CPU time required from the standard simulations and the preconditioner has been proved to be optimal with respect to the mesh size. This preconditioner can be also applied to a model adaptivity strategy which is based on an a posteriori error estimator and lets solve the expensive Bidomain model only in specific regions of the domain. These computational methods can be used to simulate the action potential propagation on fine computational meshes built on either fixed or moving real geometries.

Key Words: *preconditioning, model adaptivity, computational electrocardiology, moving domains.*

1 INTRODUCTION

The electrical activation of the heart is the biological process that generates the contraction of the cardiac muscle, pumping the blood to the whole body. In physiological conditions, the pacemaker cells of the sinoatrial node generate an *action potential*, that is a sudden variation of the cell transmembrane potential u, being u the difference between the intracellular potential u_i and the extracellular one u_e. Following preferential conduction pathways, the electrical stimulus propagates throughout the heart wall and causes the contraction the heart chambers. Due to this coupling between the electrophysiology and the mechanical behaviour, when some anomalies occur in the action potential propagation, the proper function of the heart pump can be affected.

The main motivations of mathematical modeling and numerical simulations of the cardiac electrical activity are that they can be useful, for instance, to investigate the state of the heart without invasive medical techniques, to predict the success of a surgery or the pathology development or find the optimal electrode placement for ECG.

2 NUMERICAL SIMULATION OF ACTION POTENTIAL PROPAGATION

The action potential propagation can be mathematically described by coupling a model for the ionic currents, flowing through the membrane of a single cell, with a macroscopical model that describes the propagation of the electrical signal in the cardiac tissue. The most accurate model available in the literature for the description of the macroscopic propagation in the muscle, is the *Bidomain model*, a degenerate parabolic system composed of two non-linear partial differential equations for the intracellular and extracellular potential (1) (see e.g. [1]).

$$\chi C_m \begin{bmatrix} 1 & -1 \\ -1 & 1 \end{bmatrix} \frac{\partial}{\partial t} \begin{bmatrix} u_i \\ u_e \end{bmatrix} - \begin{bmatrix} \nabla \cdot (\mathbf{D}_i \nabla u_i) \\ \nabla \cdot (\mathbf{D}_e \nabla u_e) \end{bmatrix} + \chi \begin{bmatrix} I_{\text{ion}}(u, w) \\ -I_{\text{ion}}(u, w) \end{bmatrix} = \begin{bmatrix} I_i^{\text{app}} \\ -I_e^{\text{app}} \end{bmatrix} \quad (1)$$

In the Bidomain formulation $\mathbf{D}_i, \mathbf{D}_e$ are anisotropic conductivity tensors, I_{ion} is a function of the independent variable w according to the chosen ionic model, I_τ^{app} ($\tau = i, e$) represent applied external stimuli and χ, C_m are physical parameters. The ionic models are generally composed of a system of ordinary differential equations for the ionic currents and gate variables. Problem 1 is completed by an initial condition $u(\boldsymbol{x}, 0) = u_0$ and homogeneus Neumann boundary conditions on $\partial \Omega$, corresponding to an insulated myocardium.

Due to the degenerate nature of the problem, its discretization leads to a ill-conditioned linear system and, as a consequence, the numerical resolution is very expensive. For this reason a simplified model, the *Monodomain* one has been proposed in literature. This model is by far easier to be solved, being composed of a single PDE corresponding to a well-conditioned discretized system but, due to the simplifying assumption it is based on, it is unable to capture certain patterns of propagation of the action potential that have been found experimentally and that can be predicted, instead, by the Bidomain model. For this reason it is useful to develop new strategies which allow to solve the most accurate model while reducing the computational cost.

In particular we set up a preconditioning strategy based on a suitable adaptation of the Monodomain model, which we refer to as *extended Monodomain*, used as a preconditioner for a non-symmetric formulation of the Bidomain system. This preconditioner results at the algebraic level in a lower block-triangular preconditioner that we proved to be optimal, with respect to the mesh size, using a Fourier analysis. We tested our strategy on the finite element discretization of the Bidomain problem, implementing the Monodomain preconditioner within the C++ finite elements library LifeV (www.lifev.org). We considered 3D problems on both idealized and medical images based geometries, coupling the Bidomain model with two different ionic models, the Rogers-McCulloch and the Luo-Rudy Phase I ones. We compared the performances of our preconditioner with a standard choice (more precisely ILU preconditioner implemented in Trilinos software package), with respect to the number of iterations required by the iterative algorithm to converge and the CPU time demanded. The results show that the use of Monodomain preconditioner leads to a considerable gain in both iteration counts and computational time and that this gain increases as the geometrical discretization parameter decreases. In Table 1 we show the comparison regarding CPU times and iteration counts between the standard technique (conjugate gradient method with ILU preconditioner) and the Monodomain preconditioner strategy (flexible GMRES with Monodomain preconditioner (MPrec)). The first column shows the number of nodes of the tetrahedral mesh, columns 2-3 relate to results obtained using Rogers-McCulloch ionic model while columns 4-5 refer to Luo-Rudy phase I model (see [2] for more details).

The strength of this technique is that not only it leads to an important gain in efficiency, but it can also be coupled with other strategies. In particular we developed the idea to solve the most accurate and costly Bidomain model only in some regions of interest, while in the remaining part of the tissue the simpler Monodomain model is solved. These regions can be chosen a priori, for instance according

# nodes	ILU / MPrec (RM)		ILU / MPrec (LRI)	
	time	iterations	time	iterations
12,586	1.4886	4.5229	1.5474	3.4458
62,566	1.7331	6.2097	1.2638	3.0554
172,878	1.9465	8.0000	1.4254	4.0291
841,413	2.3668	13.2229	1.9615	6.7894

Table 1: Ratio of the CPU times and ratio of iteration counts between conjugate gradient method with ILU preconditioner and flexible GMRES with Monodomain preconditioner. Rogers-McCulloch model (columns 2-3) and Luo-Rudy phase I model (columns 4-5).

to possible clinician requests, or a posteriori, on the basis of an a posteriori model error estimator. The resulting model at each time step is therefore a *Hybrid* Monodomain/Bidomain model, being the Bidomain region dependent on the error estimator pattern and varying during the simulation.

We develop a model error estimator by first evaluating the residual of the Bidomain equations computed on the Monodomain solution. We then integrate the residual, assuming the two solutions coincident at the previous time step and expressing the Bidomain conductivity extracellular tensor as a perturbation on the Monodomain one. The resulting estimator on the generic element K reads:

$$\zeta_K^2 = \int_{t^n}^{t^{n+1}} \int_{K \in \mathcal{T}_h} \nabla u_e^M \frac{\mathbf{D}_e - \lambda \mathbf{D}_i}{1 + \lambda} (\mathbf{D}_i^{-1} + \mathbf{D}_e^{-1}) \frac{\mathbf{D}_e - \lambda \mathbf{D}_i}{1 + \lambda} \nabla u_e^M,$$

where u_e^M is the extracellular potential computed with the Monodomain model. In order to implement this model adaptivity approach, we proceed according to the following algorithm:

1. Put $t = 0$ and solve the Monodomain problem;

2. for each element K of the grid:

   (a) compute ζ_K

   (b) if ζ_K is greater than a chosen threshold, activate the Bidomain model on the current element;

3. solve the Hybrid problem built at point 2b, using the Monodomain preconditioner strategy, to get u^H and u_e^H;

4. set $t = t + \Delta t$ and go to point 2.

This algorithm has been implemented in LifeV library and numerical results, obtained in 3D test cases, show that the estimator switches on the more expensive model only in small regions of the domain, in particular those involved by the propagating front at that time (see Figure 1).

This model adaptivity strategy coupled to the use of Monodomain preconditioner has proven to lead to a further gain of 10% of CPU time required for the solution of each time step. Moreover the error of the Hybrid solution, evaluated as a suitable norm of the difference between the solution of the Hybrid system and the solution of the full Bidomain system, is smaller than the error of the full Monodomain one.

The two strategies here described have been exploited in order to perform numerical simulations on very fine computational grids built on real geometries of the left ventricle. More precisely, from SPECT or MRI images we can reconstruct the epicardium and endocardium surfaces through an image segmentation process implemented in VMTK software (www.vmtk.org), and then compute a tetrahedral volume mesh on which we set up the finite element approximation of the problem.

Figure 1: Left: screenshot of the action potential propagation at $t = 60$ ms. Right: the red colour highlights the elements in which the Bidomain is switched on at $t = 60$ ms.

The computational cost associated to the assembling of the upper right block of the Hybrid matrix has been reduced by splitting it in a time-independent computation that can be performed once, and in a cheaper part to be performed *online* at each time step. This additional cost is compensated by the gain in CPU time required to solve the hybrid system when the number of active elements is small. It is worth noticing that this task will not represent an additional cost if the whole matrix of the discretized linear system has to be recomputed at each time step. This happens, for instance, in the simulation of more complex phenomena, involving the coupling between action potential propagation and heart muscle contraction: since the geometry is moving, the finite element spaces have to be rebuilt, forcing the whole matrix assembling to be performed at each time step.

To this respect the most classical way to include muscle contraction is to couple a mechanical model for the muscle to the electrophysiological model chosen. The drawbacks of this approach are that the full coupling leads to expensive computations and that a reliable mechanical model should depend on the cardiac fibers orientation, which is still a controversial aspect in this field. We then tried to incorporate the domain movement by retrieving it directly from medical images, avoiding the simulation of the mechanical behaviour of the heart. In this approch we take advantage of a surface registration algorithm in order to track the domain movement during a heart beat and we include this image-based movement in the simulation of the action potential propagation. We then solve the Hybrid PDE system with the Monodomain preconditioning together with the model adaptivity strategy, without any additional assembling cost with respect to the full Bidomain simulation.

3 CONCLUSIONS

In our exeprience, the use of efficient techniques is a crucial point in order to perform accurate simulations on real geometries in a limited amount of time. We achieve this objective by coupling two different numerical methods: the first one is a model-based preconditioner which has been proven to be optimal with respect to the mesh size and has led to a remarkable gain in CPU time. The second one is a model adaptivity strategy which allows to solve the most accurate and expensive model only where needed. This twofold approach can be used to perform accurate numerical simulations of the action potential propagation in real geometries, even in moving domain, reducing the computational effort.

REFERENCES

[1]   P. Colli Franzone and L. Pavarino, A Parallel Solver for reaction-diffusion systems in computational electrocardiology, *Mathematical models and methods in applied sciences*, Vol. 14, No. 6, 2004.

[2]   L. Gerardo-Giorda, L. Mirabella, F. Nobile, M. Perego and A. Veneziani, A model-based block-triangular preconditioner for the Bidomain system in electrocardiology, *Journal of Computational Physics*, Vol. 228, No. 10, 2009, pp. 3625-3639.

NUMERICAL METHODS FOR ACCURATE AND EFFECTIVE SIMULATIONS IN COMPUTATIONAL ELECTROCARDIOLOGY

Luca Gerardo Giorda
Department of Mathematics and Computer Science, EMORY University, 400 Dowman Dr Suite W401, Atlanta, GA, USA, `luca@mathcs.emory.edu`

Mauro Perego
Department of Mathematics and Computer Science, EMORY University, 400 Dowman Dr Suite W401, Atlanta, GA, USA, `mauro@mathcs.emory.edu`

Alessandro Veneziani
Department of Mathematics and Computer Science, EMORY University, 400 Dowman Dr Suite W401, Atlanta, GA, USA, `ale@mathcs.emory.edu`

ABSTRACT

Recent numerical techniques for the accurate and effective simulations of potential propagation in the heart are considered. On one hand, we present a second order generalization of the popular Rush-Larsen scheme for the solution to ionic models in electro-cardiology. A time adaptive implementation of the method is presented. On the other hand, we present preliminary results on the application of domain decomposition techniques for solving the coupled Monodomain and Bidomain problems in view of model adaptivity.

Key Words: *Computational electrocardiology, Rush-Larsen scheme, time adaptivity, domain decomposition methods*

1   INTRODUCTION

Numerical modeling of the cardiac activity still presents many interesting challenges in terms of accuracy and effectiveness of the methods. *In silico* physiology of the heart has been recognized as an important predictive tool for integrating properties and functions measured *in vitro* and *in vivo*. Impact of numerical models ranges from a better understanding of the physiopathology of cardiac dynamics (electrical activity, mechanics, fluid dynamics), to the prediction of the impact of certain therapies.

In this talk, we will address some methods recently developed for an accurate and effective numerical solution to the equations of electrocardiology. More precisely, we consider

1) a method for the accurate simulation of ion dynamics, which is an improvement of the popular Rush-Larsen scheme;

2) domain decomposition techniques for the simulation of the potential propagation, resorting to the solution of mixed Monodomain-Bidomain systems, in view of model adaptivity (where the computaionally intensive Bidomain problem is solved only in small regions of interest).

	c_{-1}	c_0	c_1
FE*	0	1	0
AB2*	0	$\frac{3}{2}$	$-\frac{1}{2}$
CN*	$\frac{1}{2}$	$\frac{1}{2}$	0
AM3*	$\frac{5}{12}$	$\frac{8}{12}$	$-\frac{1}{12}$

Table 1: Coefficients of the numerical schemes

2 A SECOND ORDER GENERALIZATION OF THE RUSH-LARSEN SCHEME

Let us consider the following initial value problem,

$$
\begin{cases}
\dfrac{\partial y_i}{\partial t} = a_i(t, \mathbf{y})\, y_i + b_i(t, \mathbf{y}), & n = 0, \dots, N, \quad i = 1, \dots, m \quad t \in (0, T] \\
\mathbf{y}^0 = \mathbf{y}(0).
\end{cases}
\tag{1}
$$

Upon proper identification of the vectors a and b, this problem represents several cell-membrane models for cardiac cells, including the Hodgkin-Huxley, the Beeler-Reuter, the Luo-Rudy phase I, the Winslow and the Courtemanche models [1]. The Rush-Larsen scheme [2] proposed for this kind of problems reads

$$
\begin{cases}
y_i^{n+1} = e^{a_i^n \Delta t}\left(y_i^n + \dfrac{b_i^n}{a_i^n}\right) - \dfrac{b_i^n}{a_i^n}, & n = 0, \dots, N, \quad i = 1, \dots, m \\
\mathbf{y}^0 = \mathbf{y}(0),
\end{cases}
\tag{2}
$$

where $\mathbf{y}^n$ is the approximation of the solution $\mathbf{y}(t^n)$, being $t^n = \Delta t\, h$, $T = N\Delta t$ and $\Delta t > 0$ the time step.

This scheme relies on solving exactly the linearized equation where the coefficients of problem (1) are frozen at time t^n. Our generalization reads

$$
\begin{cases}
y_i^{n+1} = y_i^n + h\Phi(a_i^{n+\frac{1}{2}} h)(a_i^{n+\frac{1}{2}} y_i^n + b_i^{n+\frac{1}{2}}), & n = 0, \dots, N, \quad i = 1, \dots, m \\
\mathbf{y}^0 = \mathbf{y}(0);
\end{cases}
\tag{3}
$$

where

$$
\Phi(x) = \begin{cases} \dfrac{e^x - 1}{x} & x \neq 0 \\ 1 & x = 0, \end{cases}
\tag{4}
$$

and $\mathbf{a}^{n+\frac{1}{2}}$ and $\mathbf{b}^{n+\frac{1}{2}}$ are approximations of $\mathbf{a}(t^{n+\frac{1}{2}})$ and $\mathbf{b}(t^{n+\frac{1}{2}})$. In particular, we select

$$
\begin{aligned}
\mathbf{a}^{n+\frac{1}{2}} &= c_{-1}\mathbf{a}^{n+1} + c_0\mathbf{a}^n + c_1\mathbf{a}^{n-1} \quad, \mathbf{b}^{n+\frac{1}{2}} = c_{-1}\mathbf{b}^{n+1} + c_0\mathbf{b}^n + c_1\mathbf{b}^{n-1}, \quad n = 1, \dots, N \\
\mathbf{a}^{\frac{1}{2}} &= c_{-1}\mathbf{a}^1 + (c_0 + c_1)\mathbf{a}^0 \quad, \mathbf{b}^{\frac{1}{2}} = c_{-1}\mathbf{b}^1 + (c_0 + c_1)\mathbf{b}^0.
\end{aligned}
\tag{5}
$$

Coefficients c_{-1}, c_0 and c_1 are selected by forcing these approximations to be exact for both constant and linear functions (yielding a second order approximation). Notice that for $\mathbf{a} = \mathbf{0}$ and specific choices for the coefficients c_i we recover classical multistep schemes, such as the Forward Euler (FE), the Crank Nicolson (CN) and the third order Adams-Moulton (AM3) schemes. We call their generalization to the case $\mathbf{a} \neq \mathbf{0}$ FE* (the Rush-Larsen scheme), CN*, AM3* respectively (see Tab. 1). In the talk, we will discuss

1. consistency, accuracy and zero-stability of the methods;

2. absolute stability;

3. positivity of the solution, which is of paramount relevance in view of the specific applications at hand.

In particular, we show that these methods are second order accurate at most (Fig. 2) and their absolute stability properties are better than the ones of the corresponding multistep method (as was already realized for the Rush Larsen method in comparison with the FE one, see Fig. 1).

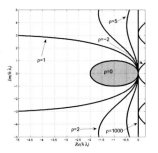 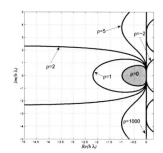 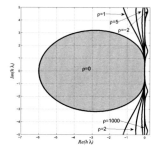

Figure 1: Absolute stability regions for the FE* (left), the AB2* (center) and AM3* methods on the model problem $y' = \lambda y$ with $\lambda = \lambda_a + \lambda_b$ a $= \lambda_a$, b $= \lambda_b y$ and $\lambda_a = \rho \lambda_b$ with ρ a real parameter.

Moreover, we will introduce *Predictor Corrector* solvers based on the appropriate coupling of an explicit and implicit methods of the form (3). The comparison between the solution computed by the explicit and the implicit solvers provide an a-posteriori error estimator suitable for *time adaptive* schemes. Numerical results for time adaptive solutions to ionic models in both the monodomain and bidomain problems will be presented, confirming our theoretical analysis (Fig. 2).

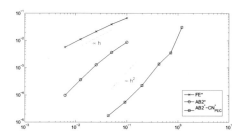

Figure 2: Simulation of Luo-Rudy I ionic model with the Monodomain model: Relative error curves as a function of the average step Δt, using FE* scheme, AB2* scheme and the time adaptive algorithm with the AB2*-CN* scheme with PEC approach.

3   DOMAIN DECOMPOSITION METHODS FOR THE COUPLED MONODOMAIN-BIDOMAIN PROBLEM

A possible approach for reducing computational costs in solving the electrocardiology problem still with good accuracy is to couple different models with different level of reliability in different part of

Figure 3: Left: Convergence factor for different matching condition as a function of the frequency (Fourier analysis). Right: Residual as a function of the iteration in a non-overlapping domain decomposition method coupling Monodomain and Bidomain problem, with different interface conditions.

the heart. As it is well known, the Monodomain model is computationally affordable and however is not able to capture some particular features of the problem. On the other hand, the Bidomain model is assumed to be accurate enough in most of the applications and however it features high computational costs. In the second part of the talk we will address some preliminary results in coupling the two problems with domain decomposition techniques. The basic idea is to devise a solver where the accurate and expensive model is solved in a small region of interest, while the most part of the domain is described by the monodomain model. The final goal is to have a *model adaptive* solver, where the region for the accurate model is automatically selected by an appropriate a-posteriori estimator.

Since the bidomain and the monodomain models are problem with different sizes (the former includes both the extra-cellular potential u_e and the transmembrane one u, the latter only u), the coupling between the two problems is non standard. In the talk, we will address some preliminary results obtained in 2D simulations on simple domains, in order to identify the best interface conditions in the numerical domain decomposition iterations (see Fig. 3 - D=Dirichlet condition, N=Neumann condition,R=Robin condition).

A Fourier analysis of the method will be presented for estimating convergence rate for different interface conditions. In the particular case of Robin-Robin boundary conditions, which exhibits the best performances (see Fig. 3 left), Fourier analysis provides also insights on the selection of good parameters for obtaining optimal convergence properties. Extensive comparisons among different approaches, different mesh size and overlapping vs. non-overlapping methods will be presented.

REFERENCES

[1]   M. Perego and A. Veneziani, An efficient generalization of the Rush-Larsen method for solving electro-physiology membrane equation, *submitted*, (2009) Tech. Rep. TR-2009-05, www.mathcs.emory.edu

[2]   S. Rush and H. Larsen, A practical algorithm for solving dynamic membrane equations, IEEE Transaction on Biomedical Engineering, BME-25 (1978), pp.389-392

[3]   L. Gerardo Giorda, M. Perego and A. Veneziani, Domain decomposition methods for coupling Monodomain and Bidomain models in electrocardiology, *in preparation* (2009)

ANALYSIS OF THE ELECTRO-MECHANICAL ACTIVATION SEQUENCE OF THE MYOCARDIUM FOLLOWING THE PATH DESCRIBED BY THE HVMB

Jordi Marcé-Nogué
Dept. RMEE, Universitat Politècnica de Catalunya, ETSEIAT Terrassa, Spain, jordi.marce@upc.edu

Francesc Roure
Dept. RMEE, Universitat Politècnica de Catalunya, ETSEIB Barcelona, Spain

Gerard Fortuny
Dept. EIM, Universitat Rovira i Virgili, Tarragona, Spain

ABSTRACT

In order to contribute in the study of the HVMB, a computational model to simulate the behaviour of the myocardial tissue, mainly based in the fibre, is presented in a computational simplified model of the HVMB. The results obtained are compared with others works in the literature to conclude that if the electro-mechanical activation sequence in the myocardium coincides with the path described by the HVMB the path and the delay observed in the shortening of the fibres are according with the expected and observed behaviour in real hearts.

Key Words: *electro-mechanical activation, myocardium, helical myocardial ventricular band*

1 INTRODUCTION

In 1975 the valencian cardiologist F. Torrent-Guasp described the heart as a Helical Ventricular Myocardial Band (**HVMB**) in which *"The ventricular myocardium is presented when it is unrolled under the form of a single big muscular band that, due to its special disposition, describes two cavities in the intact heart"* [7]. It gives a different perspective of the morphology of the heart than the current and it could explain better and most coherently the propagation of the electrical stimulus which activates the shortening of the fibres, the complex deformation movement of the heart and maybe an explanation about understanding the cardiac contraction [8]. Long before the myocardial band had been proposed, other contributions were described in order to understand the structure and behaviour of the ventricular architecture.

In order to contribute in the study of the **HVMB**, a computational model to simulate the behaviour of the myocardial tissue, mainly based in the fibre, is firstly presented and secondly defined and solved. The model should be able to describe the morphological particularities of the **HVMB** which are based in consider the path described by the band as the preferential path described by the fibres [3]. Finally, the results are compared with others works in the literature to check which behaviour will be observed in the myocardium and in the fibres if an activation sequence in the shortening of the fibres is applied along the path defined by the **HVMB**, in order to observe if the electro-mechanical activation sequence of the myocardium follows the path described by the **HVMB**.

2   METHODS

The model should be able to describe two aspects of the myocardial tissue:

On one hand it describes an active part due to the fibres. There is an internal electrical stimulus that activates the contraction of the fibres on a continuum way based on the interaction of *(a)* the electrical model that is described using the Aliev and Panfilov equations [1] and *(b)* the mechanical model that is described using the rheological model of Hill-Maxwell and is based in the Theory of Huxley of the sliding filaments and the Cross Bridge model proposed by J. Bestel, F. Clment and M. Sorine [2].

On the other hand, it describes a passive part due to the connective tissue that controls the deformation of the tissue and keeps the cardiac fibres all together and is modelled as a three-dimensional continuum element formulated with the Finite Element Method as an isoparametric hexahedrical element of 8 nodes [4].

The interaction of the Active Part and the Passive Part in the model generates the following governing equation:

$$\rho \ddot{\underline{y}} - \nabla \underline{\underline{\sigma}} = 0; \qquad \underline{\underline{\sigma}} = \underline{\underline{\sigma}}_p + \sigma_a \underline{n} \otimes \underline{n} \tag{1}$$

Where σ_p is the passive stress of the connective tissue generated by the action potential **u(t)** and σ_a is the active stress due to the contraction of the fibre. A mathematical model for the blood pressure based on the Windkessel model is included and the boundary conditions describing the behaviour of certain fixed points observed in real images are also included.

The geometry of the **HVMB** is defined starting from medical images and graphic reconstruction techniques in order to obtain a model simplification of the band and the equations are solved in a simplified **HVMB** continuum model meshed with 400 eight-node hexahedrical elements and 15 fibres inside meshed each with 50 two-node fibre elements (Figure 1). Propagation along the fibres of **u(t)** is generated in the starting point of the right segment in order to force it to follow the path described by the band and finish in the ascendant segment. A propagated deformation following the same path of the stimulus, which in this case is along the fibre, is obtained (Figure 2). In the geometrical model, the path described by the fibres coincides with the path described by the band, as some authors propose: the propagation along the **HVMB** can be studied as the propagation along the fibres.

3   RESULTS

A mapping propagation of mechanical activation in the paced heart with MRI tagging was done by Wyman [9] in order to evaluate noninvasively the mechanical activation. The mapping was done in the left ventricles (**LV**) whereas seven canine hearts were paced in situ from different sites: the base of the

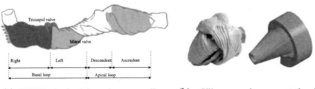

(a) **HVMB** obtained from the myocardium   (b)   Silicon   and   computational model of the **HVMB**

Figure 1: Helical Ventricular Myocardial Band

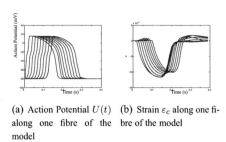

(a) Action Potential $U(t)$ along one fibre of the model   (b) Strain ε_c along one fibre of the model

Figure 2: Evolution of the different values along the time and along the fibres

left ventricle free wall (**LVb**) and the right ventricular apex (**RVa**) The propagation of this pacing along the myocardium was observed. The procedure is reproduced with the same conditions and with the same pacing protocols in the computational model. The Figures 3(a), (b) and (c) and 3(d), (e) and (f) shows that the activation time observed in the MRI described above coincide with the activation time in each part of the **HVMB** model taking into account that in the figures proposed by Wyman, the starting point of the activation is in blue and the final point in yellow (medium times in red and orange) and in the figures obtained here the colour scale ranges from blue to red (medium times between green, yellow and orange) and that in a Bull's eye the center corresponds to the apical part and the perimeter to the basal part. The correlation of results could demonstrate that the path followed by the propagation of **u(t)** coincides with the same path described by the myocardial band.

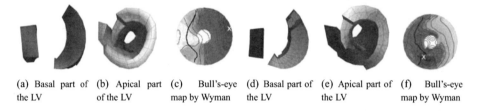

(a) Basal part of the LV   (b) Apical part of the LV   (c) Bull's-eye map by Wyman   (d) Basal part of the LV   (e) Apical part of the LV   (f) Bull's-eye map by Wyman

Figure 3: LVb (a, b, c) and RVa (d, e, f) pacing in the simplified model of the myocardial band

To observe the shortening of the fibres, firstly, in the simulation of the contraction of the fibres can be observed that the time spent by the band in doing the contraction and the relaxation is longer than the time spent by the propagation of **u(t)** (Figure 4). This phenomenon can be explained taking into account that the activation time of the action potential does not coincide with the starting time of the contraction and, in addition, that the relaxation time caused by the contraction of the fibre is longer than the depolarization time of the activation of the fibre. It coincides with the observations done, for example, by Saunders studying the electric activity and mechanical contraction of frog sartorius muscle and frog cardiac muscle [5]. Secondly, in the same simulation of the contraction of the fibres is also observed that the different fibres are shortening in different instant of time depending on its position in the myocardium. In the case of the model it is due because the activation sequence is forced to follow the path described by the **HVMB**. The fibres analysed in the Figure 4 are situated in different points of the **HVMB** and, consequently, their activation and contraction appear in different instants of time following the path of the band.

But if the shortening of the fibres is compared with an integrated overview of the left ventricular mechanical sequence, done by Sengupta [6] in which is investigated whether the onset and progression of regional left ventricular shortening and lengthening parallel the apex-to-base differences in depolarization and repolarisation, the same behaviour is observed in the shortening of the fibres and in the order of the activation sequence along the myocardial walls.

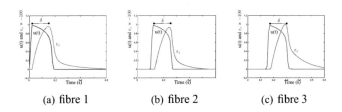

(a) fibre 1	(b) fibre 2	(c) fibre 3

Figure 4: Delay between the action potential **u(t)** and the fibre strain ε_c in different fibres situated in different positions of the myocardium

4 DISCUSSION

The main idea obtained in this work is that the path followed by the propagation of the action potential could coincide with the same path described by the myocardial band because the observations in the earlier studies coincide with the results obtained in the simulation of the simplified model of the **HVMB**. When the myocardium is electrically activated, the propagation of **u(t)** follows the path described by the preferential fibre direction, which coincides with the path described by the **HVMB**, as can be observed in the comparison of the results obtained with the observations of Wyman. When a shortening sequence is simulated, forcing the fibres to follow the path described by the band, the generated deformation in each fibre describes a delay in the shortening of the fibres depending on its position in the band. This behaviour coincides with the observations done by Sengupta about the mechanical sequence of the myocardium without consider the **HVMB** morphology.

As a consequence, it can be understood that the results obtained in this simulation agree (in a qualitative way) with the expected results and it can be concluded that if the electro-mechanical activation sequence in the myocardium coincides with the path described by the Helical Ventricular Myocardial Band, the path and the delay observed in the shortening of the fibres are according with the expected and observed behaviour in real hearts.

REFERENCES

[1] R. Aliev and A. Panfilov. A simple two-variable model of cardiac excitation,*Chaos, Solitons & Fractals*, 7, 293-301, 1996.

[2] J. Bestel. Modèle différentiel de la contraction musculaire contrôlée. Application au système cardio-vasculaire, *PhD thesis*, Université Paris-Ix Dauphine, 2000.

[3] M. Kocica et altri. The helical ventricular myocardial band: global, three-dimensional, functional architecture of the ventricular myocardium, *European Journal of Cardiovascular-thoracic Surgery*, 295, S21-S40, 2006.

[4] E. Oñate. Cálculo de Estructuras por el Método de Elementos finitos, *CIMNE*, 1995.

[5] W.B. Saunders. Physiology and Biophysics. 1982.

[6] P.P. Sengupta et altri. Apex-to-base dispersion in regional timing of left ventricular shortening and lengthening, *Journal of the American College of Cardiology*, 47, 1, 2006.

[7] F. Torrent-Guasp. *El músculo cardíaco*. Publicacions de la Fundació Joan March, 1972.

[8] F. Torrent-Guasp. Estructura y funcin del corazn. *Revista Espaola de Cardiologia*, 51, 91-102, 1998.

[9] B.T. Wyman et altri. Mapping propagation of mechanical activation in the paced heart with MRI tagging, *American Journal of Physiology*, 276, H881-H891,1999.

1st International Conference on Mathematical and Computational Biomedical Engineering – CMBE2009
June 29 – July 1, 2009, Swansea, UK
P. Nithiarasu and R. Löhner (eds)

DIFFERENCE IMAGING OF CEREBRAL STROKE IN THE HUMAN BRAIN USING EDGE FINITE ELEMENT SIMULATIONS OF MAGNETIC INDUCTION TOMOGRAPHY

Massoud Zolgharni
School of Medicine, Swansea University, SA2 8PP, UK, 390917@swansea.ac.uk
Paul D. Ledger
School of Engineering, Swansea University, SA2 8PP, UK
Huw Griffiths
School of Medicine, Swansea University, SA2 8PP, UK

ABSTRACT

The purpose of this study was to investigate the capability of a 16-channel Magnetic Induction Tomography configuration for imaging haemorrhagic cerebral stroke. An anatomically-realistic, multi-layered, head model comprising 12 tissues was used to simulate the human head. A commercial Finite-Element (FE) package (Comsol) employing edge elements was used to solve the eddy-current problem and compute the response field measured due to the stroke. Tikhonov regularization was then employed to solve the ill-posed linearized inverse problem and reconstruct an image of the stroke. The results reveal that a large, peripheral stroke saturated with 75% blood, may be imaged using the 16-channel MIT system.

Key Words: *FE modelling, magnetic induction tomography, cerebral stroke.*

1. INTRODUCTION

Magnetic induction tomography (MIT) is a non-invasive imaging modality which is used for imaging the internal distribution of the electrical conductivity of an object such as biological tissues [1]. An alternating magnetic field is applied to the object under investigation. This induces eddy currents which generate a secondary magnetic field which depends on the conductive properties of the object. The secondary field is then measured with an array of sensor coil(s). An image of the internal distribution of the conductivity may be reconstructed from the measured signals. The aim of this study was to investigate the feasibility of using MIT for imaging haemorrhagic cerebral stroke. Haemorrhagic stroke occurs due to the rupture of a blood vessel and consequent bleeding inside the brain. The idea of exploiting MIT is based on the fact that the conductivity of the blood is larger than that of the brain tissue. The finite element method using edge finite elements was used to solve the forward problem and determine an approximation of the measured signals in the sensor coils. Using this data, a linearized inverse problem was solved using Tikhonov regularization in order to reconstruct the 3D images.

2. FORWARD PROBLEM

The forward problem represents an eddy current problem in which the electric and magnetic fields, **E** and **H** respectively, satisfy Maxwell's equations

$$\nabla \times \mathbf{E} = -\mathrm{i}\mu\omega\mathbf{H} \quad , \quad \nabla \times \mathbf{H} = \sigma\mathbf{E} + \mathrm{i}\varepsilon\omega\mathbf{E} + \mathbf{J}_s \quad , \quad \nabla \cdot \varepsilon\mathbf{E} = \rho \quad , \quad \nabla \cdot \mu\mathbf{H} = 0 \qquad (1)$$

where μ is the permeability, ε is the permittivity, ρ is the electric charge density, σ is the conductivity and $i^2 = -1$. The term $\mathbf{J}_s$ represents the current sources. By application of the temporal gauge, one suitable formulation for solving these equations is the $\mathbf{A}$-formulation:

$$\nabla \times (\mu^{-1} \nabla \times \mathbf{A}) + (i\omega\sigma - \omega^2\varepsilon)\mathbf{A} = \mathbf{J}_s,$$ (2)

where $\mathbf{A}$, the magnetic vector potential, satisfies $\mu\mathbf{H} = \nabla \times \mathbf{A}$. When appropriate boundary conditions are supplied, (2) can be approximated by the finite element method (FEM) using edge elements [2]. Edge finite elements are constructed so as to ensure tangential continuity of the field on the edges of the element while allowing for a discontinuous normal component. Edge elements provide the mathematically correct approach to approximating equation (2) by the FEM. Nodal finite elements, on the other hand, enforce too strong a continuity of the field and lead to inaccurate or wrong solutions. COMSOL Multiphysics [3] is a commercial finite element package that includes this type of finite element discretisation and is employed for the finite element simulations reported here.

The MIT configuration, which consists of a circular array of 16 exciter and 16 sensor coils positioned inside a cylindrical aluminium electromagnetic shield, was simulated using the finite element method with edge finite elements [4]. The electromagnetic shield was approximated using an impedance boundary condition (IBC) and the far-field was captured by introducing infinite elements on the truncated boundaries (above and below the head). The operating frequency was fixed as 10 MHz and a realistic, multi-layered, head mesh of tetrahedral elements comprising 12 major tissues was used to simulate a stroke (figure 2). The head mesh comprised 54,019 such elements. List of the different tissues and related electrical properties used are reported previously [5]. The stroke lesion was introduced within the right temporal lobe of the brain and assumed to consist of 75% blood and 25% normal tissue. The electrical properties of the stroke region were calculated as a weighted average of the values for blood and tissue accordingly.

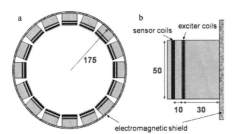

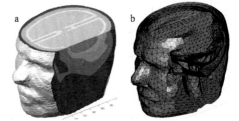

Figure 1. Concept of the 16-channel MIT system: (a) the coil array, (b) detail of an individual coil module. Dimensions in mm.

Figure 2. Head Model: (a) model with two cuts illustrating the internal tissues, (b) triangular boundary elements of the FE mesh.

Once the vector potential is obtained everywhere in the domain, the induced voltage can be calculated as the line integral of the tangential components of the $\mathbf{A}$ along a sensor coil as:

$$V = \oint_{Coil} \mathbf{E} \cdot d\mathbf{l} = -i\omega \oint_{Coil} \mathbf{A} \cdot d\mathbf{l}$$ (3)

where $d\mathbf{l}$ is length element of the coil.

Simulations were first carried out for the normal brain and the imaginary part of the voltage of the induced signals in the sensor coils recorded in the vector $\mathbf{V}_1$. Subsequently, another simulation was performed with the stroke present and the vector of the imaginary part of the voltages, $\mathbf{V}_2$, was stored. By subtracting these values, the effect of the stroke on the signals could then be expressed as the vector of voltage differences: $\Delta\mathbf{V} = \mathbf{V}_2 - \mathbf{V}_1$.

3. INVERSE PROBLEM

The forward problem described in Section 2 can be re-expressed as $\mathbf{V} = f(\sigma)$ and the inverse problem, which is of interest in imaging, consists of determining $\sigma = f^{-1}(\mathbf{V})$. This inverse problem can be re-written in the form of a minimisation problem (e.g. [6]):

$$\min_{\sigma} \left(\left\| \mathbf{V}_m - f(\sigma) \right\|^2 + \lambda \left\| \mathbf{R}\sigma \right\|^2 \right) \tag{4}$$

where $\mathbf{R}$ is a regularization matrix and λ is a scalar regularization parameter. The solution of the linearised minimisation problem for difference imaging corresponds to performing Tikhonov regularization:

$$\Delta\sigma = (\mathbf{J}^T \mathbf{J} + \lambda \mathbf{R}^T \mathbf{R})^{-1} \mathbf{J}^T \Delta\mathbf{V} \tag{5}$$

where $\mathbf{J}$ is the Jacobian matrix. For the choice of $\mathbf{R}=\mathbf{I}$ this can be written in the alternative form:

$$\Delta\sigma = \mathbf{J}^T (\mathbf{J}\mathbf{J}^T + \lambda \mathbf{I})^{-1} \Delta\mathbf{V} \tag{6}$$

which offers considerable computational advantages when the number of columns of $\mathbf{J}$ exceeds the number of rows [6]. The entries in the Jacobian matrix was determined by computing the sensitivity of the voltage pairs V_{ab} of coils a,b with respect to an element k (e.g. [5]):

$$\frac{\partial V_{ab}}{\partial \sigma_k} = \int_{\Omega_k} \mathbf{E_a} . \mathbf{E_b} \, d\Omega \tag{7}$$

Specifically, $\mathbf{E_a}$ is the electric field induced in the material when the exciter coil is activated, $\mathbf{E_b}$ is the field induced when the receiver coil is activated as an exciter and Ω_k is the volume over which the conductivity change occurs. In order that an inverse crime is not committed [6], the solution obtained on the finite element mesh was mapped to a cubic grid with regular 2 mm spacing. In this case $\mathbf{J}$ then has as many columns as there are voxels in the volume and as many rows as there are coil combinations. The entries in $\mathbf{J}$ were computed by solving the forward model for the head with a homogeneous conductivity of 1 S m^{-1}, activating all 16 exciters and 16 sensors in sequence. The electric field at the centre of each cubic voxel was then obtained from the continuous distribution available in the FE mesh of tetrahedra. This value of electric field was taken as representative of the whole (though small) cubic voxel and the sensitivity calculated using (7).

The parameter λ was selected by a subjective assessment of the smallest value, consequently giving the highest spatial resolution, which did not introduce significant noise artefacts. No noise was added to the simulated signals and it was assumed that the boundary of the eddy-current region (skin surface) was known as a-priori information. The entire eddy-current region (head) therefore remained fixed at 464,714 cubic voxels.

4. RESULTS AND DISCUSSION

Two cross-sections were extracted from the volume reconstructed image (figure 3); the image of the stroke is clearly visible although blurred in the vertical direction. However, the use of multiple planes of measurement (by scanning the coil array vertically) would be expected to reduce this blurring partcularly in the vertical direction. Also the recovered stroke is slightly shifted towards the surface of the head. This displacement is due to regularization of the inverse problem. A few artefacts can be seen on the boundaries. These artefacts are the results of ill-posed-ness of the inverse problem. By changing the level of regularization parameter, artefacts may be removed from the images at the cost of losing the exact location of the lesion.

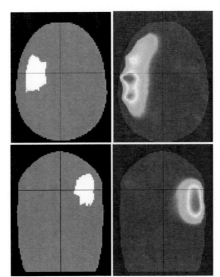

Figure 3. Left column: diagram showing true position of simulated lesion. Right column: reconstructed MIT image of conductivity change. Upper row: transverse cross-section through volume image (parallel to the plane of coil array). Lower row: coronal cross-section. ($\lambda=1\times10^{-10}$).

Performing useful clinical imaging will be more difficult than this study has suggested because a 'before-stroke' data frame ($\mathbf{V}_1$) will not normally be available. Multi-frequency imaging which exploits the frequency dependence of the tissue conductivity is the subject of present and future studies [8]. The annular coil array was simulated because it corresponded to an existing data-collection system. It may not be optimal and an array of coils covering a hemisphere, for example, might perform better for peripheral strokes than an annulus. The model will now be a useful tool for testing this and other array geometries.

ACKNOWLEDGEMENT

This work was supported by the EPSRC under grants EP/E009697/1 and EP/E009158/1. The authors thank D.S. Holder for providing the head geometry.

REFERENCES

[1]   H. Griffiths, Magnetic induction tomography, Electrical Impedance Tomography – methods, history and applications. ed. D. S. Holder, IOP Publishing, Chapter 8 ISBN 0 7503 0952 0, 2005.

[2]   O. Biro, Edge elements formulations of eddy current problems, *Computer Methods in Applied Mechanics and Engineering* 169 391-405, 1999.

[3]   Comsol Multiphysics User's Guide (2007) COMSOL AB.

[4]   M. Zolgharni, P.D. Ledger and H. Griffiths, Forward modelling of magnetic induction tomography for detecting haemorrhagic cerebral stroke, submitted to *Medical & Biological Engineering & Computing 2009.*

[5]   M. Zolgharni, P.D. Ledger, H. Griffiths and D.S. Holder Imaging cerebral haemorrhage with magnetic induction tomography: numerical modelling, *Phys. Meas.* in-press.

[6]   W. Lionheart, N. Polydorides and A. Borsic, The reconstruction problem, Electrical Impedance Tomography – methods, history and applications. ed. D. S. Holder, IOP Publishing, Chapter 1 ISBN 0 7503 0952 0, 2005.

[7]   W. Lionheart, Reconstruction algorithms for permittivity and conductivity imaging,. Proceedings of the 2nd World Congress on Industrial Process Tomography, Hannover, Germany, 4-11, 2001.

[8]   M. Zolgharni, H. Griffiths and D.S. Holder, Imaging haemorrhagic cerebral stroke by frequency-difference magnetic induction tomography: numerical modelling, IFMBE Proceedings 22 2464-7 ISBN 978-3-540-89207-6, 2008.

1st International Conference on Mathematical and Computational Biomedical Engineering - CMBE2009
June 29 - July 1, 2009, Swansea, UK
P.Nithiarasu and R.Löhner (Eds.)

TOPOLOGICAL STRUCTURES IN A PERIPHERAL BYPASS GRAFT.

Alberto M. Gambaruto
CEMAT, Department of Mathematics, Instituto Superior Técnico, Lisbon, Portugal

Adélia Sequeira
CEMAT, Department of Mathematics, Instituto Superior Técnico, Lisbon, Portugal

ABSTRACT

Present the study of topological structures in the case of a peripheral bypass graft using critical point theory and the Taylor series expansion of the velocity. Invariants of the rate-of-deformation tensor and the local solution to a system of ODEs are used to describe the local flow field. Results are discussed as a means of describing the flow field.

Key Words: *flow topology, flow field characterisation, blood flow, wall shear stress, atheroma.*

1 INTRODUCTION

The understanding of fluid flows in medicine is of importance in a number of aspects. It has been stipulated that flow parameters such as wall shear stress, including its spatial and temporal gradients, are associated with disease formation and progression such as aneurysms and atheroma. Other phenomena of physiological importance include mixing for drug delivery in both blood and inspiratory flows, air conditioning and odorant reception in the nasal cavity. The ability to associate the resultant flow field with the conduit geometry is also of great importance in predictive medicine and surgical planning. The study of topological structures in physiological flows is a means to study the flow field to give insight into relevant flow measures and description.

To study the local flow behaviour and topology we will use a critical point approach and study the invariants of the velocity rate-of-deformation tensor [Perry87].

The data set used for this study is of a distal peripheral end-to-side anastomosis located below-knee popliteal obtained from a 34 image stack from MRI (T2 TOF) with 0.254mm pixel resolution. The medical images are segmented using a constant threshold over each slice and reconstructed to yield a 3D surface definition using an implicit function formulation with cubic radial basis function interpolation, which is smoothed prior to use for numerical simulations to remove artefacts and noise brought over from medical imaging [Gambaruto08, Gambaruto09]. Fig. 1 shows steps in the reconstruction process.

2 CRITICAL POINTS, INVARIANTS OF THE RATE-OF-DEFORMATION TENSOR

Let us expand the velocity u_i, $= 1, \ldots, 3$, in terms of the space coordinates x_i using a Taylor series, giving

$$u_i = \dot{x}_i = A_i + A_{ij}x_j + A_{ijk}x_jx_k + \ldots \tag{1}$$

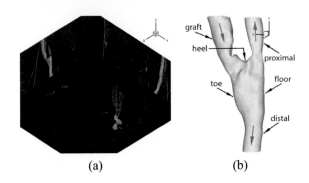

(a)   (b)

Figure 1: (a) Maximum intensity projections of medical image stack obtained from MRI and segmented contours of the lumen wall. (b) Reconstructed geometry with nomenclature and red arrows indicating the flow direction

and let the coordinate system be such that the origin follows a fluid particle by translation and no rotation. In such a reference frame $A_i = 0$, while higher order terms are finite and a local asymptotically exact solution is obtained if up to third order terms are considered. For free-slip flow, truncating the series to keep only the first-order term is permissible, and the system becomes a set of first-order ODEs.

$$\dot{x}_i = A_{ij}x_j = \frac{\partial u_i}{\partial x_j}x_i \tag{2}$$

If the flow is unsteady the solutions correspond to particle paths while if steady to streamlines. The analysis is Galilean invariant and the eigenvalues (λ_i) of the rate-of-deformation tensor (A_{ij}) can be either three real values or one real and a complex-conjugate pair, the sum of which equals zero for incompressible fluids. The corresponding eigenvectors (ζ_i) form planes to which the solution trajectories osculate. In a local coordinate system (y_i), the solution trajectories at the critical point can be written as

hr   r a   ig nva u s,$\lambda_1 \geq \lambda \geq \lambda_3$:
$$y_1 \; t \; = y_1 \; 0 \; e^{\lambda_1 t}$$
$$y \; t \; = y \; 0 \; e^{\lambda_2 t}$$
$$y_3 \; t \; = y_3 \; 0 \; e^{\lambda_3 t}$$

(3)

on r a λ_1 , on com $-$ conjuga   air ig nva u s λ + λ_3 :
$$y_1 \; t \; = y_1 \; 0 \; e^{\lambda_1 t}$$
$$y \; t \; = y \; 0 \; c \; s \; \lambda_3 t \; + y_3 \; 0 \; c \; s \; \lambda_3 t \; e^{\lambda_2 t}$$
$$y_3 \; t \; = y_3 \; 0 \; c \; s \; \lambda_3 t \; y \; 0 \; c \; s \; \lambda_3 t \; e^{\lambda_2 t}$$

It is clear that the solution trajectories can be either of node-saddle-saddle arrangement if the eigenvalues are real and a focus-stretching if a complex-conjugate pair exist, see Fig. 2. Positive λ_i identifies the critical-point along ζ_i as unstable and conversely stable if negative; while the magnitudes describe the relative degree of motion such that in the case of a complex-conjugate pair then $|\lambda_3|$ is a measure of local swirling rate, $|\lambda|$ and $|\lambda_1|$ the stretching or compression in the swirling plane (ζ , ζ_3) and along the spiralling axis (ζ_1) respectively.

The velocity gradient tensor can be further split into symmetric and anti-symmetric parts such that $A_{ij} = \;_{ij} + \Omega_{ij}$, where $\;_{ij} = \frac{\partial u_i}{\partial x_j} + \frac{\partial u_j}{\partial x_i}$ and $\Omega_{ij} = \frac{\partial u_i}{\partial x_j} - \frac{\partial u_j}{\partial x_i}$ and are the rate-of-strain and rate-of-rotation tensors. The eigenvalues of A_{ij} satisfy the characteristic equation [Chong90].

$$\lambda^3 + P\lambda + Q\lambda + R = 0 \tag{4}$$

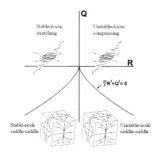

Figure 2: Three-dimensional topologies in the $Q - R$ ($P = 0$) plane, see Eq. 4. Note that the planes given by the eigenvectors ζ_i need not be orthogonal.

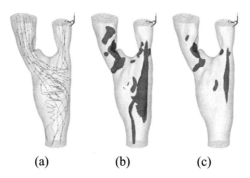

(a)　　　　　(b)　　　　　(c)

Figure 3: (a) Stream traces of massless particles and vortical structures (red) extracted as iso-surfaces of (b) $\lambda_3 = 115$ and (c) $\lambda_3 = 185 \ s^{-1}$ when the eigenvalues have one complex-conjugate pair. Note some regions appear due to local curved path motion.

where the three invariants are given by

$$
\begin{aligned}
P &= -\text{tr}\, A \\
Q &= \tfrac{1}{2}\left(P^2 - \text{tr}\, A^2 \right) = \frac{P^2 - S_{ij}S_{ji} - \Omega_{ij}\Omega_{ji}}{2} \\
R &= -\det A = \frac{-P^3 + 3PQ - S_{ij}S_{jk}S_{ki} - 3\Omega_{ij}\Omega_{jk}S_{ki}}{3}
\end{aligned}
\tag{5}
$$

Furthermore, following [da Silva08] invariants of the rate-of-shear tensor and rate-of-rotation tensor are obtained from the above equations by setting in turn S_{ij} and Ω_{ij} to zero. The full set of invariants can be used to describe the local, instantaneous dynamics of the flow.

3 RESULTS

Here the eigenvalues and eigenvectors of the rate-of-deformation tensor A_{ij} are studied. To identify vortical structures the eigenvalues must have a complex-conjugate pair, see Eq. (3). Furthermore $|\lambda_r / \lambda_3|$ should be small to give a spiralling motion and $|\lambda_3|$ large to capture fast rotating fluid (time period of revolution in the vortex plane is $T = 2\pi/\lambda_3$). An example of vortical structure identifications is shown in Fig. 3.

While the fluid domain can be decomposed into different regions depending on their local dynamics, by tracking a massless fluid particle in the domain and computing λ_i and the corresopnding ζ_i one can identify the local osculating planes of motion and distinguish the type (if node-saddle-saddle or focus-

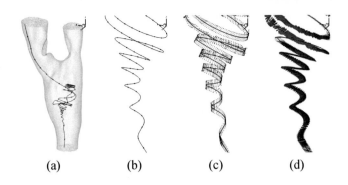

Figure 4: (a) Stream trace and detail (b), showing (c) the ζ_1 direction that represents the axial stretching/compression and (d) the ζ_2, ζ_3 plane that represents the plane of swirling motion. Note that the detail of the stream trace shown lies in a region of the f uid domain with a complex-conjugate pair of eigenvalues from the rate-of-deformation tensor.

stretching), and classify the axes along which the compression or stretching occurs. An example of this is shown in Fig. 4.

4   CONCLUSIONS

Critical point theory applied to the rate-of-deformation tensor is a powerful approach to describe the local behaviour and topology of flow field structures. We shown here the ability of observing the behaviour of vortical structures, describing the planes of swirling ans the axis of stretching/compression, through the use of the eigenvalues and eigenvectors of the rate-of-deformation tensor.

The understanding fluid flows in medicine is an established and diverse field of research. It is the goal to further this research to aid in the characterisation of the conduit geometry and the link between free-slip flow field structures to no-slip flow parameters (such as wall shear stress) that are thought to be linked to disease.

REFERENCES

[Chong90]   Chong M.S., Perry A.E. A general classification of three-dimensional flow fields. Phys. Fluids, A, 2(5):765-777.

[Gamabruto08]   Gambaruto A.M., Peir J., Doorly D.J., Radaelli A.G. Reconstruction of shape and its effect on flow in arterial conduits, J. Numer. Meth. Fluids. 57(5):473-692, 2008.

[Gamabruto09]   Gambaruto A.M., Taylor D.J., Doorly D.J. Modelling nasal air flow using a Fourier descriptor representation of geometry. J.Numer.Meth.Fluids. 29:1259-1283,2009.

[Perry87]   Perry A.E., Chong M.S. A description of eddying motions and flow patterns using critical-point concepts. Ann. Rev. Fluid Mech. 19:125-155. 1987.

[daSilva08]   da Silva C.B., Pereira J.C.F. Invariants of the velocity-gradient, rate-of-strain, and rate-of-rotation tensors across the turbulent/nonturbulent interface injets. Phys. Fluids. 20(5):055101. 2008.

1st International Conference on Mathematical and Computational Biomedical Engineering - CMBE2009

June 29 - July 1, 2009, Swansea, UK

P.Nithiarasu and R.Löhner (Eds.)

Shape Matching

A. Clark[1],

C. J. Cotter,

J. Peiro,

Department of Aeronautics, South Kensington Campus,
Imperial College London, SW7 2AZ, United Kingdom.

ABSTRACT

The study and understanding of human anatomy is important in the identification of disease and the study of its causes and development. It is known that the presence of several medical conditions is correlated with the presence of specific deformations of anatomy that might, through a better understanding of shape, be readily detectable. Here we present a method of characterising curves as descriptive signals through a matching process that generates deformations between curves using a shooting approach combined with particle mesh methods.

Key Words: *shape matching, computational anatomy, computational morphology*

1 Shape classification in a biomedical context

The ability to characterise the form of human anatomical features such as brain surfaces, the cardiovascular system and the nasal cavity has the potential to be used in the development of innovative methods for detecting abnormalities in a given sample shape by comparison with large set of standardised shapes. In the case of the nasal cavity, it is possible that topological traits might be identified and associated with certain flow characteristics. This could aid the identification of traits significant in the cause of respiratory problems and could be used to select the required surgical intervention.

2 How can shape be characterised?

Complex curves and surfaces representative of anatomy can be difficult to characterise. The motivation for the method presented here is that it might be easier to compare similar shapes through the deformations required to match one shape to another, rather than to abstractly characterise single shapes [1]. Two shapes can be compared through a matching process in which the initial shape is embedded in a time varying vector field, $u(t)$, and is deformed over a time period into the target shape. The matching process associates a descriptive signal with the initial shape that describes the evolution between the two shapes, and a scalar value that quantifies the difference between the shapes.

---

[1]contact ac03@imperial.ac.uk

3 Generating deformations

3.1 Paths between curves

A parameterised curve $Q(t, s)$ is embedded in a fluid flow generated by a time varying vector field, $u(t)$, that is

$$\dot{Q}(t, s) = \frac{\partial Q(t, s)}{\partial t} = u(Q(t, s), t). \tag{1}$$

The initial and target shapes are embedded as parameterised curves $Q_A(s)$ and $Q_B(s)$ respectively, and we seek $u(t)$ such that the initial shape evolves over time into the target shape. The boundary conditions are

$$Q_A(s) = Q(t = 0, s), \tag{2}$$
$$Q_B(s) = Q(t = 1, \eta(s)), \tag{3}$$

where $\eta(s)$ is any reparameterisation of the curve. Since there are an infinite number of paths that take $Q_A(s)$ to $Q_B(s)$, we seek the geodesic path that minimises the energy of deformation [2] of the fluid over the matching.

3.2 A constrained optimisation problem

We can use Lagrange multipliers to minimise the energy of deformation of the fluid subject to the constraint that the curve moves with the flow. The Euler-Lagrange equations then give the following for the evolution of the system

$$(1 - \alpha^2 \nabla^2)^n u = \int_0^{2\pi} P \delta(x - Q(t, s)) \mathrm{d}s, \tag{4}$$
$$\dot{Q}(t, s) = u(Q(t, s)), \tag{5}$$
$$\dot{P} = -P \cdot \nabla u(Q(t, s)). \tag{6}$$

The Lagrange multiplier, P, can be interpreted in Lagrangian dynamics as the momentum of the curve. It is this momentum distribution over the parameterised curve $Q_A(s)$ that is the characteristic signal given by the matching process.

3.3 Determining the velocity field, $u(t)$

Since the flow is constrained to follow geodesic paths, and $Q(t = 0, s) = Q_A(s)$ is fixed, we seek the momentum distribution on $Q_A(s)$, $P(t = 0, s)$ that results in the evolution of the initial shape to the target shape.

We define a *matching condition* that gives a scalar value which increases for two shapes that are less well matched. This allows us to quantify the extent to which two shapes are overlayed. By choosing an initial momentum distribution, P_0, and evolving the initial curve $Q_A(s)$ to $Q(t = 1, \eta(s))$, we can compare the resulting shape with the target shape in order to quanitify how well matched the shapes are due to P_0.

We numerically solve the optimisation problem of minimising the *matching condition* over the control variable P_0 using a shooting approach. The gradient of the *matching condition* with respect to P_0 is found using the adjoint method.

4 Results

The results of a matching between a circle and a target 'gingerbread man' shape are presented. The vector field $\boldsymbol{u}(t)$ was solved from $t = 0$ to $t = 1$ in a $2\pi \times 2\pi$ domain. Figures 1(a) and 1(b) show the initial and target shapes respectively. The momentum distribution over the initial shape that results in it evolving into the target shape is shown in Figure 1(c), and the associated descriptive signal is shown in Figure 1(d).

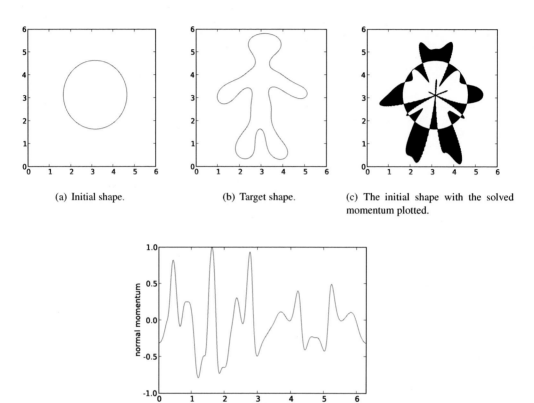

(a) Initial shape.

(b) Target shape.

(c) The initial shape with the solved momentum plotted.

(d) Characteristic momentum P_0 as a function of s.

Figure 1: Results of the circle to gingerbread man matching.

REFERENCES

[1] D'Arcy Thompson, *On Growth and Form*, Cambridge University Press, 1992

[2] Colin J. Cotter, The variational particle-mesh method for matching curves and surfaces, *J Phys A*, Volume 41, Number 34, 29 August 2008.

1st International Conference on Mathematical and Computational Biomedical Engineering – CMBE2009
June 29 – July 1, 2009, Swansea, UK
P. Nithiarasu and R. Löhner (eds)

EVALUATION OF OPTICAL FLOW COMPUTATION TECHNIQUES TO VISUALIZE MYOCARDIAL MOTION

Slamet Riyadi, Mohd Marzuki Mustafa, Aini Hussain
Department of Electrical, Electronic and Systems Engineering,
Faculty of Engineering and Built Environment, Universiti Kebangsaan Malaysia,
Bangi 43600 Selangor Malaysia. Email: riyadi, marzuki, aini@vlsi.eng.ukm.my
Oteh Maskon, Ika Faizura Mohd Nor
Universiti Kebangsaan Malaysia Medical Center, Cheras 56000 Kuala Lumpur, Malaysia,
Email: auajwad@yahoo.com, azuzayz@yahoo.ie

ABSRACT

The use of image processing technique for cardiac motion analysis has been an active research in the past decade. The visualization of myocardial motion eases the cardiologist in diagnosing cardiac abnormalities. In term of movement analysis, optical flow is the most popular technique that has been used by researchers. This paper describes the implementation and evaluation of three optical flow computation techniques to visualize the myocardial motion using ultrasound images. The three techniques are the gradient based method (GBM), the locally constant motion (LCM) and warping technique (WT). Optical flow field is computed based on healthy cardiac video on parasternal short axes view. These techniques look promising since the optical flow fields can be utilized to visualize the myocardial movement and comply with its true movement. The performances of each technique in terms of the direction, homogeneity and computing time, are also discussed.

Key Words: *Myocardial motion visualization, optical flow, ultrasound images, local and global smoothness, warping.*

1. INTRODUCTION

Myocardial infarction, or better known as heart attack, is the leading cause of death all over the world. Early detection of coronary heart disease (CHD) can be performed via anomaly motion detection of the left ventricular (LV) of the heart. LV motion analysis from clinical image sequences has been an active research area over the past decade. Various techniques have been proposed by researcher such as grids of intersection technique based on elastic non-rigid structure [1][7] and Bayesian estimation framework [9][6]. Ledesma et al developed a new spatio-temporal nonrigid registration to estimate the displacement fields from two-dimensional ultrasound sequence of the hearts [5].

In term of movement analysis in computer vision, optical flow is a popular technique to determine the displacement field of two consecutive images. Various improvements and modifications have been done by researcher whether in theory or application approaches of the optical flow. Different methods of optical flow computation have been developed on various human related real problems. In this paper, we implement and evaluate three different optical flow computation techniques to visualize the LV motion. The techniques used are gradient based method (GBM), locally constant motion (LCM) and warping technique (WT). The evaluation is performed on 2D echocardiographic images since the 2D imaging technique is commonly used in clinical practice in Malaysia.

2. MYOCARDIAL VIEW AND ITS MOVEMENT

The Cardiac Imaging Committee of the Council on Clinical Cardiology of the America Heart Association has released a standardized myocardial segmentation and nomenclature for tomography imaging of the heart [5]. In this paper, the evaluation of myocardial movement is focused only on a parasternal short axes (PSAX) view as shown in Fig. 1. The LV appears as a cavity in a centre surrounded by six myocardial segments where as normal cardiac appearance is indicated by a uniform displacement of myocardial segments. They move in radial forward and backward directions with respect to the centre of cavity, which describe the cardiac profile of systole and diastole. During one time period, the cavity size will shrink progressively during systole and it is followed by a brief instance of diastole that recovers the cavity [1]. Thus the velocity of each segment is computed accurately during one complete cycle of myocardial movement.

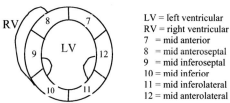

LV = left ventricular
RV = right ventricular
7 = mid anterior
8 = mid anteroseptal
9 = mid inferoseptal
10 = mid inferior
11 = mid inferolateral
12 = mid anterolateral

Fig. 1 PSAX view of echocardiography image and its segments

3. OPTICAL FLOW COMPUTATION TECHNIQUES

Optical flow field is computed by assuming that the intensity of the object remains constant from the initial point of $I(x, y, t)$ towards the latest position of $I(x+\delta x, y+\delta y, t+\delta t)$. The basic constraint of the optical flow equation can be expressed as

$$I_x v_x + I_y v_y + I_t = 0, \quad \text{or} \quad I_x u + I_y v + I_t = 0 \tag{1}$$

The intensity constancy assumption is very sensitive to brightness changes that contrarily often appear in natural cases. Therefore, it is important to introduce other assumptions to solve the estimation problem.

A. Global smoothness method
Horn-Schunck in [3] proposed global smoothness error (E_S) and data error (E_D) defined as

$$E_s = \iint_D \left(u_x^2 + u_y^2\right) + \left(v_x^2 + v_y^2\right) dx\, dy \qquad E_D = \iint_D \left(I_x u + I_y v + I_t\right)^2 dx\, dy \tag{2}$$

To determine the optical flow vector (u, v), they computed an iterative solution to minimize both errors following the equation $E_D + \lambda\, E_S$ where λ represents the determined smoothing factor.

B. Local smoothness method
In [2], Lukas-Kanade developed another approach to solve the constraint equation. By assuming that velocity (u, v) in a small neighborhood is constant, they proposed a weighted least-square in the optical flow computation for each small spatial neighborhood by minimizing equation

$$\sum_{x,y\in A} W^2(x,y)[\nabla I(x,y,t).\vec{v} + I_t(x,y,t)]^2 \tag{3}$$

The solution is given by
$$\vec{v} = [A^T W^2 A]^{-1} A^T W^2 \vec{b} \tag{4}$$
where $\quad A = [\nabla I(x_1, y_1),..., \nabla I(x_N, y_N)]$
$\qquad W = diag[W(x_1, y_1),..., W(x_N, y_N)]$
$\qquad \vec{b} = -(I_t(x_1, y_1),..., I_t(x_N, y_N))$

C. The Warping technique

Brox et al [8] summarized that using the three assumptions, namely intensity constancy, gradient constancy and smoothness assumption, velocity vectors u and v can be determined by minimizing the total energy $E(u,v) = E_{Data} + \alpha E_{Smooth}$, where $\alpha > 0$ is the regularization parameter. The derivation of intensity and gradient constancy assumption can be expressed as

$$E_{Data}(u,v) = \int_{\Omega} \Psi(|\,I(x+w) - I(x)\,|^2 + \gamma\,|\,\nabla I(x+w) - \nabla I(x)\,|^2)dx \tag{5}$$

To overcome the aperture problem, researchers introduce the smoothness assumption. Optical flow computation is not only based on a single pixel displacement but it also considers interactions between neighbouring pixels. This smoothness criterion is computed using total variation of piecewise smooth flow field which can be expressed as

$$E_{Smooth}(u,v) = \int_{\Omega} \Psi(|\,\nabla_3 u\,|^2 + |\,\nabla_3 v\,|^2)dx \tag{6}$$

The minimization computation is performed by numerical approximation combined with the down sampling strategy.

4. RESULT AND DISCUSSION

The above summarized optical flow computation procedures are used for the myocardial motion visualization based on ultrasound images. Fig. 2 shows the myocardial movement sequences where Fig. 2(a) to (d) indicate the diminishing motion of LV. These images were taken from a normal cardiac motion with PSAX view of the LV. The LV appeared in the centre of the image as a small, rounded structure with an echo-free cavity. This cavity size should diminish in a concentric manner during systole, but not to be obliterated [1].

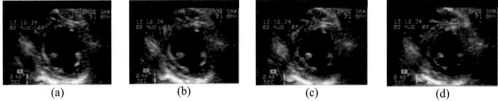

(a)   (b)   (c)   (d)

Fig. 2(a) to (d) Clinical echocardiography images showing the myocardial movement sequences of the LV as it appears in the centre of cavity and diminishes

Fig. 3 shows the initial optical flow field results for the myocardial motion visualization of two consecutive images of Fig 2(c) and (d) using three different optical flow computation methods. The arrows represent the displacement of the pixels and their directions. The different colors of arrows represent the speed of displacements that change gradually from red to blue indicating a large to small displacement representation. Based on the general visual appearance of the computed optical flow field, all methods performed an accurate visualization of myocardial motion. The optical flow movement of myocardial is represented by the red arrows and these arrows diminish as the move towards the centre of the cavity. This is in total agreement with the understanding of cardiac sequence image that during systole, the cavity size should diminish in a concentric manner.

From the results, it can be seen that the computed optical flow of the WT was the smoothest in term of the directional property in which the directions of neighbouring pixels are homogeneous and truly comply with the true movement of myocardial segments. On the other hand, the WT was not able to produce a sharp boundary of the myocardial segment. When applied onto an image of size 384x287, the WT took the longest computing time of more than 7 seconds as compared to both LCM (3.01 seconds) and GBM (0.48 seconds). This is due to the smoothing iteration process involved in the WT. The finest optical flow was obtained via the GBM or global smoothness method as shown in Figure 3(a) and it was achieved at the shortest computational time of 0.48 seconds.

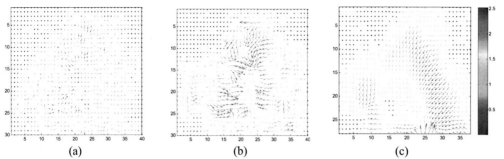

| (a) | (b) | (c) |

Fig. 3 The computed optical flow field of myocardial motion of two consecutive images of Fig. 2(c) and (d) using (a) GBM, (b) LCM and (c) WT, respectively

5. CONCLUSION

The implementation and evaluation of three different optical flow computation techniques to visualize myocardial motion using ultrasound images are described. The findings confirmed that the optical flow field has similar characteristics of the true myocardial movements in which the cavity diminishes during systole in a concentric manner. As such, it can be concluded that optical flow field can be used as a true reflection in estimating and visualizing the myocardial motion since the optical flow fields are in total agreement of the true myocardial motion.

6. ACKOWLEDGMENT

The authors would like to acknowledge Universiti Kebangsaan Malaysia (Project code UKM-GUP-TKP-08-24-080) for the financial support awarded for this research.

REFERENCES

[1]   B. Anderson, "Echocardiography: The Normal Examination of Echocardiographic Measurements", Blackwell Publishing, 2002, "Chapter 2: The 2-dimensional echocardiographic examination".

[2]   B. D. Lucas and T. Kanade, "An interative image registration technique with application in stereo vision", *Proceeding of IJCAI*, 1981.

[3]   B. K. P. Horn,. and B.G. Schuck., "Determining Optical Flow," *Artificial Intelligent, vol 9*, pp 185-203, 1981

[4]   L. Axel, R. Goncalves, and D. Bloomgarden, "Regional heart wall motion: Two-dimensional analysis and functional imaging with MR images", *Radiology* 183, pp. 745-750, 1992.

[5]   M. J. Ledesma-Carbayo, J. Kybic, M. Desco, A. Santos, M. Suhling, P. Hunziker, and M. Unser, "Spatio-temporal nonrigid registration for ultrasound cardiac motion estimation", *IEEE Transcation on Medical Imaging* 24:9, pp. 1113-1126, 2005.

[6]   M. Qazi, G. Fung, S. Krishnan, R. Rosales, H. Steck, R. B. Rao, D. Poldermans, D. Chandrasekaran, "Automated heart wall motion abnormality detection from ultrasound images using Bayesian networks", *Proceeding of IJCAI 07*, pp. 519-525, 2007.

[7]   Petland and B. Horowitz, "Recovery of non-rigid motion and structure", *IEEE Transaction on Pattern Analysis and Machine Intelligent* 13, pp. 730-742, 1991.

[8]   T. Brox, A. Bruhn, N. Papenberg and J. Weickert. "High Accuracy Optical Flow Estimation Based on a Theory for Wrapping," *Proc. 8th European Conference on Computer Vision, Springer LNCS 3024*, vol 4, pp 25-36, 2004

[9]   X. Papademetris, A. J. Sinusas, D. P. Dione, and J. S. Duncan, "3D cardiac deformation from ultrasound images", *Proceeding of MICCAI 99*, pp 420-429, 1999.

1st International Conference on Mathematical and Computational Biomedical Engineering - CMBE2009
June 29 - July 1, 2009, Swansea, UK
P.Nithiarasu and R.Löhner (Eds.)

PHYSICAL IMAGING OF MICROCRACKS IN HUMAN CORTICAL BONE

Elisa Budyn
University of Illinois at Chicago, 842 West Taylor street, Chicago, IL 60607, USA, ebudyn@uic.edu

Julien Jonvaux
University of Illinois at Chicago, 842 West Taylor street, Chicago, IL 60607, USA, jjonva2@uic.edu

Thierry Hoc
Ecole Centrale Paris, Grande voie des vignes, 92295 Chatenay Malabry, France, thierry.hoc@ecp.fr

ABSTRACT

We present an experimental/numerical procedure to model micro-cracks in human Haversian cortical bone. The micro-cracks are tracked during either tension tests or compression tests. The tissue morphology is acquired by digital imaging and the tissue elastic moduli are experimentally measured. The kinematic field providing the boundary conditions is calculated by Digital Image Correlation (DIC). The model is discretised by a Finite Element Method. The topologies of the evolving interfaces of the micro-cracks are tracked by Level Sets and the cracks are incorporated into the model using the eXtended Finite Element Method discretisation (XFEM). Based on the strain energy balance of cracks' quasi-static growth in brittle material, the local fracture toughness of micro-cracks in human Haversian cortical bone is calculated at the scale of the osteons. The model attempts to incorporate the physics of the micro-cracks growth into the imaged bone at the micro scale.

Key Words: *fracture, toughness, contact, bone, XFEM, imaging.*

1 INTRODUCTION

Micro-cracks in bone are usually involved in the remodelling process of the tissue and also the fracture risk assessment [1, 2]. Improved knowledge of fracture occurrence at the micro scale is an essential step to increased diagnostic reliability. During most daily exercise such as walking, bones undergo cyclic fatigue loading that alternates between tension and compression. Therefore the model proposes a method to determine the stress intensity factors of bone micro-cracks during the imaging of their growth at the micro scale. The micro-cracks are studied in tension or compression tests of millimetric specimens of female human cortical bone harvested from fresh cadaveric posterior femur mid-diaphysis.

2 METHODOLOGY

To study bone micro-cracks in tension, millimetric bone beam samples were placed under three point bending under light microscopopy. The beam specimen of cortical bone of square cross-section of 2 mm width measured 5 mm in length. The osteons were loaded under tranverse tension. The specimens were precracked along their osteonal longitudinal axes by 600 μm depth calibrated incisions .

The cortical bone polyphased morphology was surveyed by a digital imaging processing technique [3] in Back Scattered Electron Microscopy (BSEM). To reconstruct the physical stress field at the micro scale, the model includes the following constitutive elements as separate phases: the osteons' transversal profiles, the cement lines around them, secondary osteons whose partial areas are recognisable inside the matrix phase as shown in Figure 1(a). The Haversian canals are represented as free boundaries inside active osteons, where *in vivo* cytoplasmic fluid would flow freely.

The local elastic moduli were measured by nanoindentation and then correlated to the mineralisation levels which can be correlated to the grey scale levels in the BSEM observations. The local Poisson ratios were extrapolated from the osteonal strain fields using an approximation. A small window of observation was studied in the vicinity of the initial crack.

The experimental displacements, which provided the boundary conditions of the model, were measured over a grid by the DIC technique [4] called microextensometry (CorrelmanuV [5]). These fields were first visualised in an homogeneous equivalent continuum where they were imposed at all identified grid nodes as shown in Figure 1(b). Due to the small size of the observation window, the experimental displacement was applied along the edges of the explicit model.

The topology of the micro-cracks were surveyed digitally and tracked by level sets. The evolving interfaces of the cracks were modelled using the XFEM by adding enrichments at the nodes of the cracked elements. The model with explicit microstructure is discretised using the XFEM in non-structured quadratic triangle finite elements [6].

In order to incorporate evolving micro-cracks, the eXtended Finite Element Method (XFEM) appeared suitable. The kinematic field could be measured by Digital Imaging Correlation technique (DIC). Cortical bone was considered brittle due to its high content of hydroxyapatite. The model is under plane stress condition as the surface of the sample is observed. For quasi-static crack growth in brittle materials, the dominant strain energy could be measured given reliable local mechanical properties. The XFEM model can then directly be combined with the Digital Image Correlation to reconstruct a physical field in order to investigate the local stress intensity factors at the micro scale in human Haversian bone. The method can be related to the approach that has been applied to polycrystalline microstructures [7]. This method is able to incorporate fracture [8, 9] in explicit cortical bone microstructure as shown in Figure 1(c). The stress intensity factors were calculated using the interaction integral in Table 1. The L_2 norm of the difference between the experimental and numerical fields appears to be less than 1.3% in all cases, therefore the model adequately replicates the micro tension tests in human Haversian cortical bone and provides valuable information on three scales.

The micro compression tests were conducted on samples of the previously described size under light microscopy. These specimen were not precracked. The cortical bone morphology, mechanical properties and boundary conditions were acquired as previously mentioned. However in this model the cracks surfaces were modelled using standard FEM discretisation as this model focused on the design of the contact algorithm for multiple micro-cracks as shown in Figure 2(c). As the window of observation was larger, the experimental displacement field was imposed at all DIC imaging points inside the polyphase medium. The imaging points were incorporated into the mesh using an optimised adaptivity algorithm. The contact solution was solved by Newton-Raphson iterations [10] until convergence to the experimental displacement field was achieved. The frictional contact conditions along the crack edges were imposed at the element mid-point [11] and enforced by nodal penalties [12]. The stress intensity factors at the micro fracture tips under compression were calculated by mean of the Interaction integral over the stress field from which the pure compression field had been subtracted. The results are shown in Table 1.

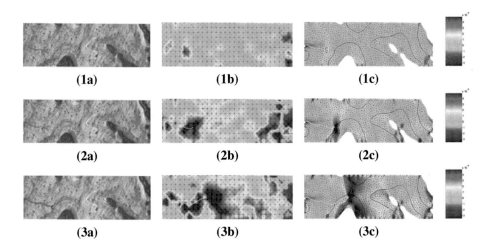

Figure 1: 1,2,3 (a) Micro-cracks Light Microscopy window in human cortical bone of 300 by 1100 μm under tension, 1,2,3(b) experimental kinematic strain field ϵ_{22} using DIC, 1,2,3 (c) Physical strain field ϵ_{22} around micro-cracks in an XFEM model with explicit microstructure and where the experimental displacements are only prescribed along the edges. The color scale is $\lfloor-0.0035; 0.0049\rfloor$ in pictures (b) and (c).

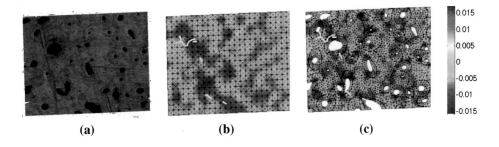

Figure 2: (a) Micro-cracks Light Microscopy window in human cortical bone of 1400 by 1900 μm under compression, (b) experimental kinematic strain field ϵ_{11} using DIC, (c) Physical strain field ϵ_{11} around micro-cracks in an FEM model with explicit microstructure and where the experimental displacements are prescribed at all DIC grid points. The color scale is $[-0.0158; 0.0170]$ in pictures (b) and (c).

Table 1: Stress intensity factors in sample $w06005$ versus the micro cracks' lengths

tension	step 1	step 2	step 3		
$K_{eq}\ (MPa\sqrt{m})$	0.34	0.67	1.45		
$a_i\ (mm)$	0.47	0.59	1.04		
compression	crack 1	crack 2	crack 3	crack 4	crack 5
$K_{eq}\ (MPa\sqrt{m})$	0.29	2.49	1.30	1.17	4.21
$a_i\ (mm)$	0.17	0.18	0.06	0.10	0.06

3   CONCLUSIONS

The model provides the fracture strength and the global response at the material scale (mm), the stress-strain fields at the microarchitectural level (10-100 μm) and the crack profiles at the micron scale (1-10 μm) and fracture parameters such as the stress intensity factors. The model emphasises the influence of the microstructure on bone failure. The model incorporates the explicit bone microstructure with its specific microarchitecture and heterogeneous mechanical behaviour of the tissue. The model confirms the local toughening mechanism [13] that is usually observed in bone and indicates some possible explanations. The model also indicates how the fracture properties could be modified in regard to possible alterations of the microstructure integrity which are not detectable by conventional clinical tools, and proposes a new procedure to diagnose pathologies.

REFERENCES

[1]   R.K. Nalla, J.H. Kinney and R.O. Ritchie, Mechanistic fracture criteria for the failure of human cortical bone,*Nature Materials, 2, 164-168,2003.*

[2]   P. Fratzl, When the cracks begin to show, *Nature Materials, 7, 610-612, 2008.*

[3]   R. Smith, *Plot Digitixer User's Manual, Plot Digitizer,* Version 2.4.1, $http$: $//plotdigitizer.source forge.net$ USA, 2007.

[4]   P. Doumalin, M. Bornert and J Crépin, Characterization of the strain distribution in heterogeneous materials, *Méc Ind, 4, 607-617, 2003.*

[5]   T. Bretheau and J. Crepin and P. Doumalin and M. Bornert M, Microextensometry: a tool for the mechanics of materials, *Revue de Métallurgie - Cahiers dInformations Techniques, 100(5), 567-, 2003.*

[6]   C. Geuzaine and J.F. Remacle, *GMSH User's Manual, GMSH,* Version 62, *Geuzaine* & *Remacle, Cleveland USA* & *Louvain Belgium, 2006.*

[7]   E. Héripré, M. Dexet, J. Crépin, L. Gélébart, A. Roos, M. Bornert and D. Caldemaison, Coupling between experimental measurements and polycrystal finite element calculations for micromechanical study of metallic materials, *Journal of Plasticity, 23, 1512-1539, 2007.*

[8]   E. Budyn and T. Hoc, Multiple scale modeling of cortical bone fracture in tension using X-FEM, *Revue Européenne de Mécanique Numérique (European Journal of Computational Mechanics), 16, 213-236, 2007.*

[9]   E. Budyn and T. Hoc, Fracture strength assessment and aging signs detection in human cortical bone using an X-FEM multiple scale approach, *Computational Mechanics, 42(4), 579-591, 2008.*

[10]   A.R. Mijar and J.S. Arora, An augmented Lagrangian optimization method for contact analysis problems, 1: formulation and algorithm, *Structural and Multidisciplinary Optimization, 28, 99-112, 2004.*

[11]   A. Dorogoy and L. Banks-Still, Shear loaded interface crack under the influence of friction: a finite difference solution, *International Journal of Numerical methods in Engineering, 59, 1749-1780, 2004.*

[12]   T. Belytschko, W.K. Liu and B. Moran, *Nonlinear Finite Elements for Continua and Structures, John Wiley and Sons, 2002.*

[13]   K.J. Koester, J.W. Ager and R.O. Ritchie, The true toughness of human cortical bone measured with realistically short cracks, *Nature Materials, 7, 676-677, 2008.*

1st International Conference on Mathematical and Computational Biomedical Engineering - CMBE2009
June 29 - July 1, 2009, Swansea, UK
P.Nithiarasu and R.Löhner (Eds.)

Monolithic Fluid-Solid Coupling and Applications in the Left Ventricle

David Nordsletten
Oxford University, Computing Laboratory, Wolfson Building, Parks Road, Oxford, OX1 3QD, UK,
david.nordsletten@dpag.ox.ac.uk

Matt McCormick
Oxford University, Computing Laboratory, Wolfson Building, Parks Road, Oxford, OX1 3QD, UK,
david.nordsletten@dpag.ox.ac.uk

Philip Kilner
Imperial College, Royal Brompton Hospital, Sydney Street, London, SW3 6NP, UK,
p.kilner@imperial.ac.uk

Peter Hunter
Bioengineering Institute, 70 Symonds Street, Auckland, NZ, p.hunter@auckland.ac.nz

David Kay
Oxford University, Computing Laboratory, Wolfson Building, Parks Road, Oxford, OX1 3QD, UK,
david.kay@comlab.ox.ac.uk

Nicolas Smith
Oxford University, Computing Laboratory, Wolfson Building, Parks Road, Oxford, OX1 3QD, UK,
nic.smith@comlab.ox.ac.uk

ABSTRACT

Understanding the underlying feedback mechanisms and mechanics of heart function is crucial for characterizing and treating heart disease – the leading cause of death in the United Kingdom [9]. To improve this understanding, an anatomically accurate model of fluid-solid mechanics in the left ventricle is presented. Using the wealth of knowledge gathered on hemodynamical and tissue mechanical factors, a numerical approach is used which allows non-conformity in an optimal monolithic scheme [14-15].

Key Words: *blood flow, cardiac tissue mechanics, fluid-solid coupling, monolithic methods.*

1 INTRODUCTION

Understanding the underlying feedback mechanisms and mechanics of heart function is crucial for characterizing and treating heart disease – the leading cause of death in the United Kingdom [9]. To improve this understanding, a number fluid mechanical models have been published in the literature. One of the leading works on mechanical modelling of the heart is that of Peskin and McQueen [7], who included both left and right ventricular chambers into their models by immersed boundary methods. Modelling the heart wall as a set of one dimensional fibers embedded in fluid, the Peskin and McQueen model incorporates many anatomically challenging features of mechanical modelling in the heart (such as the heart valves). Incorporating a more physiologically based material law for the solid, Watanabe [17] looked a blood flow and tissue mechanics in a monolithic finite element framework. Using a coarse grid of low order elements, the Watanabe model includes both mechanical and electromechanical aspects of heart function.

Building on the progress in these models, incorporating both appropriate constitutive relations and reasonable numerical grid resolutions for the underlying physics is fundamental to providing a clinically relevant modelling framework. A detailed picture of cardiac tissue architecture has been composed [4,6], showing the tissue to constitutive behavior to be orthotropic. This data has been successfully integrated into a number of constitutive models shown to provide proper material response in isolated tissue samples [2]. However, wide use of these models is limited by the complexity involved in their numerical implementation. Further, many coupled models lack sufficient resolution to accurately model underlying physics. This limitation stems largely from difficulties involved in coupling non-conforming domains as well as needs to maintain computational tractability.

In Nordsletten *et al* [14], a linear system fluid-solid system was considered, which was coupled using a third Lagrange multiplier on the fluid-solid interface. Through the proper construction of inf-sup stable spaces [1], the linear fluid-solid system was proven to admit unique solutions and optimal error estimates. These results were extended to the fully non-linear system in Nordsletten *et al.* [15], illustrating similar optimal convergence rates by numerical experiments. This method, while maintaining optimal convergence and coupling properties, accommodates arbitrary degrees of non-conformity between finite element domains – allowing refinement to be dependent on the physics of each domain.

In this paper, a model of an anatomically accurate left ventricle is presented. This model incorporates experimental measures of myocardial architecture and constitutive behavior, providing a material validity. Further, using a monolithic non-conforming finite element scheme [14-16], the numerical approximation of blood flow and tissue deformation is estimated based on their underlying physics.

2   METHODS AND MODEL DEVELOPMENT

Myocardial tissue mechanics and blood hemodynamics were modelled using the quasi-static finite elasticity (1) and Arbitrary Lagrangian Eulerian (ALE) Navier-Stokes (2) equations on the tissue and blood domains Ω_s and Ω_f [3,4,8,11-16]. Here, $\mathbf{u}$ denotes tissue displacement, $\mathbf{F}$ the Lagrangian deformation gradient tensor, σ the Cauchy stress, $\mathbf{v}$ the blood velocity, p blood pressure, $\mathbf{w}$ ALE domain velocity, $\mathcal{J}$ the ALE mapping jacobian, ρ blood density, and μ the blood viscosity.

$$\nabla_{\mathbf{x}} \cdot \sigma = \mathbf{0}, \quad \text{and} \quad \text{d} \quad |\mathbf{F}| = 1, \qquad \text{on } \Omega_s, \qquad (1)$$

$$\rho \partial_t \mathbf{v} \mathcal{J} + \mathcal{J} \nabla_{\mathbf{x}} \cdot \rho \ \mathbf{v} - \mathbf{w} \ \mathbf{v} + p \mathbf{I} - \mu \nabla_{\mathbf{x}} \mathbf{v} = \mathbf{0}, \quad \text{and} \quad \nabla_{\mathbf{x}} \cdot \mathbf{v} = 0, \qquad \text{on } \Omega_f. \qquad (2)$$

The blood and tissue were coupled at the endocardial wall using the monolithic finite element approach described in Nordsletten *et al.* [14-16]. A anatomically accurate model of the left ventricle was created, by fitting C^1-continuous endocardial and epicardial surfaces to MRI data. Surface tessellations were embedded in the endocardial surface, using the parametric triangulation algorithm of [12], for creation of coupling and fluid domains.

To provide a representative model of the complex electromechanical processes which drive ejection [10], a simple model of myocardial contraction was adopted, similar to that of Watanabe [17]. An orthonormal fiber coordinate system was incorporated, modelling the variation in fiber and sheet directions – based on experimental measures of cardiac tissue structure (see [4,6]) – seen throughout the my-

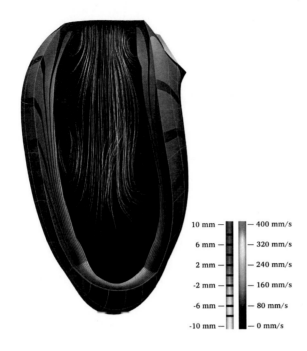

10 mm —	— 400 mm/s
6 mm —	— 320 mm/s
2 mm —	— 240 mm/s
-2 mm —	— 160 mm/s
-6 mm —	— 80 mm/s
-10 mm —	— 0 mm/s

Figure 1: *Normal left ventricle at atrial systole 450 ms , where the posteriolateral wall has been removed to show intraventricular flow. In the fluid domain, blood flow is illustrated using streamlines passing through the instantaneous vector solution (colored according to velocity magnitude). The endocardial wall is shaded black to highlight these flow features. The transmural and epicardial walls of the myocardium are shown (colored according to the dot product between displacement of fiber directions).*

ocardium. Using the myocardial constitutive law developed by Costa [2], *i.e.*

$$\sigma_F = -\varphi \mathbf{I} + \mathbf{F}_F \left(\frac{\partial W}{\partial \mathbf{F}_F} \right) ,$$

$$W\, \mathbf{E}_F = \frac{C}{2}\, e^{Q(\mathbf{E}_F)} - 1 ,$$

$$Q\, \mathbf{E}_F = \sum_{i,k \in [1,3]} \alpha_{ik}\, \mathbf{E}_{F\,ik}^{\,2}$$

passive characteristics of the myocardial constitutive behavior are included in the model. Here, φ is the tissue pressure, $\mathbf{E}$ the Green strain, α and C are of positive constants, and the subscript F denotes components expressed in the fiber coordinate system. These constitutive properties, within the monolithic fluid-solid coupling framework, maintain inherent stability, exhibiting *a priori* energy estimates for displacement and velocity [16].

3   RESULTS AND CONCLUSIONS

The numerical model of the left ventricle provides a wealth of information on simulated hemodynamics and tissue mechanics, providing a platform for quantitative analysis. Figure 1 illustrates simulated mechanical displacement within the myocardial fiber field along with intraventricular flow seen at atrial systole. With this computational tool, detailed analysis of cardiac energetics was conducted, displaying interesting synergistic effects between tissue and blood. Through this analysis, blood flow through the left ventricle is seen to provide a balance between function and mechanical energy, reducing the power required for a heart beat. However, the mechanics of the system are sensitive features of both tissue and flow which, as in pathological hearts, may have detrimental impacts of cardiac energetics and function.

Along with clinical data [5], this mathematical model of cardiac mechanics – based on sound mathematical techniques – provides valuable tool for assessing patient-specific heart function. Providing a wider breadth of information for assessment of function, such model insights may elucidate further relations between pathology and mechanics, identifying new risk factors and measures for disease diagnosis. Further, building a patient-database of simulated mechanics provides a means for filtering clinical data using mechanically relevant metrics, allowing statistical correlations between hemodynamical / tissue mechanical kinematics or energy and heart disease – improving treatment and care.

REFERENCES

[1]   I. Babuska, The Finite Element Method with Lagrange Multipliers, *Numer. Math.*, 20, 179 – 192, 1973.

[2]   K. Costa and J. Holmes and A. McCulloch, Modelling cardiac mechanical properties in three dimensions, *Phil. Trans. R. Soc. Lond. A.*, 359, 1233 – 1250, 2001.

[3]   L. Formaggia and F. Nobile, Stability analysis of second-order time accurate schemes for ALE-FEM, *Comput. Meth. Appl. Mech. Engrg.*, 193, 4097 – 4116, 2004.

[4]   P. Hunter and A. Pullan and B. Smaill, Modelling Total Heart Function, *Annual Review of Biomedical Engineering*, 5, 147 – 177, 2003.

[5]   P. Kilner and G. Yang and A. Wilkes and R. Mohiaddin and D. Firmin and M. Yacoub, Asymmetric redirection of flow through the heart, *Nature*, 404, 759 – 761, 2000.

[6]   I. LeGrice and P. Hunter and A. Young and B. Smaill, The Architecture of the Heart: A Data-Based Model, *Phil. Trans. R. Soc. Lond.*, 359, 1217 – 1232, 2001.

[7]   D. McQueen and C. Peskin, A three-dimensional computer model of the human heart for studying cardiac fluid dynamics, *Comp. Graph.*, 34, 56 – 60, 2000.

[8]   M. Nash and P. Hunter, Computational Mechanics of the Heart, *J. Elas.*, 61, 113 – 141, 2000.

[9]   National Statistics, Mortality statistics, cause, *Statistics Report, UK*, 1 – 200, 2005.

[10] D. Nickerson and N. Smith and P. Hunter, New developments in a strongly coupled cardiac electromechanical model, *Eurospace*, 7, 118 – 127, 2005.

[11] D. Nordsletten and P. Hunter and N. Smith, Conservative and non-conservative arbitrary Lagrangian-Eulerian forms for ventricular flows, *Int. J. Num. Meths. Fluids*, 56, 1457–1463, 2008.

[12] D. Nordsletten and N. Smith, Triangulation of p-order parametric surfaces, *J. Sci. Comp*, 34, 308–335, 2008.

[13] D. Nordsletten and N. Smith and D. Kay, A preconditioner for the finite element approximation to the ALE Navier-Stokes equations, *SIAM J Sci. Comp, in review*.

[14] D. Nordsletten and N. Smith and D. Kay, A Non-conforming monolithic finite element method for problems of coupled mechanics: Linear Analysis, *SIAM J. Num. Anal, in review*.

[15] D. Nordsletten and D. Kay and N. Smith, A Non-conforming monolithic finite element method for problems of coupled mechanics, *J. Comp. Phys, in review*.

[16] D. Nordsletten and N. Smith and D. Kay and P. Hunter, Fluid-Solid coupling for the Simulation of Left Ventricular Mechanics, Doctoral Thesis, *University of Oxford*.

[17] H Watanabe *et al.*, Multiphysics simulation of left ventricular filling dynamics using fluid-structure interaction finite element method, *Biophys. J.*, 87, 2074 – 2085, 2004.

1st International Conference on Mathematical and Computational Biomedical Engineering – CMBE2009
June 29 – July 1, 2009, Swansea, UK
P. Nithiarasu and R. Löhner (eds)

A NUMERICAL ACOUSTIC FLUID-STRUCTURE *IN VIVO* MODEL OF ULTRASONIC ANGIOPLASTY IN A PERIPHERAL ARTERY

Mark P. Wylie
Dublin Institute of Technology, Bolton Street, Dublin 1, mark.wylie@dit.ie
Garrett B. McGuinness
Dublin City University, Glasnevin, Dublin 9, garrett.mcguinness@dcu.ie
Graham P. Gavin
Dublin Institute of Technology, Bolton Street, Dublin 1, graham.gavin@dit.ie

ABSTRACT

The delivery of low frequency ultrasonic energy via small diameter wire waveguides represents a potential alternative therapy for the treatment of totally occluded arteries (CTOs). This type of energy manifests itself as a mechanical vibration at the distal-tip of the waveguide with amplitudes of up to 100 microns at frequencies between 20 – 45 kHz commonly reported. This type of minimally invasive surgery has recently gained regulatory approval in both the United States and Europe for the treatment of CTOs that have failed to be crossed by traditional guidewire techniques, thus facilitating standard dilation procedures and stent implantation. Disruption and ablation of diseased tissue is reported to be a result of direct mechanical ablation, cavitation, pressure wave components and acoustic streaming with some authors reporting that ablation was only evident above the cavitation threshold. This work presents a linear acoustic fluid structure finite element model of an ultrasonic angioplasty waveguide operating at 22.5 kHz. The results of a mesh density analysis show that in the region of the ball-tip the number of elements required depends on the frequency, fluid properties and amplitude of vibration. The predicted pressure amplitudes compare favorably with analytical solutions and may be useful in the prediction of the onset of cavitation, a critical effect of ultrasonic delivery. Using this method a range of waveguide frequencies, distal-tip displacements and more complex geometries could be modeled. The *in vivo* model of ultrasonic angioplasty in a peripheral artery is based on experimental work reported in the literature where the acoustic pressures in the fluid field surrounding a waveguide were measured. The model includes a tissue-air interface and predicts a standing wave in the acoustic field with a series of pressure minima and maxima similar to those experimentally determined. In conclusion the finite element model reported here will prove a useful tool in the further understanding of this emerging minimally invasive technology.

Key Words: *Ultrasound, angioplasty, acoustic, cavitation.*

1. INTRODUCTION

The majority of the atherosclerotic lesions can be treated by percuntaneous interventional dilation procedures such as coronary angioplasty and stent implantation. These procedures require that the blockage must first be accessed by a guidewire, a small diameter wire that both ensures the plaque can be crossed (a key indicator of success) and also acts as a guiderail for the balloon and stent delivery systems. Lesions resulting in a near or totally blocked artery, known as chronic total occlusions (CTO's), pose a significant challenge to dilation procedures and may represent up to 16% of all coronary plaques [1]. CTOs are often accompanied by significant calcification which can hinder successful dilation procedures and optimal stent implantation. In many cases involving CTOs invasive bypass surgery is often the only available option and in recent years this has provided an impetus to develop alternative minimally invasive techniques for challenging total occlusions.

A potential minimally invasive approach to near, totally blocked or calcified plaques involves the use of low frequency ultrasonic longitudinal waves transmitted through a wire waveguide. While the concept of using ultrasonic energy transmitted via waveguides to ablate arterial plaques has been around since the 1950s, only as recently as 2007 has this technology been approved for use in both the United States and Europe [2]. This ultrasound energy establishes a longitudinal standing wave in a wire waveguide with the frequency and amplitude being determined by the output power of the external transducer and acoustic horn. Using this configuration, frequencies in the region of 20-45 kHz and amplitudes at the waveguide distal tip of up to 50 microns are commonly reported.

At the distal tip of the waveguide tissue is thought to be disrupted by a number of mechanisms; primarily direct mechanical ablation and cavitation, and to a lesser extent acoustic streaming and pressure wave components [3]. It has been reported that this method of tissue disruption has the advantage of selective tissue removal. At the right combination of frequency and amplitude it can disrupt rigid diseased tissue while healthy elastic tissue remains largely unaffected [4]. Acoustic pressures developed at the waveguide-fluid/tissue interface appear to play a significant role with some authors observing that plaque ablation was only evident above the cavitation threshold. Indeed, as a result, frequencies are typically kept below 50 kHz as that the intensity and power required to produce cavitations rises rapidly above frequencies of 100 kHz. To further enhance cavitation an enlarged ball-tip is often located at the distal end of the waveguide. The significance of the acoustic pressure waves near the waveguide tip, the subsequent cavitation and pressures developed in surrounding fluids and tissues has led a number of researchers to investigate this phenomenon.

While the majority of this work has focused on end clinical results other researchers have performed experimental studies on the mechanical effects of ultrasonic vibrating waveguides in simulated *in vivo* conditions. Experimental studies by Makin and Everbach [5] investigated the acoustic pressures developed by an ultrasonically vibrating wire-waveguide submerged in a fluid with acoustic properties similar to blood. The experiment consisted of a 2.46mm diameter ball tipped wire oscillating in a cylinder of fluid at 22.5 kHz. Pressures were measured in the range of 12mm -250 mm from the vibrating tip; measurements at the tip were limited due to restrictions of their measuring equipment. Pressures in the acoustic field recorded clearly exhibit a standing wave structure set up by an impedance mismatch of the tissue-air interface.

This goal of this work is to develop a linear acoustic fluid-structure model of an ultrasonic wire waveguide in simulated *in vivo* conditions; in a peripheral artery such as the femoral. This model will be validated against analytical relationships and experimental results reported in the literature.

2. METHODOLOGY AND RESULTS

Finite element models were developed in ANSYS© using Acoustic Fluid29 elements in the general acoustic field and Fluid129 elements defining the infinite acoustic boundary layer condition. A fluid-structure interface defined where the ball and fluid meet. The interaction of the fluid nodes and structural nodes at the fluid-structure interface is such that the pressure in the acoustic field exerts an applied force on the structural elements that produce an effective fluid load. The governing equations for both the fluid nodes and structural nodes are:

Structural: $$[M_S](\ddot{\vec{u}}) + [K_S](\vec{u}) = (\vec{F}_S) + [R](\vec{P}) \qquad \text{(Eqn 1)}$$

Fluid: $$[M_F](\ddot{\vec{P}}) + [K_F](\vec{P}) = (\vec{F}_F) - \rho_0[R]^T(\ddot{\vec{u}}) \qquad \text{(Eqn 2)}$$

where $(\ddot{\vec{P}})$ and $(\vec{P})$ = the 2nd derivative of nodal pressure and nodal pressure respectively.

[R] = a coupling matrix that represents effective area associated with each node.

The equations given in Equation 1 and 2 can be combined into a single equation that describes load quantities at all locations in the fluid and structure as shown in Equation 3.

Combined: $$\begin{bmatrix} M_S & 0 \\ \rho_0 R^T & M_F \end{bmatrix} \begin{pmatrix} \ddot{\vec{u}} \\ \ddot{\vec{P}} \end{pmatrix} + \begin{bmatrix} K_S & -R \\ 0 & K_F \end{bmatrix} \begin{pmatrix} \vec{u} \\ \vec{P} \end{pmatrix} = \begin{pmatrix} \vec{F}_S \\ \vec{F}_F \end{pmatrix} \qquad \text{(Eqn 3)}$$

a. MESH DENSITY STUDIES

In order to understand the effect of the mesh density a finite element axisymmetric linear acoustic model of an ultrasonic vibrating ball in a single fluid type was developed. An infinite acoustic boundary using fluid elements (FLUID129) was set up along the model boundary according to defined conditions in ANSYS© i.e. this absorbing boundary must lie on an arc of radius greater than 0.2λ. Where $\lambda = c/f$ is the dominant wavelength. The following properties of the fluid elements representing blood was given as c = 1050 m/s and ρ = 1580 kg/m^3. The number of elements per wavelength (EPW) was increased until the model correlated with the generally accepted analytical solutions, see Figure 1.

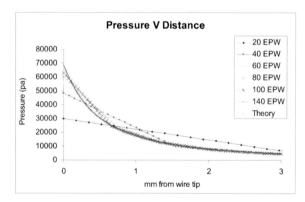

Figure 1: Pressure versus distance from ball-tip (13 micron p-p). Mesh density (elements per wavelength) results for a 22.5 kHz oscillating ball in a fluid representative of blood compared with analytical solution.

b. MODEL OF ULTRASONIC WAVEGUIDE IN SIMULATED *IN VIVO* CONDITIONS

A model representative of Makin and Everbach's [5] experimental study was created to assess the effects of an air interface on the acoustic pressures during ultrasonic angioplasty. This model and study were similar to the *in vivo* situation of the device being activated in a peripheral blood vessel. The model incorporated fluid (blood) and air properties, realistic geometries and frequencies. The results are shown in Figure 2.

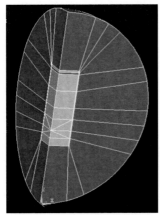
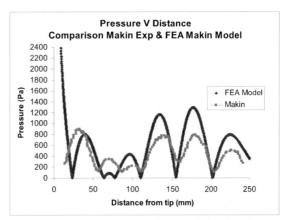

Figure 2: Experimental versus numerical pressure versus distance from ball-tip (13 micron p-p). Mesh density (elements per wavelength) results for a 22.5 kHz oscillating ball in a fluid representative of blood compared with analytical solution.

3.   CONCLUSIONS

The results of the mesh density analysis determined that at the frequency of operation and amplitude levels, commonly used in surgery, a minimum number of 140 elements/ wavelength were required to accurately capture the pressure amplitudes in the vicinity of the waveguide tip. These simulated pressure amplitudes can be used to predict the onset of cavitation, with a suitable cavitation threshold, and assess various geometric configurations, frequencies and amplitudes of vibration.

The results of the *in vivo* model of ultrasonic angioplasty in a peripheral artery shows good comparison with the experimental results in the literature and predicts a standing wave in the peripheral limb. This may have some effect on tissues away from the device and will have to be further investigated to gain a greater understanding of this emerging procedure.

REFERENCES

[1]   William NG, Wai-Hong Chen, Pui-Yin Lee and Chu-Pak Lau. Initial experience and safety in the treatment of chronic total coronary occlusions with a new optical coherent reflectometry-guided radiofrequency ablation guidewire, *The American Journal of Cardiology*, Volume 92 (6), pp 732-734, 2003.

[2]   Flowcardia Press Releases, www.flowcardia.com, accessed March 2009

[3]   Atar S, Luo H, Nagai T, Siegel RJ. Ultrasonic Thrombolysis: catheter-delivered and trans-cutaneous applications. *European Journal of Ultrasound*, 9: 39-54, 1999.

[4]   Yock PG and Fitzgerald PJ. Catheter-based ultrasound thrombolysis: Shake, rattle and reperfuse. *Circulation*, 95: 1360- 62, 1997.

[5]   Makin RS and Everbach EC. *J. Acoust. Soc. Am.*, 100(3): 1855-64, 1996.

ACCURATE PREDICTION OF BLOOD FLOW TRANSIENTS: A FLUID-STRUCTURE INTERACTION APPROACH

V. Kanyanta, A. Ivankovic, A. Karac
University College Dublin, School of Electrical, Electronics and Mechanical Engineering,
valentine.kanyanta@ucd.ie, alojz.ivankovic@ucd.ie, aleksandar.karac@ucd.ie

ABSTRACT

Numerical studies are widely employed in establishing blood flow transients in arteries. Unfortunately, many of these are based on rigid arterial geometries where the physiological interaction between the flowing blood and the dynamics of a deforming arterial wall is ignored. Although many recent studies have adopted a fluid-structure interaction (FSI) approach, they lack the necessary validation and, thus, cannot guarantee the accuracy of their predictions. This work employs a well-validated FSI model to establish the dependency of WSS transients on arterial flexibility and predict flow transients in arterial geometries. Results show a high dependency of WSS transients on arterial wall flexibility, with hoop strains of as low as 0.15% showing significant differences in these transients compared to that seen in a rigid geometry. It is also shown that flow in the atherosclerosis susceptible regions of the vascular tree is characterised by a highly disturbed flow. In these regions, WSS magnitudes are at their lowest, while the WSS spatial gradients, rate of change and oscillatory shear index are at their highest.

Key Words: *blood flow transients, wall shear stress, fluid-structure interaction.*

1 INTRODUCTION

Blood flow through a compliant artery requires appropriate fluid-structure coupling in order to account for the interaction between the flowing blood and the deforming arterial wall. Many numerical models used to predict blood flow are based on rigid arterial geometries [1, 3], where this interaction is not taken into account. Although much attention is given to the complex flow patterns in arteries, the deformation of the arterial wall during each contraction and expansion of the heart is ignored. Some recent studies now use FSI approach to predict blood flow behaviour in arteries [7]. However, many of these models still lack necessary validation and, thus, can not guarantee the accuracy of their predictions.

The current work employs a well-validated FSI model [8] to establish the effect of arterial wall flexibility on WSS transients, thus, the inadequacy of rigid arterial geometries to accurately predict blood flow transients. The model is also used to predict flow transients in a patient-specific carotid artery and, in a related study, to show the effect of local stiffening of the arterial wall due to an emerging atherosclerotic plaque on artery deformation profiles [2]. OpenFOAM, a finite volume method based C++ library [9], was used in this study.

2 NUMERICAL STUDIES

Numerical studies were employed to establish the effect of arterial flexibility on WSS transients and predict of flow transients in the carotid artery bifurcation.

2.1 WSS Transients in Straight Pipes of Varying Stiffness

A parametric study was conducted on flexible pipes of varying stiffness and a rigid pipe in order to establish the effect of pipe wall flexibility and FSI on WSS transients. Different pipe deformations were achieved by varying the pipe stiffness E, while the applied axial velocity was kept fixed at 0.76 m/s. This velocity was suddenly applied at the pipe inlet in order to initiate wave propagation along the pipe length. The resulting change in pressure Δp due to the applied velocity, V_x, is given by $\Delta p = \rho_f C_f V_x$, where ρ_f is the fluid density and C_f is the pressure wave speed [10].

For flexible pipes, E was varied from 4.6 MPa to 120 GPa, resulting in hoop strains of 2.2% to 0.0066%. With V_x kept fixed, it was possible to establish the effect of pipe stiffness on WSS transients. The geometry of the pipe was kept fixed at d = 10 mm and b = 0.5 mm. The fluid domain was modelled as a compressible Newtonian fluid with dynamic viscosity $\eta = 0.004$ Ns/m^2 (representative of the viscosity of blood), density $\rho_f = 998$ kg/m^3 and Bulk modulus K = 2.2 GPa (which are properties of water at 20°C). Since pipe deformations are relatively small (maximum hoop strain = 2.2%), the solid domain was modelled as a linear elastic solid with density $\rho_s = 1000$ kg/m^3 and Poisson ratio $\nu = 0.4995$. More details on problem set-up can be found in [8].

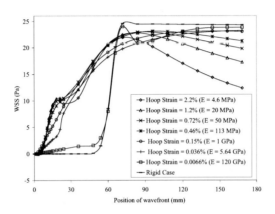

Figure 1: Variations in WSS transients due to changes in pipe stiffness, E.

Fig. 1 presents WSS transients plotted at 60 mm from the pipe inlet as a function of the position of the propagating pressure wavefront (given by $C_f * time$). The results clearly show a high dependency of WSS transients on pipe deformations. For a rigid case, there is almost sudden increase in WSS as the wavefront approach the 60 mm position from the inlet, and stays constant thereafter. This is not the case for flexible pipes were these changes are much more gradual. Hoop strains of as low as 0.15% show signicant differences in WSS transients compared to that seen in a rigid pipe. Therefore, the flexibility of the arterial wall is an important determinant of WSS transient behaviour.

2.2 Flow transients in a Patient-Specific Carotid Artery

Following the parametric study, the numerical model was employed to predict flow transients in a patient-specific carotid artery. The artery geometry and flow conditions used were based on literature values [6]. The computational mesh was generated in Gambit, using structured multi-block hexahedrals, and then imported into OpenFOAM. Cell density in the vicinity of the bifurcation region is gradually increased in order to achieve a better resolution in this region [8].

A velocity waveform was applied at the carotid inlet while pressure waveforms were specified at its outlets. The flow ratio between the external to internal carotid artery was kept fixed at 40:60 [5], using a method proposed by [6]. Fluid and solid properties remained the same as in the parametric study except for the Young's modulus which was now kept fixed at 4.7 MPa, corresponding to the stiffness of mock arteries used in related work [8].

Flow in the artery, especially in the outer edges of the bifurcation, is seen to be characterised by highly disturbed flow (Figures 2(a) and 2(b)). A vortex is also observed to form in this region during the diastole phase (Figure 2(b)). There are also noticeable changes in the position of the vortex over the entire cardiac cycle. These are reported in [8]

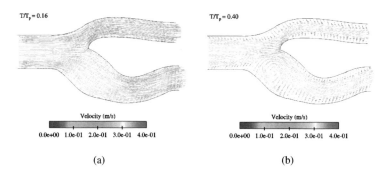

Figure 2: Velocity distribution in the patient specific carotid artery, at different stages of the cardiac cycle: (a) during systolic acceleration and (b) diastole phase.

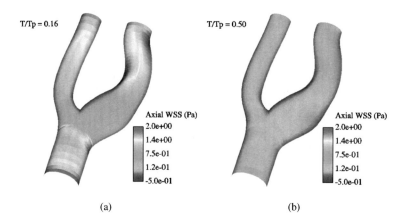

Figure 3: Velocity distribution in the patient specific carotid artery, at different stages of the cardiac cycle: (a) cardiac cycle stages, (b) t_1 and (c) t_2.

The highly disturbed flow in the carotid artery bifurcation is likely to contribute to the development of atherosclerotic plaques, which are known to affect the outer edges of the carotid artery bifurcation [4]. Circumferential flow patterns similar to those reported by [5] were also observed, and are reported in [8].

Figures 3(a) and 3(b) shows WSS distribution in the carotid artery, at two different instances of the cardiac cycle, i.e. during systole ($t/T_p = 16$) and during diastole ($t/T_p = 50$) phases. WSS is consistently lower along the outer edges of the bifurcation than anywhere else in the artery. The highest WSS spatial gradients and its rate of change also occur in these regions [8]

The predicted oscillatory shear index (OSI), which is a measure of the degree of the oscillation of WSS [8], is presented in Figure 4. Similar to WSS gradients, OSI is highest along the outer edges of the carotid bifurcation with location "'B'" showing almost complete flow reversal (≈ 0.5).

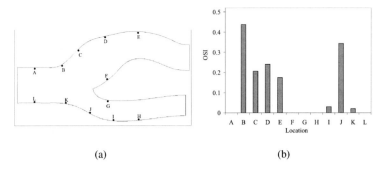

(a)   (b)

Figure 4: OSI at different locations of the carotid art35ry bifurcation.

3   CONCLUSIONS

WSS transients is highly dependent on arterial flexibility and, thus, rigid arterial geometries can not be used to accurately predict flow transients in arteries. Hoop strains of as low as 0.15% produced significant differences in WSS transients compared to those observed in a rigid geometry. Numerical prediction fo flow transients in the carotid artery bifurcation also showed highly disturbed flow with low WSS and high WSS spatial gradients, WSS tempopral gradients and OSI occur in the outer edges of the birfucation, where atheroscklerotic plaques are known to occur [4].

References

[1] A. D. Augst et al. Analysis of complex flow and the relationship between blood pressure, wall shear stress, and intima-media thickness in the human carotid artery. *J Physiol Heart Circ Physiol*, 293:H1031–37, 2007.

[2] A. Ivankovic et al. Towards early diagnosis of atherosclerosis: The finite volume method for fluid-structure interaction. *Biorheology*, 39(3-4):401–07, 2002.

[3] A.K. Politis et al. Numerical modelling of simulated blood flow in idealized composite arterial coronary grafts: transient flow. *J Biomech.*, 41:25–39, 2008.

[4] M. A. Malek et al. Hemodynamic shear stress and its role in atherosclerosis. *Journal of the American Medical Association*, 282(21):2035–42, 1999.

[5] R. Botnar et al. Hemodynamics in the carotid artery bifurcation: A comparison between numerical simulations and *in vitro* MRI measurements. *Journal of Biomechanics*, 33:137–44, 2000.

[6] R. Gin et al. A dual-pressure boundary condition for use in simulations of bifurcating conduits. *Journal of Biomechanical Engineering*, 124(5):617–19, 2002.

[7] X. L. Yang et al. Fluid-structure interaction in a pulmonary arterial bifurcation. *Journal of Biomechanics*, 40(12):2694–99, 2007.

[8] V. Kanyanta. *Towards Early Diagnosis of Atherosclerosis: Accurate Prediction of Wall Shear Stress*. Phd thesis, University College Dublin, March 2009.

[9] OpenFOAM. Programmer's guide version 1.3. www.OpenFOAM.co.uk, March 2006.

[10] E. B. Wylie and V. L. Streeter. *FLUID TRANSIENTS IN SYSTEMS*. Prentice Hall, Englewood Cliffs, New York, 1993.

1st International Conference on Mathematical and Computational Biomedical Engineering – CMBE2009
June 29 – July 1, 2009, Swansea, UK
P. Nithiarasu and R. Löhner (eds)

A FLUID-STRUCTURE INTERACTION STUDY OF BIOFILM DETACHMENT

Ashkan Safari[1], Alojz Ivanković[1], Željko Tuković[1]
[1]School of Electrical, Electronic and Mechanical Engineering, University College Dublin, Dublin, Ireland, Corresponding e-mail address: ashkan.safari@ucd.ie
Maik Walter[2], Eoin Casey[2]
[2]School of Chemical and bioprocess Engineering, University College Dublin, Dublin, Ireland. Corresponding e-mail address: maik.walter@ucd.ie

ABSTRACT

During the biofilm development process, bacterial cells may detach from the biofilm into the surrounding fluid. The key question in relation to detachment from bacterial biofilm is the mechanical response to hydrodynamic forces. In this study, a Finite Volume Method (FVM) based Fluid-Structure Interaction (FSI) solver in OpenFOAM package has been developed to model the biofilm response to flow [1]. Dynamic interaction was simulated between an incompressible Newtonian fluid and a bacterial biofilm described as a linear viscoelastic solid. Viscoelastic response of the biofilm was represented by the hereditary integral form of constitutive relation [2] while tensile relaxation modulus was expressed by the Generalised Maxwell Model (GMM) in the form of Prony series (a discrete retardation spectrum). GMM was obtained from the rheometry creep experimental data using a three-step method proposed by Dooling et al. [3]. The creep curves were all viscoelastic in nature and approximated by a linear viscoelastic model represented by Generalised Voigt Model (GVM). Elastic shear modulus (G), obtained from the three-step method, ranged from 583Pa to 1368Pa which were similar to the previous rheometry studies. In this two-dimensional model, biofilm was considered as semi-hemispherical shape (thickness of 100μm and width of 346μm) attached to the center of the bottom boundary of the square cross-section flow cell. Fluid flow through the flow cell was in laminar regime. Simulation results predicted the potential site for biofilm detachment subjected to increasing fluid flow rate through the flow cell.

Key Words: *Biofilm, Viscoelasticity, Fluid-Structure Interaction, Finite Volume Method.*

1. INTRODUCTION

Biofilms are formed when bacterial cells attach to submerged solid surfaces and accumulate to form a multilayered cellular structure. Biofilm structure may change in numerous ways such as detaching, streaming, rolling and rippling subjected to fluid stresses in a flowing system. Biofilm detachment is a term which is used for the cell cluster detachment from a biofilm and/or detachment of biofilm from the substrate. The phenomenon of detachment from biofilm is now recognised as a serious concern in public health and clinical fields. Growth of biofilm on medical devices and human organs may result in persistent infections, which may spread to other sites via detachment processes [4]. There is currently a wholly inadequate mechanistic understanding of biofilm deformation/failure in a biofilm-fluid interaction description. The nature of biofilm response is greatly influenced by material properties. Shear deformation of biofilm was modeled as a viscoelastic material using 4-elements Burger model in rheometry experiments [5] and a 2D Finite Element model of biofilm-fluid interaction was developed based on this model [6]. The aim of this study was to model a dynamic interaction between an incompressible Newtonian fluid and a bacterial biofilm described by a linear viscoelastic solid. FVM based FSI modeling has been previously developed to model fluid-structure systems [7, 8 & 9]. In this work, OpenFOAM package, which is a C++ library of FVM, was used to model the fluid-biofilm interaction problem.

2. EXPERIMENTAL

Creep analysis was carried out on mixed culture biofilms using the concentric cylinders rheometer (TA INSTRUMENTS, CSL2 100 Carimed Rheometer). Biofilm samples were cultivated using methods described previously [10]. The creep analysis was performed for 3min loading and 3min unloading subjected to constant shear stresses of 0.5 & 1Pa to monitor creep and recovery phases.

3. MODELING

A linear viscoelastic stress-strain constitutive relation was described by a hereditary integral [2]. The incremental form of this constitutive relation has been introduced in geometrically nonlinear momentum equation in an updated Lagrangian formulation to model biofilm deformation. Tensile relaxation modulus ($E(t)$) was expressed by a discrete relaxation spectrum (Prony series) and it was calculated from experimental creep data according to a three-step method as follows [3]: 1) Discrete retardation spectrum (J_i & τ_i) of a GVM (Equation-1) was fitted to experimental creep data, $J(t)$, using a non-negative least square method. It should be noted that a Genetic Algorithm (GA) was used to obtain optimal retardation times. In Equation-1, J_0 is the equilibrium compliance, J_i is retardation strength, and τ_i is retardation time, 2) GVM was solved numerically to calculate shear relaxation modulus data, $G(t)$ based on Finite Difference method [3], and 3) Discrete shear relaxation spectrum (G_i, ρ_i) of a GMM (Equation-2) was fitted to the calculated $G(t)$. In Equation-2, G_0 is the equilibrium modulus, G_i is relaxation strength, and ρ_i is relaxation time. At the end, tensile relaxation modulus ($E(t)$) was obtained from shear relaxation modulus.

$$J(t) = J_0 + \sum_{j=1}^{n} J_j \left(1 - e^{-(t/\tau_j)}\right)$$

Equation 1

$$G(t) = G_0 + \sum_{i=1}^{m} G_i e^{-(t/\rho_i)}$$

Equation 2

In fluid-structure interaction model, laminar fluid flow has been modeled by the Navier-Stokes equations in an Arbitrary Lagrangian-Eulerian (ALE) formulation. Spatial discretisation of both domains was performed using the second-order accurate unstructured cell-centred FVM. The fluid model was discretised on the moving mesh, while the viscoelastic model was discretised on the fixed mesh in an updated configuration. Automatic vertex-based mesh motion solver was used to accommodate the fluid mesh to the fluid-solid interface deformation. Temporal discretisation of both models was performed using a fully implicit second-order accurate three-time-levels difference scheme. Coupling between the domains was achieved using a strong implicit coupling algorithm. The biofilm was considered as semi-hemispherical shape attached to the center of the bottom boundary of the square cross-section flow cell (Figure-1). Thickness and width of the biofilm were 100μm and 346μm respectively, and flow cell dimensions were 3mm × 3mm × 50mm. Fluid flow through the flow cell was assumed to be in laminar regime and a fully developed flow approached the biofilm structure, therefore, a non-uniform parabolic velocity distribution was applied at inlet boundary. Water ($\mu=1\times10^{-6}$kg/mm.s, $\rho=1\times10^{-6}$kg/mm^3) flows from the left to right in X direction at V_{max} of 0.05m/s that suddenly increased to 0.1, 0.15 & 0.2m/s at the time interval of 0.0125Sec. In addition to inlet boundary, the so-called "no slip" condition was applied to the channel walls. The walls were also fixed in space; the biofilm-fluid interface was not. The normal derivative of pressure was set to zero at all boundaries, but the pressure value was specified in one point to satisfy solution convergence for pressure equation.

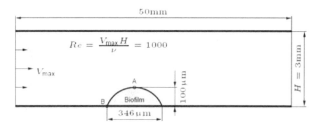

Figure 1 Fluid-biofilm interaction model description

4. RESULTS

Linear viscoelasticity behavior was observed up to the shear stress of 1Pa (data are not shown here). The experimental creep response may indicate the existence of instantaneous elastic and retardation phases (Figure-2A). The value of the instantaneous shear modulus, G, of the biofilms, obtained by GMM was in the range of 583-1368Pa. The agreement between the experimental creep data and the creep response predicted by GVM for a typical biofilm sample is illustrated in Figure-2A. GMM fitted to the numerically calculated shear stress relaxation data is shown in Figure-2B. Table-1 lists tensile relaxation modulus data used in viscoelastic solver. Viscoelastic solver was successfully validated as a good agreement was observed between experimental and numerically predicted creep response in rheometry testing.

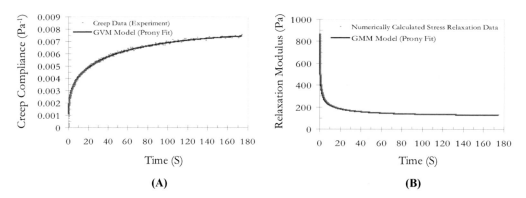

(A)   **(B)**

Figure 2: A: measured creep compliances fitted by GVM & B: calculated stress relaxation fitted by GMM

Table 1 GMM coefficients used in the viscoelastic solver *(*E(t)=2(1+υ)G(t) & υ=0.45)*

$E(t)^*$	E_0	E_1	E_2	E_3	E_4	E_5	E_6	E_7	E_8
Tensile relaxation modulus	374.4	1052	21.4	3.23	565.21	18.4	268.87	45.11	159.17
$\rho(t)$	ρ_0	ρ_1	ρ_2	ρ_3	ρ_4	ρ_5	ρ_6	ρ_7	ρ_8
Relaxation time	0	0.116	0.296	1.291	1.857	4.391	9.368	33.558	48.062

Figure-3 shows magnitude of tangential shear force at point A as well as normal and tangential tractions at point B on biofilm subjected to increasing initial flow velocities at inlet boundary (points A & B are marked in Figure 1). Simulation results showed a sudden increase in all tractions at the moment inlet flow velocity (V_{max}) was applied followed by a gradual decrease within the developing boundary layers. Observation of higher magnitude of normal and tangential tractions at point B compared to tangential shear force at point A suggests that point B may be a potential site for biofilm detachment.

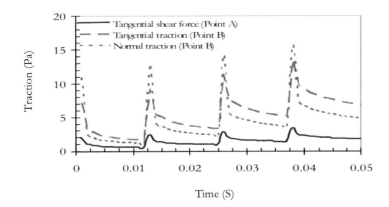

Figure 3 FSI simulation results of tractions exerted by fluid on biofilm, subjected to a 4-step inlet flow velocities of 0.05, 0.1, 0.15 & 0.2m/s at the time intervals of 0, 0.0125, 0.025 & 0.0375Sec.

5. CONCLUSIONS AND FUTURE WORK

The results have demonstrated that the linear viscoelastic response of biofilm to shear stresses can be approximated by Prony series (GVM). A sophisticated three-step method has been developed to numerically obtain respective stress relaxation response of biofilm. Simulations showed that the FSI approach may illuminate interesting details of biofilm deformation/detachment subjected to increasing flow velocities. In the next stage of this work the Cohesive Zone Model (CZM) will be implemented in such a way to allow numerical modeling of the biofilm detachment paths via Traction-Separation (TS) law. The TS law can be obtained by force-distance curve analysis in conjunction with Atomic Force Microscopy (AFM). Experimental measurement of the shear induced detachment characteristics will be conducted for FSI model validation.

REFERENCES

[1]   H. Jasak, A. Jemcov and Z. Tukovic, OpenFOAM: A C++ library for complex physics simulation. *Proc. Int. Workshop on Coupled Methods in Numerical Dynamics*, Faculty of Mechanical Engineering and Naval Architecture, University of Zagreb, Croatia, 19-21, 2007.

[2]   R. S. Lakes, Viscoelastic Solids, CRC Press, Portland, 1998.

[3]   P. J. Dooling, C. P. Buckley, and S. Hinduja, An intermediate model method for obtaining a discrete relaxation spectrum from creep data, *Rehol Acta,* 36, 472-482, 1997.

[4]   P. Stoodley, K. Sauer, D. G. Davies and J. W. Costerton. Biofilm as complex differentiated communities". *Annual Review of Microbiology*, 56, 187–209, 2002.

[5]   B. W. Towler, C. J. Rupp, A. B. Cunningham, P. Stoodley, Viscoelastic properties of a mixed culture biofilm from rheometer creep analysis. Biofouling 19, 279-285, 2003.

[6]   B. W., Towler, A. Cunningham, Stoodley, L., McKittrick, A model of fluid-biofilm interaction using a Burger material law. Biotechnology and Bioengineering 96, 259-271, 2006.

[7]   C. J. Greenshields, H. G. Weller, and A. Ivankovic. The Finite Volume Method for Coupled Fluid Flow and Stress Analysis, *Computer Modelling and Simulation in Engineering,* 4, 213-218, 1999.

[8]   A. Ivankovic, A. Karac. E. Dendrinos, and K. Parker. Towards Early Diagnosis of Atherosclerosis: The Finite Volume methods for Fluid-Structure Interaction, *Biorheology*, 39, 401-407, 2002.

[9]   A. Karac and A. Ivankovic. Behaviour of fluid filled PE containers under impact: Theoretical and numerical investigation. *International Journal of Impact Engineering,* 36, 621-631, 2009.

[10]   E. Syron, Casey, E. Model-based comparative performance analysis of membrane aerated biofilm reactor configurations. *Biotechnology and Bioengineering*

1st International Conference on Mathematical and Computational Biomedical Engineering - CMBE2009
June 29 - July 1, 2009, Swansea, UK
P.Nithiarasu and R.Löhner (Eds.)

A Partitioned Matrix-free Finite-volume Approach to Fluid-Structure Interaction Modelling

A. G. Malan

CSIR Computational Aerodynamics, Building 12, P.O. Box 395, Pretoria, 0001, South Africa, E-mail: amalan@csir.co.za

O. F. Oxtoby

CSIR Computational Aerodynamics, Building 12, P.O. Box 395, Pretoria, 0001, South Africa, E-mail: ooxtoby@csir.co.za

P. Nithiarasu

School of Engineering, Swansea University, Swansea SA2 8PP, UK, E-mail: P.Nithiarasu@Swansea.ac.uk

ABSTRACT

We develop a partitioned matrix-free finite volume algorithm for solving the equations of motion which describe strongly-coupled fluid–structure interaction systems involving viscous incompressible fluids and isotropic elastic solids. Arbitrary structural deformations are catered for by the implementation of a mesh movement algorithm along with an Arbitrary Lagrangian-Eulerian (ALE) description of the fluid domain. The characteristic-based split method, incorporating artificial compressibility, is applied to model both fluid and solid with a single equation set. In the interests of computational efficiency and scaling performance on parallel architectures, we use an edge-based, vertex-centered finite-volume discretisation methodology to discretise all governing equations in a unified manner. The developed technique is validated via application to a number of benchmark problems from the literature.

Key Words: *fluid-structure-interaction, strongly coupled, matrix-free partitioned*

1 INTRODUCTION

Biological systems involving arterial and respitory functions are highly dynamic while exhibiting an intimate coupling between fluid and structural or solid domains. As a result, recent years have seen much research going into the development of fluid-structure-interaction (FSI) modelling technology [1, 2, 3, 4, 5, 6]. Researchers are agreeing that weakly coupled solution methods applied to strongly coupled FSI systems may result in inaccurate or divergent solutions [2, 3, 5]. Further, strongly coupled FSI modelling is typically computationally highly intensive due to the restriction of fully converged solutions at each time-step, of which there are typically numerous. The latter poses the requirement for parallel computing.

In light of the above, we develop a strongly coupled FSI modelling strategy which comprises partitioned spatial discretization of the fluid and solid domains followed by fully coupled matrix-free numerical solution. The aforementioned is effected via a single solver code in a manner which allows independence in terms of both discretization as well as solution strategy employed for the fluid and solid domains, while ensuring simultaneous solution via a simple interface data transfer method. To this end, a single set of unified governing equations is proposed and appropriate constitutive equations employed to account for the molecular activity of the fluid and solid domains. The governing equations are discretized via a vertex-centered edge-based compact finite volume method [7] and solved via a matrix free artificial compressibility characteristic-based methodlogy [8]. Finally, the developed modelling technology is validated by application to a number of benchmark problems from the literature.

2 Governing Equations

The physical domain to be modelled consists of a viscous incompressible fluid and homogeneous isotropic elastic solid region. A unified governing equation set is employed to describe both fluid and solid domains and written for an arbitrary-Eulerian-Lagrangian (ALE) cartesian co-ordinate system by integration over an arbitrary moving volume $\mathscr{V}(t)$ which is translating at velocity v_j as:

$$\frac{\partial}{\partial t} \int_{\mathscr{V}(t)} \mathbf{W} d\mathscr{V} + \int_{\mathscr{S}(t)} \left(\tilde{\mathbf{F}}^j + \mathbf{H}^j - \mathbf{G}^j \right) n_j d\mathscr{S} = \int_{\mathscr{V}(t)} \mathbf{S} d\mathscr{V}, \tag{1}$$

where (omitting the energy equation) $\mathscr{S}$ denotes the surface bounding $\mathscr{V}(t)$ with outward pointing unit vector $\mathbf{n}$ and $\mathbf{F}^j = \mathbf{W} u_j$. Further, $\mathbf{S}$ is a vector of source terms (e.g. body forces) while

$$\mathbf{W} = \begin{pmatrix} \rho u_1 \\ \rho u_2 \\ \rho u_3 \\ \rho \end{pmatrix}, \quad \mathbf{H}^j = \begin{pmatrix} p\delta_{1j} \\ p\delta_{2j} \\ p\delta_{3j} \\ 0 \end{pmatrix}, \quad \mathbf{G}^j = \begin{pmatrix} \sigma_{1j} \\ \sigma_{2j} \\ \sigma_{3j} \\ 0 \end{pmatrix}, \quad \tilde{\mathbf{F}}^j = \mathbf{W}(u_j - v_j) \tag{2}$$

In the above equation set, u_j denotes velocity, p is the pressure, ρ is density and δ_{ij} is the Kronecker delta. Further, σ_{ij} denotes the deviatoric stress term. The fluid is assumed Newtonian while for the solid the generalised Hooke's law is adopted in conjunction with the Green-Lagrange tensor for large non-linear deformation:

$$\varepsilon_{ij} = \frac{1}{2} \left(\frac{\partial w_i}{\partial x_j} + \frac{\partial w_j}{\partial x_i} + \frac{\partial w_k}{\partial x_i} \frac{\partial w_k}{\partial x_j} \right) \tag{3}$$

where x_i is a fixed Eulerian cartesian reference axis and w denotes displacement.

3 Discretisation and Solution Method

3.1 Spatial Discretization

In this work we propose the use of a vertex-centred edge-based finite volume algorithm for the purposes of spatial discretization, where a compact stencil method is employed for second-derivative terms in the interest of both stability and accuracy [7]. In the case of the solid, an elemental-strain variant [6] is employed. This is the first instance in which the aforementioned approach is applied to solid or FSI modelling, and it was selected as the method allows natural generic mesh applicability, second-order accuracy without odd-even decoupling, and computational efficiency which is factors greater than element based approaches. Note that the proposed edge-based approach is also particularly well suited to shared memory parallel hardware architectures.

3.2 Temporal Discretization and Solution Procedure

The solution procedure is to allow for fully coupled solution of all descritized equations while allowing independence in terms of discretization and solution strategy employed for the fluid and solid domains. We therefore advocate a matrix-free iterative solution process where fluid-solid-interface nodes communicate pressures and displacements at each iteration. The instabilities resulting from the spatial edge-based discretization of convective terms are dealt with via a characteristic based methodlogy [9] while the stiffness resulting from incompressibility is circumvented with an artificial-compressibility split method [8].

The resulting matrix-free unified solution procedure consists of three steps per iteration. Considering the weak form governing Equation (1) with an arbitrary time-dependent volume $\mathcal{V}(t)$ which is moving at velocity v_j, the first step may be written in semi-discrete form as:

$$\frac{(\Delta W)_i^*}{\Delta t_\tau} V^\tau = - \int_{\mathcal{S}(t)} (\tilde{F}_i^j - G_i^j) n_j dS \bigg|^\tau + \frac{\Delta t_\tau}{2} (u_k - v_k) \int_{\partial \mathcal{V}(t)} \frac{\partial F_i^j}{\partial x_j} n_k dS \bigg|^\tau + SV|^\tau \tag{4a}$$

where the τ superscript denotes the previous (existing) solution or pseudo time-step and $\Delta t_\tau = t^{\tau+1} - t^\tau$. Further, ΔW_i^* is an auxiliary variable which is used in the second step as:

$$\frac{\hat{W}_4^{\tau+1} V^{\tau+1} - \hat{W}_4^\tau V^\tau}{\Delta t_{\tau_{step2}}} = -\kappa \int_{\mathcal{S}(t)} \left[F_4^k + \Delta t_\tau \left(\frac{(\Delta W)_k^*}{\Delta t_\tau} - \frac{\partial H_k^j}{\partial x_j} \right) \right] n_k dS \bigg|^\tau \tag{4b}$$

where $\kappa = 0$ for the solid and $\kappa = 1$ for the fluid domain.

The final and third incremental solution step written in semi-discrete form now follows:

$$\frac{\partial W_i}{dt} \mathcal{V} \bigg|_{\tau+1} = \frac{(\Delta W)_i^*}{\Delta t_\tau} V^\tau - \int_{\partial \mathcal{V}(t)} H_i^j n_j dS \bigg|^{\tau+1} = R_i(\mathbf{W}^{n+1}) \tag{4c}$$

for $i = 1, 2, 3$.

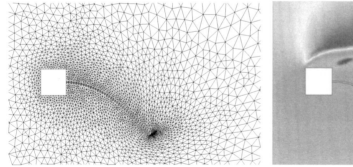 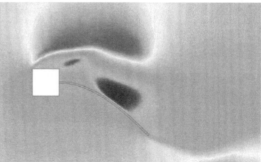

Figure 1: Block with flexible tail: deformed mesh (left) and (right) horizontal velocity at $t = 3.53$ s.

At the fluid-solid interface, traction is applied to the solid while displacement and velocity are applied to the fluid. This is done such that all governing equations are simultaneously solved to convergence. Computational points are moved dynamically throughout the iteration process where internal fluid nodes are re-positioned such that boundary displacements do not result in unacceptable deteriorating mesh quality [10]. This is of particular importance when solid displacement are large as is the case in the work under consideration.

3.3 Numerical Test

The chosen test-case is composed of a square box with fluid flowing over it and with a long thin beam attached to the centre of the downstream face as proposed by Wall and Ramm [1] (see Figure 1 for deformed configuration). We have used a fluid mesh consisting of 3251 nodes and 6311 elements and a solid mesh consisting of 40×3 quadrilateral elements. The time step size is $\Delta t = 0.005$ s. To allow the flow field to form without large transient shocks to the solid, the fluid inflow velocity was linearly ramped up to its final value of 31.5 cm s^{-1} within the first 0.02 s. In the limit-state, the beam tip is predicted to have a response of 2.0 cm and frequency of 0.8 Hz. This compares well with the results of others [2, 6].

References

[1] W. A. Wall and E. Ramm. Fluidstructure interaction based upon a stabilized (ALE) finite element method. In S. Idelsohn, E E. On Vate, and Dvorkin, editors, *Computational mechanics – new trends and applications, Proceedings of WCCM IV, CIMNE, Barcelona*, 1998.

[2] B. Hübner, E. Walhorn, and D. Dinkler. A monolithic approach to fluid–structure interaction using spacetime finite elements. *Comput. Methods Appl. Mech. Engrg.*, 193:2087–2104, 2004.

[3] C. J. Greenshields and H. G. Weller. A unified formulation for continuum mechanics applied to fluid-structure interaction in flexible tubes. *Int. J. Numer. Meth. Engng*, 64:1575–1593, 2005.

[4] K. J. Bathe and G. A. Ledezma. Benchmark problems for incompressible fluid flows with structural intercations. *Computers & Structures*, 85:628–644, 2007.

[5] W. Dettmer and J. D. Peric. A computational framework for fluid–structure interaction: Finite element formulation and application. *Comput. Meth. Appl. Mech. Engrng.*, 195:5754–79, 2006.

[6] G. Xia and C.-L. Lin. An unstructured finite volume approach for structural dynamics in response to fluid motions. *Computers and Structures*, 86:684–701, 2008.

[7] A. G. Malan and R. W. Lewis. Modeling coupled heat and mass transfer in drying non-hygroscopic capillary particulate materials. *Communications in Numerical Methods in Engineering*, 19(9):669–677, 2003.

[8] P. Nithiarasu. An efficient artificial compressibility (ac) scheme based on the characteristic based split (cbs) method for incompressible flow. *International Journal for Numerical Methods in Engineering*, 56(13):1815–1845, 2003.

[9] O. C. Zienkiewicz and R. Codina. A general algorithm for compressible and incompressible flow, part I. the split characteristic based scheme. *International Journal for Numerical Methods in Fluids*, 20:869–885, 1995.

[10] H. Braess and P. Wriggers. Arbitrary lagrangian eulerian finite element analysis of free surface flow. *Computer Methods in Applied Mechanics and Engineering*, 160:90–109, 2000.

FLUID-STRUCTURE INTERACTION IN BIOMEDICAL ENGINEERING: A COMPARISON BETWEEN BLOCK GAUSS-SEIDEL AND BLOCK NEWTON STRATEGIES

M.M. Joosten

Civil and Computational Engineering Research Centre, School of Engineering, Swansea University, Swansea SA2 8PP, Wales - U.K., 447095@swansea.ac.uk

W.G. Dettmer

Civil and Computational Engineering Research Centre, School of Engineering, Swansea University, Swansea SA2 8PP, Wales - U.K., w.g.dettmer@swansea.ac.uk

D. Perić

Civil and Computational Engineering Research Centre, School of Engineering, Swansea University, Swansea SA2 8PP, Wales - U.K., d.peric@swansea.ac.uk

ABSTRACT

In the past years, much work has been done on the computational modelling of blood flow through flexible vessels. Numerous Fluid-Structure interaction (FSI) solution strategies have been developed. In this work, two different FSI strategies are compared: The block Gauss-Seidel and the block Newton procedure. Both are partitioned strategies that resolve the strong coupling between the fluid and the structure. When using a Gauss-Seidel procedure the fluid and the structure are solved separately, with displacements and forces transferred in between. In some cases problems arise regarding the convergence behaviour. Alternatively, it is possible to use a block Newton method. In this case also the derivatives of the traction forces are transferred at the interface. The block Newton methods are often thought to be more efficient and applicable to a wider range of problems. This work includes a detailed discussion of the limitations of the Gauss-Seidel methodology and a number of numerical examples is provided, allowing for the direct comparison of the two strategies.

Key Words: *fluid-structure interaction, partitioned solution strategy, block Gauss-Seidel method, block Newton method.*

1   INTRODUCTION

In this work a comparison is made between the block Gauss-Seidel and the block Newton procedure. Both are partitioned Fluid-Structure interaction (FSI) solution strategies that resolve the strong coupling between the fluid and the structure. Using the Gauss-Seidel method, the fluid and the structure are solved separately, with displacements and forces transferred in between. With the Gauss-Seidel method problems may arise regarding the convergence behaviour. Another strategy that can be used is the block Newton method. With this method also the derivatives of the traction forces are transferred at the interface. It is often thought that the block Newton methods are more efficient and applicable to a wider range of problems.

To compare the two methods, first the Gauss-Seidel method for a 1-D model problem is analysed. The convergence behaviour of the method is investigated based on a mass, spring and dahspot system with four degrees of freedom. In order to determine how applicable the observations for the 1-D model problem are to 2-D and 3-D FSI problems, a number of numerical examples is considered. The 2-D and 3-D examples will be solved with both the block Gauss-Seidel and the block Newton method which allows for a comparison between the two methods with respect to the convergence behaviour and computational efficiency.

2   GAUSS-SEIDEL STRATEGY FOR 1-D MODEL PROBLEM

When using a Gauss-Seidel strategy some issues may arise regarding the stability of the iteration procedure [1-3]. In [4] the limitations of the Gauss-Seidel strategy are discussed based on a model problem. A one dimensional mass, spring and dashpot system with four degrees of freedom is introduced to represent a coupled second order initial value problem. One part of the problem represents domain P and the other part represents domain Q. For the Gauss-Seidel methodology, first domain Q is solved. An initial displacement is given to the domain in order to calculate the reaction force. This force is given to domain P, which can then be solved for the displacement. This process is repeated until a certain tolerance is reached.

Taking the governing equations and an appropriate time integration scheme, the entire Gauss-Seidel procedure can be described with a set of linear equations. By eliminating the force from these equations, one Gauss-Seidel iteration step can be represented in a recursive form by a single equation. This equation gives the updated interface displacement in terms of the interface displacement of the previous iteration steps. The amplification factor of the error, which determines the convergence behaviour, is easily identified in the expression. It depends on problem parameters and time step size. For small time steps this factor approaches the ratio between the mass in domain P and the mass in domain Q. If the mass in domain Q (solved for the interface force) exceeds the mass in domain P (solved for the interface displacement) instabilities will occur. It is possible to get converging simulations in such cases, but then a relaxation parameter is required. A constant relaxation parameter can be used or an Aitken relaxation parameter can be introduced.

3   COMPARISON BETWEEN BLOCK GAUSS-SEIDEL AND BLOCK NEWTON METHOD

3.1   Flow through a channel with a flexible wall

To compare the block Gauss-Seidel and block Newton method for FSI problems, first a 2-D flow through a channel with a flexible wall is considered ([5,6]). The convergence behaviour of the block Newton method for this problem is described in [6]. To analyse the convergence behaviour of the block Gauss-Seidel method the same mesh, time integration scheme and material parameters are used. However, in [6] the density of the solid wall is set to zero, and this leads to problems when using the Gauss-Seidel method. Therefore the density of the solid is set to 50 initially. The vertical displacement for a point in the flexible wall is shown in Figure 1.

The time step in Figure 1 is set to 1.0, which is relatively large compared to the smallest time period of the response of the system. The solution will therefore be relatively inaccurate. This is shown in Figure 2 where the time integration parameter ρ_∞ is varied. The chosen time integration scheme is the generalized-α method, in which the parameter ρ_∞ controls the numerical damping. In Figure 2 the response of the system is shown for $\rho_\infty = 0.0$, $\rho_\infty = 0.4$ and $\rho_\infty = 0.8$. Parameter ρ_∞ does not seem to affect the convergence, but it can be seen that the time response is affected.

To get more accurate results one would have to decrease the time step size. However, for a given density of the solid, a minimum value for the time step exists. This confirms the findings for the 1-D model problem, where it was stated that for small time steps the convergence behaviour depends on mass ratios, while for larger time steps other material and time integration parameters start to play a role. There also is a minimum value for the solid density ρ_s. For simulations with $\rho_s = 10$ no convergence could be reached, independent of the time step size. Again this is in agreement with the conclusions for the 1-D model problem. It is also in agreement with findings in [7], where results for a driven cavity with flexible bottom show that for larger densities of the flexible bottom more iterations per time step are needed.

3.2 Flow-induced oscillation of a flexible beam

The next example that is being considered describes the oscillation of a flexible beam [6]. A vorticity plot for this problem can be seen in Figure 3. The problem is solved with both the block Newton and the block Gauss-Seidel strategy. For the block Newton procedure two variations are used, the exact and inexact block Newton method (referred to as respectively strategy A and strategy B in Figure 4). For the exact block Newton method all cross-derivatives between the different fields are calculated [8]. A more simple way of implementing the method is the inexact block Newton method, where some coupling terms are approximated or neglected.

For the block Gauss-Seidel method different relaxation parameters are used. There are simulations without a relaxation parameter, with a constant relaxation parameter and with an Aitken relaxation parameter. The convergence behaviour for all these different strategies is shown in Figure 4, where the residual is shown as a function of the iteration number. It can be seen that the block Newton methods lead to fastest convergence, followed by the Gauss-Seidel method with constant or Aitken relaxation. The convergence for the Gauss-Seidel method without relaxation is very poor.

4 CONCLUSIONS

The Gauss-Seidel strategy has been analysed for a 1-D coupled model problem. It is concluded that the convergence behaviour of the method depends on the mass ratio between the two domains, especially for small time steps. To improve the performance of the method, a relaxation parameter can be introduced.

To analyse a realistic fluid-structure interaction problem, a number of numerical examples are considered. The first example solves the flow through a channel with a flexible wall. Results of the simulations

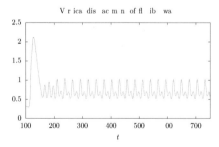

Figure 1: Channel with flexible wall, vertical displacement of a point on the membrane

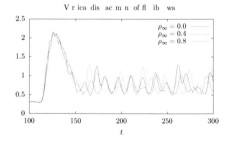

Figure 2: Vertical displacement of a point on the membrane for different values of ρ_∞

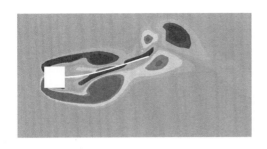

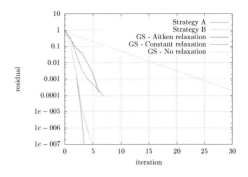

Figure 3: Oscillations of a beam, typical vorticity distribution

Figure 4: Oscillations of a beam, typical convergence of the residuals

are in agreement with findings for the 1-D model problem. These findings are also confirmed by results for a flow-induced oscillation of a flexible beam.

REFERENCES

[1] P. Causin, J.F. Gerbeau and F. Nobile, Added-mass effect in the design of partitioned algorithms for fluid-structure problems, *Computer Methods in Applied Mechanics and Engineering*, 194, 4506-4527, 2005.

[2] U. Küttler, Ch. Förster and W.A. Wall, A solution for the incompressibility dilemma in partitioned fluid-structure interaction with pure Dirichlet fluid domains, *Computational Mechanics*, 38, 417-429, 2006.

[3] Ch. Förster, W.A. Wall and E. Ramm, Artificial added mass instabilities in sequential staggered coupling of nonlinear structures and incompressible viscous flows, *Computer Methods in Applied Mechanics and Engineering*, 196, 1278-1293, 2007.

[4] M.M. Joosten, W.G. Dettmer and D. Perić, Analysis of the block Gauss-Seidel solution procedure for a strongly coupled model problem with reference to fluid-structure interaction, *International Journal for Numerical Methods in Engineering*, published online 2 december 2008, DOI: 10.1002/nme.2503

[5] M. Heil, An efficient solver for the fully coupled solution of large-displacement fluid-structure interaction problems, *Computer Methods in Applied Mechanics and Engineering*, 193, 1-23, 2004.

[6] W.G. Dettmer and D. Perić, On the coupling between fluid flow and mesh motion in the modelling of fluid-structure interaction, *Computational Mechanics*, 90, 43-81, 2008.

[7] U. Küttler and W.A. Wall, Fixed-point fluid-structure interaction solvers with dynamic relaxation, *Computational Mechanics*, 43, 61-72, 2008.

[8] W.G. Dettmer and D. Perić, A Computational Framework for Fluid-Structure Interaction: Finite Element Formulation and Applications, *Computer Methods in Applied Mechanics and Engineering*, 195, 5754-5779, 2006.

1st International Conference on Mathematical and Computational Biomedical Engineering - CMBE2009

June 29 - July 1, 2009, Swansea, UK

P.Nithiarasu and R.Löhner (Eds.)

A Finite Element Approach for Static and Dynamic Simulations of Human Red Blood Cells

Thomas Klöppel

Institute for Computational Mechanics, Technische Universität München,
Boltzmannstr. 15, 85747 Garching, Germany,
kloeppel@lnm.mw.tum.de

Wolfgang A. Wall

Institute for Computational Mechanics, Technische Universität München,
Boltzmannstr. 15, 85747 Garching, Germany,
wall@lnm.mw.tum.de

ABSTRACT

We will present a finite element model for simulating the mechanical behavior of human red blood cells (RBCs, erythrocytes). As the RBC membrane comprises a phospholipid bilayer with an intervening protein network, we propose a discretization of the membrane with two layers of three dimensional advanced solid elements. The characteristics of the very thin lipid bilayer like viscosity and bending resistance are represented by an anisotropic, viscoelastic and incompressible material. The assumption of material anisotropy provides the necessary bending stiffness. Properties of the protein network are modeled with an isotropic hyperelastic third-order material to account for shear elasticity and strain hardening at large deformations.

Starting from a flat ellipsoid, we are able to obtain a reference configuration resembling well the shape of a RBC at rest by controlling the surface area and enclosed volume. The numerical model is validated for optical tweezers studies with quasi-static deformations. Results obtained with our proposed membrane model show good agreement with experimental data. The influence of applied constraints and the employed loading conditions can clearly be seen.

Further extensions to simulate dynamical experiments including the interaction of the membrane with the cytoplasm, a Newtonian fluid inside the cell, are discussed. The effect of membrane viscosity is covered by the proposed lipid bilayer model.

Key Words: *Erythrocyte mechanics, cell membrane, finite element method*

1 INTRODUCTION

Blood is a complex fluid, i.e. a suspension of red blood cells (RBC, erythrocytes), white blood cells and platelets in a Newtonian fluid, and has long been a field of intensive research. Especially the properties of the human erythrocyte constituting more than 99% of the particulate matter in blood and 40-45% of the blood by volume play a dominant role. RBCs have a relatively simple structure, being a liquid capsule enclosed by a biological membrane. They show great ability to deform, which allows them to squeeze through capillaries with inner diameter less than 3 μm, although the average diameter of a cell is about 8 μm.

The typical biconcave discocyte shape of an erythrocyte contributes strongly to this remarkable property, since the excess of surface area for the enclosed volume allows large deformations while keeping the area constant. This shape is assumed to represent the state with minimal mechanical energy of the lipid bilayer/membrane skeleton composite under the constraint of a fixed cell volume and fixed surface area. This energy includes contributions from the bending energy E_B of the plasma membrane [3], the elastic energy E_{MS} due to shearing and stretching of the membrane skeleton, and resistance E_{AD} of the lipid bilayer against differences in area between the outer and inner leaflet. It has been reported that neither the lipid bilayer nor the protein network is completely stress-free for a RBC at rest.

To gain insight into the elastic response of the erythrocyte membrane experimental studies on single cells employing micropipettes [1] and optical tweezers [7] have been carried out. We will focus on the latter. In those experiments RBCs are prepared with rigid silica beads firmly attached to the membrane. Focusing a laser on the beads makes is possible to exert a well-controlled force and steer their movement to stretch the RBC.

Much experimental work on the dynamic motion of a RBC in shear flow has been conducted. The response to dynamical deformation of a RBC can also be analyzed using optical tweezers experiments. They provide the possibility to examine the relaxation of a single RBC and hence allow to determine the viscoelastic properties of the RBC membrane [8]. A major advantage using optical tweezers lies in the reduced number of possible input parameters.

2   RBC MODEL AND COMPUTATIONAL PROCEDURE

2.1   RBC Model

In the proposed finite element model the RBC membrane is discretized with two different layers of solid elements. The outer, thinner layer implements the properties of the lipid bilayer, namely bending elasticity, resistance against area dilatation and viscosity. Since the outer layer is relatively thin and contributes little to the membrane's in-plane shear elasticity, an isotropic material formulation would yield a negligible bending elasticity. The basic idea in the present model for the lipid bilayer is to use an incompressible or nearly incompressible viscoelastic material in combination with elastic fibers or rods initially aligned in thickness direction of the solid shell element. This additional stiffness normal to the membrane surface will provide the desired bending elasticity. The material formulation used was proposed in [4].

Since the cytoskeleton provides shear elasticity to the membrane and its bending elasticity is reported to be negligible, we employ an isotropic hyperelastic material for the inner membrane layer. To account for the hardening behavior observed in lasertrap experiments, we employ a third-order material as proposed in [7].

2.2   Computational Procedure

In order to obtain a suitable geometry of the RBC at rest, we start with a flat ellipsoidal reference configuration and adjust the area-to-volume ratio to physical values by reducing the volume enclosed by the membrane. Both, surface area and volume, are controlled with Lagrange multipliers. The resulting biconcave shape serves as starting point for the subsequent simulation of the optical tweezers experiments. One option is to keep the deformation-dependent stress field, which evolves during the transition from an ellipsoidal to a biconcave shape, within the structure. As second option it is also feasible to use the obtained shape as stress-free initial state. Thus we can study the influence of a stress-free or a prestressed reference configuration of the RBC on its elastic response.

The force on the RBC in optical tweezers experiments is exerted through rigid beads firmly attached to the membrane. Hence, any relative motion within the contact surface is suppressed. We devised a multi-point constraint allowing to restrict the motion of nodes relative to each other, where the constraint is again controlled with a Lagrange multiplier. In the present case of a uniaxial stretching, we do not allow any relative motion in force direction of the nodes within the contact surface.

To simulate dynamical experiments with optical tweezers, which show the relaxation behavior of a single cell, the viscosity of the cell will be considered. The model for the lipid bilayer proposed here is capable of reproducing the viscoelasticity of the membrane. A suitable numerical model has to additionally account for the existence of the enclosed Newtonian fluid. We will use a monolithic coupling scheme to simulate these fluid-structure-interaction effects.

3   COMPUTATIONAL RESULTS

Figure 1: Flat ellipsoidal reference state.

Figure 2: Graphical comparison between computed cell shape in red and reference shape in gray. Only an eighth of the cell is shown.

The shape of the human erythrocyte has been measured by several authors. Of special interest is the analytical formula for the cell geometry proposed in [2] and derived from direct measurements, since this formulation has been the basis for many numerical studies reported in literature. Figure 1 shows the ellipsoidal reference state for the presented finite element simulation. We compare in Figure 2 the analytically determined shape with our results. The picture shows a close match between measured and calculated shapes.

Several authors have published experimental results for the elastic response of the RBC in optical tweezers. In most cases the values of axial and transverse diameters are reported for varying stretching forces. Published simulation results of those experiments are based on different numerical methods and differ in the constraints applied. The results shown in [7] are obtained by a finite element analysis assuming a constant volume and a rigid motion of the contact surface, but without constraining the surface area. In contrast the coarse grained molecular dynamics simulations reported in [6] were performed under the constraint of constant surface area and constant volume, but the motion of the contact area has not been restricted. We are interested in the implications of such assumptions. In Figure 3 the deformed states of three different RBC models are shown at a stretching force of 50 pN. In all cases the enclosed volume is kept constant. The model shown in Figure 3 a) constrains surface area as well as the motion of the contact surface, and uses a reduced shear modulus of about a third in comparison to the other models shown in Figure 3 b) and c). Nevertheless the deviations in axial and transverse diameters lie within a range of 5% and are all found to be within the error range reported for experimental studies. This demonstrates that the loading condition as well as the assumption of a constant surface area strongly influence the outcome of the simulation and that our proposed membrane model yields results in good agreement with measured data.

4   OUTLOOK

The mechanical properties of the RBC membrane are reported to be directly connected to the progression of certain diseases. These diseases can for example alter the structure of the cell cytoplasm or the

Figure 3: Deformed state at stretching force 50 pN: a) volume, surface area and motion of the contact area constrained, shear modulus reduced; b) only volume and motion of the contact area constrained; c) volume and surface area constrained.

molecular constitution of the RBC membrane and hence affect shape and deformability. The presented membrane model allows us to modify independently the material formulations of the lipid bilayer and of the protein skeleton and to vary the connection between these two layers. We will study the effect of such variations and compare them to alterations being caused by certain diseases.

As mentioned above, many experimental studies have been performed on the motion of a cell in a simple shear flow. In those experiments a transition from tumbling to tank-treading with increasing shear rate has been observed. The transition behavior depends on cell age, membrane viscosity and the ratio between the viscosities of interior and exterior fluid. For a numerical study we will include an exterior fluid in our simulation. Furthermore this extension will allow us to simulate the flow of a cell through capillaries.

A further step towards studying the rheology of blood will be the extension to multiple RBCs exposed to a flow field. We will consider cell-cell interaction and the formation of RBC aggregates (called rouleau).

REFERENCES

[1] Boey, S. K., Boal, D. H. and Discher, D. E., Simulations of the Erythrocyte Cytoskeleton at Large Deformation. I.Microscopic Models, *Biophys. J.*, 75, 1573-1583, 1998

[2] Evans, E. and Fung, Y.-C., Improved measurements of the erythrocyte geometry, *Microvascular Research*, 4, 335-347, 1972

[3] Helfrich, W., Elastic properties of lipid bilayers: theory and possible experiments, *Z. Naturforsch.*, 28c, 693-703, 1976

[4] Holzapfel, G. A. and Gasser, T. C., A viscoelastic model for fiber-reinforced composites at finite strains: Continuum basis, computational aspects and applications, *Computer Methods in Applied Mechanics and Engineering*, 190, 4379-4403, 2001

[5] Klöppel, T. and Wall, W. A., A Finite Element Approach for Static and Dynamic Simulations of Human Red Blood Cells, *In Preparation*

[6] Li, J., Dao, M., Lim, C. T. and Suresh, S., Spectrin-Level Modeling of the Cytoskeleton and Optical Tweezers Stretching of the Erythrocyte, *Biophys. J.*, 88, 3707-3719, 2005

[7] Mills, J. P., Qie, L., Dao, M., Lim, C. T. and Suresh, S., Nonlinear Elastic and Viscoelastic Deformation of the Human Red Blood Cell with Optical Tweezers, *Mech Chem Biosyst.*, 1, 169-180, 2004

[8] Yoon, Y.-Z., Kotar, J., Yoon, G. and Cicuta, P., The nonlinear mechanical response of the red blood cell, *Physical Biology*, 5, 036007, 2008

VALIDATION OF A NUMERICAL MODEL OF THE HEMODYNAMICS IN LOWER-LIMB BYPASSES

M. Willemet, E. Marchandise, J.-F. Remacle
institute of Mechanics, Materials and Civil Engineering (iMMC), Université catholique de Louvain,
1348 Louvain-la-Neuve, Belgium.

V. Lacroix
Cliniques Universitaires St-Luc, Service de Chirurgie Cardio-Vasculaire et Thoracique,
1200 Bruxelles, Belgium

ABSTRACT

This work presents a clinical validation of a 1D-0D arterial blood flow model. In particular, the model studies the hemodynamics in bypassed arteries in the lower-limb arterial network. In addition to its clinical pathological application, this work uses patient-specific data. Through a statistical analysis of medically relevant results, we show that our numerical model reproduces well the hemodynamics in the patients bypass and lower limb arteries.

Key Words: *blood flow, bypass surgery, patient-specific validation, multiscale modeling*

1 INTRODUCTION

When atherosclerosis, a widespread cardiovascular disease, affects a patient, its arterial network suffers from physiological changes such as the change in the elasticity of the arterial wall or the increase of the arterial wall thickness due to the deposit of proteins and fat. In the worst cases, this narrowing can lead to the total occlusion of a long segment of the artery and, as a consequence, to the lack of vascularisation of the lower-limb arterial network. In such cases, bypass remains the only surgical procedure to overcome the lesion.

Nowadays, surgeon's decision to perform the bypass surgery is based on the patient's morphology, his own experience and literature advices. No numerical tool provides him with objective results from hemodynamical simulations, helping to choose the bypass that will provide the best patency rate.

2 METHOD AND RESULTS

The method is based on the resolution of the one-dimensional Euler equations of blood flow; those are coupled with the zero-dimensional RCR-windkessel model. If these coupled 1D-0D numerical models of the cardiovascular arterial circulation have been largely developed and validated in human *healthy* arteries [1,2], very few papers present their application to *pathological* cases.

This work focuses on a particular application of the clinical pathological cases, interesting in many points. Firstly, it will allow clinicians to have a better understanding of the hemodynamics in diseased states. Secondly, the use of such models for patient's specific pathological hemodynamics simulation allows us to highlight the strengths and weaknesses of the models and to improve their accuracy. Finally, it is a first response to the need of an objective predictive tool for surgeons.

The study uses our database that contains already more than 10 pathological subjects that underwent lower-limb bypass surgery. It is built following a defined protocol for medical data acquisition: standard measuring techniques are used (Doppler ultra- sound, MRI, angiography scan, arterial pressure and pulse wave velocity).

We present here a detailed analysis of the coupled 1D-0D models, the influence and sensitivity of their parameters and boundary conditions [3]. Through a statistical analysis performed using our database, we show that the numerical simulations of blood flow variables (area, velocity and pressure) fit the clinical measurements with a good agreement.

3 CONCLUSIONS

The coupled 1D-0D model is a very efficient tool for blood flow modeling, even when pathological cases are considered. The parameters of that model which are patient dependent, can be computed using simple and everyday clinical exams. Its numerical results reproduces very well the hemodynamical pulses measured in the patient. This applied approach to blood flow modeling helps the clinicians as a new tool to understand pathological hemodynamics.

REFERENCES

[1] Alastruey J, Parker K H, Peiro J, Sherwin S J, Lumped Parameter Outflow Models for 1-D Blood Flow Simulations: Effect on Pulse Waves and Parameter Estimation, *Communications in Computational Physics*, 4, 2008.

[2] Vignon-Clementel I E and Taylor C A, Outflow boundary conditions for one-dimensional finite element modeling of blood flow and pressure waves in arteries, *Wave Motion*, 39, 2004

[3] Marchandise E, Willemet M and Lacroix V, A numerical hemodynamic tool for predictive vascular surgery, *Medical Engineering and Physics*, 31, 131-144, 2009

1st International Conference on Mathematical and Computational Biomedical Engineering – CMBE2009
June 29 – July 1, 2009, Swansea, UK
P. Nithiarasu and R. Löhner (eds)

INTRAVENTRICULAR AND AORTIC BLOOD FLOW ANALYSIS AND RECONSTRUCTION USING THE EXACT SOLUTION OF NON STATIONARY HYDRODYNAMIC EQUATIONS FOR THE CLASS OF TWISTED CONVERGING VISCOUS FLOWS

G. Kiknadze
BASERT Comp. (Moscow, RUSSIA)
kiknadze@yandex.ru

A. Gorodkov
Bakulev Scientific Center for Cardiovascular Surgery (Moscow, RUSSIA)
135, Rublevskoye sch. 121552 Moscow RUSSIA
agorodkov@bk.ru

A. Bogevolnov
St.-Petersburg State University, Physical Faculty (St.-Petersburg, RUSSIA)
astislav@gmail.com

ABSTRACT

Key Words: *Twisted blood flow, exact solution of non stationary hydrodynamic equations, left ventricle, aorta.*

The lack of the knowledge on the hydrodynamics of blood flow in the transport segment of the circulation is the main impediment to the understanding of mechanism of regulation and compensation of cardiac output, and thus to the efficiency of diagnostics and adequate correction of anatomical and functional circulatory disorders, suitable cardiovascular prostheses design.

The study of blood flow hydrodynamics is in progress since more than 50 years, however even the most sophisticated modern measuring equipment that is capable to carry out detailed 3D measurement of the flow velocity field in different parts of circulatory system does not allow one to proceed to the analysis of mechanism of blood flow transportation, and stays on the statement that the blood flow is a kind of twisted flows.

The Bakulev Scientific Center of Cardiovascular Surgery was dealing with this problem since early 60-s. The main purpose of the study was to ameliorate the design of implantable cardiovascular substitutes such as mechanical heart valve prostheses, vascular prostheses, assist devices and totally implantable heart pump in order to minimize distortion of velocity and shear fields of the flow. As elsewhere this study in Bakulev Center did not come to essential result because of absence of appropriate quantitative methods of analysis and modeling of twisted blood flow.

The situation has radically changed on the end of 80-s when the exact solution of non stationary hydrodynamic equations for the radially converged twisting viscous flows was firstly published in the former USSR. On the base of exact solution the series of new tornado-like technologies was successfully initiated, and a number of effective innovations were applied in industry.

The exact solution allows to link definitely the geometrical parameters of blood flow and of circulatory bed where the flow is realized without flow rupture and stagnation. The non stationarity of flow is defined by the time-dependent parameters unambiguously determined from the instant geometrical configuration of the channel changing during cardiac cycle.

Knowing that the blood flow is deprived of rupture or stagnation zones, it is sufficient to compare the dynamic geometry of left ventricular-aortic channel, so as the instant orientation of the intraventricular trabecules relief with the streamlines of the twisting flow described by the exact solution.

The study was performed in four stages.

Firstly we have studied the geometry of the left ventricular-aortic channel using the corrosion casts techniques considering that the cast reflects the instant statement of the flow at some moment of the cardiac cycle. It was shown that the longitudinal-radial projection of channel so as the trabecules orientation corresponds closely to the streamlines of the tornado-like twisting flow described by the exact solution. This flow is generated inside left ventricle due to interaction of blood mass with spirally oriented trabecules and papillary muscles and is maintained in the aorta due to its elasticity and convergence. Using specially designed methods of data treatment we have calculated the meanings of flow parameters from the exact solution that correspond to instant flow structure imprinted in the channel cast.

The second stage consisted in measurement of dynamic aortic lumen by means of MRI. It was shown that during whole cardiac cycle the longitudinal aortic profile corresponds to the profile of the tornado-like twisting flow, whereas the characteristics of the flow itself change significantly corresponding to flow evolution due to cardiac contraction. Therefore the structural flow parameters in aorta were calculated for one cardiac cycle.

At the third stage we have performed the 4D mapping of the flow velocity field in the ascending and descending aorta using MRI flow quantification. 6 transversal sections of aorta were studied each crossed by 7 saggital and 7 radial sections. The velocity vectors were measured in the intersection points in three orthogonal direction during the entire cardiac cycle. The reconstructed velocity field was treated using the exact solution. It was shown that on the peak ejection the dominating twisted jet is injected in the aorta from the left ventricle. The interaction of this jet with the residual aortic blood leads to forming of a number of secondary direct and reverse twisting streams that together compose an ensemble with mutually compensated cumulative circulation. Thus the aorta does not undergo an important tangential exposure. The secondary flows appear in consistency with the exact solution and provide the link between main twisting jet and elastic aortic wall forming a 3D boundary layer. As far as the blood flows out from aorta, the intensity of main twisting jet decreases, but the flow twisting inside aorta never interrupts due to cyclic injections of twisting jets. The transversal dynamic pressure gradient in the aorta occurring because of twisting, reaches 600 Pa at the peak systole.

Therefore the flow in the aorta is a structurally organized flow possessing ambiguously defined streamlines which twisting never stops. The mechanism of twisting originates in the intraventricular helical trabecules and papillary muscles relief dynamically changing its configuration with cardiac contraction and relaxation. The formed twisting jet is injected in the aorta, and the jet evolution is definitely described by the exact solution.

At the fourth stage a two-axial model of intraventricular flow was developed which implies flow evolution in correspondance with the exact solution along the inflow axis of the left ventricle during diastole, and outflow axis of the left ventricle during systole. The model supposes that:

A/ the movement of blood is divided into two components : the first is the longitudinal displacement along the converging channel; the second is the tangential twisting around the flow axis;

B/ the direction of twisting in reference to forward motion of blood can never be changed during cardiac cycle;

C/ the radius of flow twisting is essentially less than the radius of flow axis curvature, thus the latter was considered as a straight line,

D/ the ventricular cavity geometry supposes the successive presence of two axes corresponding to the inflow and outflow streams.

The cardiac cycle consists of following four stages:

A/ inflow stream from the left atrium which velocity field should be sewed together with the velocity field of residual intraventricular flow keeping twisting inside the left ventricular cavity (the mitral valve opened);

B/ the turn of the jet from the inflow axis to the outflow axis (both valves closed);

C/ ejection of twisted jet in the aorta (aortic valve opened);

D/ inertial twisting of residual mass of blood inside the left ventricle (both valves closed).

The mathematical approach to cardiac cycle modeling was based on consecutive switching on and switching off the forces applied to forward motion of flow along the converged channel and twisting motion of flow around the axis. The model parameters correspond to individual totality of twisting flow properties, and can be applied as a diagnostic criteria for the flow statement estimation in patients suffering from cardiovascular disorders.

REFERENCES

[1]   Kiknadze G.I. and Krasnov Yu.K., *Dokl.Akad. Nauk SSSR*, 1986, vol. 290. no 6, pp. 1315-1319.

[2]   Kiknadze G.I., Oleinikov V.G., Gachechiladze I.A., Gorodkov A.Yu., Dobrova N.B., Baquey Ch., Barat J.-L., *Doklady Biophysics*, 1996, vols 349-351, pp. 59-62.

[3]   Бокерия Л.А., Городков А.Ю., Кикнадзе Г.И., Соколов М.В., *Бюлл. НЦССХ им. А.Н. Бакулева РАМН*, 2002, т. 3 № 7, с. 99-112.

BUILDING COUPLED 3D–1D–0D MODELS IN COMPUTATIONAL HEMODYNAMICS

Pablo J. Blanco

Laboratório Nacional de Computação Científica, Petrópolis, Brazil, 25651-075, pjblanco@lncc.br
Instituto Nacional de Ciência e Tecnologia em Medicina Assistida por Computação Científica,
Petrópolis, Brazil

Márcio R. Pivello

Universidade Federal de Uberlândia, Brazil, 38400-902, pivello@mecanica.ufu.br
Instituto Nacional de Ciência e Tecnologia em Medicina Assistida por Computação Científica,
Petrópolis, Brazil

Santiago A. Urquiza

Laboratorio de Bioingeniería, Universidad Nacional de Mar del Plata, Mar del Plata, Argentina, 7600,
santiago.urquiza@gmail.com
Instituto Nacional de Ciência e Tecnologia em Medicina Assistida por Computação Científica,
Petrópolis, Brazil

Raúl A. Feijóo

Laboratório Nacional de Computação Científica, Petrópolis, Brazil, 25651-075, feij@lncc.br
Instituto Nacional de Ciência e Tecnologia em Medicina Assistida por Computação Científica,
Petrópolis, Brazil

ABSTRACT

Nowadays, in the computational hemodynamics field there is an increasing need for reproducing accurately physiological blood flow regimes encountered in the cardiovascular system, as well as to simulate coupled global/local phenomena, with the purpose of retrieving as much information as possible from the numerical simulations. In this context, the present work is concerned with the variational derivation of the so-called geometrical multi-scale models which provide mainly two advantages aligned to the needs identified above, giving rise to the 3D–1D–0D coupled models. Also, two examples of application to show the potentialities of these dimensionally-heterogeneous coupled models in computational hemodynamics are provided.

Key Words: *computational hemodynamics, multi-scale modelling, variational approach, 3D–1D–0D models, physiological regimes.*

1   INTRODUCTION

In last years, numerical simulation have played a main role in the field of computational hemodynamics. Several approaches can be identified in this field. We can work, on one hand, with simplified mathematical models to model the global behavior of the arterial system [1,6]. On the other hand, full three-dimensional simulations help researchers to analyze the local behavior of blood flow [3,8].

With these two alternatives at hand, other questions emerged for which 3D or 1D standalone models might not give accurate answers. Studying the interaction between local and global phenomena under real physiological regimes led researchers to integrate simple and complex representations. Thus, coupled 1D and 3D models yielded new mathematical challenges and new possibilities [2,4,5,9].

Specifically, in this work we present a consistent variational derivation of a 3D–1D–0D multi-scale model of the cardiovascular system taking into account for the local circulation (3D), global circulation (1D) and peripheral circulation (0D). Then, we use the coupled model in applications to show the potentialities of the technique. Section 2 presents some remarks about the use of coupled models, as well as the mathematical formulation. Section 3 is devoted to the applications. Final comments are drawn in Section 4.

2 MATHEMATICAL FORMULATION

A multi-scale approach to this problem is able to couple several elements of interest in the analysis: (i) all the complexity of 3D blood flow circulation in complex arterial districts such as bifurcations, tortuous vessels, valves among others; (ii) all the complexity of the systemic response such that, for a given heart beat (input) we obtain the conformation of the cardiac pulse (the output); (iii) all the influence of peripheral beds, taking into account the peripheral resistance and compliance that determines the overall state of the arterial network as well as rules the blood flow distribution. In what follows the multi-scale model of the arterial tree will be developed (see [2] for more details).

Let a domain Ω split into three parts $\Omega = (\Omega_0 \cup \Omega_1 \cup \Omega_3)^\circ$ through two coupling interfaces (Γ_{01} and Γ_{13}) for the coupling between the 0D and 1D, and the 1D and 3D respectively. The fluid velocity and pressure are denoted by $(\mathbf{u}_0, p_0)$, $(\mathbf{u}_1, p_1)$ and $(\mathbf{u}_3, p_3)$ for the 0D, 1D and 3D correspondingly. The kinematical hypotheses considered for each sub-domain are the following $\mathbf{u}_0 = u_0 \mathbf{e}_z$, $\mathbf{u}_1 = u_1(z)\mathbf{e}_z$ and $\mathbf{u}_3 = \mathbf{u}_3(\mathbf{x})$ where $\mathbf{e}_z$ is the unit axial vector. As a consequence, it is $p_0 = p_0$, $p_1 = p_1(z)$, $p_3 = p_3(\mathbf{x})$. Over the lateral boundary of Ω_3 we consider adherence of the fluid flow, while in its free outlet we take homogeneous Neumann boundary conditions. Over the inlet of Ω_0 we consider a Neumann boundary condition p_t. The blood is a Newtonian fluid and the area in the 0D and 1D models is denoted by A_0 and A_1 respectively. The length of the 0D model is L_0, and the 1D interval is I_1.

The extended variational principle is the following: find $((u_0, u_1, \mathbf{u}_3), (p_1, p_3), t_{01}, t_{13}) \in \mathcal{U}_d \times \mathcal{P}_d \times \mathcal{T}'_d$ such that

$$\left(A_0 \rho L_0 \tfrac{du_0}{dt} + 8\pi\mu L_0 u_0\right)v_0 + \int_{I_1} \left[A_1\rho\tfrac{\partial u_1}{\partial t}v_1 + A_1\rho u_1\tfrac{\partial u_1}{\partial z}v_1 - A_1 p_1\tfrac{\partial v_1}{\partial z} - p_1\tfrac{\partial A_1}{\partial z}v_1 + 8\pi\mu u_1 v_1\right]dz$$
$$+ \int_{\Omega_3}\left[\rho\tfrac{\partial \mathbf{u}_3}{\partial t}\cdot\mathbf{v}_3 + \rho(\nabla\mathbf{u}_3)\mathbf{u}_3\cdot\mathbf{v}_3 - p_3\,\mathrm{div}\,\mathbf{v}_3 + 2\mu\varepsilon(\mathbf{u}_3)\cdot\varepsilon(\mathbf{v}_3)\right]d\mathbf{x} =$$
$$- A_0 p_t v_0 + t_{01}(v_0 - v_1)\big|_{\Gamma_{01}} + s_{01}(u_0 - u_1)\big|_{\Gamma_{01}}$$
$$+ t_{13}\left(v_1 - \tfrac{1}{|\Gamma_{13}|}\int_{\Gamma_{13}}\mathbf{v}_3\cdot\mathbf{e}_z\,d\Gamma\right)\big|_{\Gamma_{13}} + s_{13}\left(u_1 - \tfrac{1}{|\Gamma_{13}|}\int_{\Gamma_{13}}\mathbf{u}_3\cdot\mathbf{e}_z\,d\Gamma\right)\big|_{\Gamma_{13}}$$
$$\forall((v_0, v_1, \mathbf{v}_3), s_{01}, s_{13}) \in \mathcal{V}_d \times \mathcal{T}'_d, \quad (1a)$$

$$\int_{I_1}\left[\tfrac{\partial A_1}{\partial t} + \tfrac{\partial}{\partial z}(A_1 u_1)\right]q_1\,dz + \int_{\Omega_3} q_3\,\mathrm{div}\,\mathbf{u}_3\,d\mathbf{x} = 0 \qquad \forall(q_1, q_3) \in \mathcal{P}_d, \quad (1b)$$

with proper initial boundary conditions and $A_1|_{\Gamma_{13}} = |\Gamma_{13}|$. Note that p_0 is not an unknown in the 0D model, but the pressure drop, that is $A_0\Delta p_0 = t_{01} - A_0 p_t$. Also, $\mathcal{U}_d = \{(u_0, u_1, \mathbf{u}_3) \in \mathbb{R} \times H^1(I_1) \times \mathbf{H}^1(\Omega_3); \mathbf{u}_3|_{\Gamma_{L_3}} \text{ satisfies b.c.}\}$, $\mathcal{P}_d = L^2(I_1) \times L^2(\Omega_3)$, $\mathcal{V}_d$ is the space associated to the linear manifold $\mathcal{U}_d$, and $\mathcal{T}'_d = \mathbb{R} \times \mathbb{R}$. The area A_1, and the domain Ω_3 are unknowns, so problem (1) is closed with the following constitutive relations for the arterial walls

$$p_1 = p_r + \tfrac{E\pi R_r h_r}{A_1}\left(\sqrt{\tfrac{A_1}{A_r}} - 1\right) + \tfrac{k\pi R_r h_r}{A_1}\tfrac{1}{2\sqrt{A_r A_1}}\tfrac{\partial A_1}{\partial t} \qquad \text{in } I_1, \quad (2)$$

$$p_3 = p_r + \tfrac{Eh_r}{R_r^2}\zeta_3 + \tfrac{kh_r}{R_r^2}\tfrac{\partial\zeta_3}{\partial t} \qquad \text{over } \Gamma_{L_3}, \quad (3)$$

where r indicates reference values, E is the Young modulus, k the viscoelastic coefficient, R the radius of curvature, h the thickness, A_1 the area of the 1D domain and ζ_3 the displacement of the arterial wall in the direction of the normal $\mathbf{n}_3$ in the 3D model over Γ_{L3}. Then, the velocity over Γ_{L3} is obtained by doing $\mathbf{u}_3|_{\Gamma_{L3}} = \frac{\partial \zeta_3}{\partial t}\mathbf{n}_3$. For the derivation of the Euler–Lagrange equations and for the approximation of the problem see [9].

3   EXAMPLES OF APPLICATION

In all the examples presented here we make use of the 1D model given in [1] and the heart cardiac ejection used is given in [7]. Firstly, a 11 cm-long vessel district corresponding to the iliac bifurcation was embedded in the 1D model of the arterial tree. In this example we analyze the physiological blood flow at the iliac bifurcation for different spatial discretizations (case (i): 41000 nodes, case (ii): 77000 nodes, case (iii): 208000 nodes) and put attention in both the global and local solutions. In figure 1 we see how the global solution (mean pressure and flow rate) is affected by the 3D spatial discretization in the case (i), mainly at the proximal location in the flow curve.

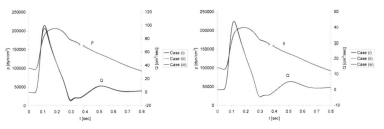

(a) Abdominal aorta (proximal location).   (b) Left iliac artery (distal location).

Figure 1: Solution at the global scale (1D model) over the coupling interfaces.

When looking at the OSI index (see Figure 2) we see that the differences are small, and the main characteristics are the same in the three cases.

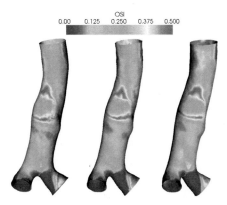

Figure 2: OSI indicator (from left to right cases (i), (ii) and (iii)).

Secondly, we study the influence in local hemodynamics, again under physiological regimes, to the size of a cerebral aneurysm. We employ three different sizes. In this case, we aim at comparing the intra-aneurismal blood flow behavior, comparing the values of the WSS index. This is done for two time instants. In Figure 3, we see that the blood flow produces a larger value of the shear stress in the region just after the aneurysm when the pathology is more critical.

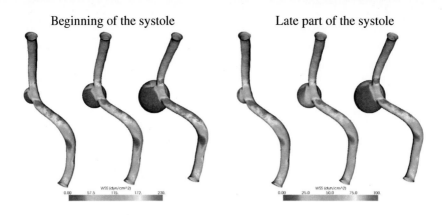

Beginning of the systole   Late part of the systole

Figure 3: Behavior of shear stresses over the endothelium.

4   CONCLUSIONS

In this work we have presented a closed framework to deal, in a variational context, with multi-scale computational hemodynamics. Thus, we have presented the model as well as examples of application that give evidences about the performance and potentialities of coupled 3D–1D–0D models with the aim of simulating the blood flow in 3D arterial vessels under the physiological conditions resulting from systemic interaction.

REFERENCES

[1]   A.P. Avolio, Multi–branched model of the human arterial system, *Med. Biol. Engrg. Comp.*, 18, 709-718, 1980.

[2]   P.J. Blanco, R.A. Feijóo and S.A. Urquiza, A unified variational approach for coupling 3D–1D models and its blood flow applications, *Comp. Meth. Appl. Mech. Engrg.*, 196, 4391-4410, 2007.

[3]   J.R. Cebral, P.J. Yim, R. Lohner, O. Soto and P.L. Choyke, Blood flow modeling in carotid arteries with computational fluid dynamics and MR Imaging, *Acad. Radiol.*, 9, 1286-1299, 2002.

[4]   L. Formaggia, J.F. Gerbeau, F. Nobile and A. Quarteroni, On the coupling of 3D and 1D Navier–Stokes equations for flow problems in compliant vessels, *Comp. Meth. Appl. Mech. Engrg.*, 191, 561-582, 2001.

[5]   F. Migliavacca, R. Balossino, G. Pennati, G. Dubini, T.-Y. Hsia, M.R. de Leval and E.L. Bove, Multiscale modelling in biofluidynamics: Application to reconstructive paediatric cardiac surgery, *J. Biomech.*, 39, 1010-1020, 2006.

[6]   N. Stergiopulos, D.F. Young and T.R. Rogge, Computer simulation of arterial flow with applications to arterial and aortic stenoses, *J. Biomech.*, 25, 1477-1488, 1992.

[7]   J.C. Stettler, P. Niederer and M. Anliker, Theoretical analysis of arterial hemodynamics including the influence of bifurcations, part I, *Ann. Biomed. Engrg.*, 9, 145-164, 1981.

[8]   C.A. Taylor, T.J.R. Hughes and C.K. Zarins, Finite element modeling of blood flow in arteries, *Comp. Meth. Appl. Mech. Engrg.*, 158, 155-196, 1998.

[9]   S.A. Urquiza, P.J. Blanco and M.J. Vénere and R.A. Feijóo, Multidimensional modeling for the carotid blood flow, *Comp. Meth. Appl. Mech. Engrg.*, 195, 4002-4017, 2006.

Estimation of Contact Force Distribution between Stent and Vascular Wall to Design Suitable Stent Shape

Daisuke Yoshino
Department of Mechanical Systems and Design, Tohoku University
6-6-01, Aramaki-Aoba, Aoba, Sendai, Japan
yoshino@elm.mech.tohoku.ac.jp

Katsumi Inoue
Department of Mechanical Systems and Design, Tohoku University
6-6-01, Aramaki-Aoba, Aoba, Sendai, Japan
inoue@elm.mech.tohoku.ac.jp

ABSTRACT

A medical device of mesh-shaped tubular structure called stent is frequently used to expand the stenosis of a blood vessel. The stents are required to satisfy scaffolding property, namely sufficient radial force to ensure vessel patency. But if the force caused by expansion of blood vessel is too large, blood vessel wall may be dameged. Therefore, the evaluation of radial force to support blood vessel is important, so that a suitable stent is designed. In this paper, the contact force distribution between a self-expandable stent and blood vessel wall is computed using a finite element method. In addition, stress state of the stent into an artery is obtained from contact force distribution. Finally, it is discussed that the analysis presented in this paper is useful to design a suitable stent for patients.

Key Words: *self-expandable stent, blood vessel, shape design, patient's condition.*

1 INTRODUCTION

A stent is a tubular medical implement used for the treatment of stenoses developed in arteries. If the endothelial cells of a blood vessel are damaged because of stimulus by hypertension, diabetes mellitus, etc., fat accumulates thickly onto vessel walls, eventually causing arteriosclerosis. The stents are required to satisfy scaffolding property, namely sufficient radial force to ensure vessel patency.

The risk for damage of vascular wall is increased by the excessive force at stent ends generated by the expansion of blood vessel. In case vascular wall is damaged, neointimal proliferation is encouraged in the lesion area. As a result, in-stent restenosis arises. To solve this problem, a medicine such as immunosuppressant and drug eluting stents (DES) have already been used in clinical practice (for example [1] and [2]). However, no papers have reproted that the neointimal proliferation is inhibited by improvement of bare metal stents (BMS) themselves, as far as the authors know.

In this paper, a self-expandable stent called SENDAI stent is targeted. Focusing attention on importance of scaffolding property of a stent, the contact force distribution between a stent and vascular wall is computed using a finite element method. In addition, stress state of the stent into artery is obtained from the distributed contact force, and usefulness of the presented analysis is discussed.

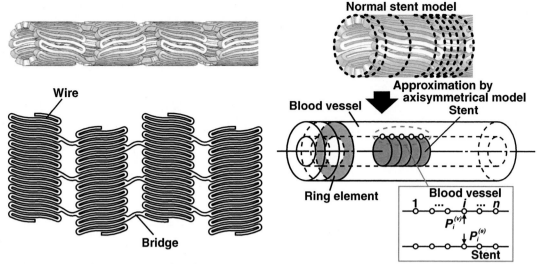

Figure 1. 2D drawing and 3D model of SENDAI stent   Figure 2. Axisymmetrical model for analysis

2 SENDAI STENT

SENDAI stent is a self-expandable stent on which the authors conduct cooperative research with Tohoku University School of Medicine and Tohoku Institute of Technology. The two-dimensional (2D) drawing of SENDAI stent is illustrated in Figure 1. Every wire part consists of 12 pieces of wavy wire and the strut part connects them by 3 bridge wires. The stent is made of Nitinol tube of 1.85 mm in diameter, 40-80 mm long and about 0.25 mm thick.

The authors have presented a design support system of self-expandable stent [3], [4], and the three-dimensional (3D) models in Figure 1 are generated by the system.

3 DISTRIBUTION OF CONTACT FORCE BETWEEN STENT AND VASCULAR WALL

The expansion of the stent in a blood vessel induces a pressure in the contact surfaces of the stent and the vessel. The analysis of the pressure, or contact force; based on a complicated shape of stent shown in Figure 1 is not very easy but a time-consuming task. A simplified method of analysis is presented by using the axisymmetrical models shown in Figure 2 instead. Assuming an axisymmetrical deformation of the stent due to uniformly distributed radial force, the stent is modeled the rings indicated by broken lines in Figure 2. Each wire part is represented by five rings. The blood vessel, which is longer than the stent, is similarly modeled by the rings, where the intervals of the rings are same as those of the stent.

Let's consider contact points i (i = 1, 2, ..., n) along the contact line on stent and vascular wall. When a unit radial force is applied to a point i of model k ($k = s, v$; which corresponds to stent and vessel, respectively), the displacement in radial direction at a point j denoted by $r_{ji}^{(k)}$ are calculated by a finite element method. Introducing influence matrix $[H^{(k)}]$ which is defined by $r_{ji}^{(k)}$ in the following from

$$[H^{(k)}] = [\, r_1^{(k)}, r_2^{(k)}, ..., r_n^{(k)} \,] \tag{1}$$

where

$$\{r_i^{(k)}\} = (\, r_{1i}^{(k)}, r_{2i}^{(k)}, ..., r_{ni}^{(k)} \,)^T.$$

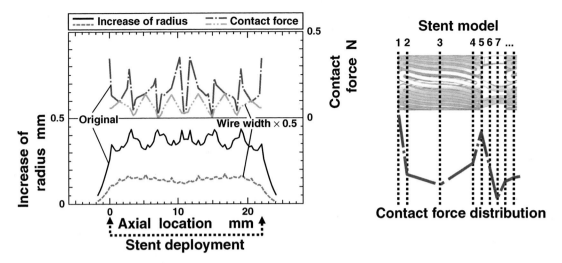

Figure 3. Contact force distribution and increase of radius of femoral artery

The contact force $\{P^{(k)}\}$ along the contact line is related to the displacement in radial direction $\{r^{(k)}\}$ at each point so as to satisfy the following equation

$$[H^{(k)}]\{P^{(k)}\} = \{r^{(k)}\}. \tag{2}$$

Therefore, the following expressions; namely, the equilibrium equation and the condition of contact, should be satisfied at every points of contact. Here, $R_i^{(s)}$, $R_i^{(v)}$ denote initial radii of stent and blood vessel on a point i in the contact area, respectively.

$$P_i^{(v)} + P_i^{(s)} = 0, \quad P_i = P_i^{(v)} = -P_i^{(s)} \tag{3}$$

$$R_i^{(v)} + r_i^{(v)} = R_i^{(s)} + r_i^{(s)} \tag{4}$$

Consequently, the equation of the cpntact force and accompanying displacement is derived from equation (2), (3) and (4) as follows

$$[H^{(v)} + H^{(s)}]\{P\} = \{R^{(s)} - R^{(v)}\}. \tag{5}$$

In case SENDAI stent with a diameter of 10 mm is inserted into femoral artery with an internal diameter of 6.2 mm, the contact force distribution and increase of radius of femoral artery are shown in Figure 3. Young's modulus and Poisson's ratio of Nitinol are assumed as 28 GPa and 0.3, respectively. Also, Young's modulus and Poisson's ratio of femoral artery are 0.49 MPa and 0.49. The excessive forces to expand the artery are induced at the ends of each wire. In case of the stent with one-half wire width, the peaks of contact force are considerably decreased; on the other hand the expansion-ability of stent reduces. The analysis clearly demonstrates the importance of shape design of stent to realize a suitable stent for patients.

4 STRESS STATE OF STENT INTO ARTERY

The contact force distribution is applied to stent models to simulate the stress of the stent into the artery. The stress distribution and maximum von Mises stress in the representative areas are shown in Figure 4. The difference between stress values of Area 1 and ones of Area 2 is not so large. Altogerther, extreme increase of stress doesn't occur at both wire ends and the connection between wire and bridge.

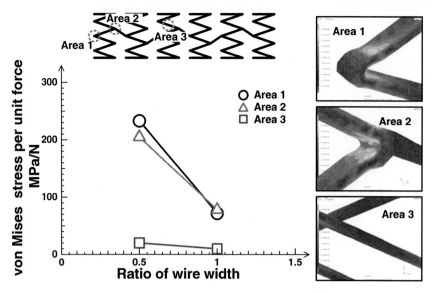

Figure 4. Stress state of stent into femoral artery

5 CONCLUSIONS AND FUTURE WORK

In this paper, the contact force distribution between a stent and vascular wall was computed using finite element method. In addition, stress state of stent into the artery was obtained by the distributed contact force.

The authors have presented a simplified determination of the mechanical properties of stent from the patient's condition and clinical requirement [3], [4]. The design variables in stent shape design will be discussed in the future work by combining the analysis in this paper with the above-motioned preliminary design of stents

REFERENCES

[1] M.-C. Morice, P. W. Serruys, J. E. Sousa, J. Fajadet, E. B. Hayashi, M. Perin, A. Colombo, G. Schuler, P. Barragan, G. Guagliumi, F. Molnar and R. Falotico, A Randmized Comparison of a Sirolimus-Eluting Stent with a Standard Stent for Coronary Revascularization, *The New England Journal of Medicine*, 346, pp.1773-1780, 2002.

[2] D. Fukuda, M. Sata, K. Tanaka and R. Nagai, Potent Inhibitory Effect of Sirolimus on Circulating Vascular Progenitor Cells, *Circulation, Journal of the American Heart Association*, 111, pp.926-931, 2005.

[3] D. Yoshino, K. Inoue and Y. Narita, Mechanical Properties of Self-Expandable Stents: A Key to Product Design of Suitable Stents, *Proceeding of the Seventh International Symposium on Tools and Methods of Competitive Engineering*, pp.659-672, 2008.

[4] D. Yoshino, K. Inoue and Y. Narita, Understanding the Mechanical Properties of Self-Expandable Stents: A Key to Successful Product Development, *Journal of Mechanical Engineering Strojniški Vestnik*, 54, 6, pp.471-485, 2008.

1st International Conference on Mathematical and Computational Biomedical Engineering – CMBE2009
June 29 – July 1, 2009, Swansea, UK
P. Nithiarasu and R. Löhner (eds)

A LUMPED PARAMETERS MODEL TO STUDY LEFT VENTRICLE DISEASES AND TO PREDICT SURGICAL THERAPIES

V. Gramigna, G. Fragomeni
Department of Experimental and Clinical Medicine, Magna Graecia University,
Catanzaro, ITALY, {gramigna, fragomeni}@unicz.it

ABSTRACT

Heart failure (HF) is a pathology increasingly prevalent and has become a major challenge for health care providers. Improved knowledge of its pathogenesis has led to an increase in the number of pharmacologic and non-pharmacologic therapies used. Although it begins with an inability of the cardiac pump to meet the energetic requirements of the body, over time, the syndrome of heart failure perturbs many systems, from the heart itself to the periphery [1]. Currently applied strategies for early diagnosis of HF are not sufficient. A computer model able to simulate this pathology and to analyse heart pathological parameters is necessary to assess the prognosis of HF and to find an adapted treatment. Aim of the present work is to develop a non linear time-varying elastance (NTVE) model in order to investigate this pathology. Particularly, this model allows to evaluate effects of Left Ventricle (LV) in three different pathological working conditions. This model allows the simulation of all three pathologies varying the specific parameters internal to the model itself. Moreover it permits a comparison between physiological and pathological LV parameters. It can be seen as a means for diagnosis and indication of medical and/or surgical therapies. In particular Dor procedure [2] (endoventricular circular patch plasty repair of LV with associated coronary grafting) is a relative new surgical technique that applies to patients with ventricular dysfunction after an infarction. This surgical procedure consists of reducing and reconstructing LV chamber by using an endoventricular circular patch and grafting diseased coronary vessels. The above-mentioned model could be seen as a means to simulate the results of this technique and to analyze how, in comparison with pathological conditions, it could improve LV functions.

Key Words: *Heart Failure, Lumped Parameter Model, Ventricle remodelling.*

1. INTRODUCTION

Traditionally, haemodynamic definitions of heart failure have been used to classify and describe HF giving rise to terms such as high and low output cardiac failure, right, left or congestive cardiac failure. This definitions are based on the patient's signs and symptoms [3].The history of mathematical models is closely related to the evolution of mathematics. A model can be as simple as one equation, but the contemporary available computing power has opened the doors for much more complicated models. The main advantage of mathematical models is that they are cheap and flexible instruments [3]. Aim of this work is to validate computer model in physiological conditions and analyse LV failure comparing ventricular parameters in physiological and pathological conditions. This model can be used as a means for the diagnosis and indication of medical and/or surgical therapies. In comparison with the other studied lumped parameters models, it is able to simulate HF by means of variations of internal parameters and, consequently, to evaluate in advance the fundamental characteristics of LV following surgical therapies. For example, Dor procedure, a relatively new surgical technique that applies to patients with ventricular dysfunction, consists of reducing and reconstructing LV chamber by using an endoventricular circular patch. The above-mentioned model could be seen as a means to simulate this surgery and to analyze how, in comparison with the pathological conditions, it could improve LV functions.

2. MODEL AND METHODOLOGY

LV is represented by a NTVE model, including internal resistance. The latter allows to evaluate internal dissipation of energy during ejection [4, 5, 6]. In this model, it is possible to link the instantaneous blood pressure and volume inside the ventricle, during the whole cardiac cycle, by means of differential equation [3, 7, 8]. Differential elastance is the slope of a function, which can be used to indicate both the relation when the ventricle is at rest -end-diastolic pressure-volume relationship (EDPVR) - and the relation when the ventricle is maximally stimulated -end-systolic pressure-volume relationship (ESPVR)-.EDPVR function is described by equation which can be seen as the sum of a straight line and an equilateral hyperbole. The slope of the line is equal to E_{min} while the hyperbole has vertical asymptote represented by ventricular volume saturation V_{sat}. Graphically, ESPVR function is a parable characterized by downward concavity, vertex having coordinates (V^*, P^*). Atrium is described by means of similar relations, but with different parameters [10, 11]. A Guyton's model has been used to represent the venous circuit [7], while the output of the ventricle is loaded by a Noordergraaf's model of the arterial systemic circuit [8, 12]. Valves are represented by means of a resistor and a diode (Fig. 1).

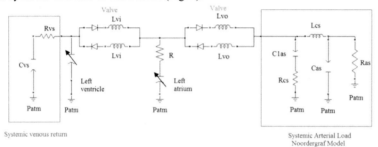

Fig.1: Guyton's and Noordegraaf's models

3. COMPUTER SIMULATION AND DISCUSSION

HF is defined as a state in which the heart is unable to meet the demands for blood flow without an excessive use of physiological compensatory mechanism. The most prominent physiologic compensatory mechanism is the increase in stroke volume associated with increased pre-load (Frank-Starling mechanism). Symptoms of HF usually result from pulmonary venous congestion secondary to high pulmonary venous pressure produced by the need for high ventricular filling pressure [4]. Different working conditions for LV have been considered and computer simulations have been carried out. In order to use the above-mentioned model to simulate pathological working conditions of LV, the model has been validated with physiological parameters. Results coming from physiological simulation are concurring with literature [4]. Cases a), b) and c) show three different pathological working conditions for LV in presence of HF.

Case a) LV pathological model in presence of valve incompetence
This case includes any condition in which the systolic and diastolic function of the heart is normal. However, there is a high workload on the heart, such as the need for greater stroke. This situation appears, for example, in the presence of LV pathologies, such as valve incompetence. When the valve is incompetent, the heart has to work harder. It has to pump more blood than earlier, because a portion of it goes back into the heart and has to be pumped out again. Afterload impedance is elevated, leading to a smaller stroke volume from any given end-diastolic pressure [4].This pathological situation in computer model can be simulated by modifying the numerical value of arterial systemic resistance and the pressure of saturation of parable, which represents ESPVR function in atrium. Figure 2-*a* shows physiologic elastance curves and PV loop for the physiological and pathological conditions in *case a*. Pressure, flow rate and volume waveform are shown in Figure 3-*a*.

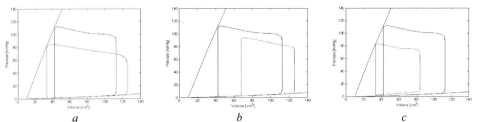

Fig.2: Schematic diagram illustrating three types of heart failure syndromes. Each panel compares a normal PV-loop (*black loop*) with a PV-loop for HF (*red loop*). *a) case a, b) case b, c) case c*

Case b) LV pathological model in presence of reduced contractility

In this case, HF involves conditions associated with a decreased systolic function of the heart . In healthy conditions, the increased filling of LV results in an increased contractility and, thus, in a rise in cardiac output. In HF this mechanism fails as the LV is loaded with blood to the point where heart muscle contraction becomes less efficient. With a downward shift of ESPVR, the stroke volume from any given end-diastolic volume decreases. To maintain stroke volume, the circulatory system increases left ventricular diastolic volume and pressure into the symptomatic range [13]. In order to simulate this pathological situation in computer model, it is possible to modify the pressure of saturation of parable (which represents ESPVR function in LV). In fact, a decrease of this parameter produces a downward shift of ESPVR. Consequently, since EDPVR remains unchanged, the stroke volume decreases. Figure 2-*b* shows physiological elastance curves and PV-loop for both physiological and pathological conditions in *case b*. Pressure, flow rate and volume waveform are shown in Figure 3-*b*.

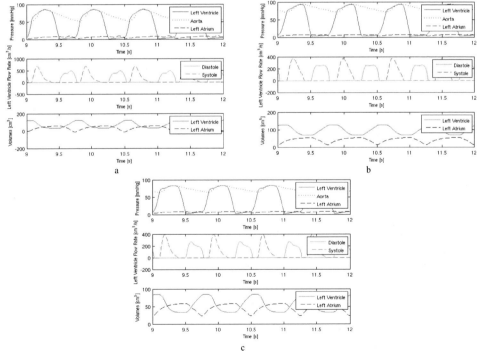

Fig.2 Pressure, flow rate and volume waveform. *a) case a, b) case b, c) case c.*

Case c) LV pathological model in presence of diastolic dysfunction

Finally, case *c* appears in presence of LV pathologies, such as diastolic dysfunction. This term refers to changes in ventricular diastolic properties that have an adverse effect on stroke volume. In this case diastolic function is impaired, so that ventricular diastolic filling is inadequate. The diastolic pressure-volume relationship line has shifted to the left [6, 12]. The parameter which can be modify in order to simulate this pathological situation is E_{min}. In fact, as shown in Figure 2-c, when decreasing E_{min}, the diastolic pressure-volume relationship line has shifted to the left, so that the stroke volume from any given end-diastolic pressure is decreased Figure 3-c shows pressure, flow rate and volume waveform for *case c*.

4. CONCLUSIONS

Aim of this study was to validate LV time-varying elastance model and to investigate behaviors of a left ventricle in presence of three typologies of heart failure. This model can be seen as a means for diagnosis and indication of medical and/or surgical therapies. As future work, it would be useful to apply this model in order to simulate other LV pathologies and to plan surgical interventions. In particular Dor procedure is a relatively new surgical technique that applies to patients with ventricular dysfunction after an infarction for either akinesia or dyskinesia. It consists of reducing and reconstructing LV chamber by using an endoventricular circular patch and grafting diseased coronary vessels. Post-infarction are characterized by changes in shape and function (remodeling) frequently complicated by functional mitral regurgitation leading to cardiac dysfunction and clinical HR. It has been shown that Dor procedure improves pump function, clinical status and survival, even in patients with severe cardiac dysfunction [2]. The above-mentioned model could be seen as a means to simulate this surgery and to analyze how, in comparison with the pathological conditions, it could improve LV functions.

REFERENCES

[1]   B. Mettauer, J. Zoll, A. Garnier, R. Ventura-Clapier, Heart failure: a model of cardiac and skeletal muscle energetic failure, *Pfugers Arch Eur J Physiol*, 452, 653-666, 2006.

[2]   M. Di Donato, M. Sabatier, V. Dor, G. F. Gensini, A. Toso, M. Maioli, A. W. H. Stanley, C. Athanasuleas, G. Buckberg, Effect of the Dor Procedure on left ventricular dimension and shape and geometric correlates of mitral regurgitation one year after surgery, *The American association for Thoracic Surgery*, 121, 0022-5223, 2001

[3]   W. J. C. Hobbs and L. Cotter, Management of heart failure , *Current Anaesthesia & Critical Care*, 12, 273-280, 2001.

[4]   A. C. Guyton, C. E. Jones, T. G. Coleman, Cardiac Output and its Regulation, *Circulatory Physiology Second Edition edn*, W.B. Saunders; 1973.

[5]   P Segers, N Stergiopulos, N Westerhof, Relation of effective arterial elastance to arterial system properties, *Am J Physiol Heart Circ Physiol*, 282, H1401-H1046, 2002.

[6]   M. S. Maurer, D. Spevack, D. Burkhoff, I. Kronzon, Diastolic dysfunction: can it be diagnosed by Doppler echocardiography?, *J Am Coll Cardiol*, 44, 1543-9, 2004.

[7]   H. Suga, Ventricular energetics, *Physiol Rev*, 70 , 247-277, 1990.

[8]   F. M. Colacino, M. Arabia, F. Moscato, GA. Danieli, Modeling, analysis, and validation of a pneumatically driven left ventricle for use in mock circulatory systems, *Med Eng Phys*, 29 (8), 829-839, 2007.

[9]   H. Suga, Time course of left ventricular pressure-volume relationship under various extents of aortic occlusion, *Jpn Heart J.*, 11, 373-8, 1970.

[10]   J. Alexander Jr, K. Sunagawa, N. Chang, K. Sagawa, Instantaneous pressure-volume relation of the ejecting canine left atrium, *Circ Res*, 61 (2), 209-219, 1987.

[11]   R. Y. Grimes, R. A. Levine, P. G. Walker, A. P. Yoganathan, Dynamics of systolic pulmonary venous flow in mitral regurgitation: mathematical modeling of the pulmonary venous system and atrium, *J Am Soc Echocardiogr*, 8, 631-642, 1995.

[12]   R. Nishio, S. Sasayama and A. Matsumori, Left ventricular pressure-volume relationship in a murine model of congestive heart failure due to acute viral myocarditis, *J Am Coll Cardiol*, 40, 1506-14, 2002.

[13]   G. Drzewiecki, J. Wang, J. Li, J. Kedem, H. Weiss, Modeling of mechanical dysfunction in regional stunned myocardium of the left ventricle, *IEEE Trans Biomed Eng*, 43 (12),1151-1163, 1996.

A MODEL OF NEONATAL PULMONARY ATRESIA WITH INTACT VENTRICULAR SEPTUM AND RV-DEPENDENT CORONARY FLOW: CAN COLLATERALS PROTECT THE HEART FROM ISCHEMIA?

Jonathan P. Mynard
Heart Research Group, Murdoch Children's Research Institute, Australia,
jonathan.mynard@mcri.edu.au

Malcolm R. Davidson
Department of Chemical and Biomolecular Engineering, University of Melbourne, Australia,
m.davidson@unimelb.edu.au

Daniel J. Penny
Heart Research Group, Murdoch Children's Research Institute, Australia, dan.penny@rch.org.au

Joseph J. Smolich
Heart Research Group, Murdoch Children's Research Institute, Australia, joe.smolich@mcri.edu.au

ABSTRACT

We developed a model of the neonatal arterial and coronary circulations in the context of pulmonary atresia with intact ventricular septum (PAIVS). PAIVS is characterised by a blocked pulmonary valve orifice and elevated right ventricular (RV) pressure and is often associated with an abnormal connection (fistula) between the RV cavity and a coronary artery (e.g. the left anterior descending artery, LAD). A proximal coronary stenosis is also common and can result in RV-dependent coronary flow, where decompression of the RV by surgical repair of the atresia leads to compromised coronary flow (ischemia). Using a combined one-dimensional (1D) and lumped parameter (0D) model, we simulated PAIVS to investigate the effects of an RV-LAD fistula, LAD stenosis and RV decompression on coronary blood flow patterns. We also simulated coronary collaterals, which develop in response to inadequate blood flow, and found that these provide little protection against ischemia in the setting of PAIVS with RV-LAD fistula and LAD stenosis, since collateral flow is preferentially directed to the low resistance fistula.
Key Words: *newborn circulation, ventriculo-coronary fistula, congenital heart disease*

1 INTRODUCTION

Pulmonary atresia with intact ventricular septum (PAIVS), which occurs in approximately 1 per 10,000 of live births [1], is a congenital heart defect in which the communication between the RV and pulmonary trunk fails to develop. Since the RV pumps into a 'dead end', RV pressure is elevated and the *left* ventricle supplies blood flow to the lungs via the aorta and ductus arteriosus (DA, a fetal shunt that normally closes at birth). Although rare, PAIVS causes death if untreated and, in two-fifths of cases, is complicated by the presence of a direct connection (fistula) between the RV and a coronary artery. Approximately 50% of these display 'RV-dependent coronary flow', in which a region of heart muscle (myocardium) is primarily or exclusively supplied by RV blood rather than aortic blood via the coronary arteries, and which is often associated with a coronary stenosis (narrowing) proximal to the fistula [1]. A known risk of RV-dependent coronary flow is that the RV decompression that occurs with surgical correction of the atresia can reduce coronary flow to dependent myocardial regions, leading to ischemia and heart failure.

Coronary collaterals are conduits that develop in response to inadequate myocardial blood flow, and in many settings (e.g. coronary artery stenosis in adults), provide an alternate source of flow that reduces the risk of irreversible myocardial ischemia. However, whether coronary collaterals provide similar protection in PAIVS and RV-dependent coronary flow is unknown. The aim of this study was thus to develop a computer model of PAIVS and 1) to investigate coronary flow associated with PAIVS, an RV-LAD fistula, an LAD stenosis proximal to the fistula, and RV decompression, and 2) to ascertain whether coronary collaterals are likely to provide protection against ischemia in the context of RV-dependent coronary flow.

2 MAIN BODY

Fig. 1a shows a schematic of the computer model, which consists of 1) 1D arterial segments, 2) ventricles/valves, 3) 0D peripheral vascular beds and 4) 0D intramyocardial coronary circulation.

1D arterial segments. A full description of the 1D equations and their numerical solution is found in [2]. Briefly, the governing equations for a single vessel in 1D are

$$\frac{\partial}{\partial t}\begin{bmatrix} U \\ A \end{bmatrix} + \frac{\partial}{\partial x}\begin{bmatrix} UA \\ \frac{U^2}{2} + \frac{P}{\rho} \end{bmatrix} = \begin{bmatrix} 0 \\ -8\pi\mu\frac{U}{A} \end{bmatrix} \tag{1}$$

where A is cross-sectional area, U is axial velocity, P is pressure, μ and ρ are blood viscosity and density (assumed to be 0.04 poise and 1.06 g/cm^3 respectively). P is related to A via the relation $P = P_{ext} + \beta\left(\sqrt{A} - \sqrt{A_0}\right)$, where external pressure P_{ext} is assumed zero, A_0 is the unstressed cross-sectional area and β is a wall stiffness parameter. For treatment of boundary conditions and branching points, Eq. (1) is expressed in terms of forward- (W_+) and backward-propagating (W_-) characteristics, such that $W_\pm = U \pm 4c$ (where wave speed $c = A^{\frac{1}{4}}\sqrt{\frac{\beta}{2\rho}}$), with the quasi-linear equation

$$\frac{\partial}{\partial t}\begin{bmatrix} W_+ \\ W_- \end{bmatrix} + \frac{\partial}{\partial x}\begin{bmatrix} U+c & 0 \\ 0 & U-c \end{bmatrix}\begin{bmatrix} W_+ \\ W_- \end{bmatrix} = 0 \tag{2}$$

At branching points, U and A for each vessel are calculated by extrapolating the outgoing characteristics [2] and assuming conservation of mass ($Q_{in} = Q_{out}$) and total mechanical energy ($P + \frac{1}{2}\rho U^2$).

Ventricle/valve model. The forward component of ventricular pressure (P_{LV+} or P_{RV+}) is prescribed via the incoming characteristic (W_{v+}) and is composed of two sigmoid curves [2] fused in mid-systole (Fig. 1b), producing isovolumic contraction (IC), ejection (E), isovolumic relaxation (IR) and diastolic filling (DF) phases. Total ventricular pressure is the sum of the prescribed component and a backward-running component arising from the transmission of any backward-running arterial waves (W_{a-}) across the valve [2]. The valve transmits W_{v+} to the arterial side ($W_{v\to a+}$) via $\Delta W_{v\to a+} = T\Delta W_{v+}$, where T is a transmission coefficient equal to 0 for a closed valve, 1 for an open valve, and changes according to a cubic function when opening or closing. The valve also reflects W_{a-} such that $\Delta W_{a\to a+} = R\Delta W_{a-}$, where $R = 1 - T$. The total forward-running arterial characteristic is then $W_{a+} = \Delta W_{v\to a+} + \Delta W_{a\to a+} + W_{a+}^0$, where W_{a+}^0 is the initial value.

0D Peripheral Vascular Beds. At the terminal ends of the 1D arterial tree, the standard 3-element Windkessel model (Fig. 1c) is used to represent the downstream vasculature, with a characteristic impedance (Z_c) in series with the parallel connection of a vascular bed resistance (R_{vb}) and compliance (C_{vb}).

0D intramyocardial coronary circulation. The left and right coronary arteries (LCA and RCA) arise from the aortic root (Fig. 1a) and the LCA branches into the circumflex (Cx) and LAD. These 1D segments terminate in a 0D model of the intramyocardial vasculature [3] (Fig. 1c), consisting of 1)

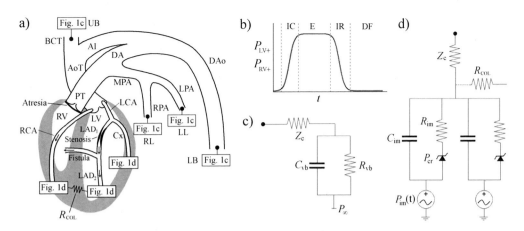

Figure 1: a) Schematic of the model indicating left/right ventricles (LV/RV), valves, 1D arterial segments (PT=Pulmonary Trunk, AoT=Aortic Trunk, BCT=Brachiocephalic Trunk, AI=Aortic Isthmus, DA=Ductus Arteriosus, MPA/LPA/RPA=Main/Left/Right Pulmonary Arteries, DAo=Descending Aorta, LCA/RCA=Left/Right Coronary Arteries, Cx=Circumflex Coronary Artery, LAD=Left Anterior Descending Coronary Artery; note that 1D segments are based on lamb anatomy), vascular beds (UB=Upper Body, LB=Lower Body, LL/RL=Left/Right Lungs), pulmonary atresia, RV-LCA fistula, LCA stenosis and coronary collateral represented by R_{COL}. Arrows indicate directions of positive flow. b) Shape of the prescribed forward component of ventricular pressure. c) 0D model of peripheral vascular beds. d) 0D model of intramyocardial coronary circulation.

a characteristic impedance (Z_c), 2) an inner muscle layer (subendocardium), where intramyocardial pressure (P_{im}) due to contracting myocardium is assumed to equal ventricular pressure, and 3) an outer muscle layer (subepicardium), where P_{im} is assumed to equal 40% of ventricular pressure. Both layers are represented by a 2-element Windkessel (resistance, R_{im}, and compliance, C_{im}) with a zener diode representing critical closing pressure (P_{cr}) and P_{im} to represent vessel compression. Collateral flow is modelled by connecting the LAD and RCA 0D models with a resistance (R_{COL}) (Fig. 1a,d).

Modelling PAIVS. Pulmonary atresia is modelled by setting $T = 0$ for the whole cardiac cycle. Peak P_{RV+} and P_{LV+} for atresia are set to 103 and 57 mmHg respectively, but $P_{RV+} = P_{LV+}$ upon RV decompression (since we have assumed an open DA). The RV-LAD fistula is modelled as a 1D segment (Fig. 1a) with P_{RV+} prescribed at the terminal as a backward component of pressure. The proximal LAD (LAD$_1$) stenosis is modelled as a 90% diameter reduction half-way along the vessel (see Fig. 1a).

Results. With a functional RV valve and $P_{RV+} = P_{LV+}$, LAD, Cx and RCA flow waveforms (Fig. 2a) exhibit the typical coronary flow morphology, with low flow during systole due to myocardial compression, and majority flow in diastole when the heart is relaxed. Introduction of pulmonary atresia and elevated RV pressure (Fig. 2b) causes a 104% increase in LV output (compensating for the absent RV output). A 16% fall in mean aortic pressure causes a 24% reduction in both LAD and Cx flows, however the reduction in RCA flow (42%) is more severe due to the increased RV P_{im}. Adding an RV-LAD fistula leads (Fig. 2c) to a dramatic difference between LAD$_1$ and LAD$_2$ waveforms (previously identical). In systole, the high RV cavity pressure forces flow across the fistula, leading to significant retrograde LAD$_1$ flow but augmentation of LAD$_2$ forward flow. During diastole, the low RV cavity pressure sucks blood out of the LAD, leading to antegrade LAD$_1$ flow; however diastolic LAD$_2$ flow is still positive since LV P_{im} also falls (i.e. an LV intramyocardial suction effect overcomes the RV suction effect). RV decompression (Fig. 2d) significantly reduces RV-LAD flow during systole whereas diastolic flow is relatively unchanged. Importantly, however, there is only a moderate reduction in mean LAD$_2$ flow, showing that *RV-dependent coronary flow does not occur with a fistula alone.* Fig. 2e shows that the addition of an LAD$_1$ stenosis (and elevated P_{RV+}) effectively abolishes LAD$_1$ flow, but in LAD$_2$, the normal coronary flow morphology is reversed. Thus forward flow occurs during systole, with RV blood flowing across the fistula and into the myocardium (via LAD$_2$). However, due to higher coronary compression in the subendocardium during systole, more flow reaches the subepicardium than

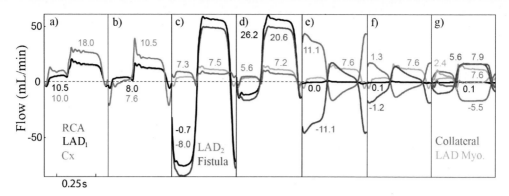

Figure 2: Flow waveforms for a) functional pulmonary valve, b) pulmonary atresia, c) atresia with fistula before and d) after RV decompression, e) atresia with fistula and LCA_1 stenosis before and f) after RV decompression, and g) with collateral flow included. Mean flows are given in mL/min. 'LAD Myo.' is the region of myocardium supplied by the LAD and is the same as LAD_2 flow in all cases except g)

the subendocardium, with a subendocardial-to-supepicardial flow ratio of 0.8, compared to the normal ratio of ~ 1.1. Such a reduced subendocardial flow is known to stimulate development of coronary collaterals. Without these collaterals, RV decompression (Fig. 2f) leads to an 88% reduction in LAD_2 flow compared to a 23% reduction without the stenosis (Fig. 2d), demonstrating that in the presence of a fistula, *the stenosis is primarily responsible for RV-dependent coronary flow*. Importantly, RV decompression in the presence of the LAD stenosis causes complete cessation of subendocardial flow, while only a small amount of flow reaches the subepicardium (1.3 mL/min). Including an RCA-LAD coronary collateral connection (Fig. 2g) results in 7.9 mL/min of collateral flow, where we note that in this case LAD_2 is equal to myocardial plus collateral flows, whereas previously $LAD_2 =$ myocardial flow. However, only 14% of this collateral flow is directed into the myocardium, with negligible augmentation of subendocardial flow, while the remaining 86% flows to the low resistance RV-LAD fistula.

3   CONCLUSIONS

Results from the combined 0D/1D computer model indicate that in the setting of PAIVS and RV-LAD fistula, a) myocardial ischemia due to RV decompression is likely when a proximal LAD stenosis is present, and b) that coronary collaterals may provide very little protection against ischemia since collateral flow is preferentially directed towards the low resistance fistula. These results illustrate that computer modelling is a powerful tool for investigating coronary blood flow dynamics in complex congenital malformations.

REFERENCES

[1]   R.M. Freedom, R.H. Anderson and D. Perrin, The significance of ventriculo-coronary arterial connections in the setting of pulmonary atresia with an intact ventricular septum. *Cardiology in the Young*, 15, 447-468, 2005.

[2]   J.P. Mynard and P. Nithiarasu, A one dimensional arterial blood flow model incorporating ventricular pressure, aortic valve and regional coronary flow using the locally conservative Galerkin (LCG) method, *Communications in Numerical Methods in Engineering*, 24, 367-417, 2008.

[3]   R. Beyar and S. Sideman, Time-dependent coronary blood flow distribution in left ventricular wall. *American Journal of Physiology - Heart & Circulatory Physiology* 252, H417-433, 1987.

Evaluation of computational and analytical models for blood perfusion in perforator flaps

D. Drikakis[1], C. Milionis[1], S. K. Pal[2], S. Patel[1] and E. Shapiro[1]*

ABSTRACT

Arterial flow in the context of plastic or reconstructive surgery is of primary importance to the successful outcome of the procedure. Analytic formulae which are frequently used for the estimates of flow rates in these applications introduce a number of assumptions about the geometry of the artery, the character of the flow and media properties of blood. This paper presents a computational fluid dynamics (CFD) study of a ligated perforator artery using real geometry taken from ex vivo intraoperative angiography. An analytical model is derived for this case under assumptions typically made in the literature and comparisons between the CFD study and the analytical model are presented. The results demonstrate that inherent limitations introduced by these assumptions can lead to pressure drop being under-predicted by up to 30 times. Additional case study is presented allowing to pinpoint the source of the difference to the effects of the real geometry. Observed behaviour highlights the need for CFD modelling of arterial networks.

Key Words: *blood flow, perforator flaps, analytical model, CFD of arterial flows*

1 INTRODUCTION

In free flap surgery, where tissue is excised from one area of a patients body in order to reconstruct another area, the survival of this flap once reattached has a significant dependency on the specifics of the arterial network chosen to supply oxygenated blood to the reconstructed area. The failure of such procedures arises when the tissue flap is insufficiently perfused with oxygenated blood. This can lead to full or partial necrosis of the tissue flap (see, for example, [1, 2]).

Pre-operative measurements of pressure distribution and the flow rate of blood within the chosen arteries present significant challenge. Furthermore it is difficult for surgeons to carry out such measurements during the surgical operation. Hence in order to increase the survival rate of free flap surgery it is important for the surgical staff to be able to pre-operatively assess the arterial properties quickly and accurately.

Coscia and Rubino [3] have investigated from a hemodynamic point of view, the recent operative technique of using perforator flaps instead of more traditional axial flaps in reconstructive surgery. The idea behind the use of perforator flaps is to only harvest the tissue which is required for reconstruction. Once the peripheral pedicle has been identified, the pedicle is traced from periphery to the source vessels whist all branching vessels are ligated. All other tissue is left in situ. This type of flap have been reported in the literature to have a decreasing effect on the morbidity of the donor site [4]. Coscia and Rubino describe the use of a analytical model to predict the fluid flow in the network of a perforator

---

[1]Fluid Mechanics and Computational Sciences Group, Cranfield University, Cranfield, Bedfordshire, MK43 0AL, UK
[2]St Andrew's Centre for Plastic Surgery and Burns, Broomfield Hospital, Chelmsford, Essex, UK
*Authors names in alphab etical order. Corresponding author: D. Drikakis, d.drikakis@cranfield.ac.uk

flap. The construction of the model includes several assumptions including straight circular pipe model for the artery geometry, steady Hagen-Poiseuille flow and Newtonian behaviour of blood. However in-vivo measurements performed for both pre- and post operatively on three patients [3] showed up to 200% deviation from flow rates predicted by the analytical model.

The above discrepancies prompted the investigation into the effects of the assumption made in the analytical model on the actual pressure drop observed presented in this paper. The most appropriate tool for the evaluation of these assumptions is the Computational Fluid Dynamics (CFD) modelling. The use of CFD as a tool to assess arterial blood flow has attracted a wide variety of interest in recent years with the majority of this work being in the context of larger arteries such as the abdominal aorta, coronary artery and the carotid artery [5]. CFD modelling of free flap arterial networks has been conducted with high-resolution methods for a simplified geometry by Patel et al. [6], however to the authors knowledge there has been no CFD investigation of the real geometry of perforator arterial network performed to date. In order to obtain the real geometry of a perforator artery, an ex-vivo intraoperative angiography study by Ohijimi et. al. [7] is utilised. The geometry reported in this paper corresponds to the perforator flap used for the oral carcinoma surgery (see [7], case 11). Further a analytical model is derived under the same assumptions as used by Coscia and Rubino [3] for the linear variation of the perforator diameter with length observed in the chosen flap. CFD simulations of the complete geometry are then performed and results examined in order to shed light on the validity of the assumptions embedded in the analytical model. Non-Newtonian effects are also quantified.

2   MODELLING APPROACH

Coscia and Rubino's [3] analytical model was based on a number of assumption discussed in the introduction of this paper. One of the main assumptions was that the model was based on the artery having a radius a varying according to the following linear form [8] of the tube state equation:

$$a(p) = a_0 + \alpha p, \tag{1}$$

where α is the constant of vessel's compliance, a_0 is the initial radius and p is the local pressure. The geometry reconstruction from the angiogram indicated that the variation of the radius in our case is closer to linear law, given by:

$$a(s) = \frac{s}{L}(a_L - a_0) + a_0, \tag{2}$$

where s is the distance along the centreline of the perforator artery from the inlet and a_0 and a_L denote the initial and the final radius, $a_0 \leq a_L$. The conservation of momentum written locally for a fully developed Hagen-Poiseuille flow in a straight artery with the axis aligned with x is then given by

$$a(x)^4 \frac{dp}{dx} = -\frac{8\mu Q_u}{\pi}, \tag{3}$$

where μ is the constant dynamic viscosity and Q_u is the volume flux. Equation (3) can be integrated between $x = 0$ and $x = L$ to obtain the pressure drop along the artery in the following form

$$p_{out} - p_{in} = \frac{8\mu Q_u}{3\pi a_0^4} C^4 \frac{1}{3} \left(\frac{1}{(L+C)^3} - \frac{1}{C^3} \right), \tag{4}$$

where p_{out} and p_{in} denote outlet and inlet values of pressure, and $C = La_0/(a_L - a_0)$.

Numerical simulations were performed using the commercial software FLUENT (v6.3.26). In order to address Non-Newtonian effects, the Carreau Model was chosen following [9]. The summary of blood viscosity parameters used for both Newtonian and Non-Newtonian simulations can be found in [10]. Computations were performed using the pressure-based second order solver. Grid-dependency study was conducted using grids ranging from 0.5m to 2.25m cells ensuring that numerical solutions are grid-converged to within 2%.

3   RESULTS AND DISCUSSION

The reconstructed geometry of a realistic artery of a perforator flap is presented in Figure 1(a). The reconstruction process involved digitising the angiograms presented by Ohijimi et al. [7], and modelling the artery as a system of connected tubes with linear variation of diameter. The process is reported in detail in [11]. The overall length of the artery along the centreline is $\sim 15cm$. The initial diameter of the artery is $1.5mm$ and the diameter at the outlet is $0.5mm$. Simulations were performed for three different flow rates ranging from $5.2 \cdot 10^{-5}\frac{kg}{s}$ to $2.6 \cdot 10^{-4}\frac{kg}{s}$ according to flow data reported by Rubino et. al [12] for both Newtonian and Non-Newtonian fluids. The pressure drop obtained via the numerical simulations was found to be almost 30 times higher than that predicted by the analytical model. This pattern remained true for all three different flow rates. Furthermore the differences in the pressure drop observed between simulations with Newtonian and Non-Newtonian blood model models were within 11% for all flow rates simulated.

In order to explain this large difference between the numerical simulation and analytical model, one needs to re-examine the rationale behind the analytical model and attempt to evaluate assumptions employed separately.

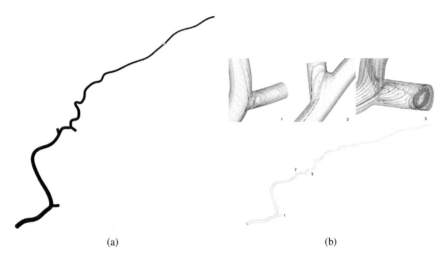

(a)   (b)

Figure 1: Reconstructed artery geometry (a) and areas of flow recirculation (b).

In order to be able to separate the modelling assumptions, it is useful to conduct an intermediate simulation for a straight artery with linearly varying diameter but the same overall length. In this case, the only difference between the full numerical model and the analytical model is the assumption of the fully developed Hagen-Poiseuille flow, which allows us to evaluate its importance. Results of the simulations performed for the Newtonian blood model showed that the pressure drop along the pipe according to the analytic model underpredicted CFD results by $\sim 20\%$, which indicates that the Hagen-Poiseuille flow assumption cannot be responsible for the high deviation from the analytical formula. This observation allows to conclude that the difference between the analytical formula and the numerical model arises primarily because of the effects of the real geometry in comparison with the straight pipe assumption of the analytical model. Indeed, the actual perforator artery geometry in Figure 1(a) has a number of bends and back-flow areas. Furthermore, as shown on Figure 1(b), ligated branches result in large recirculation zones which lead to pressure losses along the perforator artery. The analytical model is unable to account for these important flow features, hence reducing the validity of such models.

4 CONCLUSIONS

An extension to the analytical model of Coscia and Rubino [3] has been presented and compared with numerical simulations of a ligated perforator artery. Numerical simulations demonstrated that the assumptions made in designing the analytical model have a significant effect on the predicted pressure difference along the artery and can lead to pressure drop being under-predicted by up to 30 times. Additional tests conducted lead to the conclusion that the assumption responsible for this drastic effect is that of the simplified geometry. Pressure losses from bends and within the ligated branches in a real perforator artery lead to an increase in pressure drop required to drive the flow through the perforator artery. Viscosity effects from modelling the fluid as either Newtonian or Non-Newtonian were found to be small in comparison to geometrical effects. The differences observed demonstrate that it is necessary to develop more realistic analytical models taking into account the geometry effect in order to assist medical practitioners in the selection of perforator arteries for reconstructive surgery.

References

[1] Alderman, A., Wiltins, E., Kim, H. M., Lowery, J., Complications in postmastectomy breast reconstruction: Two-year results of the Michigan breast reconstruction outcome study, Plastic & Reconstructive Surgery, 109(7), pp. 2265–2274, 2002

[2] Paige, K., Bostwick, J., Bried, J., Jones, G., A comparison of morbidity from bilateral, unipedicled and unilateral, unipedicled TRAM flap breast reconstructions, Plastic & Reconstructive Surgery, 101(7), pp. 1819–1827, 1998

[3] Coscia, V. and Rubino, C., Hemodynamic enhancement in reconstructive surgery: Mathematical model and clinical findings, *Mathematical and Computer Modelling*, 42, pp. 1151-1161, 2005

[4] Allen, R.J. and Treece, P., Deep inferior epigastric flap for breast reconstruction, *Ann. Plast. Surg.* 32, 32-38, 1994

[5] Ku, D. N., Giddens, D. P. and Downing, J. M., Pulsatile flow and atherosclerosis in the human carotid bifurcation, *Arteriosclerosis*, 5, pp. 293–302, 1985

[6] Patel, S., Drikakis, D. and Pal. S., Computational fluid dynamics of flow through a free flap in reconstructive surgery, *International Journal of Dynamics of Fluids* 1, pp. 1-10, 2005

[7] Ohjimi, H., Era, K., Tanahashi, S., Kawano, K, Manabe, T. and Naitoh, M. Vivo Intraoperative Angiography for Rectus Abdominis Musculocutaneous Free Flaps, Plastic & Reconstructive Surgery, 109(7), pp. 2247-56, 2002

[8] Yen, R.T., Fung, Y.C. and Bingham, N., Elasticity of small pulmonary arteries in the cat, *J. Biomech. Eng.* 102, 170-177, 1980

[9] Shibeshi S.S. and Collins, W.E., The rheology of blood flow in a branched arterial system, *Appl. Rheology*, 15(6), pp. 398-405, 2006

[10] Johnston, B.M., Johnston, P.R., Corney, S. and Kilpatrick, D., Non-Newtonian blood ow in human right coronary arteries: steady state simulations, *Journal of Biomechanics*, vol. 37, pp. 709-720, 2004

[11] Milionis, C., CFD study of blood perfusion in reconstructing microsurgery, *MSc Thesis*, Cranfield University, *to be submitted*, 2009

[12] Rubino, C., Coscia, V., Cavazzuti, A.M. and Canu, V., Haemodynamic enhancement in perforator flaps: The inversion phenomenon and its clinical significance. A study of the relation of blood velocity and flow between pedicle and perforator vessels in perforator flaps, *J. Plastic, Recon. & Aesth. Surg.*, 59, pp. 636-643, 2006

1st International Conference on Mathematical and Computational Biomedical Engineering – CMBE2009
June 29 – July 1, 2009, Swansea, UK
P. Nithiarasu and R. Löhner (eds)

A MODEL OF VASCULAR MICROBUBBLE TRANSPORT THROUGH A VESSEL BIFURATION

Andres J. Calderon
University of Pennsylvania, Philadelphia, PA, USA
Brijesh Eshpuniyani
IIT-Kanpur, Kanpur, India
J. Brian Fowlkes
University of Michigan, Ann Arbor, MI, USA
Joseph L. Bull
University of Michigan, Ann Arbor, MI, USA joebull@umich.edu

ABSRACT

Transport of a pressure-driven semi-infinite bubble through a liquid-filled bifurcating channel was investigated using the boundary element methods. This work was motivated by a novel developmental gas embolotherapy technique for selective occlusion of blood flow to tumors. Transport of microbubbles determines the homogeneity of occlusion that can be obtained when the microbubbles lodge. The homogeneity of bubble splitting was found to increase with bubble driving pressure. These findings provide a basis for further development of treatment strategies for gas embolotherapy.

Key Words: *Gas embolotherapy, cancer, microcirculation, acoustic droplet vaporization.*

1. INTRODUCTION

A boundary element model is used to investigate the transport of long vascular microbubbles through bifurcations. This study is motivated by a novel gas embolotherapy technique [1-9] that we are developing for the potential treatment of cancer by using gas emboli to infarct tumors. Gas embolotherapy is described in more detail elsewhere [1, 2]. The gas bubbles originate from superheated liquid perfluorocarbon droplets that are small enough to pass through capillaries and are injected into the bloodstream. The liquid droplets are stabi-lized by a protein or lipid shell. They are vaporized at the desired location for treatment via high intensity ultrasound, a process termed acoustic droplet vaporization (ADV), to produce gas bubbles whose volumes are approximately 125 to 150 times the droplet volume. The resulting gas bubbles are large enough to occlude capillaries, and in the absence of flow they have persistence times sufficiently long to induce tissue infarction. In other studies, we have computationally investigated the potential of ADV to damage or rupture vessels [7, 8]. Achieving complete tumor necrosis requires infarction of most of the tumor. Understanding the transport and splitting of the gas bubbles, which are long compared to the vessel diameter, is necessary in order to design delivery strategies. In previous experimental steadies we have investigated the transport of a long through single [3] and multiple bifurcations [5], and have investigated lodging of microbubbles [4].

This study examined the behaviour of a pressure-driven semi-infinite bubble, surrounded by blood, as it passes through a geometrically symmetric bifurcation. This work aims elucidate underlying biofluid mechanics related to vascular microbubble transport and to provide guidance in achieving a uniform delivery of bubbles to the vasculature in and around tumors in gas embolotherapy.

2. MAIN BODY

The model presented here considers the time-dependent motion of a semi-infinite bubble through a geometrically symmetric two-dimensional bifurcating channel (Fig. 1). The liquid surrounding the bubble is incompressible and Newtonian. Reynolds numbers in the microcirculation are low (Re << 1). For ease of comparison with transport in both arterioles and capillaries, the governing equations were non-dimensionalized using channel half-width a as the length scale, σ/μ as the velocity scale, σ/a as the pressure scale, and $a\mu/\sigma$ as the time scale, where σ is surface tension and μ is the liquid viscosity. The flow is governed by the dimensionless continuity and Stokes equations.

$$\nabla \cdot \vec{u} = 0 \qquad\qquad (1)$$
$$-\nabla p + \nabla^2 \vec{u} + Bo\vec{e}_g = 0 \qquad\qquad (2)$$

Dimensionless velocity and pressure are denoted by $\vec{u}$ and p, respectively. $Bo = \rho g a^2/\sigma$ is the Bond number, where g is the acceleration due to gravity, ρ is density, and $\vec{e}_g$ is the unit vector in the direction of gravity.

The pressure in the semi-infinite bubble, P_{bub}, and the pressures at the top and bottom outlets of the two daughter channels of the bifurcation, P_t and P_b respectively, were specified to impose pressure driven flow. The bubble starts in the parent channel and is considered to contact the channel wall. A Tanner law is used to model the slip of the moving contact line. Stress and kinematic boundary conditions are imposed at the bubble interface. We solved the governing equations to determine the evolution of the bubble interface, using the boundary element method [6, 10, 11]. The velocity and pressure fields within the liquid domain were computed at various times.

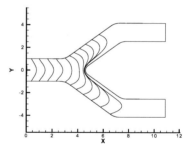

Figure 1 shows examples of bubble interface evolution as a bubble splits in the bifurcation for two values of the bubble pressure. This decrease in viscous resistance will allow the bubble to increase in speed. The higher bubble pressure in the top frame results in faster bubble transport. The net viscous resistance downstream of the bubble decreases, as the bubble nears the outlets of the daughter branches. In both frames, the daughter channel outlet pressures are asymmetric, with the top daughter channel outlet at a dimensionless pressure of 1 and the bottom daughter channel outlet at a dimensionless pressure of 0. The bubble propagates into the bottom daughter channel at a faster rate than the bubble propagates into the top daughter channel

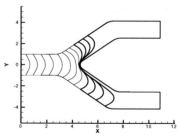

The splitting ratio is defined as the ratio of bubble length in lower daughter tube vs. bubble length in upper daughter tube. The results show that splitting ratio increases with bubble pressure. We observed that there is a critical pressure below which the bubble does not split and the entire bubble enters the channel with less pressure. This is similar to the effect of capillary number on bubble splitting observed in previously published constant flow bench top experiments in which a critical capillary number below which splitting does not occur was identified [3].

Figure 1. Evolution of bubble interface for a bifurcation angle of 78° for P_{bub} = 6 and P_t = 1 (top frame), and P_{bub} = 4 and P_t =1 (bottom frame). P_b = 0 in both frames.

3. CONCLUSIONS

The splitting ratio for a semi-infinite bubble passing through a bifurcation was found to increase with increasing driving bubble pressure. These findings suggest the feasibility of achieving bubble splitting within the microcirculation in our novel gas embolotherapy approach, and provide insights regarding strategies to obtain even splitting of microbubbles, which will facilitate uniform flow occlusion in or near the tumor.

4. ACKNOWLEDGEMENTS

This work was funded by the National Institute of Health grants R01 EB006476 and EB003541

REFERENCES

[1]   J.L. Bull, Cardiovascular bubble dynamics, *Critical Reviews in Biomedical Engineering*, 33, 299–346, 2005.

[2]   J.L. Bull, The application of microbubbles for targeted drug delivery, *Expert Opinion on Drug Delivery*, 4, 475-493, 2007.

[3]   A.J. Calderon, J.B. Fowlkes, and J.L. Bull, Bubble splitting in bifurcating tubes: a model study of cardiovascular gas emboli transport., *J. Appl. Physiol.*, 99, 479-487, 2005.

[4]   A.J. Calderon, Y. Heo, N. Futai, S. Takayama, J.B. Fowlkes, and J.L. Bull, A microfluidic model of bubble lodging in microvessel bifurcations, *Applied Physics Letters*, 89, Art. No. 244103, 2006.

[5]   B. Eshpuniyani, J.B. Fowlkes, and J.L. Bull, A bench top experimental model of bubble transport in multiple arteriole bifurcations, *International Journal of Heat and Fluid Flow*, 26, 865-872, 2005.

[6]   B. Eshpuniyani, J.B. Fowlkes, and J.L. Bull, A boundary element model of microbubble sticking and sliding in the microcirculation, *Int. J. Heat Mass Trans.*, 51, 5700–5711, 2008.

[7]   T. Ye and J.L. Bull, Direct Numerical Simulations of Micro-Bubble Expansion in Gas Embolotherapy., *J. Biomech. Eng.*, 126, 745-759, 2004.

[8]   T. Ye and J.L. Bull, Microbubble expansion in a flexible tube, *J. Biomech. Eng.*, 128, 554-563, 2006.

[9]   O.D. Kripfgans, J.B. Fowlkes, D.L. Miller, O.P. Eldevik, and P.L. Carson, Acoustic droplet vaporization for therapeutic and diagnostic applications, *Ultrasound Med. & Biol.*, 26, 1177-1189, 2000.

[10]   J.L. Bull, A.J. Hunt, and E. Meyhofer, A theoretical model of a molecular-motor-powered pump., *Biomedical Microdevices*, 7, 21-33, 2005.

[11]   A.J. Calderon, "A multiphase flow study of bubbles traveling through bifurcations for a novel gas embolotherapy application," Ph.D. Thesis, University of Michigan, Ann Arbor, MI, 2006.

1st International Conference on Mathematical and Computational Biomedical Engineering - CMBE2009
June 29 - July 1, 2009, Swansea, UK
P.Nithiarasu and R.Löhner (Eds.)

COMPUTATIONAL MODELLING OF LEFT VENTRICULAR ASSIST DEVICES

*D. Carswell, T. N. Croft, D. McBride, A. K. Slone and M. Cross

Civil and Computational Engineering Centre, School of Engineering, Swansea University, Singleton Park, Swansea, SA2 8PP, UK

* d.carswell@swansea.ac.uk

G. Foster

Calon-Cardio Technology, Institute of Life Sciences, Swansea University, Singleton Park, Swansea, SA2 8PP, UK

ABSTRACT

This paper outlines the work being done at Swansea University on the computational modelling of Left Ventricular Assist Devices (LVADs). These LVADs are designed to operate between $10\,000$ and $50\,000\,\mathrm{r\cdot min^{-1}}$ and up to around $27\,\mathrm{kPa}$ ($200\,\mathrm{mmHg}$). The Quemada viscosity model has been incorporated into the model so that the properties of blood are modelled to a greater extent, as it is a non-Newtonian fluid. A rotor-stator arrangement is employed by current pump designs which means that multiple frames of reference must be used in order to accurately model the flow. Post processing tools allow particle tracking for a more complete visualisation of flow patterns within the pump and also aid the prediction of haemolysis and thrombosis. Results of flow rate with increasing rotation rate are presented.

Key Words: *computational fluid dynamics, haemolysis, particle tracking.*

1 INTRODUCTION

Left Ventricular Assist Devices (LVADs) have been growing in development in recent years. Many devices have received approval for clinical use including the Thoratec VAD, HeartMate LVAS and the Novacor LVAS [1]. Each pump design falls into the category of either axial or centrifugal where axial pumps can, generally, be made smaller than centrifugal pumps so they lend themselves better as implantable devices [2]. While experimental analysis and particulars of these devices is desirable, it is often required to optimise pump performance and blade designs prior to committing any particular design for manufacture using Computational Fluid Dynamics (CFD). Experimental procedures have to deal with human blood that readily coagulates when kept stationary so anti-coagulants are often used but affect blood properties [3]. More importantly, CFD can give an approximation of the expected level of haemolysis, linked to shear rate ($\dot{\gamma}$) and exposure time (t), of any particular pump which will ultimately determine its success or failure. Outlined herein is a suitable procedure employing the use of multiple frames of reference as flow traverses the rotating and stationary parts of the device.

2 COMPUTATIONAL PROCEDURE

For flow in rotating domains, a relative velocity $\mathbf{u_r}$ is defined relative to the absolute velocity, $\mathbf{u}$, by

$$\mathbf{u_r} = \mathbf{u} - \omega\mathbf{r}$$

where $\mathbf{u}$ is the absolute velocity, ω is the rotation speed in rad·s^{-1} and $\mathbf{r}$ is the distance from the rotation axis. Here, the solved velocity is the absolute velocity therefore the unsteady, incompressible Navier–Stokes equations must be written using this new term, yielding

$$\rho\frac{\partial \mathbf{u}}{\partial t} + \rho\mathbf{u_r}\frac{\partial \mathbf{u}}{\partial \mathbf{x}} + \rho\omega\mathbf{r} = -\frac{\partial p}{\partial \mathbf{x}} + \mu\left(\frac{\partial^2 \mathbf{u}}{\partial \mathbf{x}^2}\right)$$

Blood viscosity is non-Newtonian and is modelled utilising the Quemada viscosity model given by

$$\mu = \frac{\mu_p}{(1 - 0.5k_Q H)^2}$$

where

$$k_Q = \frac{k_0 + k_\infty\sqrt{\gamma_r}}{1 + \sqrt{\gamma_r}} \quad \text{and} \quad \gamma_r = \frac{\dot{\gamma}}{\gamma_c}$$

and the standard model constants, $k_0 = 4.0$, $k_\infty = 1.5$ and $\gamma_c = 5.0\,\text{s}^{-1}$ [4]. The percentage of haematocrit H present in healthy human blood varies from patient to patient but is usually given between 45 and 48 % [5, 6]. Plasma viscosity μ_p is also required by the model. While blood exhibits Newtonian behaviour above shear rates of $100\,\text{s}^{-1}$ [4] it is not known whether shear rates less than this will be experienced. Most numerical studies assume fully Newtonian behaviour with a prescribed laminar viscosity of 0.0036 Pa·s [3, 7-9].

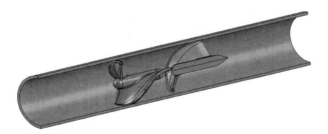

Figure 1: Cutaway view of the pump showing rotor and stator components.

A sample pump exploiting a rotor-stator design is pictured in Figure 1. It is divided into three main domains comprising the rotating middle section and two stationary domains either side of this, one containing the stator component. An unstructured mesh comprising tetrahedrals is used to mesh the rotor and stator parts while a fully hexahedral mesh is generated in regions free of these components. Pyramids are used to link the differing element types together. Typically, meshes contain 500 000 elements and 120 000 nodes. Objectively, the pump performance is required so suitable boundary conditions must be applied that do not make any assumptions on the mass flow rate, therefore, pressure boundary conditions are imposed at both the inlet and outlet, the inlet being fixed and the outlet being variable between 6.7 kPa (50 mmHg) and 27 kPa (200 mmHg). A stationary wall is imposed on the outer casing and stator and zero rotational velocity relative to the rotating frame is specified on the rotor. The vertex-based discretisation scheme is used as it is much more forgiving of high orthogonality angles in complex meshes [10].

3 RESULTS AND DISCUSSION

For the time being, all experiments and simulations were conducted in water where $\rho = 1\,000\,\text{kg·m}^{-3}$ and $\mu = 0.001\,\text{Pa·s}$. Preliminary numerical investigations revealed that a steady flow rate was obtained after approximately 0.05 s of a transient solution. Using a Δt dependent on rotation rate, where $\Delta t < 0.005\,\text{s}$, a transient simulation was run in parallel using eight CPUs taking approximately 2 hours to complete.

Figure 2 shows the comparison between gathered experimental data at increasing flow rates versus results of simulations conducted here. The current set of experiments were conducted in a crude manner

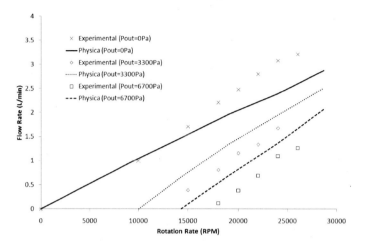

Figure 2: Graph of experimental and numerical results.

in order to gain the rough estimates required for validation of the numerical work. There are known experimental factors that have not been taken into account when setting up the numerical model. The main factor is the losses incurred in the length of pipe attached to the pump outlet in order to achieve a pressure head. A siphoning effect is created at 0 Pa leading to an underprediction in the numerical results. Newly-devised, more precise experimental results will soon be available that should correlate better with the numerical predictions shown here.

Tracking particles through the domain allows detailed analysis of region of the pump where flow is likely to damage red blood cells (RBCs). Shear rates below 450 Pa·s for a period of less than 620 ms present negligible damage to RBCs [11]. Other researchers [3] have shown that low flow rates induce haemolysis more because of the increased time RBCs experience high shear rates. Particles are released from the centre of each face on the inlet and are tracked for the whole length of the pump using a very small time step, typically 1×10^{-5} s, in order to produce an accurate path. Tracks have shown that, at $500\,\text{rad·s}^{-1}$, RBCs experience high shear rates for around 50 ms in the vicinity of the rotor component.

The next stage involves converting this data to an index of haemolysis. Giersiepen [13] proposed that the index of haemolysis (IH) is linked to shear stress (τ) and exposure time (t) by

$$IH = C\tau^{\alpha}t^{\beta} \tag{1}$$

where $C = 3.62\times10^{-5}$, $\alpha = 2.416$ and $\beta = 0.785$ [11]. It was subsequently found that these parameters overestimate the level of haemolysis [11]. A different set of parameters ($C = 1.8\times10^{-6}$, $\alpha = 1.991$ and $\beta = 0.765$) were used by Song et al. [12] but the differences between these two sets of parameters has not been investigated yet.

4 CONCLUSIONS

There is a reasonable correlation between the numerical and experimental results currently, although better experimental readings are expected in the near future that should confirm a better relationship. Particle tracking has successfully been used to monitor shear-stress levels throughout the pump and will later be used as the basis for computing an index of haemolysis for each pump design. The model will be used to test many more pump designs, some axial, some centrifugal, to increase the flow rate for a comparatively slower rotation rate.

REFERENCES

[1]   X. Song et al. Design and Transient Computational Fluid Dynamics Study of a Continuous Axial Flow Ventricular Assist Device. *American Society of Artificial Internal Organs*, 215:224, 2004.

[2]   W.-K. Chan et al. Numerical Investigation of the Effects of the Clearance Gap Between the Inducer and Impeller of an Axial Blood Pump. *Artificial Organs*, 29(3):250–258, 2005.

[3]   A. Arvand, M. Hormes and H. Reul. A Validated Computational Fluid Dynamics Model to Estimate Hemolysis in a Rotary Blood Pump. *Artificial Organs*, 29(7):531–540, 2005.

[4]   A. Marcinkowska-Gapinska et al. Comparison of Three Rheological Models of Shear Flow Behavior Studied on Blood Samples from Post-Infarction Patients *Med. and Bio Eng Comput*, 45:837–844, 2007.

[5]   D. Arora, M. Behr and M. Pasquali. Hemolysis Estimation in a Centrifugal Blood Pump Using a Tensor-based Measure. *Artificial Organs*, 30(7):539–547, 2006.

[6]   A. Bloom et al. Haemostatis and Thrombosis, 3rd Edition. Vol. I, 1994.

[7]   L. Chua et al. Numerical Simulation of an Axial Blood Pump. *Artificial Organs*, 31(7):560–570, 2007.

[8]   S. Klaus et al. Investigation of Flow and Material Induced Hemolysis with a Couette Type High Shear System. *Mat.-wiss u. Werkstofftech*, 32:922-925, 2001.

[9]   M. Grigioni et al. A Parametric Model of Cannula to Investigate Hemolysis by using CFD. *In Proceedings of the 22nd. Annual EMBS International Conference, July 23-28, 2000, Chicago, IL.*

[10]   D. McBride, N. Croft and M. Cross. Combined Vertex-Based – Cell-Centred Finite Volume Method for Flows in Complex Geometries. *In Proceedings of the Third International Conference on CFD in the Minerals and Process Inductries, CSIRO, Melbourne, Australia, 10-12 December, 2003.*

[11]   R. Paul et al. Shear Stress Related Blood Damage in Laminar Couette Flow. *Artificial Organs* 27(6):517–529, 2003.

[12]   X. Song et al. Computational Fluid Dynamics Prediction of Blood Damage in a Centrifugal Pump. *Artificial Organs*, 27(10):938–941, 2003.

[13]   M. Giersiepen et al. Estimation of Shear Stress Related Blood Damage in Heart Valve Prostheses: In Vitro Comparison of 25 Aortic Valves. *International Journal of Artificial Organs*, 13(5):300–306, 1990.

1st International Conference on Mathematical and Computational Biomedical Engineering – CMBE2009
June 29 – July 1, 2009, Swansea, UK
P. Nithiarasu and R. Löhner (eds)

Pulsatile flow investigation in a model Cavopulmonary connection

Chitra K.
Research scholar, Dept. of Applied Mechanics, IITMadras, Chennai-600036, India
muralikmc@gmail.com
S. Vengadesan
Assistant Professor, Dept. of Applied Mechanics, IITMadras, Chennai-600036, India
vengades@iitm.ac.in
T. Sundararajan
Professor, Dept. of Mech. Engineering, IITMadras, Chennai-600036, India
tsundar@iitm.ac.in
P. Nithiarasu
Professor, School of Engineering, Swansea University, Swansea SA2 8PP, UK
p.nithiarasu@swansea.ac.uk

ABSTRACT

An investigation of haemodynamics in the total cavopulmonary connection (TCPC) has been carried out by means of experimental and computational fluid dynamic techniques. In the experimental work, dye visualization and particle image velocimetry (PIV) has been used. The Computational Fluid Dynamics (CFD) approach is based on an AC-CBS (Artificial Compressibility Characteristic Based Split) scheme. The blood is assumed to be incompressible and Newtonian. Flow pattern in the TCPC model is measured using the PIV technique for a Reynolds number of 565. The numerical study has been carried out on a similar geometry and for the flow parameters used in the experiments. For the sake of simplicity, an equivalent two dimensional geometry of TCPC has been considered for the numerical study. Comparison of experimentally observed results with the present numerical predictions shows a good correlation between them.

Key words: *Total Cavopulmonary connection, haemodynamics, flow visualization, recirculation zone*

1. INTRODUCTION

Total Cavopulmonary Connection is an alternate surgical method to Fontan procedure (Fontan and Baudet 1971) developed by de Level *et al.* (1988) for correcting single ventricle congenital heart problems. Quantifying the recirculation zone size and wall shear stress is important for understanding the development of arterial diseases. A haemodynamic study in a model cavopulmonary vascular system can throw light on important fluid mechanical aspects which have bearing on the long term utility of the system after surgical repair. Even though fluid flow studies on TCPC have been carried out by several authors using *in-vitro* and *in-vivo* methods, there is insufficient data under pulsatile flow conditions. Hence, in the present study transient CFD simulations have been carried out for TCPC geometry (Fig. 1(a)) using an optimum offset size which minimizes energy loss (Chitra *et al.* 2009). The CFD based results have been validated with experimental observations of flow visualization and PIV.

2. Physical model studies

The flow pattern in TCPC is investigated using dye visualization technique on a 1:1.6 scale model. The optimal offset between SVC (Superior vena cava)and IVC (Inferior vena cava) streams at TCPC is 0.4375D (where D is the diameter of SVC/IVC) which results in minimum energy loss (Chitra *et al.* 2009) has been considered for scale model (Fig. 1(a)). Different coloured liquids are sent through the two inlets (i.e. IVC and SVC) at a prescribed flow rate ratio corresponding to the Reynolds number of 565. The observed flow patterns have been videographed using a digital video camera. The still pictures of flow patterns are later obtained using image processing. The tests have been later carried out to pulsatile motion with the frequency of pulsation set at 0.78 Hz. The experimental set up has also been used for PIV measurements by replacing the fluid with seeding particles of hollow glass spheres of $10\mu m$. The flow region of interest is illuminated with the double pulsed Nd-YAG laser sheet (100mJ intensity) and images have been captured with a CCD camera. In the present experimental set up, the confluence region of TCPC as shown in Fig. 1(a) is considered for measuring the flow field.

3. Numerical Solution Methodology

The Characteristics Based Split (CBS) scheme described earlier is fully explicit and effective in solving incompressible fluid dynamics problems (Nithiarasu 2003, 2004). Based on this formulation and solution methodology, a numerical model has been developed and tested for steady and transient flow problems. The results are comparable with published solutions (Chitra *et al.* 2009). The validated numerical model has been extended to investigate the haemodynamics in cavopulmonary vascular system after TCPC surgical procedure with the digitized geometry of the TCPC, as used in experiments. While a parabolic inlet velocity profile has been used for steady flow, velocity profile is allowed to oscillate at the SVC and IVC inlets with a phase lag for the case of pulsatile flow simulation.

4. Results and discussion

The flow pattern using dye visualization procedure for steady flow condition in TCPC is shown in Fig. 1(a). For the same condition, the flow pattern measurement obtained using PIV at the confluence region is shown in Fig. 1(b). Two dimensional numerical results at steady flow condition is shown in Fig. 1(c). The comparison between experiments and numerical results shows good correlation between them. Numerical simulation has been extended for pulsatile flow corresponding to non-dimensional pulse period of T = 1. Here, the volume flow rate ratio of left to right pulmonary artery is obtained as 1.28. The actual measured volume flow rate ratio is 1.34±7% as obtained from experiments and this value is in reasonable agreement with the numerical results.

In PIV flow patterns are obtained at mid section of the confluence region in the horizontal plane for pulsatile flow condition. The flow patterns obtained at different instances of pulsatile cycle, from experimental observations are compared with the numerical results as shown in Figs. 2(a)-2(d). It is observed from the flow pattern under transient flow condition that the recirculation zones and vortex at the confluence region of TCPC change with time. The numerical results also have accurately captured the flow features.

5. Conclusions

Haemodynamic studies in total cavopulmonary connection have been carried out with experimental and numerical procedures. Flow pattern for steady and pulsatile flow conditions have been compared between experimental and CFD results. The flow rate ratio values at the exit of left and right pulmonary arteries were also compared. The results clearly show a good agreement between experimental and numerical data. In the case of steady flow condition, the recirculation zones and central vortex at the confluence region do not change with time. But under pulsatile flow situation, the recirculation zones and vortex at the confluence region change periodically which can produce alternating wall shear stresses along the artery wall.

REFERENCES

[1]   Fontan F, and Baudet E., Surgical repair of tricuspid atresia, Thorax, 26, 240-248, 1971.

[2]   de Leval M.R., Kilner P., Gewillig M., and Bull C., Total cavopulmonary connection: A logical alternative to atrio pulmonary connection for complex Fontan operations Experiment studies and early clinical experience, J. Thor. Cardio. Surgery 96, 682-695, 1988.

[3]   Nithiarasu, P., An efficient Artificial Compressibility (AC) scheme based on the Characteristic Based Split (CBS) method for incompressible flows, Int. Journal for Numerical Methods in Engineering, 56, 1815-1845, 2003.

[4]   Nithiarasu, P, Mathur J.S., Weatherill N.P. and Morgan, K., Three dimensional incompressible flow calculations using the characteristic based split (CBS) scheme", International Journal for Numerical Methods in Fluids, 44, 1207 – 1229, 2004.

[5]   Nithiarasu, P., A fully explicit Characteristic Based Split (CBS) scheme for viscoelastic flow calculations, International Journal for Numerical Methods in Engineering, 60, 949-978, 2004.

[6]   Chitra K., Vengadesan S., Sundararajan T., Nithiarasu P., (2009), An investigation of Haemodynamics in TCPC, Jl. Communications in Numerical Methods in Engg., 2009. –In press.

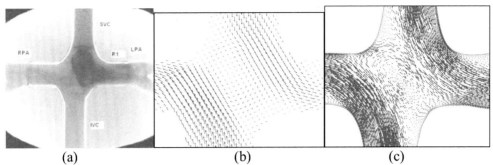

(a)   (b)   (c)

(a) Dye flow visualization, (b) PIV, (c) Present numerical study (CBS-scheme)
RPA-Right pulmonary artery, LPA- Left pulmonary artery
SVC- Superior vena cava, IVC –Inferior vena cava

Figure 1 Steady flow pattern comparison of experimental and numerical results

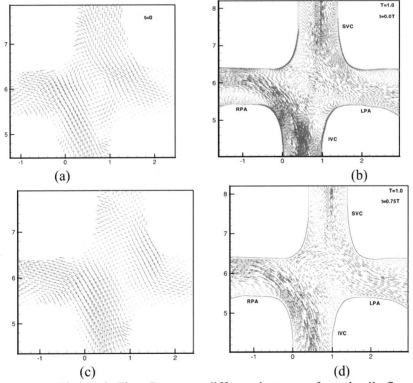

(a)   (b)

(c)   (d)

Figure 2 Flow Pattern at different instances for pulsatile flow condition
(a), (c)-PIV , (b), (d)- present numerical result

1st International Conference on Mathematical and Computational Biomedical Engineering - CMBE2009
June 29 - July 1, 2009, Swansea, UK
P.Nithiarasu and R.Löhner (Eds.)

A new immersed fluid-structure computational framework for haemodynamic applications

A. J. Gil*, A. Arranz Carreño, J. Bonet and O. Hassan
Civil and Computational Engineering Centre, School of Engineering
Swansea University, Singleton Park, SA2 8PP, UK
*Corresponding author: a.j.gil@swansea.ac.uk

ABSTRACT

In this paper, a new computational methodology, based on the original Immersed Boundary Method (IBM) pioneered by Peskin [1], is outlined with the final aim of modelling cardiovascular phenomena, specifically, heart-valve related problems. The principal characteristic of such "immersed techniques" is the representation of any deformable body immersed within an incompressible viscous flow field as a momentum forcing source in the Navier-Stokes equations used to represent the fluid mechanics. In the wake of the original IBM, which was based upon a finite difference scheme along with the use of discrete Dirac delta interpolating functions, a more sophisticated formulation is derived in order to model more complex mechanisms of interaction. A series of examples will be presented in order to demonstrate the robustness and applicability of this new methodology.

Key Words: *heart valve modelling, fluid-structure interaction, immersed boundary method.*

1 INTRODUCTION

In recent years, medical Fluid Structure Interaction (FSI) problems have received a wealth of attention from the computational mechanics community due to the advances in the modelling of both fluid and solid and galvanised by significant developments in terms of affordable computational resources. Nowadays, those FSI problems involving large structural deformations are of primary interest. As an example, the interaction of a viscous incompressible fluid (blood) with a deformable membrane (heart valves, arteries, veins) represents an extraordinary challenge which commands considerable interest from numerous researchers.

From the mathematical perspective, the main difficulty of these FSI problems is the existence of non-linear boundary conditions imposed on moving interfaces where the position of the interface is part of the overall problem's solution. However, the optimal choice of specific numerical strategies for the discretisation of the fluid, the solid and the interface is still an open field. Arbitrary Lagrangian Eulerian (ALE) formulations are classical approaches for the engineering analysis of FSI problems [2, 3, 4]. In those approaches, the fluid phase is resolved in a reference spatial domain over which the incompressible Navier-Stokes equations are formulated in an ALE format along with the introduction of kinematic boundary conditions to define the solid interface.

A disadvantage in the above approaches relates to the fact that mesh update or remeshing algorithms, required for the movement of the referential fluid mesh, can be computationally expensive in terms of the overall scheme. Furthermore, in the case of highly deformable medical FSI problems such as the opening and closure of heart valves, it may be impossible to represent the complete interaction process because of the extreme distortion which tends to appear in the moving fluid mesh when large-deformation membranes are modelled, which could even introduce topological changes within the problem to be solved.

In order to circumvent those difficulties, the Immersed Boundary Method (IBM), as described by the pioneering paper of Peskin [1], was initially introduced with the purpose of studying flow patterns around heart valves. Nonetheless, several disadvantages of the IBM have been identified and reported [5]. Firstly, the assumption of a small strain linear elastic fibre-like one dimensional solid structure, which may be regarded as carrying mass but occupying no volume whatsoever. This hypothesis limits considerably the realistic representation of immersed solid structures. Second, it has been broadly reported that diffusive effects may be generated at the interface of the fluid with the solid structure, as a result of the smoothed representation of the discrete Dirac Delta function. In order to overcome some of the drawbacks of the IBM, a more sophisticated formulation is presented in this paper.

2 METHODOLOGY

The proposed technique follows the basic principle of immersed techniques [1, 6, 7]. Two independent meshes will be established for each of the phases, namely a Lagrangian mesh for the structure domain and an Eulerian mesh for the fluid domain. The coexistence of fluid and structure requires the development of fluid structure interaction terms f^{FSI} which will be included into the momentum equations of the fluid. Furthermore, a corresponding compatibility equation between the velocity of the fluid and the solid at the interface is required to close the coupled system. Specifically, for medical considerations, a standard non-slip condition will be regarded. The incompressible time-dependent Navier-Stokes fluid equations,

$$\nabla \cdot \boldsymbol{u} = 0 \tag{1}$$

$$\rho \frac{\partial \boldsymbol{u}}{\partial t} + \rho \, \boldsymbol{u} \cdot \nabla \boldsymbol{u} + \nabla p - \mu \Delta \boldsymbol{u} - \boldsymbol{f}^{FSI} = 0 \tag{2}$$

are solved by using a fractional step method to uncouple velocity $\boldsymbol{u}$ and pressure p unknowns, where ρ is the density of the fluid, μ is the viscosity of the fluid and t denotes time. The spatial semi-discretisation is carried out on a standard Marker-and-Cell (MAC) staggered cartesian grid [8], where the pressure field is defined at the cell centre and the velocity and force cartesian components are defined at the cell edges. The staggering of the variables in this fashion helps not only to the stabilisation of the scheme by removing well-known spurious saw modes but it also enables the accurate enforcement of the incompressibility condition at the cell centres. The viscous term is discretised in space by means of a standard central difference stencil and in time by using the Crank-Nicolson scheme. The convective term is discretised in space by means of a higher order upwind scheme and in time with the Adams-Bashforth extrapolation method. Moreover, the system of algebraic equations resulting from the incompressibility constraint is solved accurately and in an extremely efficient manner by means of the Fast Fourier Transform (FFT) method.

The structure is discretised as a collection of particles immersed within the fluid. Suitable kernel functions satisfying reproducibility conditions are used in order to transfer information between the Eulerian fluid mesh and the Lagrangian structure mesh and viceversa. In the case of a two-dimensional problem, the velocity vector $\boldsymbol{u}^a$ at a structure particle a occupying the location $\boldsymbol{x}^a$ is interpolated as follows,

$$\boldsymbol{u}^a = [u^a \ v^a]^{\mathrm{T}} \, ; \quad u^a = \sum_{A \in I^a} u^A \phi_x^A(\boldsymbol{x}^a); \quad v^a = \sum_{A \in I^a} v^A \phi_y^A(\boldsymbol{x}^a) \tag{3}$$

where A denotes a fluid cell edge, I^a represents the set of fluid cell edges A within the support of the kernel centred at structure particle a and $\phi_x^A(\boldsymbol{x}^a)$ and $\phi_y^A(\boldsymbol{x}^a)$ stand for the kernel functions centred at fluid cell edge A and associated with the cartesian directions ox and oy, respectively. The term $\boldsymbol{f}^{FSI} = \begin{bmatrix} f_x^{FSI} & f_y^{FSI} \end{bmatrix}^{\mathrm{T}}$ in equation (2), in the absence of inertia effects, is formulated for a fluid cell edge A as follows,

$$f_x^{FSI,A} = \int_{\Omega_0^s} \left(P_x'^s - P_x' \right) \cdot \boldsymbol{\nabla}\phi_x^A(\boldsymbol{x}^s)dV; \quad f_y^{FSI,A} = \int_{\Omega_0^s} \left(P_y'^s - P_y' \right) \cdot \boldsymbol{\nabla}\phi_y^A(\boldsymbol{x}^s)dV \qquad (4)$$

where Ω_0^s represents the structure domain in its initial configuration, $\boldsymbol{P}' = \begin{bmatrix} P_x' & P_y' \end{bmatrix}^{\mathrm{T}}$ and $\boldsymbol{P}'^s = \begin{bmatrix} P_x'^s & P_y'^s \end{bmatrix}^{\mathrm{T}}$ symbolise the deviatoric component of the first Piola-Kirchhoff stress tensor for the fluid and the immersed solid structure, respectively, where the stress tensors are constructed after suitable time integration of the velocity spatial gradient tensor $\boldsymbol{l}$, which for a structure particle a is obtained as follows,

$$\boldsymbol{l}^a = \begin{bmatrix} l_x^a & l_y^a \end{bmatrix}^{\mathrm{T}}; \quad l_x^a = \sum_{A \in I^a} u^A \boldsymbol{\nabla}\phi_x^A(\boldsymbol{x}^a); \quad l_y^a = \sum_{A \in I^a} v^A \boldsymbol{\nabla}\phi_y^A(\boldsymbol{x}^a) \qquad (5)$$

3 NUMERICAL EXAMPLES

A series of numerical simulations will be presented in order to demonstrate the robustness and flexibility of the developed computational framework. The examples will range from classical problems, such as flow over a rigid cylinder, cylinders dropping under gravity within a tank and a lid-driven cavity problem with rigid squares moving inside, to problems more closely related to cardiovascular applications such as a deformable membrane subjected to a pulsatile flow –see figures 1 and 2.

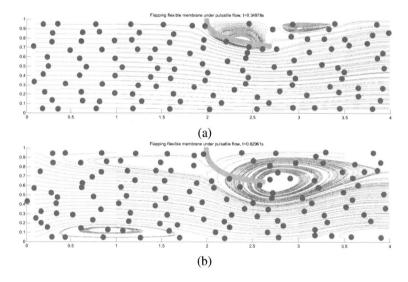

(a)

(b)

Figure 1: (a) and (b) Deformable valve (with passive tracers) subjected to pulsatile flow.

4 CONCLUSIONS

A new computationally immersed methodology is presented for solving large deformation fluid structure interaction cardiovascular problems. The solid is regarded as immersed within the fluid domain in such a way that the interaction between both phases is evaluated by means of a force field which is applied as a source term within the Navier-Stokes equations. This forcing term accounts for both inertia effects (due to difference in density between both phases) and deviatoric stress effects (due to different

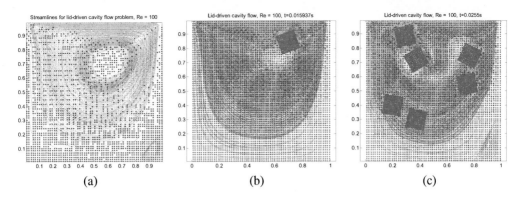

(a)   (b)   (c)

Figure 2: (a) Lid driven cavity problem, Re=100. (b) Lid driven cavity problem with an immersed rigid square, Re=100. (c) Lid driven cavity problem with a series of immersed rigid squares, Re=100.

constitutive behaviour between both phases). The transferring of data between the Eulerian fluid mesh and the Lagrangian structure mesh, is carried out in a conservative manner by means of suitable kernel functions ensuring reproducibility conditions. The overall numerical strategy has been proven to be very robust and flexible in dealing with highly complex extreme deformation problems.

ACKNOWLEDGEMENT. This work was financially supported by the UK Engineering and Physical Sciences Research Council (EPSRC) through the grant EP/F03010X.

REFERENCES

[1] C. Peskin, Flow patterns around heart valves: a numerical method, *Journal of Computational Physics*, 10, 252-271, 1972.

[2] T. E. Tezduyar, A new strategy for finite element computations involving moving boundaries and interfaces. The deforming-spatial-domain/space time procedure, part I: the concept and the preliminary numerical tests, *Computer Methods in Applied Mechanics and Engineering*, 94, 339-351, 1992.

[3] P. Le Tallec and J. Mouro, Fluid structure interaction with large structural displacements, *Computer Methods in Applied Mechanics and Engineering*, 190, 3039-3067, 2001.

[4] W. Dettmer and D. Perić, A computational framework for fluid-structure interaction: Finite element formulation and applications, *Computer Methods in Applied Mechanics and Engineering*, 195, 5754-5779, 2006.

[5] P. N. Watton, X. Y. Luo, X. Wang, G. M. Bernacca, P. Molloy and D. J. Wheatley, Dynamic modelling of prosthetic chorded mitral valves using the immersed boundary method, *Journal of Biomechanics*, 40, 613626, 2007.

[6] W. K. Liu, Y. Liu, D. Farrell, L. Zhang, X. S. Wang, Y. Fukui, N. Patankar, Y. Zhang, C. Bajaj, J. Lee, J. Hong, X. Chen and H. Hsu, Immersed finite element method and its applications to biological systems, *Computer Methods in Applied Mechanics and Engineering*, 195, 1722-1749, 2006.

[7] R. Lohner, S. Appanaboyina and J. R. Cebral, Comparison of body-fitted, embedded and immersed solutions of low Reynolds-number 3-D incompressible flows, *45th Aerospace Sciences Meeting and Exhibit*, 2007.

[8] F. H. Harlow and J. E. Welch, Numerical calculation of time-dependent viscous incompressible flow of fluid with free interface, *The Physics of Fluids*, 8, 21822189, 1965.

Patient-Specific Computational Modelling of a Carotid Bifurcation Using the Locally Conservative Galerkin (LCG) Method

R. L. T. Bevan, P. Nithiarasu* and R. Van Loon
Civil and Computational Engineering Centre, School of Engineering
Swansea University, Swansea SA2 8PP, UK
*Corresponding author. Email: P.Nithiarasu@swansea.ac.uk

ABSTRACT

Blood flow through a patient-specific carotid bifurcation is studied. The locally conservative Galerkin (LCG) spatial discretisation has been applied along with an artificial compressibility and characteristic based split (CBS) scheme to solve the Navier-Stokes equations. Derived haemodynamic parameters associated with atherosclerosis have been analysed. Parameters investigated include the time averaged wall shear stress (WSS), the oscillating shear index (OSI) and the maximum wall shear stress temporal gradient (WSSTG). Results were in good agreement with other reported work in the field.

Key Words: *blood flow, wall shear stress, carotid bifurcation, explicit local flux conservation, local conservation, LCG, CBS*

1 INTRODUCTION

The analysis of haemodynamics within a carotid artery bifurcation is of interest with regards to the genesis and diagnosis of atherosclerotic plaques. Since cardiovascular disease is the principle cause of death in the United States, Europe and regions of Asia [1], this topic is of particular importance. From clinical observation, atherosclerotic disease typically occurs at sites with complex haemodynamics such as artery bifurcations and regions of high curvature. These regions usually have low or oscillatory wall shear stresses (Younis *et al* [2]). The geometry of the artery influences the haemodynamics within the artery. Since each individual has varying geometry, the location of plaque accrual will also be affected.

In the locally conservative Galerkin (LCG) method, the interface flux is reintroduced into the continuous Galerkin framework, thus allowing the interface flux to be explicitly conserved over an element [3–5]. This explicit form provides controlled flexibility, allowing for the introduction of discontinuities along an element boundary as well as allowing the variability of the polynomial order of approximation within each element. These properties are useful for multiscale and fluid-structure interaction studies in biofluids.

The LCG method involves utilising a time-stepping algorithm, as an iterative mechanism, coupled with a post-processing stage to determine the interface fluxes. This approach removes the standard element assembly process, and an element-wise solution process is employed. Transient solutions can be recovered through use of a dual time stepping approach when artificial compressibility is employed. The LCG method is both locally and globally conservative.

2 GOVERNING EQUATIONS

2.1 The Navier-Stokes equations for incompressible flow

The artificial compressibility based Navier-Stokes equations may be written as

Continuity

$$\frac{1}{\beta^2}\frac{\partial p}{\partial t} + \rho\frac{\partial u_i}{\partial x_i} = 0 \tag{1}$$

Momentum

$$\frac{\partial u_i}{\partial t} + \frac{\partial u_j u_i}{\partial x_j} + \frac{1}{\rho}\frac{\partial p}{\partial x_i} - \frac{1}{\rho}\frac{\partial \tau_{ij}}{\partial x_j} = 0 \tag{2}$$

$$\tau_{ij} = \mu\left(\frac{\partial u_i}{\partial x_j} + \frac{\partial u_j}{\partial x_i} - \frac{2}{3}\frac{\partial u_k}{\partial x_k}\delta_{ij}\right) \tag{3}$$

where u_i are the cartesian components of the velocity vector, p represents the pressure, ρ is the fluid density, and β is an artificial compressibility parameter [6]. The deviatoric stress components τ_{ij} are related to the velocity gradients by Equation (3). Non-dimensional forms of the above equations are employed, along with appropriate reference quantities. The problem definition is completed by selecting appropriate initial and boundary conditions.

2.2 Semi-discrete form of the characteristic based split (CBS) scheme

The characteristic based split (CBS) scheme is a well established algorithm in the continuous Galerkin context, for both incompressible and compressible flow simulations. The artificial compressibility form has been incorporated into the CBS scheme since 2003. For an overview of the CBS scheme, the reader is referred to the work of Nithiarasu *et al.* [7].

The present work couples the semi-discrete CBS scheme with the LCG spatial discretisation procedure to obtain an element-wise solution strategy. Ignoring third order and higher terms, the three steps of the CBS scheme are defined respectively as:

$$\frac{u_i^\dagger - u_i^n}{\Delta t} = -\left(\frac{\partial u_j u_i}{\partial x_j}\right)^n + \frac{\partial}{\partial x_j}\left(\frac{1}{Re}\frac{\partial u_i}{\partial x_j}\right)^n + \frac{\Delta t}{2}u_k\frac{\partial}{\partial x_k}\left(\frac{\partial u_j u_i}{\partial x_j}\right)^n \tag{4}$$

$$\frac{1}{\beta^2}\frac{p^{n+1} - p^n}{\Delta t} = -\rho\frac{\partial}{\partial x_i}\left(u_i^\dagger - \Delta t\left(\frac{\partial p}{\partial x_i}\right)^n\right) \tag{5}$$

$$u_i^{n+1} = u_i^\dagger - \Delta t\left(\frac{\partial p}{\partial x_i}\right)^n + \frac{\Delta t^2}{2}u_k\frac{\partial}{\partial x_k}\left(\frac{\partial p}{\partial x_i}\right)^n \tag{6}$$

2.3 LCG Spatial Discretisation

As with the continuous Galerkin method, the variation of each of the variables is approximated by the standard finite element spatial discretisation as

$$u_i \approx \tilde{u}_i = \mathbf{N}\mathbf{u_i} \quad \text{and} \quad p \approx \tilde{p} = \mathbf{N}\mathbf{p} \tag{7}$$

where $\mathbf{N}$ are the shape functions. In order to reintroduce the interface flux, the terms in the Equations (4), (5) and (6) are integrated by parts. For the full discrete form of the governing equations, the reader is referred to Thomas *et al* [5].

2.3.1 Calculation of face fluxes

The interface flux will generally contain contributions from both convective and diffusive components. The face flux component containing the convection field is based on nodal values of the continuous solution from the previous time-step (n). However, for linear tetrahedral elements, the gradients of the diffusion field are not immediately available. Determining a mean of the element gradients is employed to evaluate the scalar-derivatives at a common node connected to a group of elements. This procedure is simple, keeping the numerical flux calculation costs to a minimum. Together, the diffusive and convective components give a total nodal flux approximation. The face flux is then constructed from these nodal values. To ensure local conservation, the flux crossing a common face shared by two elements is made equal and forced to act in an opposing direction.

2.3.2 Correction Factor

In principle, the equal and opposite fluxes introduced at the interfaces of the elements will vanish when the solution is averaged over a node. The only difference between the continuous Galerkin and the LCG method described here is thus the differences in the use of the mass matrix. In order for the LCG method to produce the same results to that of the continuous Galerkin method, a correction factor, based upon this difference, must be implemented when seeking a solution to a transient problem involving a non-uniform mesh.

3 RESULTS AND DISCUSSIONS

The patient-specific carotid bifurcation geometry was constructed from a set of anonymous CT images provided by Singleton Hospital, Swansea, UK. The CT scans consisted of 390 axial slices from the thorax to the nasal passage. Data preparation, segmentation and mesh generation was performed using the data software AMIRA (Mercury Computer Systems, Chelmsford, MA, USA). The blood dynamic viscosity and density were taken to be $\mu = 0.035$ g/cm s and $\rho = 1.0$ g/cm^3. A no-slip boundary condition was applied to the walls of the artery. Velocity profiles were applied to the inlet and outlet surfaces. A velocity profile was developed from the fully developed unsteady solution known as Womersley flow [2], with the harmonics used to construct the profile based upon a measured aortic velocity waveform. A detailed description can be found in Mynard *et al* [8].

The Womersley velocity profile was discretised into 40 real time steps. The peak velocity was set to 66 cm/s while the peak mean velocity was 45 cm/s. The inlet velocity profile was determined and mapped to the surface of the inlet of the common carotid artery (CCA). Based upon the inlet mass flow rate the velocity profiles for the interior carotid artery (ICA) and the exterior carotid artery (ECA) were determined and applied, with the outlet flow split between the ICA (60% flow rate of inlet) and the ECA (40% flow rate of inlet).

Several derived haemodynamic parameters were investigated in order to predict the locality of atherogenesis. These parameters were the time averaged wall shear stress (WSS), the oscillating shear index (OSI), and the maximum wall shear stress temporal gradient (WSSTG). The WSS results are shown in Figure (1). The results obtained were in good agreement with the results of Younis *et al* [2]. The OSI analysis predicted a potential region of atherogenesis, with this region being farthest from a local narrowing of the CCA and along the outer wall, which is in close agreement with the findings of Kaazempur-Mofrad *et al* [9].

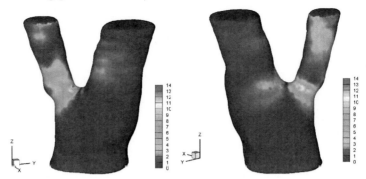

Figure 1: Wall Shear Stress (Pa) distribution within the carotid bifurcation (a) Posterior (b) Anterior

4   CONCLUSION AND FUTURE WORK

This short paper describes the application of a promising method to study flow through patient-specific geometries. The characteristics of atherosclerosis prohibit the use of generalised modelling and therefore a method that provides a timely solution is sought. Due to the element-wise solution strategy, the locally conservative method can be easily parallelised. It is therefore, highly suitable for development as a tool within the diagnosis and decision making process. Future work on the model involves development of the model to include fluid-structure interaction.

REFERENCES

[1] R. Ross. Mechanisms of disease - atherosclerosis - an inflammatory disease. *New England Journal of Medicine*, 340(2):115–126, 1999.

[2] H. F. Younis, M. R. Kaazempur-Mofrad, R. C. Chan, A. G. Isasi, D. P. Hinton, A. H. Chau, L. A. Kim, and R. D. Kamm. Hemodynamics and wall mechanics in human carotid bifurcation and its consequences for atherogenesis - investigation of inter-individual variation. *Biomechanics and Modeling in Mechanobiology*, 3:17–32, 2004.

[3] P. Nithiarasu. A simple locally conservative Galerkin (LCG) finite element method for transient conservation equations. *Numerical Heat Transfer, Part B Fundamentals*, 46:357–370, 2004.

[4] C. G. Thomas and P. Nithiarasu. An element-wise, locally conservative Galerkin (LCG) method for diffusion and convection-diffusion problems. *International Journal for Numerical Methods in Engineering*, 73(5):642–664, 2008.

[5] C. G. Thomas, P. Nithiarasu, and R. L. T. Bevan. The locally conservative Galerkin (LCG) method for solving incompressible Navier-Stokes equations. *International Journal For Numerical Methods in Fluids*, 57:1771–1792, 2008.

[6] P. Nithiarasu. An efficient artificial compressibility (ac) scheme based on the charcteristic based split (cbs) method for incompressible flows. *International Journal for Numerical Methods in Engineering*, 56:1815–1845, 2003.

[7] P. Nithiarasu, R. Codina, and O. C. Zienkiewicz. The characteristic based split scheme - a unified approach to fluid dynamics. *International Journal for Numerical Methods in Engineering*, 66:1514–1546, 2006.

[8] J. P. Mynard and P. Nithiarasu. A 1D arterial blood flow model incorporating ventricular pressure, aortic valve and regional coronary flow using the locally conservative galerkin (LCG) method. *Communications in Numerical Methods in Engineering*, 24:367–417, 2008.

[9] M. R. Kaazempur-Mofrad, A. G. Isasi, H. F. Younis, R. C. Chan, D. P. Hinton, G. Sukhova, G. M. LaMuraglia, R. T. Lee, and R. D. Kamm. Characterization of the atherosclerotic carotid bifurcation using MRI finite element modeling, and histology. *Annals of Biomedical Engineering*, 32:932–946, 2004.

1st International Conference on Mathematical and Computational Biomedical Engineering – CMBE2009
June 29 – July 1, 2009, Swansea, UK
P. Nithiarasu and R. Löhner (eds)

The Effects of External Compression on Tissue Deformation in the Lower Leg

Ying Wang[1], Nigel B. Wood[1], David N. Firmin[2], X. Yun Xu[1]
[1]Department of Chemical Engineering, [2]Cardiovascular Magnetic Resonance Unit,
National Heart and Lung Institute, Imperial College London, UK

ABSTRACT

The compression device is a well established mode of prophylaxis against deep vein thrombosis (DVT), although the exact mechanisms by which DVT is prevented are poorly understood. In this study, the lower legs of four healthy subjects were imaged by magnetic resonance (MR) with, and without, the presence of a compression stocking. Segmentation of MR images before and after compression shows that the deformations of the deep posterior compartment (DPC) were smaller than the other three muscle compartments (anterior compartment, lateral compartment, superficial posterior compartment). This is likely to be due to several factors: i) DPC is enclosed by the other three muscle compartments and by the bones of the lower leg, which makes it less sensitive to external pressures than the other muscle compartments; ii) DPC, located between tibia and fibula, has a relatively large area attached to these two bones of the lower leg, restricting its out-of-plane deformations. This study presents finite element models of a lower leg cross section with and without restriction to the out-of-plane deformation of DPC. The comparison between the simulation and segmentation results from MR images shows that the restriction of the 'out-of-plane' deformation of DPC improves the agreement between the simulation and MR measurement in terms of the degree of vein compression.

Key Words: *deep vein thrombosis, finite element analysis, deep posterior compartment.*

1. INTRODUCTION

The compression device is a well established mode of prophylaxis against deep vein thrombosis (DVT) [1], but the exact mechanisms by which DVT is prevented are poorly understood and there is a need for further study. Employing the finite element method, previous authors have investigated the change in cross section of deep vessels in the lower leg [2] and bulk deformation of calf tissue [3] under compressions, assuming a uniform strain-stress boundary condition for all the materials of the lower leg.

Segmentation of MR images before and after compression showed that the deep posterior compartment (DPC) deformed less than the other three muscle compartments (anterior compartment (AC), lateral compartment (LC), and superficial posterior compartment (SPC)). In order to reproduce the observed response of DPC to external compression, we present finite element models of a calf cross section with and without restriction of the 'out-of-plane' deformation of DPC. The predicted deformations of the lower leg are compared with MR images of the compressed lower leg.

In this study, the lower legs of four healthy subjects were scanned with, and without, the presence of a compression stocking using MR imaging. This was followed by analysis *via* a finite element model (FEM) with a combination of different strain-stress boundary conditions for the components of the lower leg (Model A), compared with the results from uniform plane stress boundary conditions (Model B).

2. METHODS

Four healthy male subjects were scanned using a Siemens Avanto 1.5T scanner. The scans were performed with the subject in the prone position and an appropriately sized knee length stocking (Mediven Travel) was used in each case. The subjects were imaged first without compression before partial withdrawal of the patient table from the scanner to allow application of the stocking by an assistant. Following this they were returned to the original position within the scanner and a further set of images acquired.

A single transverse section, approximately 7 cm below the popliteal artery bifurcation, was studied in all four subjects. The MR images were segmented manually using in-house code developed in MATLAB (Mathworks) [4]. Model geometry was generated using images without the stocking. The main focus was on the deformations of the medial peroneal veins (MPV) and therefore, only the MPV was segmented. Ansys 11.0 (Ansys Inc.) was employed to build the 2D FE model. In this study, two FE models employing different strain-stress boundary conditions are presented. In Model A, the plane strain boundary condition is applied to the DPC, while all the other components of the lower leg employ the plane stress boundary condition. For model B, a uniform plane stress boundary condition is applied to all the materials of the lower leg. An example of Model A is shown in Figure 1.

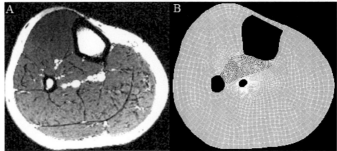

Figure 1: Transaxial section of calf of subject 1: (A) MR image of the calf, (B) Finite element model of segmented calf components: plane strain assumption for the DPC (purple), plane stress for the other regions of the section (green).

The 2D structure of the leg was assumed to be comprised of 3 components: muscle and fat, MPV, and bones. The area was meshed using 183 plane elements. (Fig. 1) Muscle and fat were treated as a homogenous material with Young's modulus as 1.2×10^4 Pa [1]. The wall thickness of the MPV was taken to be 0.8 mm, with a wall thickness/radius ratio of 0.2. The Young's modulus of the veins was taken to be 1.33×10^5 Pa [5]. All materials were assumed to have a Poisson's ratio of 0.49.

A pressure load of 10 mmHg was applied to the internal surface of the MPV to simulate the blood pressure within the veins, whilst a 40 mmHg pressure was applied as the external pressure. Bones were taken as rigid and incompressible. The elements attached to the bone were assumed to be fixed in space. Two different assumptions, plane strain (Model A) and plane stress (Model B) were applied to the DPC, whilst plane stress was applied to the other parts of the lower leg. The MPV running alongside the boundary between the DPC and SPC, was assumed to be located in the SPC. It was also assumed that there was no sliding between DPC, SPC and MPV.

3. RESULTS

Comparisons of the simulation results of Model A (Fig. 2) and Model B (Fig. 3) show that by applying plane strain boundary condition to DPC, the deformation of DPC is restricted. Because the MPV lies on the boundary between DPC and SPC, deformation of the DPC significantly affects the translation of the centroid of the MPV. In the simulation results of Model B, MPV moves deep into the transverse section while being compressed whereas the MPV of Model A remains at approximately the same position. Comparison of the simulation results with MR images shows that Model A (Fig. 4-1), in which the out-of-plane deformation of DPC is restricted, produces a better agreement with segmented results from MR images (Fig. 4-3) in terms of vein compression than Model B (Fig. 4-2).

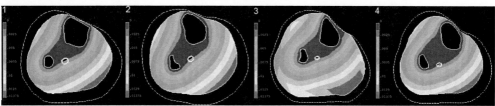

Figure 2: Deformations in transaxial sections of the lower leg simulated using Model A. The undeformed finite element geometry is shown as a white ellipse: 1-Subject 1, 2-Subject 2, 3-Subject 3, 4-Subject 4.

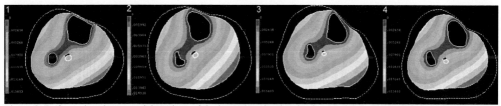

Figure 3: Deformations in transaxial sections of the lower leg simulated using Model B. The undeformed finite element geometry is shown as a white ellipse: 1-Subject 1, 2-Subject 2, 3-Subject 3, 4-Subject 4.

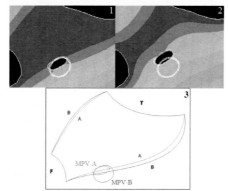

Figure 4: (1 & 2) Deformations of transaxial sections of lower leg generated by simulation (1-Model A, 2-Model B) and (3) segmented boundaries from MR images of Subject 4). The undeformed finite element geometry is shown as a white ellipse (1 & 2). (3) Segmented geometry of DPC and MPV with and without compression: B-before compression, A-after compression, T-tibia, F-fibula. In the segmentation results, because of the small deformation of DPC, the MPV, located on the boundary of DPC, remains at approximately the same position while being compressed, which is similar to the simulation results of Model A with restriction to the out of plane deformation of the DPC. In the simulations results of Model B, the MPV moves deep into the transverse section and the displacement of the centroid of the MPV is larger than that obtained from MR imaging.

Table 1: Simulated Area Reduction Resulting From Compression

		Subject 1	Subject 2	Subject 3	Subject 4
% Reduction	**A: DPC with Plane Strain**	59.0	54.6	48.8	56.5
	B: DPC with Plane Stress	52.2	48.1	39.4	49.4

According to the simulation results, Model A produced larger area reduction of MPV ($54.7 \pm 5.9\%$) than Model B ($42.3 \pm 7.9\%$) (Table 1). Comparing with area reduction estimated from MR images ($64.1 \pm 6.9\%$), restricting the out of plane deformation of DPC has improved the agreement between the simulation results and in vivo measurements in terms of area reduction of veins. However, it needs to be pointed out that the simulated bulk deformations of the other three muscle compartments produced by both models are larger than the measured deformations.

4. DISCUSSION

Segmentations of the undeformed and deformed MR images showed that under compression, the deep posterior compartment (DPC) had much smaller deformation than the other three muscle compartments, and deep vessels were compressed alongside the boundaries of DPC. The small displacement of the boundaries of DPC is likely to be due to several factors. One is that DPC is located deep in the leg and therefore, is not very sensitive to the external pressures. Another is that it has two opposite aspects attached to tibia and fibula respectively, resulting in a restriction of its out-of-plane deformations.

Based on the observed response of DPC to external compression, the plane strain assumption was applied to it, while the plane stress assumption was applied to the other parts of the model. The combination of different strain-stress boundary conditions improved the agreement between the simulation and imaging results in terms of the displacement and area reduction of veins. However, the simulations produced larger bulk deformation of lower leg than those shown in *in vivo* images. Although factors, such as tissue properties and geometry of the lower leg, may have influence on the compression pressure that actually applied to subjects, it is suggested that in reality the deep veins are much more sensitive to the external pressure than that predicted by the present model. According to the anatomy of the lower leg, the deep vessels are surrounded by connective tissues enclosing the muscle compartments. The interactions between the vessels and surrounding tissues may play an important role in the deformation and compression of deep veins. .

5. CONCLUSIONS

MR images of healthy subjects with and without compression stockings showed that different muscle groups have different responses to the external pressure. Based on these observations, a 2D FE model with different strain-stress boundary conditions for different compartments has been developed. The potential of the FEM to predict the deformation and compression of deep veins has been demonstrated. It is suggested that application of the boundary conditions should be based on the actual responses of the components of the lower leg. In the future this model may have merit in optimizing the design of compression devices.

REFERENCES

[1]   R.J. Morris, J.P. Woodcock, Evidence-based compression: prevention of stasis and deep vein thrombosis, Ann Surg, 239,162–171, 2004.

[2]   G. Dai, J.P. Gertler, R.D. Kamm, The effects of external compression on venous blood flow and tissue deformation in the lower leg, J Biomech Eng, 121, 557–564, 1999.

[3]   A.J. Narracott, G.W. John, D.R. Hose, R.J. Morris, J.P. Woodcock, P.V. Lawford, Influence of Intermittent Compression Cuff Design on Calf Deformation: Computational Results, 29th Annual International Conference of the IEEE EMBS, 6334-6337, 2007.

[4]   S.P. Downie, The Effects of Compression on the Lower Limb Venous System, PhD thesis, Imperial College London, 2008.

[5]   Y.C. Fung, *Biomechanics: Mechanical properties of living tissues*, 321-391, Springer -Verlag, New York, 1993.

1st International Conference on Mathematical and Computational Biomedical Engineering – CMBE2009
June 29 – July 1, 2009, Swansea, UK
P. Nithiarasu and R. Löhner (eds)

POROVISCOELASTIC ANISOTROPIC ANALYSIS OF THE UNCONFINED COMPRESSION TEST ON ARTICULAR CARTILAGE

Son K. Hoang
PoroMechanics Institute, The University of Oklahoma, 100 East Boyd St., Suite P119,
Norman, OK 73019, USA, sonhoang@ou.edu
Younane N. Abousleiman
PoroMechanics Institute, The University of Oklahoma, 100 East Boyd St., Suite P119,
Norman, OK 73019, USA, yabousle@ou.edu

ABSRACT

The poroviscoelastic analytical simulation of the unconfined compression test is extended in this paper to account for the transversely isotropic nature of the porous medium, thus mimicking the response of fluid-saturated anisotropic viscoelastic biomaterials such as articular cartilage subjected to laboratory loading conditions. The stresses, fluid pressure, fluid flux, strains, and displacements are simulated through exact modeling of the intrinsic nature of the anisotropic viscoelastic matrix structure as well as the compressible interstitial fluid flow under general time-dependent displacement or force loading; thus simulating realistic responses of test samples in biomechanics experimental setups, including cyclic loading. The presented solution will not only serve as a benchmark for validating numerical schemes and simulations but also assist in calibrating laboratory poromechanical material characterization and modeling of anisotropic poroviscoelastic biological tissues such as articular cartilage.

Key Words: *poroviscoelasticity, unconfined compression, articular cartilage, analytical techniques.*

1. INTRODUCTION

The coexistence of poro- and visco-elastic phenomena has been observed experimentally on a variety of biological materials.[1-2] Similarly, anisotropic viscoelastic properties have also been reported on many tissues.[3-4] Therefore, an anisotropic poroviscoelastic approach would be of importance in the study of biomaterials.

For articular cartilage in particular, the tissue is composed of pore fluid, 60-85 percent by weight, and an anisotropic inhomogeneous viscoelastic matrix made up with proteoglycan aggregates and collagen fibers. The anisotropy and heterogeneity of the matrix are due in part to the orientation, size, and distribution of the collagen fibers. The cells, or chondrocytes, are limited in number and contribute little to the mechanical behavior of the tissue. However, cartilage components are produced by the cells, and cell behavior may be susceptible to stresses, strains, fluid pressure, as well as fluid flux caused by external mechanical forces, especially since articular cartilage does not have a blood supply. Moreover, it has been speculated that the pore fluid squeezed out during mechanical loading of the tissue may play an important role in joint lubrication. Ultimately, knowledge of stress, strain, and pore pressure distribution as well as pore fluid flow is essential to the understanding of cartilage biomechanics.

The groundwork for formulating viscoelasticity within the mechanics of fluid-saturated porous media was laid out by Biot (1956).[5] Using the theory of poroviscoelasticity, the analytical solutions for the wellbore and cylinder problems with material isotropy subjected to quasi-static stress and pore pressure variations have been derived by Abousleiman et al (1996).[6] Also for material isotropy, one-dimensional poroviscoelastic solution for spherical geometry has been derived by Wong et al. (2008).[7] Incorporating material anisotropy, the solution to the orthotropic poroviscoelastic rectangular strip problem has been worked out by Hoang and Abousleiman.[8]

This paper extends the poroviscoelastic analytical solution for the cylindrical geometry problem (Abousleiman et al., 1996) to encompass material transverse isotropy. The solution could be used not only to validate numerical schemes but also directly to simulate and analyze unconfined compression tests of biomaterials under general time-dependent loading conditions.

2. PROBLEM DESCRIPTION AND ANALYTICAL APPROACH

This study aims to derive the poroviscoelastic solution for the stresses, strains, pore pressure, fluid flux, and displacements of transversely isotropic biological tissues subjected to the unconfined compression test, one of the most common laboratory testing configurations in biomechanics. The cylindrical sample thickness and radius are denoted as H and R, respectively. A general time-dependent axial force $F(t)$ is applied through the perfectly rigid, frictionless, and impermeable loading plates. The tested sample is transversely isotropic, with the axis of material symmetry coinciding with the axis of geometrical symmetry, as illustrated in Fig. 1. With the aforementioned conditions, the experimental setup becomes a generalized plane-strain axisymmetric problem, with all shear stresses and shear strains vanish, and all dynamic and kinematic variables except u_z independent of z.

Extending the correspondence principle of elasticity-viscoelasticity to poroelasticity-poroviscoelasticity, the constitutive relations in cylindrical coordinates for a transversely isotropic poroviscoelastic material under compression-positive convention are as follows:

$$\widetilde{\sigma}_{rr} = \overline{M}_{11}\widetilde{\varepsilon}_{rr} + \overline{M}_{12}\widetilde{\varepsilon}_{\theta\theta} + \overline{M}_{13}\widetilde{\varepsilon}_{zz} + \overline{\alpha}_1\widetilde{p} \tag{1}$$

$$\widetilde{\sigma}_{\theta\theta} = \overline{M}_{12}\widetilde{\varepsilon}_{rr} + \overline{M}_{11}\widetilde{\varepsilon}_{\theta\theta} + \overline{M}_{13}\widetilde{\varepsilon}_{zz} + \overline{\alpha}_1\widetilde{p} \tag{2}$$

$$\widetilde{\sigma}_{zz} = \overline{M}_{13}\widetilde{\varepsilon}_{rr} + \overline{M}_{13}\widetilde{\varepsilon}_{\theta\theta} + \overline{M}_{33}\widetilde{\varepsilon}_{zz} + \overline{\alpha}_3\widetilde{p} \tag{3}$$

$$\widetilde{p} = \overline{\alpha}_1\overline{M}\widetilde{\varepsilon}_{rr} + \overline{\alpha}_1\overline{M}\widetilde{\varepsilon}_{\theta\theta} + \overline{\alpha}_3\overline{M}\widetilde{\varepsilon}_{zz} + \overline{M}\widetilde{\zeta} \tag{4}$$

with σ_{ij} = the stress tensor, ε_{ij} = the strain tensor, $M_{ij}(t)$ = time-dependent stiffness tensor, p = pore pressure, ζ = the variation of fluid content, and $\alpha_i(t)$ = time-dependent effective stress coefficient tensor. The tilde and the bar accents denote mathematical manipulations involving Laplace transform as follows:

$$\widetilde{X} = \text{Laplace transform}\{X(t)\} \text{ and } \overline{X} = s\widetilde{X}$$

with s is the Laplace transform parameter. Other governing relations include Darcy's law, strain-displacement relations, equilibrium in radial direction, and continuity equation, as follows:

$$\widetilde{q}_r = -(k_1/\mu)\partial\widetilde{p}/\partial r \tag{5}$$

$$\widetilde{\varepsilon}_{rr} = \partial\widetilde{u}_r/\partial r \tag{6}$$

$$\widetilde{\varepsilon}_{\theta\theta} = \widetilde{u}_r/r \tag{7}$$

$$\partial\widetilde{\sigma}_{rr}/\partial r + (\widetilde{\sigma}_{rr} - \widetilde{\sigma}_{\theta\theta})/r = 0 \tag{8}$$

$$s\widetilde{\zeta} - \frac{k_1}{\mu}\left(\frac{\partial^2}{\partial r^2} + \frac{1}{r}\frac{\partial}{\partial r}\right)\widetilde{p} = 0 \tag{9}$$

The solution is derived analytically by exploiting the formal similarity between the poroelastic and poroviscoelastic governing equations and boundary conditions in the Laplace transform domain. Detailed derivation is presented elsewhere.[9]

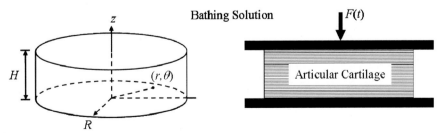

Fig. 1: Schematic of the unconfined compression test

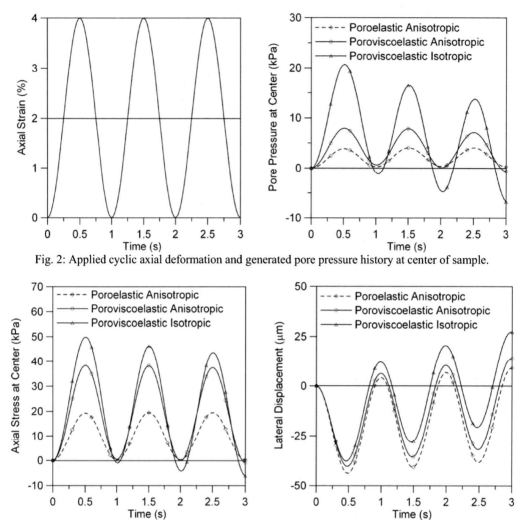

Fig. 2: Applied cyclic axial deformation and generated pore pressure history at center of sample.

Fig. 3: Evolution of axial stress at center of sample and lateral displacement of side of sample.

3. NUMERICAL EXAMPLE

In this section, the response of an articular cartilage plug with dimensions of $R = 2.5$ mm and $H = 1000$ μm under unconfined compression is investigated to illustrate the applicability of the presented solution. To demonstrate the viscoelastic nature of the matrix, the drained moduli $M_{ij}(t)$ are assumed to behave according to the familiar generalized Kelvin model. Other rheological models for the viscoelasticity of the matrix can be easily employed in the same manner. Similarly, experimentally measured relaxation functions can also be used for $M_{ij}(t)$. Initial stiffness values are assumed as follows: $M_{11}(0^+) = 0.373$ MPa, $M_{12}(0^+) = 0.021$ MPa, $M_{13}(0^+) = 0.019$ MPa, $M_{33}(0^+) = 0.800$ MPa. All moduli are assumed to retain 50% of initial values at long time and to have the same characteristic relaxation time of 60 s. Other material properties are time-independent as follows: $\phi = 0.852$, $k_1 = 1.0 \times 10^{-15}$ m^2, $K_f = 2.3$ GPa, $K_s = 3.0$ MPa, and $\mu = 0.001$ Pa·s. Although the porous matrix of articular cartilage has long been recognized as a viscoelastic material, the tissue has sometimes been modeled as a poroelastic medium to simplify the analysis. The typical approach is to measure the long-time stiffness coefficients to determine the appropriate poroelastic parameters. Therefore, to illustrate the poroviscoelastic behavior of the tissue, the response of a counterpart poroelastic sample is also investigated. Following the common analysis method, the stiffness coefficients are taken as $M_{ij\text{-elastic}} = M_{ij\text{-viscoelastic}}(\infty)$. Furthermore, an isotropic poroviscoelastic sample is also investigated to demonstrate the effects of material anisotropy. For illustration purposes, it is assumed that M_{33} and M_{13} are determined to be as above; however, M_{11} and M_{12} are not evaluated but assumed to be the same as M_{33} and M_{13} based on the (incorrect) assumption of material isotropy.

Cyclic loading is of particular interest in the laboratory context. In this example, a cyclic compressive strain from 0 to 4% with a frequency of 1 Hz is employed as shown in Fig. 2. Figs. 2 and 3 demonstrate the evolution of pore pressure and axial stress at the center of the samples, and the lateral displacement of the side of the samples with time. Although the trends are similar, it is clear that the poroelastic analysis underestimates the magnitude of pore pressure and stress which is consistent with observations from earlier studies.[2] Similarly, it is evident that the failure to account for material anisotropy could give rise to erroneous predictions of the articular cartilage responses to external loading.

4. CONCLUSIONS

The analytical solution for poroviscoelastic transversely isotropic samples under unconfined compression has been presented, accommodating any time-dependent axial force or displacement loading scenario. In addition, the solution can be used with any conceptual spring-dashpot model for the stiffness moduli or creep/relaxation functions obtained from experiments, offering researchers great flexibility in analyzing and interpreting experimental results. Therefore, the presented solution for this practical problem will not only serve as a benchmark for validating numerical schemes and simulations but also assist in calibrating and interpreting laboratory results on biological tissues.

ACKNOWLEDGEMENT

The financial support of the PoroMechanics Industrial Consortium at the University of Oklahoma is gratefully acknowledged.

REFERENCES

[1]   A.F. Mak, The apparent viscoelastic behavior of articular cartilage-the contributions from the intrinsic matrix viscoelasticity and interstitial fluid flows, *Journal of Biomechanical Engineering*, 108(2), 123–130, 1986.

[2]   S. Cheng and L.E. Bilston, Unconfined compression of white matter, *Journal of Biomechanics*, 40(1), 117–124, 2007.

[3]   T. Iyo, Y. Maki, N. Sasaki, and M. Nakata, Anisotropic viscoelastic properties of cortical bone, *Journal of Biomechanics*, 37(9), 1433–1437, 2004.

[4]   D.D. Deligianni, A. Maris, and Y.F. Missirlis, Stress relaxation behaviour of trabecular bone specimens, *Journal of Biomechanics*, 27(12), 1469–1476, 1994.

[5]   M.A. Biot, Theory of deformation of a porous viscoelastic anisotropic solid, *Journal of Applied Physics*, 27(5), 459–467, 1956.

[6]   Y. Abousleiman et al., Poroviscoelastic analysis of borehole and cylinder problems, *Acta Mechanica*, 119(1–4), 199–219, 1996.

[7]   H. Wong, M. Morvan, F. Deleruyelle, C.J. Leo, Analytical study of mine closure behavior in a poro-visco-elastic medium, *Int. J. Numer. Anal. Meth. Geomech.*, 32, 1737–1761, 2008.

[8]   S. Hoang and Y. Abousleiman, Poroviscoelastic two-dimensional anisotropic solution with application to articular cartilage testing, *Journal of Engineering Mechanics*, in press.

[9]   S. Hoang and Y. Abousleiman, Poroviscoelasticity of transversely isotropic cylinders, to be presented at the 4th Biot Conference, New York, NY, June 8–10, 2009.

1st International Conference on Mathematical and Computational Biomedical Engineering – CMBE2009
June 29 – July 1, 2009, Swansea, UK
P. Nithiarasu and R. Löhner (eds)

CHARACTERISATION OF A SURROGATE LUNG MATERIAL MADE OF POLYURETHANE FOAM AND FLUID-FILLED GELATINE MICROCAPSULES

Hamid Khalili Parsa, Alojz Ivankovic, Aleksandar Karac
School of Electrical, Electronic and Mechanical Engineering, University College Dublin,
Dublin, Ireland,
{Hamid.Parsa, Alojz.Ivankovic, Aleksandar.Karac}@ucd.ie

ABSTRACT

In this study, a surrogate lung material, developed to mimic the lungs behaviour in low and high rate impact tests in order to better understand the damage mechanism in the lungs resulting from car crashes, collisions and explosion [1], is tested and characterised. This aims to eliminate the practice of live animal testing. The surrogate lung consists of polyurethane foam mixed with gelatine microcapsules filled with Barium Sulphate solution. Thus, both the foam and microcapsules must be individually characterised in addition to the surrogate lung itself when treated as a continuum material. For this, a number of compression tests were carried out on each material to ascertain their mechanical properties. On the other hand, the damage to the surrogate lung specimens as represented by burst microcapsules was analysed by carrying out CT scans before and after testing. The results show that the modulus of elasticity increases with the test speed. CT scan results clearly demonstrated the magnitude and distribution of damage within the specimen.

Key Words: *Surrogate lung, polyurethane foam, microcapsule, CT scan, damage analysis.*

1. INTRODUCTION

The exposure of the human thorax to external loads can cause severe injuries to internal organs, particularly to lungs, and can cause death. Most critical are rapidly changing loads caused by impacts and blasts, resulting from car crashes, collisions and explosion. Over 1.2 million people are killed in road crashes every year according to the World Report on Road Traffic Injury Prevention 2004. Most common lungs injuries are oedema and haemorrhage [2-4]. These injuries impair oxygen transport mechanism and cause secondary injuries to the brain. This is due to the fact that the lungs are more susceptible to damage than the other organs in the human thoracic region.

Presently the damage mechanisms in lungs are not fully understood. The current methods of modelling blunt impact on the thorax include the use of a combination of lungs from mammals and artificial models. In order to eliminate the practice of live animal testing, this research which is a continuation of previous research [5,6], aims to develop a surrogate lung material that will reproduce the dynamic response of a human lung under various loading conditions. It is also aimed to develop a numerical model of the surrogate lung to simulate and predict damage to the lungs. The outcome of this work will provide necessary input data for subsequent numerical and experimental analysis of the blast impact and predicting primary blast injuries to human lungs.

2. MATERIALS AND METHODS

There are two main criteria that the surrogate lung material must fulfil: (a) Its stress wave speed should be similar to that of a real lung (more than 30 m/s); (b) It must be able to reproduce the extent and the distribution of damage resulting from impact at appropriate pressures similar to the lung overpressure at injury level (above 4 bars) [7]. A closed-cell polyurethane foam with a theoretical wave speed of 39.15 m/s was used to mimic the spongy material of the lungs. Gelatine microcapsules filled with Barium Sulphate solution were used to simulate the damage of alveoli in blast tests in terms of haemorrhage and bursting pressure while the Barium Sulphate solution is detectable under X-rays for easy scanning and analysis of the damage distribution. Hence, the surrogate lung was manufactured by mixing the polyurethane foam and gelatine microcapsules.

For characterisation of the microcapsules, initially, the diameter of each microcapsule was measured using an optical microscope. In this research, a number of low rate compression tests were carried out on individual microcapsules of diameter of 750 μm to investigate their mechanical properties and bursting pressure. Each microcapsule was compressed between two parallel plates made of steel at constant rate of 200 μm/min until bursting occurred. The load-displacement curve was obtained using a 10 N load cell (Tinius Olsen Ltd, UK) and the profile of the deforming microcapsule was recorded by a Nikon digital camera attached to an optical microscope. An analytical model derived by Feng and Yang [8] was employed and solved numerically using a MathCAD application, developed for this purpose. The model considers the deformation of a hyperelastic spherical membrane, filled with an incompressible fluid. In principal, fluid was not modelled in the analysis, but the incompressibility was achieved by pertaining the contact volume occupied by microcapsule membrane. Two material models were used to represent the rubber-like behaviour of the microcapsule: neo-Hookean and 2-term Mooney-Rivlin [9,10]. The material model parameters were iterated until the prediction for both the load-displacement and the profile of the deforming microcapsule were in good agreement with experimental data, particularly in terms of bursting pressure.

A number of compression tests were carried out on the cylindrical specimens (diameter of 51mm and height of 30mm) including foam and surrogate lung material, using the Hounsfield machine with a 100N load cell to ascertain their mechanical properties. Two parallel plates were used for this purpose and they were both lubricated by PTFE/Silicone lubricant to minimise friction and ensure uniaxial compression during the test. The tests were performed at various rates between 5 and 500mm/min and they were repeated to ensure accuracy. The load-displacement curve was obtained and then converted to an engineering stress-strain curve.

Some preliminary high rate tests were done and the damage to the surrogate specimens as represented by burst microcapsules was analysed by carrying out CT scans on the specimens before and after testing using the CT scanner available at St. Vincent's University Hospital in Dublin. Firstly a virgin sample was scanned which was later completely crushed, inducing near 100% damage. This sample was then rescanned to compare the difference between two specimens.

3. RESULTS

Figure 1a shows the comparison between the different material models and the experimental data on the microcapsules. The results show that both Mooney-Rivlin and neo-Hookean material with modulus of elasticity of 180 MPa and 198 MPa, respectively, and wall thickness of 4 μm agree well with experimental results. A bursting pressure of 5 bar was calculated at 45.5% deformation which is comparable to the lung overpressure at injury level. The simulated deformed profile of the compressive microcapsule at various deformation stages i.e. undeformed, 19.2% and 45.5% is shown in Figure 1b. A comparison between the experimental recorded deformation and the numerical simulated profile of the compressive microcapsule shows that they are in excellent agreement.

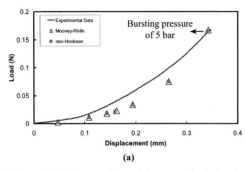
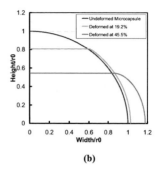

(a)   (b)

Figure 1: (a) Comparison of the numerical simulation of microcapsule compression tests with the experimental data, (b) the simulated deformed profile of the compressive microcapsule at various deformation stages

Figure 2 demonstrates the stress-strain curve of both the foam and surrogate lungs at various rates of compression. The results show that the modulus of elasticity increases with the test rate. The measured values for modulus of elasticity (E) were 42 kPa and 70 kPa for the foam and surrogate lung specimens, respectively. Now, using the density of material, one can calculate the stress wave velocity through $c = \sqrt{E/\rho}$; values of 18 and 20 m/s for foam and surrogate lungs, respectively, are obtained.

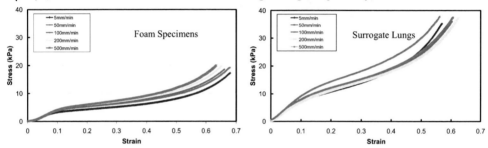

Figure 2: Stress-strain curves of foam and surrogate lung specimens

Regarding the damage analysis, Figure 3 illustrates the difference between the virgin and tested surrogate lung specimen. The white shiny spots in the virgin specimen are the microcapsules. In each CT slice of the virgin surrogate lung (1mm), the average number of microcapsules was approximately 47. This was assigned as a number of microcapsules in any undamaged plane and was compared with the planes of the impacted samples by counting the remaining microcapsules after impact. The ratio of damaged to undamaged microcapsules was used to define the percentage of damage occurring in the specimen. This was then graphed as a function of location from the anterior to posterior of the impact site. Figure 4 shows the statistical distribution of the burst microcapsules through the sample before and after damage (0% and 100% damage).

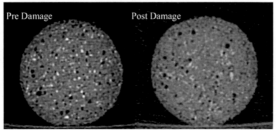

Figure 3: Comparison of a surrogate lung before and after test

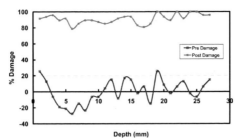
Figure 4: Statistical distribution of burst microcapsules before and after damage

4. CONCLUSIONS AND FUTURE WORK

In conclusions, a numerical model of the uniaxial compression of a single fluid-filled gelatine microcapsule has been developed. Experimental results agree well with numerical simulations in terms of the deformed shape and bursting pressure. Based on the experimental data and numerical simulations a microcapsule bursting pressure of 5 bar was obtained which is comparable to the reported lung overpressure at which injury occurs. Thus, it may be concluded that these microcapsules can be effectively utilised in the surrogate lung specimens for the detection of damage in impact experiments. Furthermore, compression tests combined with the numerical simulation have proven to be an efficient and accurate tool for the determination of the material properties of microcapsules. It is also concluded that the surrogate lung specimens developed in this work exhibit similar stress wave speeds to those of real lungs while CT scan results clearly demonstrate the magnitude and distribution of damage within the specimen as represented by burst microcapsules. These results can be used as a quantitative measure of the damage by comparing the state of the microcapsules between virgin and tested specimens.

High rate compression tests on microcapsules are currently in progress. Here, drop-weight tests are conducted on stationary microcapsules, and the loading rate is varied by varying the drop height. Further high rate impact tests will be carried out on the surrogate lung material containing smaller microcapsules similar in size to alveoli (350μm) using a drop weight tower.

REFERENCES

[1]   H. Khalili Parsa, A. Ivankovic, A. Karac, Development of a surrogate lung for predicting blast trauma, *Bioengineering in Ireland 14*, p34, 2008.

[2]   Y.C. Fung, R.T. Yen, Z.L. Tao, S.Q. Liu, A hypothesis on the mechanism of trauma of lung tissue subjected to impact load, *Journal of Biomechanical Engineering*, 110, 50-56, 1988.

[3]   R.T. Yen, Y.C. Fung, S.Q. Liu, Trauma of lung due to impact load, *Journal of Biomechanics*, 21, 745-753, 1988.

[4]   R.L. Maynard, D.L. Coppel, K.G. Lowry, Blast injury of the lung, In: G.J. Cooper, H.A.F. Dudley, D.S. Gann, R.A. Little, R.L. Maynard (Eds.), *Scientific Foundation of Trauma*. Butterworth Heinemann, Oxford, 214-224, 1997.

[5]   C. Walsh, *Construction of a surrogate human lung*, Final year project, UCD, 2005.

[6]   O. Alakija, A. Ivankovic, A. Karac, Finite Volume solution to high rate wave propagation through a lung alveoli stack , *IUTAM Symposium on Biomechanics of Impact*, 281-288, 2005.

[7]   Q. Grimal, A. Watzky, S. Naili, A one-dimensional model for the propagation of transient pressure waves through the lung. *Journal of Biomechanics*, 35, 1081-1089, 2002.

[8]   W.W. Feng, W.H. Yang, On the contact problem of an inflated spherical nonlinear membrane, *Journal of Applied Mechanics*, 40, 209-214, 1973.

[9]   M. Mooney, A theory of large elastic deformation, *Journal of Applied Physics*, 11, 582-592, 1940.

[10]   R.S. Rivlin, Large elastic deformations of isotropic materials, IV. *Further development of the general theory, Philos. Trans. Roy. Soc., London*, Ser. A 241, 379–397, 1948.

Analysis and optimization of a scoliosis surgical correction procedure

J. F. Aguilar Madeira

IDMEC/IST-Instituto Superior Técnico, Av. Rovisco Pais, 1049-001 Lisbon, Portugal,
jaguilar@dem.ist.utl.pt
and ISEL-Instituto Superior de Engenharia de Lisboa

H. L. Pina

IDMEC/IST-Instituto Superior Técnico, Av. Rovisco Pais, 1049-001 Lisbon, Portugal,
hpina@dem.ist.utl.pt

E. B. Pires

ICIST and DECivil, Instituto Superior Técnico, Av. Rovisco Pais, 1049-001 Lisbon, Portugal,
bpires@civil.ist.utl.pt

J. Monteiro

Orthopaedic Department, Hospital de Santa Maria, University of Lisbon Medical School, Portugal,
jmmonteiro@netcabo.pt

ABSTRACT

This paper describes a FEM model developed to simulate the surgical correction of scoliotic vertebral column, to compute the forces involved in the correction and a Genetic Algorithm employed for the optimization of the tightening sequence employed in this surgical procedure.

Key Words: *Computational Biomechanics, Scoliosis, Finite Element Method, Genetic Algorithms and Parallel Computation.*

1 INTRODUCTION

Scoliosis is a medical condition characterized by an abnormal curvature of the vertebral column characterized by a lateral S-shaped deviation of the vertebrae with respect to their natural alignment. This condition can be alleviated by surgery and some techniques are reviewed in [1].

A biomechanical model based on the finite element method (FEM) was previously developed in order to numerically simulate real clinical cases of surgical correction of scoliosis. To obtain the forces applied in the surgery an analysis using a FEM analysis was performed.

Also we are interested in finding the optimal tightening sequence that minimizes the corrective forces applied during the surgery. For the usual number of vertebrae involved an exhaustive search is generally out of the question, so a Genetic Algorithm is applied to determine the optimal tightening sequence.

2 ANALYSES AND OPTIMIZATION

Scoliosis is a medical condition characterized by an abnormal curvature of the vertebral column characterized by a lateral S-shaped deviation of the vertebrae with respect to their natural alignment. This feature can be viewed in the frontal plane (see Figure 1).

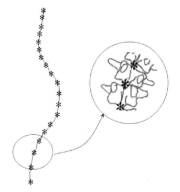

Figure 1: Scoliotic spine   Figure 2: One-dimensional model of the spine

Besides producing these deformations in the frontal plane, scoliosis also: (i) aggravates the natural curvatures in the sagittal plane, not only in the thoracic region but also in the lumbar region (pathologies known as thoracic kyphosis and lumbar lordosis, respectively), and (ii) causes the unlevelling of the shoulders.

This condition can be alleviated by surgery and some techniques are reviewed in [1]. The analysis carried on this paper concentrates in the Resina-Alves method ([4]) which consists in a straightening procedure based on the tightening of the column by two metallic rods implants. These rods act as levers with fulcrum at the curve apex so that their fixation to the column produces a reduction of the deformation (see Figure 3).

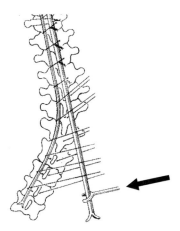

Figure 3: Resina-Alves method

The initial geometry of the scoliotic spine is obtained by digitalization and computer graphics treatment of presurgery X-rays of the patient.

The tightening sequence of the vertebrae to the rods determines the magnitude of the forces applied to the column and as the scoliotic curve pattern is somewhat unique to the patient this requires an individualized analysis. Also it is desirable to keep those forces as small as possible compatible to the intended correction and within the patient's bearing capacity.

A biomechanical model based on the finite element method (FEM) was previously developed (see [1], [3] and [2]) in order to numerically simulate real clinical cases of surgical correction of scoliosis. This computational model consists of one-dimensional finite elements with spatial deformation (linear and angular) in which: (i) the column is represented by its axis that coincides with the axis of the body of the vertebrae; (ii) the vertebrae are assumed to be rigid and (iii) the deformability of the column is concentrated in linear elastic springs that connect the successive rigid elements (see Figure 2). The two metallic rods used as implants for the surgical correction are modeled as linear elastic beam elements. The analyses include both flexural and torsional effects in the column as a result of the scoliosis itself and of the corrective procedure. To obtain the forces at the connections between the metallic rods and the vertebrae geometrically non-linear analyses are performed using a standard FEM software package.

Numbering the vertebrae involved in the surgical procedure as $1, \ldots, n$, we are interested in finding the optimal tightening sequence which is equivalent to find the permutation of integers $1, \ldots, n$ that minimizes the correction forces applied by the surgeon to the patient's column. Thus we are faced with a combinatorial optimization problem, isomorph to the Traveling Salesman Problem, with $n!$ candidate solutions. For the usual number n of vertebrae involved an exhaustive search is generally out of the question, so a Genetic Algorithm is applied to determine the optimal tightening sequence. As the fitness evaluation requires one computing intensive FEM analysis per candidate solution a parallel implementation of the Genetic Algorithm was developed allowing several fitness evaluations to be carried out simultaneously.

3 CONCLUSIONS

It is concluded that: (i) the finite element model was able to predict with reasonable accuracy the forces applied by the surgeon ([2]); (ii) for the particular case studied (involving 11 vertebrae) and relative to a conventional procedure based only on the surgeon's expertise, an optimal tightening sequence is able to achieve a 40% reduction of the forces applied.

References

[1] P. B. Dinis, E. B. Pires, J. A. C. Martins, S. Domingues, and N. Perdig ao. Surgical correction of scoliosis by the Resina-Alves method: numerical simulation of a clinical case. In M. Doblaré, M. Cerrolaza, and H. Rodrigues, editors, *Proceedings of the International Congress of Computational Bioengineering*, volume 2, pages 471–476, 2003.

[2] S. J. Palma, E. B. Pires, P. B. Dinis, and J. A. C. Martins. Resultados numéricos adicionais relativos à correcção cirúrgica de uma escoliose pelo método de Resina-Alves. In J. C. de Sá et al., editor, *Métodos Numéricos e Computacionais em Engenharia CMNE/CILAMCE*, 2007.

[3] S.J. Palma, E.B. Pires, R.P. Rodrigues, J.G. Ferreira, and J.A.C. Martins. Correcção cirúrgica de escolioses pelo método de Resina-Alves: medição in vivo de forças e sua comparação com os resultados de uma simulação numérica. In H. C. Rodrigues and al., editors, *Actas do 2º Encontro Nacional de Biomecânica*, pages 299–304. IST Press, 2007.

[4] J. Resina and A. F. Alves. A technique of correction and internal fixation for scoliosis. *The Journal of Bone and Joint Surgery*, 59-B (2):159–165, 1997.

Regularized Learning Algorithm for Prediction of Blood Glucose Concentration in "No Action Period"

Sergei Pereverzev

Sivananthan Sampath

Johann Radon Institute for Computational and Applied Mathematics
Austrian Academy of Sciences
Altenbergerstrasse 69, A-4040 Linz
sergei.pereverzev@oeaw.ac.at, sivananthan.sampath@oeaw.ac.at

ABSTRACT

In this article we propose a simple approach to predict blood glucose concentration in the no action period based on statistical learning theory and regularization networks which allows a prediction with the accuracy 2 mmol/l for 2 hours time horizon. We also present numerical experiments with proposed algorithm.

Key Words: *statistical learning, regularization, Reproducing Kernel Hilbert space, Diabetes, Prediction of blood glucose level.*

1 INTRODUCTION

Failure to maintain Blood Glucose Level (BGL) in normal range (3.9 - 10 mmol/l) leads to high/low blood sugar (hyper/hypoglycemia). Disordered metabolism and abnormal BGL is refered as Diabetes Mellitus (DM) and it is due to insuffient levels of the hormone insulin. The main diabetes therapy is based on insulin injections, and an excess of insulin causes hypoglycemia or in long run affects a liver. However, the insulin (rapid-acting insulin) reaches peak action in 45 to 90 minutes. Therefore, for more effective treatment (or to avoid hypo/hyperglycemia events) one needs to know the BGL in advance, say one hour ahead.

In [3] it has been observed that a statistical analysis of BGL may be improved by separating data for different times of day, and an explanation has been given that different processes may control BGL in different day periods, in the morning and in the evening, for example. This observation hints at constructing predictors for each of such periods. Using this hint we propose a prediction method which can be effective for "no action periods", such as a sleep or fasting.

As a state of art, in [4], [5] time series analysis has been used to predict BGL 30 and 60 minutes into the future. Using recent results of statistical learning theory we propose a new prediction algorithm, which in experiments with available data allows a BGL prediction with clinically acceptable accuracy 2 mmol/l 2 hours ahead.

Within the framework of learning theory [2] our problem can be stated as follows. We are given blood glucose levels y_i at time moments t_i, $= 1, 2, \ldots, n$, and need to predict a level y at time t, $t - t_n > 60$ (minutes). We assume that a time moment t does not determine uniquely a level y, but rather a probability distribution on the set of possible values of BGL. This can be formalized assuming that a probability distribution $\rho(t, y)$ is defined over the set of pairs (t, y). This distribution is unknown, but we are provided with training data $\mathbf{z} = \{(t_1, y_1), \ldots, (t_n, y_n)\}$ obtained by sampling n times the set of pairs (t, x) according to $\rho(t, x)$. The problem consists in, given $\mathbf{z}$, providing an estimator, that is, a function $f(t)$ that can be used to predict a value y for given t. The error we make when we predict y by $f(t)$ can be measured by expected risk

$$\mathcal{E}(f) = \int (y - f(t))^2 \rho(t, y) \; t \; y.$$

We assume that the expected risk is defined on a "large" function space $\mathcal{H}$, and we denote by $f_{\mathcal{H}}^\rho$ the function which minimizes $\mathcal{E}(f)$, i.e. $f_{\mathcal{H}}^\rho = \arg\min\{\mathcal{E}(f), f \in \mathcal{H}\}$. This function cannot be found in practice, because the distribution $\rho(t, y)$ that defines the expected risk is unkown, but using training data $\mathbf{z}$ one can approximate $f_{\mathcal{H}}^\rho$ by the minimizer of a Tikhonov-type functional

$$f_{\mathbf{z}}^\lambda = \arg\min\{\frac{1}{n}\sum_{i=1}^{n}(y_i - f(t_i))^2 + \lambda\|f\|_{\mathcal{H}}^2\}. \tag{1}$$

If $\mathcal{H} = \mathcal{H}$ is chosen as Reproducing Kernel Hilbert Space (RKHS) with the norm $\|\cdot\|_{\mathcal{H}_K} = \|\cdot\|$ generated by a Mercer kernel $K(t, \tau)$, then the predictor $f_{\mathbf{z}}^\lambda$ has the form

$$f_{\mathbf{z}}^\lambda(t) = \sum_{i=1}^{n} c_i K(t, t_i),$$

where $C = (c_i) = (n\lambda + K)^{-1}Y$, $Y = (y_i)$, $K = (K(t_i, t_j))$, and is the unit matrix of size n.

Immediate concerns with the kernel-based predictor $f_{\mathbf{z}}^\lambda$ are the choice of the regularization parameter λ and the choice of the kernel itself. In the next section we address these issues using a new approach called the quasi-balancing principle, that can be seen as a combination of the quasi-optimality criterion [6], and the balancing principle introduced in the context of learning in [1].

2 Prediction Algorithm and Numerical Experiments With Clinical Data

We use the quasi-balancing principle to construct the predictor $f_{\mathbf{z}}^\lambda$ from a given initial regularization parameter λ_0 and the kernel K.

The Balancing Principle: Let $\{f_{\mathbf{z}}^{\lambda_i}\}$ be the predictors (1) constructed for some $\mathcal{H} = \mathcal{H}$ and $\lambda_i = \lambda_0 q^i$, $= 0, 1, \ldots, M$, $q > 1$. Define

$$\lambda_{\mathcal{H}_K} = \max\{\lambda_i : \|f_{\mathbf{z}}^{\lambda_i} - f_{\mathbf{z}}^{\lambda_j}\| \le C \; /\lambda_j\sqrt{n}, j = 0, 1, \ldots, \; - 1\},$$
$$\lambda_{emp} = \max\{\lambda_i : \|f_{\mathbf{z}}^{\lambda_i} - f_{\mathbf{z}}^{\lambda_j}\|_{\{x_l\}} \le C_{emp}/\sqrt{\lambda_j n}, j = 0, 1, \ldots, \; - 1\},$$

where $\|g\|_{\{x_l\}}^2 = n^{-1}\sum_{i=1}^{n}g^2(x_i)$, and C , C_{emp} are some design constants.

The following result is proved in [1].

Theorem 2.1. *With a high probability the choice*

$$\lambda_+ = \min\{\lambda_{\mathcal{H}_K}, \lambda_{emp}\}$$

guarantees the risk of optimal order, i.e. $\mathcal{E}(f_{\mathbf{z}}^{\lambda_+}) \asymp \mathcal{E}(f_{\mathcal{H}_K}^\rho)$ as $n \to \infty$.

The Quasi-Balancing Principle: It reduces the computational cost compare to the balancing principle. The choice of the regularization parameter is given by

$$\lambda_+^{QB} = \min\{\lambda_{emp}^{QO}, \lambda_{\mathcal{H}_K}^{QO}\},$$

where

$$\lambda_{emp}^{QO} = \lambda_k, \quad = \arg\min\{\sigma_{emp}(\nu) : \nu = 1, 2, ..., M\}, \quad \sigma_{emp}(\nu) = \|f_{\mathbf{z}}^{\lambda_\nu} - f_{\mathbf{z}}^{\lambda_{\nu-1}}\|_{\{x_i\}},$$

$$\lambda_{\mathcal{H}_K}^{QO} = \lambda,, \quad l = \arg\min\{\sigma_{\mathcal{H}_K}(\nu) : \nu = 1, 2, ..., M\}, \quad \text{and } \sigma_{\mathcal{H}_K}(\nu) = \|f_{\mathbf{z}}^{\lambda_\nu} - f_{\mathbf{z}}^{\lambda_{\nu-1}}\|, \cdot$$

Note that the quasi-balancing principle is a heuristic rule that can be used in case of a small sample size n, and it does not require any a priori knowledge of $\rho(t, y)$.

The construction of the predictor

The clinical data are given for some fixed day period, where no external actions appear, such as meals or insulin injection. More precisely, three days records $\{(t_i, y_i^{(j)}) : \ = 1, 2, \ldots, 11\}$, $j = 1, 2, 3$, with the frequency $t_i - t_{i-1} = 15$ (minutes) are given for a particular patient. Using the records for the first two day as training data, we choose the kernel K for sufficiently small λ_0 as

$$K = \arg\min\left\{\sup_{4 \leq i \leq 7} |f_{2,,}^{\lambda_+}(t_l) \quad y_i^{(2)}|, K \subset \mathbb{K}, \sup_{4 \leq i \leq 7} |f_{1,,}^{\lambda_0}(t_l) - y_i^{(1)}| \leq 2 \, (\text{mmol/l})\right\}, \tag{2}$$

where $\mathbb{K} = \{K(t, \tau) = (t\tau)^\alpha + \beta e^{-\gamma(t-\tau)^2} : (\alpha, \beta, \gamma) \in [10^{-3}, 3] \times [10^{-3}, 5] \times [10^{-6}, 1]\}$, and $f_{j,,}^\lambda$ are the predictors (1) constructed for $\mathcal{H} = \mathcal{H},, \lambda = \lambda_0, \lambda_+$, and $\{(t_i, y_i^{(j)})_{i=1}^3\}$, $j = 1, 2$.

In our experiments we approxiamtely solve the minimization problem (2) by the full search over the grid of parameters $\alpha_\ell = 10^{-3}\ell$, $\beta_\ell = 10^{-3}\ell$, $\gamma_\ell = 10^{-5}\ell$, $\ell = 0, 1, 2, \ldots$

In this way we find a kernel for predicting BGL one hour ahead in the time interval $[t_3, t_7] = [45, 105]$ from measurements collected within the period $[t_1, t_3] = [15, 45]$. For predicting BGL in the time interval $[t_7, t_{11}] = [105, 165]$, i.e. 2 hours ahead, we use predicted values $f_{j,,}^{\lambda_+}(t_i)$ instead of real measurements $y_i^{(j)}$, $= 5, 6, 7$. The kernel for this prediction is chosen similar to (2). In both time intervals we use quasi-balancing principle for choosing regularization parameter λ_+.

Numerical Experiments

The performance of proposed prediction algorithm is checked on the third day, where the data $(t_i, y_i^{(3)})$, $= 1, 2, 3$, are used for training, while the data $(t_i, y_i^{(3)})$, $= 4, \ldots, 11$, are used to check the prediction accuracy.

The clinical records of 10 patients have been provided by Novo Nordisk A/S. Each of three days records is formed by BGL-measurements with 15 minutes frequency during 3 hours after injection followed by a standard breakfast. For 7 patients our algorithm is able to predict BGL with accuracy 2 mmol/l 2 hours ahead. Typical example of successful prediction can be seen on the figure below (Day 3). For this particular patient the kernels $K(t, \tau) = (t\tau)^{0.4455} + 0.005e^{-0.001(t-\tau)^2}$ and $K(t, \tau) = (t\tau)^{0.01} + 4e^{-0.00028(t-\tau)^2}$ have been chosen by the algorithm for a prediction in time intervals $[45, 105]$ and $[105, 165]$ respectively. The quasi-balancing principle has been implemented with $\lambda_0 = 10^{-4}$, $q = 1.01$. In the figure real measurements are labelled by "*", while predicted values used for further prediction are labelled by "o".

Patient: ANA1235, Subject ID - 9

| Day 1: Kernel and regularization parameter specification | Day 2: Test Kernel and regularization parameter specification | Day 3: Prediction using first 3 measurements |

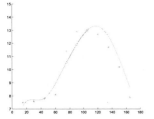 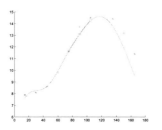 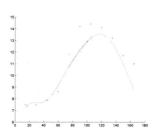

3   CONCLUSIONS

The proposed method is simple, it requires less frequent measurements than predictors based on time series analysis (15 minutes versus 1-3 minutes). With available data in 70% of cases we are able to predict the blood glucose concentration for 2 hours time horizon in no action period using 30 minutes past information with clinically acceptable accuracy of 2 mmol/l.

4   ACKNOWLEDGEMENTS

The work of second author is supported by EU-project "DIAdvisor" performed within 7-th Framework Programme of EC. We are grateful to Novo Nordisk A/S for providing clinical records for the experiments.

References

[1] E. De Vito, S. Pereverzev and L. Rosasco, Adaptive kernel methods using the balancing principle, Technical Report CBCL paper 275, CSAIL-TR-2008-062 , Massachusetts Institute of Technology, Cambridge, MA, 2008.

[2] T. Evgeniou, M. Pontil and T. Poggio, Regularization networks and support vector machines, *Adv. Comp. Math.*, **13**:1-50, 2000.

[3] J. J. Liszka-Hackzell, Prediction of blood glucose levels in diabetic patients using a hybrid AI technique, *Computers and Biomedical Research*, **32**:132-144, 1999.

[4] J. Reifman, S. Rajaraman, A. Gribok and W. K. Ward, Predictive monitoring for improved management of glucose levels, *Journal of Diabetes Sci. and Tech.*, **1**(4):478-486, 2007.

[5] G. Sparacino, F. Zanderigo, S. Corazza, A. Maran, A, Facchinetti, and C. Cobelli, Glucose concentration can be predicted ahead in time from continuous glucose monitoring sensor time-series, *IEEE Trans. on Biomedical Eng.*, **54**(5):931-937, 2007.

[6] A. N. Tikhonov and V. B. Glasko, Use of the regularization method in non-linear problems, *Zh. vychisl. Mat. mat. Fiz.*, **5**:463-473, 1965.

1st International Conference on Mathematical and Computational Biomedical Engineering – CMBE2009
June 29 – July 1, 2009, Swansea, UK
P. Nithiarasu and R. Löhner (eds)

THERMAL ANALYSIS OF INFANT RADIANT WARMER

Marek Rojczyk
Institute of Thermal Technology, Silesian University of Technology
ul. Konarskiego 22, 44-100 Gliwice, Poland, marek.rojczyk@polsl.pl
Ireneusz Szczygieł
Institute of Thermal Technology, Silesian University of Technology
ul. Konarskiego 22, 44-100 Gliwice, Poland, ireneusz.szczygiel@polsl.pl

ABSTRACT

The main objective of this study it to understand the heat transfer phenomena between an infant placed in a radiant warmer and the environment. A complete geometrical model was constructed using CATIA solid modeller software. The model was used in the Computational Fluid Dynamics (CFD) analysis with the usage of commercial code FLUENT. The buoyancy induced flow is reduced to two-dimensional geometry. The analysis involves besides the flow, convection and radiation heat transfer as well as the turbulence modelling. Analyses were focused on three main problems: the infant heat losses, the infant thermal stabilisation and the complete incubator usage. This results will be used to optimise the incubator parameters. The computations in 3D model and extended conditions will be developed in the future.

Key Words: *radiant warmer, premature infant, CFD, heat transfer, fluid mechanics.*

1. INTRODUCTION

Birth is a wonder. Unfortunately through environment pollution, genetic defects, population's oldness, sterile aspect of life, stimulants and trends (likely to be slim), less women are able to give a birth in a right-term which is 37–42 week of pregnancy [6]. Premature infants are weaker and their organs are not well developed. Therefore, thanks to many researches and inventing of incubators, there is a rescue for those children.

The best solution is to place them in a closed incubator and to guarantee the optimal thermal conditions for development. However, in case of newborns' threat to life, free access to infants is the most important aspect. In that case an open incubator should be used.

A purpose of this project is to build a numerical model and to understand the phenomena of heat transfer between an infant and surrounding environment in a radiant warmer in order to ensure the optimal temperature of body. The focus was on natural convection, radiation and conduction only and not on other aspects of the heat transfer. Other possible occurrences like for example evaporation, are more advanced and will be developed in further work.

2. RADIANT WARMER INCUBATOR – A SAVING LIFE MACHINE; FUNDAMENTALS OF THERMAL CONTROL

2.1 Heat transfer from a human body

The human body as normal temperature is about 37°C, and the effect of energy balance: heat generation and losses into the environment. The heat balance equation is presented by ASHRAE [1]:

$$M - W = Q_{sk} + Q_{res} = (C + R + E_{rsw} + E_{dif}) + (C_{res} + E_{res}) \tag{1}$$

Where: M – metabolic energy production; W — mechanical work, Q_{sk} – skin heat loss; Q_{res} – heat loss through respiration; C – convective skin heat loss; R – radiative skin heat loss; E_{rsw} – evaporative skin heat loss (through sweating); E_{dif} – evaporative skin heat loss (through moisture diffusion); C_{res} – convective heat loss from respiration; E_{res} – rate of evaporate heat loss from respiration.

2.2 Infant thermoregulation

Premature infants (born before 32 week) with Very Low Birth Weight (<1500 gram) have handicapped thermoregulation system. This ability is formed in the last trimester of pregnancy. Additionally foetal exchanges 85% of heat trough placenta and only 15% through the skin which is thin and not well developed. Therefore, after delivery there should be ensured a neutral environment with neutral temperature. This parameter is not the same for every infant and depends on body weight and birth age. Generally even low fluctuation of body temperature can be dangerous for infants' life. Consequently, closed incubators and radiant warmer are really necessary [6].

2.3 Radiant warmer

Model of the open incubator used in present study was built on the bases of "Babytherm 8010 Radiant Warmer", constructed by Dräger Medical – Germany, which is installed in "Upper Silesian Child and Mother's Centre of Health" in Katowice [2]. Figure 1 shows the simple model of the incubator created in CATIA (left) [3]. The incubator consists of two main elements of heat production: a lamp (1) with infrared bulbs, and a bed (2) with a heating up mattress. The incubator is sophisticated apparatus so it is also equipped with such installations as intubation, make x-ray photo, check balance, defibrillator, etc. [2].

The GAMBIT preprocessor was used to create 2D geometry (middle), and to discretise the whole domain in the considered region (right) [5]. In ideal case the domain dimensions should be equal to the size of the hospital room under consideration, however, due to the limitation of the number of mesh cells, the domain is reduced to 1.5x1.5m. Due to the restrictions of the hardware and computational time it is important to find a compromise between number of cells and solution accuracy. A unstructured (triangular) mesh which is comprised of 54000 elements was used.

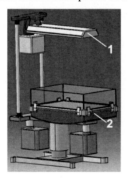 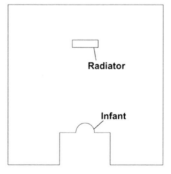 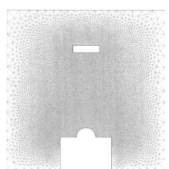

Figure 1: CATIA model (left), 2D GAMBIT model (middle), mesh (right).

3. COMPUTATIONAL FLUID DYNAMICS ASPECTS

FLUENT solver was used to solve heat and flow phenomena. A 2D model was analysed. The following settings were assumed. Firstly, all of processes are considered as a steady–state. The fluid as an incompressible ideal gas was admitted. Air is viscous and analyzed by $k-\varepsilon$, RNG (renormalization group) turbulence model. Radiation is considered by Discrete Ordinate radiation model [4].

4. VARIANTS OF CALCULATIONS AND THEIR SOLUTIONS

A few kinds of boundary conditions which present normal cases of a warm bed usage were studied:

- The way body behaves in the natural environment (case without a radiator lamp with a natural convection only).

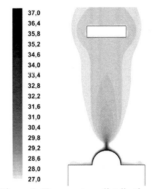

Figure 2: Temperature distribution, °C

In this case the air around the bed is heated up by the body and then moves up. Figure 2 presents the contours of the temperature distribution. Body temperature (without any protection) rapidly decreases because of the heat losses into the environment.

- The infant's thermal stabilisation (infant is heated through mattress only).

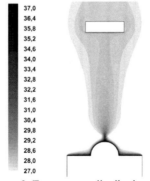

Figure 3: Temperature distribution, °C

The main phenomena in this case are a natural convection and radiation (Fig.3). However, the air does not start heating up from the body but also from the top of the bed (in fact there is a gel mattress which conducts heat from the aluminium heater plate). Due to simplifications, mattress has the same temperature as the body. Higher mattress temperature influences also the surrounding near the baby. Therefore, there is no visible turbulence.

- Complete incubator operation.

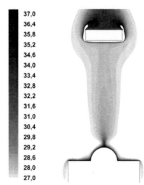

Figure 4: Temperature distribution, °C (white colour near radiator shows that the temperature is bellow the temperature range)

The full radiant warmer model is presented in the Figure 4. There were added the heat sources (in radiator) to conditions which were analyzed in the previous cases. It emits the electromagnetic waves in infra-red spectrum which increases the temperature of all encounter bodies especially of infant's skin. The operating radiator introduces meaningful changes. In that event a bigger amount (than in the previous cases) fluid is heated up and rise.

5. CONCLUSIONS

As mentioned previously, actual researches prove that more children were born too early. Therefore, proceeding the delving in order to improve devices and reach the best parameters which do not depend on infants, and guarantee healthy growth, is indispensable. This project implements it. Preliminary computations show that the model is feasible to be constructed. The 2D model solutions are promising and further researches should be provided for more complicated cases. Before considering the evaporation, the 3D model should to be constructed.

Further researches with focus on the optimal boundary conditions for radiator, bed top, baby and at the inlet and outlet. The experiment in real conditions will be provided in order to define the boundary conditions in a proper way.

REFERENCES

[1]   ASHARE *Fundamentals Handbook*. Physiological principles, comfort and health, Atlanta 1989.

[2]   Babytherm 8040/8010 radiant warmer. Instruction for use. Dräger Medical AG & Co. KGaA

[3]   CATIA Version 5 Release 12 User's Documentation Home Page. Dassault Systemes 1994–2003

[4]   Fluent 6.3. User guide, Lebanon, NH, USA: Fluent Inc.; 2006

[5]   Gambit 2.3. Modeling Guide, Lebanon, NH, USA: Fluent Inc.; 2004

[6]   Radshaw M., Rivers R., Rosenblatt D. *Born too early. Special care for your preterm baby.* Oxford University Press Inc. 1985

1st International Conference on Mathematical and Computational Biomedical Engineering – CMBE2009
June 29 – July 1, 2009, Swansea, UK
P. Nithiarasu and R. Löhner (eds)

A parallelized transient boundary element model of laser hyperthermia-photodynamic therapy in the oesophagus.

Prof K.E. Donne
Swansea Metropolitan University, Wales, UK, ke.donne@smu.ac.uk
Dr A. Marotin
Swansea Metropolitan University, Wales, UK, arnaud.marotin@smu.ac.uk
D. Rees
Swansea Metropolitan University, Wales, UK, dave.rees@smu.ac.uk

ABSTRACT

Key Words: *Boundary element method, photodynamic therapy, hyperthermia, oesophageal cancer.*

1. INTRODUCTION

This paper is concerned with the development of a transient boundary element method (BEM) based model to describe the photochemical and photothermal mechanisms playing a significant role in the treatment strategy of the oesophageal cancer. The medical condition known as Barett's oesophagus which has developed into an invasive adenocarcinoma is the typical situation which could benefit from modelling the action of both mechanisms [1]. Indeed, photodynamic therapy (PDT) is nowadays a considered treatment for early-stage and advanced oesophageal cancer [1, 2]. Moreover, according to the investigation of Eicher et al. [3], a synergetic effect was found by simultaneously applying PDT and hyperthermia (HT). Hence, by combining both PDT and HT therapies the efficiency of the treatment could be improved.
The basic principle of PDT consists in the administration of a photosensitiser. After a period of time, depending on the application, most of the photosensitiser is cleared from healthy tissue whereas its concentration in tumour cells has not decreased much. The remaining photosensitiser is then activated by exposure to a low-power drug-specific wavelength, mainly transmitted via optical fibres to or into the tumour. The combination of the photosensitiser activated using the appropriate wavelength with oxygen, produces cytotoxic agents resulting in the inactivation of tumour cells [4]. The reader is referred to Langmack et al. [5] who have introduced a kinetic model to quantify the rate and amount of damage produced by PDT.
HT involves irradiating tissue at a higher power than in PDT to raise the tumour tissue to a temperature in the range 42-45°C for a specified period of time, usually 30 to 60min [6, 7]. Temperature values within this range are not directly harmful to normal cells, while malignant ones are destroyed as they are more sensitive to high temperatures.

2. MODEL DESCRIPTION

The three-dimensional geometry of the oesophagus used in the BEM model developed for the current application is obtained from medical CT scan data originating from the Visible Human Project [8]. The lower part of the oesophagus is reconstructed using the image processing software Velocity Pro [9] which outputs the final boundary surface geometry in an STL format (see Figure 1). To by-pass the common problem of "non-watertight" STL files, the extracted oesophagus part is resurfaced using the surface modeller ALIAS [10]. A high-quality surface and volume mesh is then generated using the mesh generator in UGS I-DEAS [11]. I-DEAS is also used to create a tumour sub-volume, representative of an invasive oesophageal cancer progressing into the wall [12, 13]. The surface mesh of the oesophagus part and buried tumour considered is shown in Figure 2.

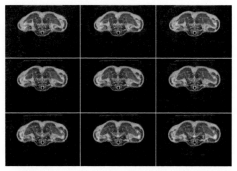
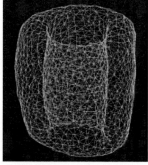

Figure 1 Reconstruction of the lower part of the oesophagus from medical CT scan data, using the image processing software Velocity Pro.

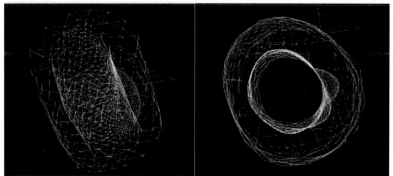

Figure 2 Snapshots of the oesophagus and tumour mesh considered.

To calculate the light propagation in the oesophagus, the BEM method is developed to take into consideration two contiguous homogeneous zones with different optical properties (normal site and tumour site). The modelling of the radiative problem, using the diffusion approximation of the transport theory, includes the Henyey-Greenstein phase function that takes account of anisotropic scattering in the diffusion approximation for the boundary surface elements where the photon are incident [14]. In this way, the predominantly forward scattering behaviour of tissue is reproduced using an algorithm that is much more efficient than the current approximation, inventing fictitious buried isotropic point sources in the tissue, to represent a collimated beam.

For the PDT model, the diffuse light source, representative of the typical catheter delivering the appropriate 630nm wavelength in the oesophagus, is incorporated as a photon current through the boundary by modifying the Robin boundary condition along the illuminated part of the oesophageal wall as described by Schweiger et al. [15]. Once the photon deposition at 630nm is calculated, the computation of the photodynamic damage dose takes place according to the kinetic model introduced by Langmack et al. [5].

We then proceed with the calculation of the photon deposition at 1064nm, followed by a transient thermal BEM using the bioheat equation [16] to model HT. The latter BEM model considers convective boundary conditions, which provide a reasonable effective loss term to the surrounding tissue. A separate calculation was undertaken with Dirichlet boundary conditions at the external wall to represent the mass of body tissue at 37°C. It allowed the determination of the appropriate heat transfer coefficient for the Robin boundary conditions implemented in these calculations, in order to produce the equivalent heat loss at the exterior wall.

Following Skinner et al. [17] the Arrhenius damage integral noted Ω_A is evaluated throughout the tissue region under consideration. In the bioheat equation, the blood perfusion term is a sink term which depends on the local perfusion rate w_b. It is important to take account of the decrease in w_b in the vasculature as the desired therapeutic damage increases. Once $\Omega_A(r, t)$ is determined, the instantaneous blood perfusion rate is found from: $w_b(r, t) = w_{init} \exp(-\Omega_A)$, where w_{init} is the initial perfusion rate before treatment begins [17, 18].

3. RESULTS

The BEM solution of the radiative transport problem has been validated against an existing Monte Carlo code [19] for both wide and narrow light sources. As for the BEM solution of the transient thermal transport problem, numerous benchmark tests have been performed, comparing the latter transient BEM method against analytical solutions for simple geometries and against finite difference and finite volume codes for irregular geometries and pulsed laser sources [14].

The photochemical damage calculation due to the PDT therapy is performed according to the protocol implemented by Globe et al. [20] (fluence rate of 68mW/cm^2 and a total light dose of 85J/cm^2). This damage is obtained by incorporating the results from the radiative transport solution into the Langmack et al. [5] kinetic model.

The resulting thermal damage after 30min of irradiation at 1064nm, is validated against the experiment implemented by Eicher et al. [3]. The calculation of thermal damage is carried out by evaluating the Arrhenius integral in a subroutine in the transient thermal BEM model. The damage parameter Ω_A is dimensionless and exponentially dependent on temperature. Mohammed et al. [21] argued that a limit of $\Omega_A > 0.6$ can be considered as a threshold of final tissue destruction as $\Omega_A = 0.6$ corresponds to a reduction in concentration of native molecules to 50%. The results show that only tissue in the tumour region undergoes significant damage ($\Omega_A > 0.6$). At HT characteristic low temperatures, the illumination time plays a critical role. Therefore damage may increase gradually should the light exposure be kept on for longer.

The combined radiative and transient thermal BEM has been coded in C++ on a 16 node, 128 processes High Performance Computer Cluster using the Message Passing Interface (MPI) protocol. For the clinical problem described in this paper, which has 1701 boundary elements and 2132 volume elements, the total calculation time was 65.72 seconds, which was fifty times faster than the sequential code.

4. CONCLUSIONS

Through the realistic and representative clinical case study of oesophageal cancer considered, this paper shows that a transient radiative-thermal transport solver, based on the BEM, can be successfully applied to real clinical study. Indeed, the results are consistent with previous clinical experimental work using a ballon catheter approach and indicate that the method has significant potential for modelling PDT and HT therapies using body scan data. For both the radiative and thermal algorithms, careful consideration of the numerical errors in the determination of the Green's terms has led to a framework of rules for choosing element subdivision level and quadrature order. The philosophy behind this work is to provide numerical tools that could contribute to the analysis of real-world clinical problems, which consist of irregular geometries, complex tissue structures and light-based therapies that are not clearly understood. The integrated radiative-thermal model developed could be used to undertake detailed parametric studies of light-based treatments provided that the careful consideration of errors minimisation is followed.

Besides, the BEM has a major attraction in that it is easily converted into a parallel code. This latter feature is brought to light in the present work, where a MPI-based parallel implementation on a High Performance Cluster has achieved a time-effective version for solving realistic clinical problems. Nevertheless, there is scope for further optimisation of the MPI version, which currently does not include parallelisation of any matrix inversions.

REFERENCES

[1]   Thompson Cancer Survival Center. Center of Excellence for Treatment of Barrett's Esophagus. http://www.thompsoncancer.com/tcsc-home.cfm

[2]   National Institute for Health and Clinical Excellence. http://www.nice.org.uk/

[3]   J. Eichler, J. Liebetruth, R.A. London and L. Ziegenhagen, *Temperature distribution for combined laser hyperthermia-photodynamic therapy in the esophagus*, Medical Engineering & Physics, Vol.22, pp.307-312, 2000.

[4]   W.M. Sharman, C.M. Allen and J.E. van Lier, *Photodynamic therapeutics: basic principles and clinical applications*, Drug Discovery Today, Vol.4, No.11, pp.507-517, 1999.

[5]   K. Langmack, R. Mehta, P. Twyman and P. Norris, *Topical photodynamic therapy at low fluence rates – theory and practice*, Photochemistry and Photobiology B: Biology, Vol.60, No.1, pp.37-43, 2001.

[6]   M. Tunc, U. Camdali, C. Parmaksizoglu and S. Cikrikci, *The bio-heat transfer equation and its applications in hyperthermia treatments*, Computer-Aided Engineering and Software,Vol.23, No.4, pp.451-463, 2006.

[7]   A.J. Welch and M.J.C. van Gemert, *Optical-thermal response of laser-irradiated tissue*, New York: Plenum Press, 1995.

[8]   M.J. Ackerman, *The Visible Human Project*, IEEE, Vol.86, No.3, pp.504-511, 1998.

[9]   Velocity^2 Pro. Image3D LLC, 470 Lawndale Drive, Salt Lake City, Utah 84115. http://www.v2software.com

[10]   Alias Studio, Autodesk Media and Entertainment Solutions. http://usa.autodesk.com/

[11]   MAYA   HTT's   TMG-Thermal   advanced   heat   transfer   simulation   software. http//www.mayahtt.com/

[12]   Private communication with William Davies, Clinical Scientist, Head of Clinical Engineering. Singleton Hospital, Medical Physics Department, Swansea.

[13]   Private communication with Dr Samuel Webster, Lecturer in Anatomy, School of Medicine, University of Wales Swansea.

[14]   A. Marotin, *An investigation into the boundary element method for multi-dimensional modeling of light-tissue interaction*, PhD Thesis, University of Wales, Swansea Institute of Higher Education, Swansea, 2007.

[15]   M. Schweiger, S.R. Arridge, M. Hiroaka and D.T. Delpy, *The finite element method for the propagation of light in scattering media: boundary and source conditions*, Medical Physics, Vol.22, No.11, pp.1779-1792, 1995.

[16]   J. Liu, *Bioheat Transfer Model*, Wiley Encyclopedia of Biomedical Engineering, 2006.

[17]   M.G. Skinner, M.N. Lizuka, M.C. Kolios and M.D. Sherar, *A theoretical comparison of energy sources—microwave, ultrasound and laser—for interstitial thermal therapy*, Physics and Medicine in Biology, Vol.43, pp.3535-3547, 1998.

[18]   Y.S. Liew, *An investigation into embedded photodynamic therapy*, PhD Thesis, University of Wales, Swansea, 2005.

[19]   G.M. Daniel, *Optical and thermal transport modelling of laser-tissue interaction*, PhD Thesis, University of Wales, Swansea Institute of Higher Education, Swansea, 2002.

[20]   J. Globe, A. Smythe, C.J. Kelty, M.W.R. Reed, N.J. Brown and R. Ackroyd, *The effect of photodynamic therapy (PDT) on esophageal motility and acid clearance in patients with Barrett's esophagus*, Photochemistry and Photobiology B: Biology Vol.85, pp.17-22, 2006.

[21]   Y. Mohammed and J.F. Verhey, *A finite element method model to simulate laser interstitial thermotherapy in anatomical inhomogeneous regions*, Biomedical Engineering Online, Vol.4, No.2, pp. 1-16, 2005.

1st International Conference on Mathematical and Computational Biomedical Engineering – CMBE2009
June 29 – July 1, 2009, Swansea, UK
P. Nithiarasu and R. Löhner (eds)

A molecule dissociation method based on multi-objective optimization

Kun Yang
Department of Engineering Mechanics, State Key Laboratory of Structural Analysis for Industrial Equipment, Dalian University of Technology, Dalian 116024, China, Email: yangkun@dlut.edu.cn
Xicheng Wang
Department of Engineering Mechanics, State Key Laboratory of Structural Analysis for Industrial Equipment, Dalian University of Technology, Dalian 116024, China, Email: guixum@dlut.edu.cn
Hualiang Jiang
Drug Discovery and Design Center, State Key Laboratory of Drug Research, Shanghai Institute of Materia Medica, Chinese Academy of Sciences, Shanghai 201203, China, Email: hljiang@mail.shcnc.ac.cn

ABSTRACT

As complementary approaches for experimental measurements, steered molecular dynamics (SMD) can provide atomic-level descriptions of underlying events. This technique has already been used to provide qualitative insights into many fields, including identification of ligand binding/unbinding pathways and clarification of the elastic properties of proteins among others. However, the pulling direction of the spring in SMD is chosen randomly or by guesswork on the basis of structural information. A disadvantage arises from the fact that the force applied to the ligand in the chosen direction may not move along a favorable pathway, and some SMD simulations may suffer from inefficiency. In this paper, we propose a molecule dissociation method with pulling direction optimization to overcome the above difficulties. A multi-objective optimization method is developed to adaptive direction adjustments. The novel method has been successfully used to dissociate some substrate-bound complex structures. The results shows that the proposed method can give a better dissociation pathway, which has a lower energy barrier, shorter dissociation time and decreased motion trajectory compared with those of a conventional SMD simulation method.

Key Words: *Steered molecular dynamics, dissociation pathway, genetic algorithm, multi-objective optimization.*

1. INTRODUCTION

Numerous functions of cells involve the mechanical properties of biopolymers. A wealth of information about the mechanical properties of structural proteins has been revealed by single molecule experiments, in which mechanical forces are used to stretch proteins. The techniques employed for these studies include atomic force microscopy [1], laser optical tweezers [2], biomembrane force probes [3] and surface force apparatus experiments [4]. However, these experimental techniques cannot resolve sufficient details in terms of protein structures. As complementary approaches for experimental measurements, steered molecular dynamics (SMD) can provide atomic-level descriptions of underlying events. This technique has already been used to provide qualitative insights into many fields, including identification of ligand binding/unbinding pathways and clarification of the elastic properties of proteins among others [5-7].

In SMD simulations, time-dependent external forces are applied to a system. Analysis of the dissociation process yields important structural information about the structure-function relationships of ligand-receptor complexes and binding pathways. However, the pulling direction of the spring in SMD is chosen randomly or by guesswork on the basis of structural information. A disadvantage arises from the fact that the force applied to the ligand in the chosen direction may not move along a favorable pathway, and some SMD simulations may suffer from inefficiency.

In the present paper, we propose an SMD method with adaptive direction adjustments to overcome the above difficulties. We developed a multi-population genetic algorithm based on information entropy to optimize the pulling direction. The proposed method can accelerate molecular dynamics simulations, find an optimal pathway and allow ligand unbinding from a deeply buried active site to the protein exterior.

2. Methods and Application

As mentioned above, a force is applied to the ligand along a chosen direction in SMD simulations. The direction is accepted or rejected based on factors such as conservation of the secondary structure of the protein, deformation of the protein, magnitude of the force applied and average velocity of the ligand along the unbinding pathway among others. The conventional SMD method may suffer from inefficiency if a force is applied to the ligand in a rejected direction. The conventional SMD method can be improved by optimizing the direction of the force during the simulation. A multi-population genetic algorithm based on information entropy is used to find the optimal pulling direction. The optimal phase is embedded in the GROMACS version 3.2 software [8-9] with the GROMOS96 force field. The improved program can be used efficiently to explore the binding and unbinding properties of biomolecules and their responses to external mechanical manipulations at the atomic level.

2.1   Optimization design model
The adaptive direction adjustment problem of SMD simulations can be written as an optimization problem:

$$Max \left\| d_{lig}^{new}(\mathbf{r}) - d_{lig}^{init}(\mathbf{r}) \right\|$$
$$Min \left\| E_{lig}^{new}(\mathbf{r}) - E_{lig}^{init}(\mathbf{r}) \right\| \tag{1}$$
$$s.t. \begin{cases} -\pi \le \phi \le \pi \\ 0 \le \theta \le \dfrac{\pi}{2} \end{cases}$$

where $\| d_{lig}^{new}(r) - d_{lig}^{init}(r) \|$ and $\| E_{lig}^{new}(r) - E_{lig}^{init}(r) \|$ are the ligand's distance and total energy

changes between the forthcoming and initial positions with a pulling direction of r_t for the duration of certain time steps. To obtain the same scale, each item of the optimization function should be normalized.

The pulling direction r_t is determined by the initial position r_0, procession angle ϕ and nutation angle θ.

The nutation angle θ is allowed to vary between 0 and $\pi/2$ rad to ensure the pulling direction r_t in the

hemispherical space along the initial direction r_0, and the procession angle ϕ varies between $-\pi$ and π. Problem (1) is a multi-objective optimization problem. It can be transformed into a single objective problem (2) by the weighted coefficient method:

$$\max F(\mathbf{d}) = \alpha \| d_{lig}^{new}(\mathbf{r}) - d_{lig}^{init}(\mathbf{r}) \| - \beta \| E_{lig}^{new}(\mathbf{r}) - E_{lig}^{init}(\mathbf{r}) \|$$
$$s.t. \begin{cases} -\pi \le \phi \le \pi \\ 0 \le \theta \le \dfrac{\pi}{2} \\ \alpha + \beta = 1 \end{cases} \tag{2}$$

where α and β are weighted coefficients. Problem (2) is solved by a genetic algorithm, and its constraints can easily be treated by means of GAs encoding of the variable space in chromosomes.
2.2   Multi-population genetic algorithm based on information entropy
We used a new iteration scheme in conjunction with a multi-population genetic strategy based on an information entropy searching technique with a narrowing down space to solve problem (2). By application of the information entropy principle, an entropy-based optimization model can be given, and obtain easily and explicitly

$$p_j^* = \exp(\gamma F_j(d)) / \sum_{j=1}^{m} \exp(\gamma F_j(d)) \tag{4}$$

γ is called as quasi-weight coefficient (here $\gamma = -1$)[10] .

The $(1 - p_j)$ can be used as the coefficients of narrowing searching space in the modified genetic algorithm. Design space is defined as the initial searching space $D(0)$. M populations with N members are generated in the given space. The searching space of each population is narrowed according to the following formula:

$$D(K) = (1 - p_j)D(K - 1)$$

$$\underline{d}_i(K) = \max\{[d_i^*(K) - 0.5(1 - p_j)D(K)], \underline{d}_i(0)\} \quad (5)$$

$$\overline{d}_i(K) = \min\{[d_i^*(K) + 0.5(1 - p_j)D(K)], \overline{d}_i(0)\}$$

where $\underline{d}_i(K)$ and $\overline{d}_i(K)$ are the modified lower and upper limits of the i_{th} design variable at the K_{th} iteration, respectively. $d_i^*(K)$ is the value of the i_{th} design variable of the best member in the jth population. When the optimal solution occurs in the l_{th} population, then $(1 - p_l^*) = 0$, and its searching space is not narrowing. Then, the convergence criterion of the proposed method can be defined as follows: when the searching space in the best population has been reduced to a very small area (a given tolerance), the global optimal solution can be obtained approximately.

2.3 Applications to metyrapone dissociating from cytochrome P450 3A4 [11]

The proposed method has been applied to dissociate the substrate-bound complex structure of cytochrome P450 3A4-metyrapone. Adaptive direction adjustments can make the metyrapone dissociate more easily and rapidly compared with the conventional SMD. Compared with the conventional SMD, the total dissociation time of the improved SMD simulation is reduced from 672 to 457 ps.

SMD with adaptive direction adjustments can effectively reduce the computing time and decrease the height of the peak force. We compare some datum in Table 1. It can directly show that the novel SMD is better than the conventional SMD.

Table 1 P450 3A4 Results of the conventional and improved SMD simulations

	Conventional SMD	SMD with direction optimization
Dissociation time (ps)	672	457
Maximum force (pN)	742.59	592.68
Integrated force (pN·ns)	249.4	151.81
Total work (kJ·mol−1)	626.44	420.04

To prove the feasibility of the new method, we presented a direction named Channel 2. Li et al. [12] have pointed out that Channel 2 is an impossible pathway for dissociating the substrate-bound complex structure of cytochrome P450 3A4-metyrapone. Only two modifications of the direction are needed to dissociate the ligand successfully.

2.4 Application to Glutamine-binding protein (GlnBp) [13]

Glutamine-binding protein (GlnBp) is one of the ligand-specific periplasmic binding proteins in the Escherichia coli permease systems, predicted to play an important role in transferring Gln from the periplasmic space to the cytoplasmic space.

In order to compare both the temporal and spatial characteristics with the mechanics property, we calculate dissociation time, maximum force, integrated force and total work, as shown in Table2.

Table 2 GlnBp Results of the conventional and improved SMD simulations

	Conventional SMD	SMD with direction optimization
Dissociation time (ps)	1964	1505
Maximum force (pN)	875.74	748.01
Integrated force (pN·ns)	559.87	353.45
Total work (kJ·mol−1)	337.13	212.76

3. CONCLUSIONS

In this paper, we proposed a novel SMD method with adaptive direction adjustments. The method has been successfully used to dissociate the substrate-bound complex structure of cytochrome P450 3A4-metyrapone and Glutamine-binding protein. By means of adding adaptive direction adjustments to the conventional SMD simulation, a better dissociation channel can be found. The simulation results show that the improved SMD method has a shorter dissociation time, smaller maximum force and lower energy barrier than the conventional SMD. The results also show that the new SMD method can easily find a successful dissociation pathway even along a failed direction at the beginning of the simulation.

The new SMD method is also suitable for macrobiomolecules with multiple routes or complicated curved routes for ligand passage. It may also be efficient for protein folding/unfolding processes.

Acknowledgement

The authors gratefully acknowledge financial support for this work from the National Natural Science Foundation (No.10772042) and High Science and Technology Project (No2006AA01A124) of China.

REFERENCES

[1]   G. Binnig, C.F. Quate and C. Gerber, Atomic force microscope, *Physcal Review Letters*, 56, 930-933, 1986.
[2]   K. Svoboda and S.M. Block, Biological applications of optical forces, *Annual Review of Biophysics Biomolecular Structure*, 23, 247-285, 1994.
[3]   E. Evans, K. Ritchie and R. Merkel, Sensitive force technique to probe molecular adhesion and structural linkages at biological interfaces, *Biophysical Journal*, 68, 2580-2587, 1995.
[4]   J.N. Israelachvili, Intermolecular and surface forces, *Academic Press*, 1992.
[5]   S. Izrailev, S. Stepaniants, B. Isralewitz, D. Kosztin, H. Lu, F. Molnar, W. Wriggers and K. Schulten,, Steered molecular dynamics, In Computational Molecular Dynamics: Challenges, Methods, Ideas, *Lecture Notes in Computational Science and Engineering*, P. Deuflhard, J. Hermans, B. Leimkuhler, A. E. Mark, S. Reich and R. D. Skeel, editors. Springer-Verlag, Berlin, Germany. 4, 39-65, 1999.
[6]   B. Isralewitz, J. Baudry, J. Gullingsrud, D. Kosztin and K. Schulten, Steered molecular dynamics investigations of protein function, *Journal of Molecular Graphics Modelling*, 19, 13-25, 2001.
[7]   Y. Xu, J. Shen, X. Luo, I. Silman, J.L. Sussman, K and Chen, H. Jiang, How does huperzine A enter and leave the binding gorge of acetylcholinesterase? Steered molecular dynamics simulations, *Journal of American Chemical Society*, 125, 11340-11349, 2003.
[8]   H.J.C. Berendsen, D. van der Spoel and R. van Drunen, GROMACS: A message-passing parallel molecular dynamics implementation, *Computer Physics Communications*, 91, 43-56, 1995.
[9]   E. Lindahl, B. Hess and D. van der Spoel, GROMACS 3.0: A package for molecular simulation and trajectory analysis, *Journal of Molecular Modeling*, 7, 306-317, 2001.
[10]   L. Kang, H.L. Li, H.L. Jiang and X.C. Wang, An improved adaptive genetic algorithm for 412 protein–ligand docking, *Journal of Computer-Aided Molecular Design*, 23, 1~12, 2009.
[11]   P.A. Williams, J. Cosme, D.M. Vinkovic, A. Ward, H.C. Angove, P.J. Day, C. Vonrhein, I.J. Tickle and H. Jhoti, Crystal structures of human cytochrome P450 3A4 bound to metyrapone and progesterone, *Science*, 305, 683-686, 2004.
[12]   W. Li, H. Liu, X.M. Luo, W.L. Zhu, Y. Tang, J.R. Halpert and H.L. Jiang, Possible pathway(s) of metyrapone egress from the active site of cytochrome P450 3A4: a molecular dynamics simulation, *Drug Metabolism and Disposition*, 35, 689-696, 2007.
[13]   Y.J. Sun, J. Rose, B.C. Wang and C.D. Hsiao, The structure of glutamine-binding protein complexed with glutamine at 1.94 A resolution: comparisons with other amino acid binding proteins, *Journal of Molecular Biology*, 278, 219-229, 1998.

Molecular Dynamics investigation of salt-dependent diffusion coefficients of ssDNA oligomers in aqueous solution.

Massimo Lai, Dimitris Drikakis
FMaCS group, Aerospace Sciences Department, Cranfield University
Cranfield, Bedfordshire,MK43 0AL, United Kingdom
m.lai@cranfield.ac.uk
d.drikakis@cranfield.ac.uk

ABSTRACT

We report the results of molecular dynamics simulations of diffusion coefficients of ssDNA tetramers in different salt conditions. After the correction for finite-size effects, the results agree well with the values extrapolated from experimental results available for longer strands. We also show that diffusion coefficients appear to be sequence-dependent, but the dependency tends to disappear when the salt concentration rises to 1.0M.

Key Words: *ssDNA, diffusion coefficients, molecular dynamics, explicit water model, polymer transport, finite-size effects*

1 INTRODUCTION

The aim of this work was to evaluate the effect of salt concentration on the diffusive properties of DNA oligomers of different sequence. Salt concentration plays a double role, modifying the carrier fluid viscosity and the mechanical properties of the ssDNA chain [4, 6]. This interplay determines the resulting diffusive behaviour. The effect on the conformation has been investigated calculating the equivalent hydrodynamic radius of the strands. The averaged properties of short oligomers can be used as constitutive elements of a finely discretised model of ssDNA for implementation in particle-fluid models for the simulation of transport phenomena in DNA biosensors.

2 METHOD

All simulations have been carried using the LAMMPS parallel MD simulator using the CHARMM27 force field [9, 5]. All bonds and angles involving H atoms were constrained with SHAKE. The cutoff for non-bonded interactions was set to 10 Angstrom and long-range electrostatics were computed by PPPM method using a grid space of 1 Angstrom. The 3' and 5' ends of the nucleic acid chain were capped with hydroxyl groups, the tetranucleotides AAAA and TTTT were solvated in cubic boxes of explicit TIP3P water, modified according to the parametrization suggested by Price and Brooks in order to reproduce the solvent structure more accurately [1].

The systems have been then neutralized with 3 Na^+ ions and NaCl has been added up to two different concentrations, 0.1M and 1.0M respectively. The boxes for AAAA in 0.1 and 1.0M solutions included 6755 waters, $8Na^+$ and 5 Cl^- and 6631 waters, $65Na^+$ and 62 Cl^- respectively. The boxes for TTTT contained 6761 waters, $8Na^+$ and 5 Cl^-, and 6646 waters, $65Na^+$ and 62 Cl^-. All runs were performed at 298K and 1 atm in the NpT ensemble using Nose-Hoover thermostat and barostat [10]. The systems have been minimized and then equilibrated for 1ns with a timestep of 0.5fs, and then run for 4 more nanoseconds to allow ion equilibration around the molecule [3]. Each of the 4 cases has been run in 3 independent simulations with randomized initial configurations, for a total simulated time of 300ns. Radius of gyration and center of mass position of the ssDNA were stored every 0.2 ps.

The diffusion coefficients were calculated from the random fluctuations of the molecule centre of mass using the well-known Einstein relation for diffusion in three dimensions,

$$D = \lim_{t \to \infty} \frac{\partial \langle M D t \rangle}{\partial t} \tag{1}$$

The slope of a linear fitting of the Mean Square Displacement (MSD) over a time window Δt was evaluated after computing the MSD by window-averaging over the production run, as illustrated for example by [7]. The chosen window length was $\Delta t = 100$ps, while the spacing between the time origins of the windows was 10ps. The MSD converges very neatly to the expected linear behaviour, and the uncertainty on the slope is several orders of magnitude smaller than the absolute value, thus providing a solid estimate.

A suitable treatment for keeping account of the effect of PBC and the limited size of the simulation box was developed by Yeh and Hummer, based on an empirical correction of the original theoretical analysis for point-like particles by Dünweg and Kremer [11, 2]. The simulated diffusion coefficient D_s computed by means of Eq. (1) is first corrected for finite-size effects as:

$$D = D_s + \frac{{}_BT\xi\alpha}{\pi\eta L}, \tag{2}$$

Where ${}_BT$ is the reduced temperature, η is the dynamic viscosity of the used water model, $\xi = 2.873$ is a constant that synthetises the correlation effect summed over all periodic images of a cubic lattice, $\alpha = 0.7$ is an empirical correction for finite-size molecules, and L is the linear size of the box [11, 2]. Assuming that viscosity alone doesn't have a remarkable effect on the hydrodynamic radius of the molecules, the Stokes-Einstein equation provides the scaling relationship for diffusion in two solvents of different viscosity (in our case, real and model water), as

$$\eta_w D_w = \eta D, \qquad D_w = \frac{\eta}{\eta_w} D, \tag{3}$$

where D_w is the estimated diffusion coefficient in real water. The dynamic viscosity of TIP3P water is known to be very low, and it has been reported by some authors to be $0.31 \pm 0.01 mPa \cdot s$. However our measurements (results unpublished), show that the Price-Brooks TIP3P has comparatively higher viscosity. The experimental values for water viscosity in no-salt, 0.1M, and 1.0M NaCl solutions are respectively $0.89 \pm 0.02 mPa \cdot s$, $0.90 \pm 0.02 mPa \cdot s$ and $0.97 \pm 0.02 mPa \cdot s$. [4]. The comparison with model water in similar conditions, and the corresponding correction factors as summarized in Tab. (1). For the solutions at 0.1M and 1.0M NaCl the solvent viscosity correction factors η/η_w are respectively 0.50 and 0.49. The corrected diffusion coefficients are summarised in Tab. (2).

3   RESULTS AND CONCLUSIONS

Salt concentration is known to have an effect on both fluid viscosity [4] and ssDNA persistence length [6], which influences the chain persistence length and therefore its conformation in solution and, potentially, its hydrodynamic radius. We have used molecular dynamics simulations to investigate the effect of salt concentrations on the diffusive properties of ssDNA oligomers. Finite-size effects have been taken into consideration by means of opportune correction coefficients. The discrepancy between the viscosity of real and model water has also been considered.

The nucleotide sequences of the simulated ssDNA strands were chosen as two limit cases, polyadenine and polythymine, which show respectively the maximum and minimum base stacking tendency and therefore the maximum and minimum expected persistence length. The calculated diffusion coefficients are very close to those extrapolated from the experimental measurements, which indicates a Zimm scaling [8]. The results indicate a higher diffusivity of the thymine oligomers in low-salt conditions, while in high-salt there is almost no difference between the polyadenine and polythymine, within the measurement accuracy. For both sequences the diffusion is lower in high-salt, but this is due to the increased solvent viscosity. We can therefore conclude that, at least for short chains, sequence-dependent mechanical features of ssDNA are more relevant in low-salt conditions and tend to be less evident as the counter-ion concentration increases.

C(NaCl)	$\eta_{PB-TIP3P}$	η_{H_2O}(exp.)	$\eta_{PB-TIP3P}/\eta_{H_2O}$
0	0.43 ± 0.02	0.89	0.48
0.1M	0.45 ± 0.01	0.90	0.49
1.0M	0.48 ± 0.01	0.97	0.50

Table 1: Viscosity of real water, (extrapolated from [4]), and Price-Brooks TIP3P water (Lai, unpublished) at 298K and 1 atm, at different NaCl molar concentrations (values in $mPa \cdot s$).

Sequence	C(NaCl)	D_s	D_w	R_h	R_g
AAAA	0.1M	0.415 ± 0.014	0.299 ± 0.007	0.811 ± 0.019	0.582 ± 0.035
AAAA	1.0M	0.379 ± 0.007	0.275 ± 0.003	0.818 ± 0.007	0.573 ± 0.038
TTTT	0.1M	0.447 ± 0.020	0.315 ± 0.009	0.770 ± 0.021	0.557 ± 0.022
TTTT	1.0M	0.379 ± 0.009	0.275 ± 0.004	0.818 ± 0.009	0.558 ± 0.01

Table 2: Computed (D_s) and corrected (D_w) diffusion coefficients (in $10^{-5} cm^2/s$), corrected hydrodynamic radius R_h (in nm), and radius of gyration R_g (in nm).

REFERENCES

[1] C.L. Brooks D.J. Price. A modified TIP3P water potential for simulation with Ewald summation. *Journal of Chemical Physics*, 121(20):10096–10103, 2004.

[2] B. Dunweg and K. Kremer. Molecular dynamics simulations of a polymer chain in solution. *J. Chem. Phys.*, 99(9):6983–6997, 1993.

[3] M. Feig and B. M. Petitt. Sodium and chlorine ions as part of the DNA solvation shell. *Biophys. Jour.*, 77(4), 1999.

[4] Z. Hai-Lang and H. Shi-Jun. Viscosity and density of water + sodium chloride + potassium chloride solutions at 298.15K. *J. Chem. Eng. Data*, 41(3), 1996.

[5] A.D. MacKerell and N.K. Banavali. All-atom empirical force field for nucleic acids: II. application to molecular dynamics simulations of DNA and RNA in solution. *Journal of Computational Chemistry*, 21(2):105–120, 2000.

[6] M. C. Murphy, I. Rasnik, W. Cheng, T. M. Lohman, and T. Ha. Probing single-stranded DNA conformational flexibility using fluorescence spectroscopy. *Biophysical Journal*, 86(4):2530–2537, 2004.

[7] D. Nevins and F.J. Spera. Accurate computation of shear viscosity from equilibrium molecular dynamics simulations. *Molecular Simulation*, 33(15), 2007.

[8] A. E. Nkodo, J. M. Garnier, B. Tinland, H. Ren, C. Desruisseaux, L. C. McCormick, G. Drouin, and G. W. Slater. Diffusion coefficient of DNA molecules during free solution electrophoresis. *Electrophoresis*, 22(12):2424–2432, 2001.

[9] S.J. Plimpton. Fast parallel algorithms for short-range molecular dynamics. *J. Comp. Phys.*, 117:1–19, 1995.

[10] B.L. Hoolian S. Melchionna, G. Ciccotti. Hoover NpT dynamics for systems varying in shape and size. *Molecular Physics*, 78(3), 1993.

[11] I. C Yeh and G. Hummer. Diffusion and electrophoretic mobility of single-stranded RNA from molecular dynamics simulations. *Biophysical Journal*, 86(2):681–689, 2004.

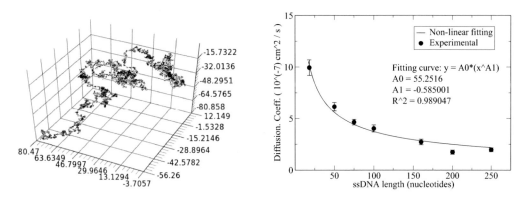

Figure 1: Brownian motion of a simulated trajectory (left) and fitting curve for the experimental values of ssDNA diffusion coefficients, from [8] (right).

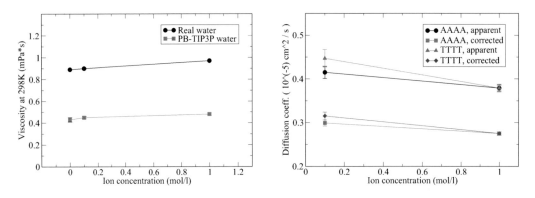

Figure 2: Discrepancy between real water and model water viscosity (left) and plot of simulated diffusion coefficients (right).

1st International Conference on Mathematical and Computational Biomedical Engineering – CMBE2009
June 29 – July 1, 2009, Swansea, UK
P. Nithiarasu and R. Löhner (eds)

BEHAVIOUR OF TENSEGRITY CELLS ASSEMBLY DURING SINGLE CELL GROWTH

Eligiusz W. Postek
University of Sheffield, Computer Science, Computational Systems Biology, Regent Court, 211 Portobello, S1 4DP Sheffield, UK, e.w.postek@sheffield.ac.uk
Rod Smallwood
University of Sheffield, Computer Science, Computational Systems Biology, Regent Court, 211 Portobello, S1 4DP Sheffield, UK, r.smallwood@sheffield.ac.uk
Rod Hose
University of Sheffield, Medical Physics and Clinical Engineering, Beech Hill Road, S10 2RX, Sheffield, UK, d.r.hose@sheffield.ac.uk

ABSTRACT

The tensegrity structures form the cells of living organisms. We will deal with the cell monolayer. The particular cell is an elementary icosahedron. We are interested in the influence of the cell growth on the displacement and stress patterns in the cell matrix. The problem is geometrically nonlinear and visco-elastic.

Key Words: *Tensegrity, cell colonies, cell growth*

1. INTRODUCTION

The tensegrity structures form the cells of living organisms [1]. The role of cytoskeleton (CSK) is continuously discovered. The cytoskeleton can be modelled as a tensegrity structure consisting of equivalent microtubules acting as struts and actins which are the tendons [2]. We are observing the behaviour of the assembly of the cells in the situation of growth of a single cell. The cell growths because of the extension of the struts. We observe three exemplary modes of the extension, namely, all struts are growing, two parallel struts are growing and one strut is growing. We are not answering the question why the struts are starting to grow. The signal can come from an external agent [3].

2. MATHEMATICAL FORMULATION

We adopt the incremental formulation in the Updated Lagrangian frame. The equation of equilibrium reads

$$\left(\int_{\Omega^t} \mathbf{B}_L'^{\mathsf{T}} \, {}_t^t \bar{\delta} \mathbf{B}_L' \, d\Omega^t \right) \Delta \mathbf{q} + \int_{\Omega^t} \mathbf{B}_L^{\mathsf{T}} \Delta \mathbf{S} \, d\Omega^t = \int_{\Omega^t} \mathbf{N}^{\mathsf{T}} \Delta \mathbf{f} \, d\Omega^t + \int_{\partial\Omega_\sigma^t} \mathbf{N}^{\mathsf{T}} \Delta \mathbf{t} \, d\left(\partial\Omega_\sigma^t \right) \quad (1)$$

where $\mathbf{B}_L^{\mathsf{T}}$ and $\mathbf{B}_L^{\mathsf{T}}$ are the nonlinear and linear operators, $\mathbf{N}$ is the shape functions matrix, $\Delta \mathbf{S}$ is the stress increment, $\bar{\tau}$ is the Cauchy stress matrix, $\Delta \mathbf{q}$ is the displacement increment, $\Delta \mathbf{f}$ and $\Delta \mathbf{t}$ are the body forces and the boundary tractions increments. The integration is done over the domain Ω and its boundary Ω_σ.

The constitutive model is visco-elastic such as the stress increment depends on total stress **S**, the shear modulus (G), the bulk modulus (K) and the strain increment Δ**E** as follows

$$\Delta \mathbf{S} = \mathbf{D}^{const}\left(\mathbf{S}, G, K\right)\!\Delta\mathbf{E} \qquad (2)$$

with the relaxation function

$$G(t) = G_o + \sum_{i=1}^{n} G_i \exp\left(\frac{-t}{\lambda_i}\right) \qquad (3)$$

where t is the time and λ_i are the relaxation times of the particular parallel dampers. These above describe the generalized Maxwell model.

3. NUMERICAL EXAMPLE

The icosahedral tensegrity structure is presented in Fig. 1. The cytoskeleton can slide on the surface. The right side of cellural matrix is fixed. We adopt the following data, namely, height of the cell 19 μm, cross-sectional areas of the tendons (filaments) 10nm², cross-sectional areas of the struts (microtubules) 190 nm², Young's modulus of the tendons 2.6GPa and the struts 1.2GPa, initial prestressing forces 20 nN, maximum loading 0.1N, relaxation time 1.0 sec, G_i/G_o ratio 0.91. The honeycomb pattern of the cells is shown in Fig 1a and the elementary icosahedral tensegrity structure which models the individual cells is shown in Fig 1b. The 6 pairs of the parallel struts are marked in blue color and the remaining bars are the tendons.

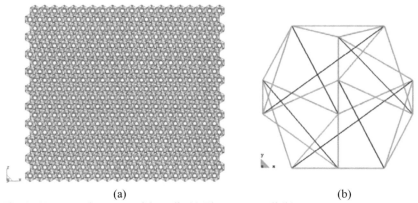

(a)   (b)

Fig. 1. Honeycomb pattern of the cells (a) Elementary cell (b)

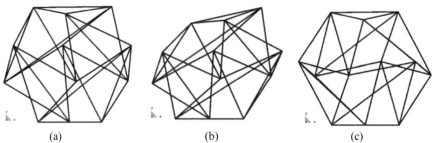

(a)   (b)   (c)

Fig. 2. Exemplary modes of growth. All microtubules are growing, growth mode A (a) Two parallel microtubules, growth mode B, (b) One microtubule, growth mode C (c).

The three considered elementary modes of growth are shown in Fig. 2. It is interesting to note that the growth of two parallel struts ovals the cell which is the growth mode B. The same happens to mode C, however it is less intence. The modes presented above correspond with Fig. 3 where the growing cell is placed close to the middle of the cellular matrix.

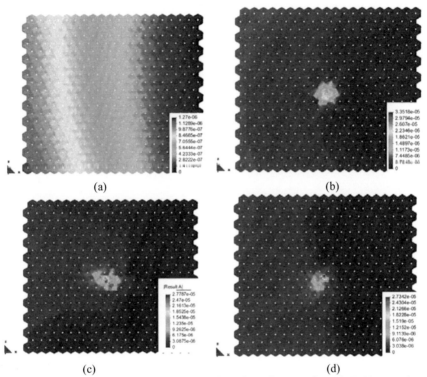

(a)

(b)

(c)

(d)

Fig 3. Displacement patterns. Tension (a) growth mode A (b), growth mode B (c), growth mode C (d).

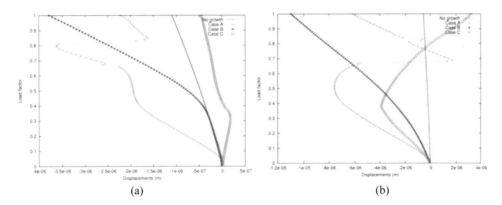

(a)

(b)

Fig. 4. Load factor versus horizontal displacement, point on the loaded edge (a) and the point on the surface close to the growing cell (b).

The cellular matrix is loaded with horizontal load and the single cells which are growing are introduced into. We may notice that the symmetry of the displacement pattern of the homogeneous cellular structure (Fig 1a) is slightly skewed. This is because of unsymmetry of the particular cells what makes the equivalent material anisotropic. We may notice that the two close to symmetry modes B and C gives relatively symmetric displacement patterns. The difference is mostly in the intensity of the perturbation of the displacement fields, Figs 1b and 1c. The most irregular pattern is introduced by mode B.

We observe the two characteristic horizontal displacements, Fig. 4. The points are chosen in the middle of the horizontally loaded edge and on the surface close to the growing cell. We may note that the introducing of the growing cell causes irregularities in the path of equilibrium. The less irregular path is in the case when the growing cell does not exist and the most irregular is in the case A.

4. CONCLUSIONS

Analysing all the above we may note that the behaviour of the living tissue is significantly different from the performance of the dead one. The tissue where the divisions do not occur behaves in regular and predictable way. The behaviour of the living tissue where the growing cells appearing is not as regular. The growing cells stand for appearing and disappearing of the inclusions and the dislocations in the material.

REFERENCES

[1]   C. Ainsworth, Stretching the imagination, *Nature,* 456, 1 Dec, 696-699, 2008.

[2]   D. Stamenovic, Effect of cytoskeletal prestress on cell rheological behaviour, *Acta Biomaterialia*, 1, 255-262, 2005.

[3]   M. Pogson, M., R. Smallwood, E. Qwarnstrom, M. Holcombe, Formal agent-based modelling of intracellular chemical interactions, *Biosystems*, 85, 37-45, 2006.

1st International Conference on Mathematical and Computational Biomedical Engineering - CMBE2009

June 29 - July 1, 2009, Swansea, UK

P.Nithiarasu and R.Löhner (Eds.)

TRUSS MODEL FOR STRESS CONTROLLED MORPHOGENESIS

Jose J. Muñoz

Laboratori de Càlcul Numèric (LaCàN)

Applied Mathematics III

Universitat Politècnica de Catalunya

Campus Nort UPC, 08034 Barcelona, Spain

e-mail: j.munoz@upc.edu, web page: http://www-lacan.upc.edu

Vito Conte

Materials Research Group

Division of Engineering

King's College London

Strand, London WC2R 2LS, UK

Mark Miodownik

Materials Research Group

Division of Engineering

King's College London

Strand, London WC2R 2LS, UK

ABSTRACT

We resort to the usual decomposition of the deformation gradient into an active and a passive component, and deduce the constitutive law and equilibrium equations when the two components are not independent. In the model described here the active part of the deformation is related to the hyperelastic passive part through a control function that simulates a feedback mechanism that has been experimentally observed during embryo development. Using a variational approach, we first write the equations for continua and study the effects of the control function in these equations. We particularise the results for a system of trusses, which allows us to obtain a simplified set of equations. In our derivations, we apply special attention to the conditions that a thermodynamically compliant formulation should satisfy.

We particularise these equations and conditions for the relevant elements of the cytoskeleton, namely, microfilaments and microtubules. We apply the model to simulate the shape changes observed during invagination of the Drosophila Melanogaster embryo. As a salient result, the model reveals that the incompressibility constraint of the yolk furnishes a necessary pressure on the epithelium that eventually eases its internalisation.

Key Words: *Morphogenesis, Development, Drosophila, Growth, Trusses, Invagination*

1   INTRODUCTION

Mesodermal invagination is one of the first movements with large deformations of the epithelium cells during embryo development. It has been experimentally tested that the genetical expression of the main genes involved in this process may be mechanically induced and expressed[1,5]. This feedback mechanism has strongly motivated the development of models where the active mechanisms are stress-controlled ⸴ . We here apply these ideas in a continuum approach and in a thermodynamically consistent manner, and particularise them to a system of truss elements, which will eventually represent the relevant elements of the cytoskeleton, namely microfilaments and microtubules. The resulting model is an improvement to the author's previous two-[3] and three-dimensional models .

2   CONTINUUM MODEL

We will resort to the usual decomposition of the deformation gradient $\boldsymbol{F}$ into an active component $\boldsymbol{F}$ and an elastic component $\boldsymbol{F}_e$ (see Figure 1). Consistent expressions of the elastic and active stresses, denoted by $\boldsymbol{P}_e$ and $\boldsymbol{P}$ respectively, can be deduced from reduced dissipation inequality, which in the present case reads,

$$\mathcal{D} := \boldsymbol{P}_e : \boldsymbol{L}_e + \boldsymbol{P} : \boldsymbol{L} - \rho^0 \dot{\psi} \geq 0,$$

with $\mathcal{D}$ the dissipated energy, and $\boldsymbol{L}_e = \dot{\boldsymbol{F}}\boldsymbol{F}^{-1}$, and $\boldsymbol{L} = \dot{\boldsymbol{F}}\,\boldsymbol{F}^{-1}$ the kinematic conjugates to $\boldsymbol{P}_e$ and $\boldsymbol{P}$, respectively.

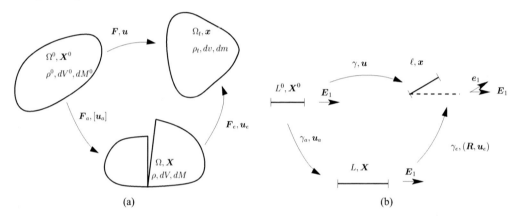

(a)   (b)

Figure 1: Maps between the reference configuration, the relaxed configuration, and the deformed configuration for the continuum model (a), and the truss model (b).

Two sets of equilibrium equations are deduced by minimising the following functional,

$$\Pi\left(\boldsymbol{u}\,,\boldsymbol{u}_e\right) = \int_\Omega \rho\psi\left(\boldsymbol{u}\,,\boldsymbol{u}_e\right)\,V + \Pi_{ext}$$

with respect to *independent* variations $\delta\boldsymbol{u}$ and $\delta\boldsymbol{u}_e$. After inserting the following dependence between active and elastic deformations,

$$\dot{\boldsymbol{F}} = \boldsymbol{\beta}\,\boldsymbol{F}_e\,.\tag{1}$$

with β a general stress-control function, we may couple the two sets of equilibrium equations into a single equation.

3   TRUSS MODEL

Motivated by the mechanism in the actin-myosin complex depicted in Figure 2, and the simplicity to measure the material properties in the cytoskeleton elements rather than in the continuum cell, we have particularised the previous model to a system of trusses. The equivalent maps are given in Figure 1b, where the tensors $\mathbf{F}$, $\mathbf{F}$ and $\mathbf{F}_e$ have been replaced by γ, γ and γ_e, respectively. Due to the linear interpolation of the total displacements $\mathbf{u}$, the latter may be expresses as,

$$\gamma = 1 + u\ X_1^0\ ' = \frac{\ell}{L^0}, \quad \gamma = 1 + u\ X_1^0\ ' = \frac{L}{L^0}, \quad \gamma_e = 1 + u_e\ X_1\ ' = \frac{\ell}{L},$$

where L^0, L and ℓ are the reference, relaxed and deformed length of the truss, respectively (see Figure 2 for the physical representation of these lengths).

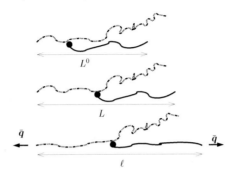

Figure 2: Scheme of the physical representation of the growth process in the actin-myosin complex.

we particularise our mode to a total stored free energy density given by $\psi = \frac{1}{}\ u_e'\ = \frac{1}{}\ \left(\frac{\ell-L}{L}\right)$, with a material parameter, assumed constant for each truss. The dependence in (1) between the active deformations and the elastic deformations is now replaced by the following linear relationship:

$$\dot{u}\ = \beta\ u_e' - \sigma \tag{2}$$

with β a material parameter, and σ the target stress at which homeostatic equilibrium takes place.

4 NUMERICAL RESULTS

We have modelled the cross-section of the Drosophila Melanogaster embryo, and applied a stress controlled active deformation (non-zero parameter β in Eqn. (2)) to the apical elements of the mesoderm (cells at the bottom in Figure 3), and to the radial trusses. For some combinations of the stiffness , consistent with experimental measurements, we have obtained the deformed configurations in Figure 3. We note that the cytoplasm and the yolk have been modelled through an incompressibility condition for each cell unit, and for the whole inner volume of the cross-section. Interestingly, when the yolk is not modelled, no invagination could be achieved.

5 CONCLUSIONS

We have applied the common gradient decomposition to the cellular structural elements, in conjunction with a stress controlled growth process. The method has allowed us to identify some of the key mechanisms that trigger invagination. In this regard, it has been found that the internal pressure furnished by the yolk of the embryo has a determinant role in the invagination of the mesoderm in the Drosophila embryo.

REFERENCES

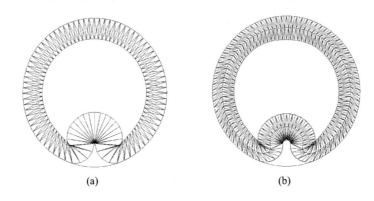

(a)   (b)

Figure 3: Deformed cross-section of the embryo using different typologies of the cytoskeleton.

[1] E Brouzés, W Supatto, and E Farge. Is mechano-sensitive expression of twist involved in mesoderm formation? *Biol. Cell*, 96:471–477, 2004.

[2] V Conte, J J Muñoz, and M Miodownik. 3D finite element model of ventral furrow invagination in the Drosophila melanogaster embryo. *J. Mech. Behav. Biomed. Mater.*, 2:188–198, 2008.

[3] J J Muñoz, K Barrett, and M Miodownik. A deformation gradient decomposition method for the analysis of the mechanics of morphogenesis. *J. Biomechanics*, pages 1372–1380, 2007.

[4] A Ramasubramanian and L A Taber. Computational modeling of morphogenesis regulated by mechanical feedback. *Biomech. Model. Mechanobiol.*, 7:77–91, 2008.

[5] B I Shraiman. Mechanical feedback as a possible regulator of tissue growth. *Proc. Nat. Acad. Sci. USA*, 102(9):3318–23, 2005.

[6] L A Taber. Theoretical study of beloussovs hyper-restoration hypothesis for mechanical regulation of morphogenesis. *Biomech. Model. Mechanobiol.*, 2008. DOI 10.1007/s10237-007-0106-x.

[2] O.C. Zienkiewicz and R.C. Taylor. *The finite element method*, 4th. Edition, Vol. **I**, McGraw Hill, 1989., Vol. **II**, 1991.

1st International Conference on Mathematical and Computational Biomedical Engineering – CMBE2009
June 29 – July 1, 2009, Swansea, UK
P. Nithiarasu and R. Löhner (eds)

OBJECTIVE BALANCE ASSESMENT:
FEMALE CLAUDICANTS PERFORM POORLY IN
COMPUTERIZED DYNAMIC POSTUROGRAPHY

Katherine A. Mockford
Academic Vascular Surgical Unit, Alderson House, Hull Royal Infirmary, Hull, HU3 2JZ,
katherinemockford@hotmail.com

Fayyaz A. K. Mazari
Academic Vascular Surgical Unit, Alderson House, Hull Royal Infirmary, Hull, HU3 2JZ,
fayyaz.mazari@hcy.nhs.uk

Alastair R. Jordan
Department of Sport, Health and Exercise Science, University of Hull, Cottingham, HU6
7RX, A.R.Jordan@2006.hull.ac.uk

Natalie Vanicek
Department of Sport, Health and Exercise Science, University of Hull, Cottingham, HU6
7RX, N.Vanicek@hull.ac.uk

Ian C. Chetter
Academic Vascular Surgical Unit, Alderson House, Hull Royal Infirmary, Hull, HU3 2JZ,
ian.chetter@hey.nhs.uk

Patrick. A. Coughlin
Academic Vascular Surgical Unit, Alderson House, Hull Royal Infirmary, Hull, HU3 2JZ,
patrick.coughlin@hey.nhs.uk

ABSTRACT

Key Words: *Intermittent claudication, computerized dynamic posturography, balance, gender.*

1. INTRODUCTION

Impaired balance is a recognized, specific risk factor for falling[1]. Falls are of increasing prevalence with age and the associated morbidity is both significant and costly[2]. Intermittent claudication, a clinical manifestation of lower limb atherosclerosis, is characterized by ischemic pain, most commonly in the calf muscles, and is brought on by exercise and relieved by rest. Claudication is a common problem in the elderly affecting approximately 4.5% of the population over the age of 55[3]. The aim of this study was to compare balance between male and female claudicants and to assess such patients' insight into their own risk of falling.

2. MAIN BODY

Methods

Sixty eight claudicants (50 men, 18 women), underwent objective balance assessment by computerized dynamic posturography (CDP), using the EquiTest (NeuroCom® International Inc., Clackamas, OR, USA) system. This incorporates the Sensory Organization Test (SOT) and the Motor Control Test (MCT). SOT determines body sway relative to the maximum limits of stability under 6 different sensory conflict conditions to assess the contribution of each sensory system (Figure 1). MCT involves anterior and posterior translations of the patient's support surface and assesses the timing, strength and symmetry of the lower limb response. SOT and MCT scores are compared to NeuroCom's healthy control population data and are considered abnormal when lower than 95% of age matched controls[4].

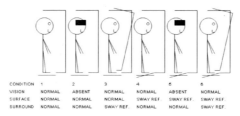

Figure 1. The 6 sensory conditions of the Sensory Organization Test. Patients are asked to close their eyes in order to remove visual inputs (conditions 2 and 5). Sway referencing occurs as the support surface (conditions 4, 5 & 6) or surroundings (conditions 3 & 6) tilt in response to the subjects' anterior-posterior sway, thus disrupting somatosensory or visual stimuli respectively.

In addition, patients underwent a standard assessment of lower limb ischemia including ankle brachial systolic pressure indices (ABPI) both pre and post exercise. Exercise consisted of a treadmill test (10% incline, 1.6 miles per hour). Patients were asked to walk for as long as possible. Intermittent claudication distance (ICD) was the distance recorded at which they experienced onset of pain and maximum walking distance (MWD) was the distance recorded when unable to walk further. Patient reported walking distance (PRWD) was also noted. Patients completed a visual analogue scale assessment of their fear of falling, the Activities-specific Balance Confidence (ABC) scale[5].

Results

Female claudicants performed significantly worse in the objective assessment of balance using CDP (Chi-Squared test, P = 0.003) (Table 1). Thirteen of the eighteen female patients (72%) demonstrated abnormal balance (Table 1). Composite equilibrium SOT scores were significantly lower for female claudicants (Mann Whitney U test, P = 0.014), with median scores of 62 for females and 72.5 for males (Figure 2). Performance on the Motor Control Test was not significantly different between the sexes.

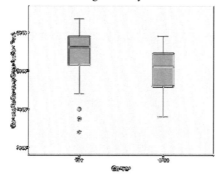

Figure 2. A comparison of the composite equilibrium scores for the Sensory Organization Test between male and female claudicants (P = 0.014). This is a weighted average of scores for all 6 conditions described in Figure 1 resulting in an overall score of balance. The median values are marked by a horizontal line within each interquartile range (IQR, shown as boxes). The range is marked by the whiskers and outliers (circles) are values 1.5-3.0 IQR lower than the first quartile.

Further examination of the SOT scores for each condition revealed significantly poorer scores on conditions 4 and 6 for female claudicants (Mann Whitney U Test, P < 0.05) (Figure 3).

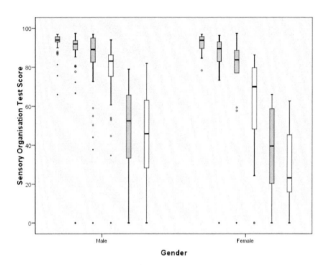

Figure 3. The Sensory Organization Test scores for conditions 1-6 for male and female claudicants. Conditions 1-6 (described in Figure 1) are represented from left to right on the chart. Scores for conditions 4 and 6 were significantly different between genders (Mann Whitney U test, P < 0.05) and are highlighted in white. The median values are marked by a horizontal line within each interquartile range (IQR, shown as boxes). The range is marked by the whiskers, outliers (circles) are values 1.5-3.0 IQR lower than the first quartile, and extreme outliers (stars) are values >3.0 IQR lower than the first quartile.

Table 1. A comparison between male and female claudicants undergoing objective assessment of balance

	Male Claudicants $n = 50$	Female Claudicants $n = 18$ (26%)	*P* value§ (>0.05 = NS)
Patient characteristics			
Age, median (IQR)	71 (66-76)	70 (65-81.5)	NS*
Computerized dynamic posturography			
Sensory Organization Test score - median (IQR)	72.5 (62.25-78)	62 (51-69.5)	0.014*
Sensory Organization Test outcome - proportion with normal score (%)	34/50 (68%)	5/18 (28%)	0.003**
Motor Control Test score - median (IQR)	150 (144-159)	145 (136-150)	NS*
Motor Control Test outcome - proportion with normal score (%)	37/48 (77%)	12/15 (80%)	NS***
Indicators of lower limb ischemia			
Patient Reported Walking Distance (PRWD) †	182 (102-294)	95 (39-388)	NS*
Intermittent Claudication Distance (ICD) †	43 (28-70)	36 (29-111)	NS*
Maximum Walking Distance (MWD) †	72 (50-198)	77 (43-178)	NS*
ABPI pre exercise, most affected leg	0.76 (0.62-0.94)	0.60 (0.57-0.71)	0.012*
ABPI post exercise, most affected leg	0.38 (0.23-0.71)	0.27 (0.19-0.35)	NS*
Fear of falling			
Activities specific Balance Confidence (ABC) score - median (IQR)	83 (65-96)	75 (35-92)	NS*

§ P values denote the significance of tests comparing male and female claudicants, alpha level set at 0.05,
Significant differences are highlighted by the shaded areas
Mann Whitney U test *, Chi-squared test **, Fischer's "exact" test ***
IQR = interquartile range
† = all distances measured in meters
ABPI = ankle brachial pressure index

All indicators of lower limb ischemia were not significantly different between male and female claudicants in this study, other than ABPI pre exercise in the affected limb. Fear of falling as measured by the ABC score tended to be lower in females, although this did not achieve statistical significance (Mann Whitney U test, P = 0.25).

Discussion

To our knowledge this is the first study to compare CPD results between adult males and females using the EquiTest system and to demonstrate poorer balance among a female population. While acknowledging the relatively small sample size in this study, this is an important finding, as being able to identify patients with an increased likelihood of falling is vital in enabling the initiation of preventative strategies. Poor female performance cannot be explained by age, as there was no statistical difference between genders in relation to age. Again the difference is not likely to result from greater disease severity in women as there was no significant difference in any of the walking distances or in post exercise ABPI between males and females. It is noted that the pre exercise ABPI was significantly lower in females which is consistent with the findings of The Edinburgh Artery Study, explained by height differences between men and women[3]. Lower scores in conditions 4 and 6 of the SOT achieved by women suggest poor use of visual cues (condition 4) and reliance on visual cues even when inaccurate (condition 6). The explanation for this finding is not known. It may be that women participating in this study found coordinating visual and somatosensory inputs more difficult than their male counterparts due to poor visuo-spatial task proficiency, however this is unproven. There was no significant increase in fear of falling among women highlighting a relative ignorance to potential falls risk among both sexes.

3. CONCLUSIONS

Impaired balance is very common among female claudicants, and this may predispose to a high incidence of falls. We demonstrated no increased fear of falling among females, thus possibly rendering these patients at greater risk, due to a lack of awareness of their potential for falling.

Fall preventions strategies, in particular balance and strength training, should be directed at female patients to combat the high cost, both medical and financial, of falls. In order to specifically target higher risk patients of both sexes, objective balance assessment can be safely performed using computerized dynamic posturography in older claudicants.

REFERENCES

[1] Tinetti ME, Speechley M, Ginter SF, Risk factors for falls among elderly persons living in the community, *New England Journal of Medicine,* 319(26),1701-7, 1988.

[2] Stevens JA, Corso PS, Finkelstein EA, Miller TR, The costs of fatal and non-fatal falls among older adults, *Injury Prevention,* 12(5), 290-5, 2006.

[3] Fowkes FG, Housley E, Cawood EH, Macintyre CC, Ruckley CV, Prescott RJ, Edinburgh Artery Study: prevalence of asymptomatic and symptomatic peripheral arterial disease in the general population, *International Journal of Epidemiology,* 20(2), 384-92, 1991.

[4] NeuroCom International Inc. EquiTest System Version 8.0 Data interpretation manual. Clackamas, Oregon: NeuroCom International Inc.; 2001.

[5] Miller WC, Deathe AB, Speechley M, Psychometric properties of the Activities-specific Balance Confidence Scale among individuals with a lower-limb amputation, *Archives of Physical and Medical Rehabilitation,*84(5), 656-61, 2003.

1st International Conference on Mathematical and Computational Biomedical Engineering – CMBE2009
June 29 – July 1, 2009, Swansea, UK
P. Nithiarasu and R. Löhner (eds)

BIOMECHANICAL ADAPTATIONS WHEN LANDING ON FOOTBALL TURF

Philippa L. Jones
Sports Biomechanics Research Group, Cardiff School of Sport, University of Wales Institute, Cardiff, UK, CF24 6XD, phjones@uwic.ac.uk
David G. Kerwin
Sports Biomechanics Research Group, Cardiff School of Sport, University of Wales Institute, Cardiff, UK, CF24 6XD, dkerwin@uwic.ac.uk
Gareth Irwin
Sports Biomechanics Research Group, Cardiff School of Sport, University of Wales Institute, Cardiff, UK, CF24 6XD, girwin@uwic.ac.uk
Len Nokes
Cardiff School of Engineering, Cardiff University, UK, CF24 3AA, Nokes@cardiff.ac.uk

ABSTRACT

The aim of the study was to investigate variations in lower limb biomechanics during jump landings on natural (NT) and artificial Football Turf (FT). In this preliminary study, one footballer performed 40 single leg jump landings following a ball heading movement on NT and FT. Three-dimensional kinematic data (CODA, 200Hz) and ground reaction force data (Kistler, 1000Hz) were collected for each trial. Segmental clusters on the foot, shank and thigh of the landing limb, enabled three-dimensional kinematics to be determined. There was evidence of alterations in the movement profiles as landing trials progressed on FT. Knee flexion and adduction moved closer to the mean NT profiles. Ankle eversion reduced and vertical ground reaction force profiles mimicked NT profiles by the end of the familiarisation period. Distinct alterations in landing technique at the knee and ankle indicated a time related response to the familiarisation period.

Key Words: *Artificial turf, injury, landing, movement adaptation.*

1 INTRODUCTION

Football Turf (FT), as described by the Fédération Internationale de Football Association (FIFA), is a third generation artificial surface developed specifically for football performance. Alterations to the Laws of the Game in 2004 acknowledged FT as an official surface for competitive football. The use of FT surfaces in professional competition continues to rise, but its suitability remains in question by the football community, based largely on the limitations of previous generations of artificial turf [1]. FIFA recommend that familiarisation sessions of 1-hour should occur prior to play on an unfamiliar surface [2]. Nothing is known about adaptations that may occur within this period. It is therefore desirable to determine if and when adaptations occur and to consider id the modulations to joint kinematics have any implications for injury. The purpose of this preliminary study was to monitor joint and ground reaction responses during a 1-hour period of familiarisation on a modern FT when performing landings from a heading task.

2 METHODS

Data Collection: A female footballer (age 24yrs, height 1.64m and mass 56.8kg) provided informed consent to participate in the study, with all procedures approved by the University's Ethics Committee. The participant was experienced at senior competitive level on natural turf, but had never playing on FT. An automated motion analysis system CODA, (Charnwood Dynamics Ltd, Leicestershire, UK) was used to collect the trajectories of active LED markers at 200Hz for 5 seconds per trial. Cluster marker sets were utilised with additional markers placed on anatomical landmarks of the lower limb for 10 static trials (2-6 second duration). Ground reaction force data were collected for the landing leg using a force plate (Kistler 9287BA, Switzerland) sampling at 1000Hz. Turf samples, housed in purpose built metal trays (900mm x 600mm x 50mm) were mounted on the force plate and changed between trials. The participant performed 20 landings on each surface in a randomized order over a 1-hour period, wearing her own football boots (Predator Pulse II FG, Adidas). Each trial comprised a single step approach into a jump to head a suspended size 5 official football followed by a single leg landing on turf and a two-step forward sprint (Figure 1). The ball height was selected to mimic a challenging heading action.

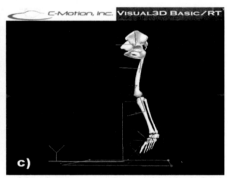

Figure 1: a) Participant performing experimental protocol and b) cluster set used to enable c) skeletal representation of lower limb during movement using Visual 3D software.

Data Processing: The kinematic data were processed using motion analysis software (Visual 3D, C-motion Inc., USA) enabling three dimensional analysis and skeletal illustrations for each movement trial (Figure 1). Each trial was normalised to 100% from the instant when vertical ground reaction force exceeded 10N and the instant when Fz dropped below 10N. The raw data were filtered at a cut off frequency of 19Hz, determined by a Residual Analysis and flexion-extension, adduction-abduction and internal rotation of the knee joint and plantar-dorsiflexion and inversion-eversion of the ankle, along with vertical (Fz), anterior-posterior (Fy) and medio-lateral (Fx) ground reaction forces were exported.

Data Analysis: The 20 trials performed under FT were divided into 4 groups, FT1 (trials 1-5), FT2 (trials 6-10), FT3 (trials 11-15) and FT4 (trials 16-20). The 20 trials performed under NT remained as a single group. Mean (±SD) profiles were calculated for knee flexion-extension, adduction-abduction, internal-external rotation, Fx, Fy and Fz for all 5 groups (FT1-FT4 and NT). Percentage root mean square differences (%RMSD) were calculated for joint angles for FT1-FT4 against the mean NT profile.

3 RESULTS

The mean of trials 1-5 (FT1) demonstrated the greatest %RMSD between NT and FT in knee flexion-extension and adduction-abduction, which then reduced in subsequent trials (Table 1). The %RMSD between NT and FT in knee internal-external rotation was similar across the FT conditions (Table 1). The %RMSD in ankle plantar-dorsiflexion between NT and FT was relatively low throughout with a slight increase in FT2 and FT3 (Table 1). FT1 demonstrated the least %RMSD in ankle inversion-eversion between NT and FT which increased in subsequent trial groupings (Table 1).

The angle profiles for the knee and ankle when landing on FT and NT are presented in Figure 2, with means provided for trials 1-5 (FT1), 6-10 (FT2), 11-15 (FT3) AND 16-20 (FT4) under FT. A tendency towards additional knee flexion and adduction was observed during FT1 and FT2 before movements altered to more closely mimic those demonstrated under NT (Figure 2a). Ankle plantar-dorsiflexion angles were extremely consistent throughout the FT trials and closely mimicked that demonstrated under NT (Figure 2b). A tendency towards similar ankle eversion angle profiles under FT1 and FT2 in comparison to

Table 1: Overall percentage difference of mean angle profiles between NT and FT trial groups.

	Movement	FT 1 (1-5) RMSD (%)	FT 2 (6-10) RMSD (%)	FT3 (11-15) RMSD (%)	FT4 (16-20) RMSD (%)
Knee	Flexion-extension	33	12	5	4
	Adduction-abduction	44	30	21	18
	Internal-external rotation	19	11	18	18
Ankle	Plantar-Dorsiflexion	5	7	8	5
	Inversion-eversion	11	13	23	36

NT was observed whilst less ankle version was noted under FT3 and FT4 (Figure 2b). FT1 demonstrated an Fx profile that closely mimicked that of NT which then deviated with subsequent FT trial groupings (figure 2c). Altered Fy profiles were demonstrated during FT1-FT3 whilst FT4 appears to more closely resemble performance on NT (Figure 2c). FT1 demonstrated an altered Fz profile in comparison to NT whilst FT2-FT4 more closely mimicked performance on NT (Figure 2c).

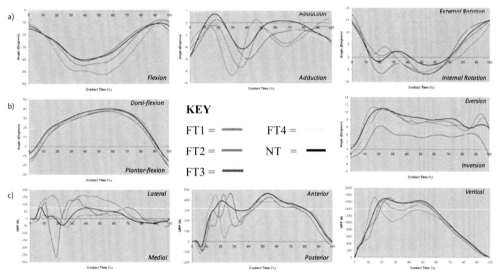

Figure 2: a) Angle profiles of the knee and b) ankle when landing on FT (FT1-FT4) and NT. c) Ground reaction force profiles (Fx, Fy, Fz) when landing on FT (FT1-FT4) and NT.

4 DISCUSSION

Knee and ankle and ground reaction forces were studied for a single experienced footballer as she performed a game specific landing task on familiar NT and novel FT surfaces. The trials were tracked over 1-hour to monitor alterations in lower limb biomechanics.

Shift towards NT mean angle profiles: Knee flexion-extension and adduction-abduction angle profiles during FT1 and FT2 demonstrated clear movements away from the mean profile under NT (Figure 2). The increase in knee flexion displayed in FT1 and FT2 suggests a potential anticipatory landing strategy where the participant may have perceived landing under FT to be more demanding than under NT, as knee flexion has been closely linked with enhanced force dissipation and shock absorption [3]. However, later trial groupings (FT2-FT4) demonstrated a distinct shift towards the knee profiles produced under NT (Table 1 and Figure 2) suggesting that initial kinematic differences at the knee may be due to a lack of FT experience. These changes may be due to the participant's perceived need to acquire appropriate movement characteristics [4] rather than to the altered surface properties, as might initially have been expected. Matas

[5] supported this idea when comparing normal with treadmill running. They showed differences from natural conditions for approximately 4 minutes whilst subsequent kinematics were similar. FT1 demonstrated a distinctively sharper gradient in vertical ground reaction force and therefore greater loading rate compared to later trials (FT2-FT3), which began to mimic the profile demonstrated under NT.

Shift away from NT mean angle profiles: Ankle inversion-eversion angle profiles during FT1 and FT2 appear to in part mimic the profile demonstrated under NT (Figure 2). This suggests that during the initial trials on FT the participant may have utilised her normal landing strategy. However, as she performed further trials, eversion reduced (Figure 2). This may highlight a true kinematic adaptation to landing strategy when performing on a new novel surface, which may alter performance and hence raise implications for injury. Possible rationale for this potential medial to lateral movement at the ankle may be due to the shoe-surface interaction. Whilst the medial-lateral forces demonstrated during early landings on FT (FT1) appeared to closely resemble NT performance, the force profiles subsequently altered as additional trials were performed (Figure 2). Specifically, early onset medial forces were increased under FT3 and FT4, which may highlight important differences in landing technique and subsequent loading of the body.

Familiarisation period: These preliminary observations during a familiarisation period resulted in lower limb kinematic alterations as the participant became accustomed to the task on the new FT surface. FIFA stipulates that a visiting team must be allocated a minimum of two 1-hour training sessions before competition to ensure surface familiarity [2]. Evidence was found that changes occurred within the 1-hour time frame but these adaptations varied across the lower limb joints.

5   CONCLUSIONS

The present study is a preliminary investigation into how a footballer adapted her landing movement technique during a 1-hour familiarisation period. Knee and ankle angle kinematics were found to alter as more trials were performed on FT, with selected profiles shifting closer or further away from the mean NT angle profiles. Such distinct alterations in movement during the familiarisation period indicated adaptations in technique when landing on this novel surface. Further trials involving a range of players under different task conditions need to be conducted to check the consistency of these observed responses in order to further examine technique modification and subsequent injury potential when competing on FT.

Acknowledgement

This work was funded by UWIC Bursary Awards for Research Students and University of Wales Bursary.

REFERENCES

[1]   S. W. Baker, Performance standards for professional soccer on artificial turf surfaces, *Journal of Sports Turf Research Institute,* 66: 83-92, 1990.

[2]   FIFA, *FIFA quality concept for artificial turf guide.* Zurich: FIFA, 2008.

[3]   M. J. Decker, M. R Torry, D. J. Wyland, W. I. Sterett and J. R. Steadman, Gender differences in lower extremity kinematics, kinetics and energy absorption during landing. *Clinical Biomechanics*, 18, 662-669, 2003.

[4]   K. M. Newell, Coordination, control and skill. In D. Goodman, R. B. Wilberg, and I. M. Franks (Eds.), Differing perspectives in motor learning, memory and control (pp. 295–317). Amsterdam: North-Holland, 1985.

[5]   A. Matsas, N. Taylor and H. McBurney, Knee joint kinematics from familiarised treadmill walking can be generalised to overground walking in young impaired subjects. *Gait and Posture*, 11, 46-53, 2000.